Liquids and Solutions

Structure and Dynamics

Peeter Kruus

Department of Chemistry
Carleton University
Ottawa, Ontario
Canada

MARCEL DEKKER, INC. New York and Basel

Library of Congress Cataloging in Publication Data

Kruus, Peeter, 1939-
Liquids and solutions.

Includes index.
1. Solution (Chemistry) 2. Liquids. I. Title.
QD541.K88 541'.042'2 76-1795
ISBN 0-8247-6427-7

MARCEL DEKKER, INC.

270 Madison Avenue, New York, New York 10016

Current printing (last digit):
10 9 8 7 6 5 4 3 2 1

PRINTED IN THE UNITED STATES OF AMERICA

PREFACE

This book has developed from a graduate course given twice at Carleton University, Ottawa, Canada, and a series of seminars given at the Physics Institute, Odense University, Denmark. The discussion is, for the greater part, at a level where a graduate student or a senior undergraduate student in physical chemistry or chemical physics should be able to follow it. Because of the growing interest in the structure and dynamics of aqueous systems shown by people working with biological systems, students and researchers in biology with a strong physics chemistry background may also find the book of use.

The purpose of the book is to bring readers with a standard undergraduate physical-chemistry background to a level where they can appreciate the articles and advanced books dealing with this topic which have been appearing with considerable frequency lately. An attempt is thus made to present the underlying models, assumptions, and principles present in the more important theoretical approaches and experimental methods used for the elucidation of structure and dynamics in liquids and solutions.

To keep the book within reasonable length, detailed discussion of the various phenomena involved is not possible. It is also not necessary as numerous good references are available for more specialized topics. Thus an overview is given which attempts to give some unity to the various specializations which have developed in this field. References to more detailed and advanced descriptions are included throughout. Some of the more common references which are referred to in several chapters are listed at the end of the book together with collections of relevant papers given at recent meetings of interest under "General References."

The book is arranged into three main parts. Part A describes the bases of the theoretical approaches used as generally as possible. Part B describes the underlying theory behind the various experimental methods used, the types of apparatus used, and then discusses examples of the types of phenomena which can be studied by these methods. Several of the examples in each chapter are taken from quite recent work, so that the reader can be left with some feeling of the "state of the art" in each case.

Parts A and B are presented assuming that the reader is familiar with the material in part C, which contains basic topics not specific to liquids. Many of the topics will have been covered in a standard physical chemistry curriculum. Thus it can be used as a review for those topics which the reader has covered previously or as a guide for studying unfamiliar topics. The discussion in part C is not comprehensive enough to be used alone for the study of unfamiliar topics.

Part C is included as it was possible to trace back most of the difficulties encountered by students taking the course to weaknesses in their knowledge of basic principles which they have forgotten or have never had.

The topics covered are generally not concerned with the internal structure of molecules and other effects (e.g., chemical reactions) determined primarily through "chemical" interactions, where there is significant overlap of the electronic distributions of the species concerned. Thus the geometry of the electronic distributions of species involved will be assumed as known.

The discussion also does not in general cover "uncommon" aspects of liquids, e.g., glasses, melts, liquid metals, quantum liquids. Some of the experimental methods are, nevertheless, also applicable to the study of such systems. Aspects applicable especially to some "uncommon" liquids (e.g., argon) made up of spherically symmetrical molecules are introduced, as the essential characteristics of the liquid state are most easily seen in such systems. A discussion of critical phenomena in liquids and mixtures is also included. Much of the discussion, however, deals with aqueous systems.

For the sake of brevity, the discussion is limited to topics directly concerned with those emphasized in the book. Thus many topics which would normally be included under these chapter headings are not present. This is valid for part C in particular. The description of experimental techniques in part B also does not cover any details of less specialized aspects, e.g., amplifiers, lenses, recorders.

The symbols used in the book are summarized in the glossary. They are, as much as possible, in agreement with the recommended SI symbols. Because of the blending of specialized fields, a symbol nevertheless can have many meanings. In several instances the SI symbols have been altered slightly to avoid conflict with symbols used in the vast majority of cases in a speciality. For similar reasons, in several cases the units of common use in the speciality are used rather than SI units.

The author is indebted to many people for help in preparation of the manuscript. Special thanks are due to those who read and criticized portions of the first draft: Dr. W. J. L. Buyers, Atomic Energy of Canada; Drs. G. C. Benson, D. W. Davidson, J. E. Piercey, and I. C. P. Smith, National Research Council of Canada; Dr. E. M. Valeriote, Defence Research Board of Canada; Dr. A. R. Davis, Department of the Environment, Canada; Dr. R. A. Shigeishi, Carleton University, Ottawa; Dr. H. L. Friedman, State University of New York, Stony Brook. Special thanks are also due to Mrs. M. J. McGuire for typing of the final draft; Mrs. A. Kruus for typing of the preliminary draft, preparation of diagrams and consistent encouragement; and Dr. O. S. Mortensen and the Physics Institute, University of Odense for their hospitality during the preparation of the preliminary draft. Any errors, omissions, or misinterpretations remaining in the manuscript are the sole responsibility of the author.

Ottawa, Canada

Peeter Kruus

CONTENTS

Part A

THEORETICAL APPROACHES

Part A describes the more common ways of treating structure and dynamics from the theoretical point of view. The discussion begins with a review of intermolecular forces in Chap. 1, and then proceeds to describe theoretical approaches to the structure of pure liquids (Chaps. 2 and 3), nonelectrolyte solutions (Chap. 4), electrolyte solutions (Chap. 5), and dynamics in liquids and solutions, both from the hydrodynamic (Chap. 6) and the molecular (Chap. 7) points of view. Some of the approaches described seem to have been superseded by recent advances in other approaches. However, in cases where there is considerable literature, these superseded approaches are included.

Some newer approaches which seem promising are also included even if little literature exists at this time. In most cases, such approaches are not dealt with in any detail. Attempts are made to simply outline the aspects in the approaches which are novel, and references are given to detailed papers.

The discussion in Part A is from a point of view independent of experimental method. In Part B, various experimental methods will be discussed, with the discussion related back to the material in Part A.

Chapter 1

FORCES IN LIQUIDS

INTRODUCTION

The structure and dynamics in a liquid system is ultimately determined by the forces present between particles (molecules and/or ions) in the system. In this chapter, the types of forces present will be discussed.

It is assumed that the distribution of charge and other properties of individual particles is known. It is, of course, such properties which determine the forces present, but the elucidation of the properties of individual particles by molecular orbital (MO) calculations, gas-phase spectrometry, etc. is outside the scope of this book. An exception is made in the case of interactions involving water molecules, where some MO calculations have been carried out on water dimers and hydrated ions.

Most of the discussion concerns the "pair potential" $v(r)$, which describes the potential energy v as a function of the distance r between two particles. The assumption that the total potential energy can be treated as the sum of pair interactions is not strictly valid in liquids. Thus, forces involving three particles are also examined briefly.

The simplest form of an intermolecular potential is a "hard-sphere" potential where for $r \leqslant 2a$, $v(r) = \infty$, and for $r > 2a$, $v(r) = 0$. Thus 2a is the "hard-sphere diameter" of the species involved. When two species, a and b, are involved, then $a = \frac{1}{2}(a_a + a_b)$. Such a model allows no attraction.

A simple model showing attraction is the square-well potential. It is shown in Fig. 1.1 overlapping the more realistic "Lennard-Jones 6-12" potential. At high temperatures, where $kT \gg$ depth of the potential well, the shape of the well is not of much importance, and a simple model is often satisfactory. The 6-12 potential sketched in Fig. 1.1 is probably the most commonly used potential. It is of the form

$$v(r) = 4\varepsilon\left[\left(\frac{\sigma}{r}\right)^{12} - \left(\frac{\sigma}{r}\right)^{6}\right]$$

or

$$= \varepsilon\left[\left(\frac{r^{\#}}{r}\right)^{12} - 2\left(\frac{r^{\#}}{r}\right)^{6}\right]$$

i.e.,

$$(r^{\#})^{6} = 2\sigma^{6} \tag{1.1}$$

The discussion in Sec. 1.1 will show that the attractive $(1/r)^6$ part of this potential has a good theoretical foundation. The repulsive part is set with a power 12 for convenience.

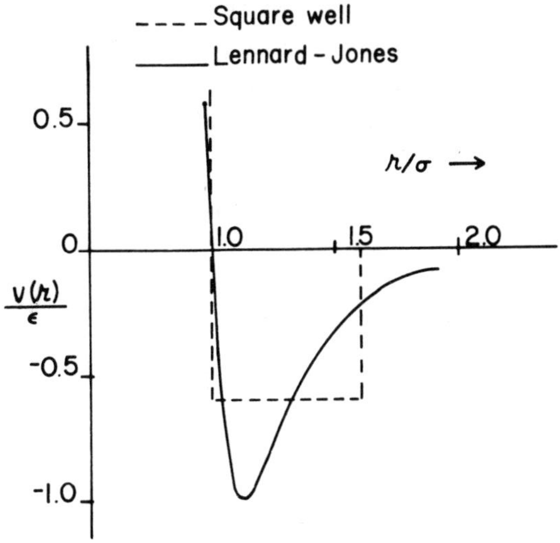

Fig. 1.1. The Lennard-Jones 6-12 potential with a square well potential superimposed.

The repulsive part of the pair potential involves "short-range forces," i.e., forces present at values of r so small that the charge distributions of the molecules overlap. Also some attractive forces, such as charge transfer and cases of hydrogen bonding, are short-range. These are discussed in Sec. 1.2.

Forces pertaining to water molecules are discussed in Sec. 1.3. Because of their importance, they have been investigated in greater detail. Unique features in the charge distribution of the water molecule make it difficult to describe these interactions by the general methods outlined in Sec. 1.1.

There is no discussion here of the forces present in liquid metals. Such liquids are different, in that neutral "molecules" do not exist in them. A liquid metal can be represented as two intermixed fluids, one made up of positive metal ions, and the other of conduction (essentially free) electrons. The forces in the liquid are, to a large degree, determined by the presence of the "gas" of free electrons. Thus a "pair potential" is, in a strict sense, not a valid physical concept for the liquid metal. "Pseudomolecules" can, however, be pictured as present, with the electrons distributed about the metal ions to form molecules. An effective pair potential between such "molecules" can be defined, and relationships based on the pair potential can be exploited (see Chaps. 15 and 16).

1.1 LONG-RANGE FORCES

(a) *Description of Molecules in Terms of Multipoles*

A molecule (or ion) can be described as a distribution of charge ρ with nuclei described by discrete positive contributions and electrons by a continuous distribution. A less exact description of this charge distribution is in terms of the electrical moments (or multipoles) of the molecule: net charge $\mathcal{Q}$, dipole moment $\underline{p}$, quadrupole moment $\underline{\underline{Q}}$, octopole moment, etc.

Such a description in terms of multipoles is usually satisfactory for intermolecular force calculations when intermolecular distances are large. It is also often possible to measure these moments experimentally, while the actual distribution ρ remains unknown.

In the following calculations, the molecule will be assumed to consist of a distribution of charges q_i each located at a point (x_i, y_i, z_i) about the origin of a coordinate system. The potential $\phi(P)$ at some point $P(x, y, z)$ a distance r from the origin due to this distribution will be calculated. In Sec. (b) we will then place a molecule at P.

$\phi(P)$ can be simply written as the sum of coulombic potentials (Eq. (20.1))

$$\phi(P) = \Sigma\phi_i(P) = \Sigma\frac{q_i}{4\pi\varepsilon^\circ r_i}$$

$$= \Sigma\frac{q_i}{4\pi\varepsilon^\circ} \cdot \frac{1}{[(x - x_i)^2 + (y - y_i)^2 + (z - z_i)^2]^{\frac{1}{2}}} \qquad (1.2)$$

As the distance r_i between q_i and P is assumed >> x_i, y_i, z_i, the ϕ_i (actually $1/r_i$) can be expanded in terms of a Taylor series

$$\phi_i(P) = \frac{q_i}{4\pi\varepsilon^\circ r_i} = [\phi_i]_0 + \left[\frac{\partial\phi_i}{\partial x_i}\right]_0 x_i + \left[\frac{\partial\phi_i}{\partial y_i}\right]_0 y_i + \cdots$$
$$+ \frac{1}{2}\left[\frac{\partial^2\phi_i}{\partial x_i^{\,2}}\right]_0 x_i^{\,2} + \cdots + \left[\frac{\partial^2\phi_i}{\partial x_i \partial y_i}\right]_0 x_i y_i + \cdots \quad (1.3)$$

Here $[\phi_i]_0$ is $\phi_i(P)$ calculated for $(x_i, y_i, z_i) = (0, 0, 0)$. Equation (1.3) can be simplified with appropriate substitutions such as,

$$\left[\frac{\partial\phi_i}{\partial x}\right]_0 = \frac{q_i}{4\pi\varepsilon^\circ}\left[\frac{\partial(1/r_i)}{\partial x_i}\right]_0 = \frac{q_i x}{4\pi\varepsilon^\circ r^3} \quad (1.4)$$

When forms of the type (1.4) have been substituted into (1.3), and the results have been summed as in (1.2), $\phi(P)$ can be written as

$$\phi(P) = \frac{Q}{4\pi\varepsilon^\circ r} + \frac{1}{4\pi\varepsilon^\circ r^2}\left\{\frac{x}{r}p_x + \frac{y}{r}p_y + \frac{z}{r}p_z\right\} + \frac{1}{4\pi\varepsilon^\circ r^3}\left\{\frac{1}{2}\left(\frac{3x^2}{r^2} - 1\right)Q_{xx}\right.$$
$$\left. + \cdots + \frac{3xy}{r^2}Q_{xy} + \cdots\right\} + \frac{1}{4\pi\varepsilon^\circ r^4}\left\{\cdots\right. \quad (1.5)$$

Equation (1.5) can also be expressed in terms of Legendre polynomials [1]. Thus $Q=\Sigma q_i$ is the net charge on the molecule; p_x is the component of $\underline{p}$ in the x direction, given by

$$p_x = \Sigma q_i x_i = \int \rho x dx \quad (1.6)$$

An integral form for p_x is shown to indicate that continuous distribution could be used.

The quadrupole moment $\underline{\underline{Q}}$ is in the form of a tensor. The nine components are of the form $Q_{xy} = \Sigma q_i x_i y_i$, etc. By a suitable transformation, the tensor $\underline{\underline{Q}}$ can be diagonalized to have only components Q_{xx}, Q_{yy}, Q_{zz}. For a symmetric species, e.g., CH_4, $Q_{xx} = Q_{yy} = Q_{zz} \neq 0$. Yet the contribution to $\phi(P)$ from such a symmetric $\underline{\underline{Q}}$ is zero, as

$$\left[\frac{1}{2}\left(\frac{3x^2}{r^2} - 1\right) + \frac{1}{2}\left(\frac{3y^2}{r^2} - 1\right) + \frac{1}{2}\left(\frac{3z^2}{r^2} - 1\right)\right] Q_{xx} = 0 \quad (1.7)$$

Thus, often the quadrupole moment is defined as only that portion of $\underline{\underline{Q}}$ which departs from symmetry.

When r is not >> dimensions of the molecule, then a multipole expansion is not an accurate way of describing the charge distribution. In some cases the charge distribution in individual chemical bonds present in the molecule can be considered in terms of bond (or functional group) dipoles [1].

(b) *Interactions Between Permanent Charge Distributions*

The interaction between the permanent charge distributions of two molecules labeled *a* and *b* will now be considered. Molecule *a* is the molecule at the origin described in Sec. (a). Molecule *b* is described by a charge distribution centered about P with charges q_j at $(x + x_j, y + y_j, z + z_j)$ or $[P + (x_j, y_j, z_j)]$.

The potential energy of the system is then

$$V = \Sigma q_j \phi[P + (x_j, y_j, z_j)] \tag{1.8}$$

Again, $\phi[P + (x_j, y_j, z_j)]$ can be expressed in terms of a Taylor expansion, in this case about the point P. It is of a form

$$V = \Sigma q_j [\phi]_P + \Sigma \left\{ q_j x_j \left[\frac{\partial\phi}{\partial x}\right]_P + q_j y_j \left[\frac{\partial\phi}{\partial y}\right]_P + \cdots \right. \\ \left. + \Sigma \left\{ \frac{1}{2} q_j x_j^2 \left[\frac{\partial^2\phi}{\partial x^2}\right]_P + \cdots + q_j x_j y_j \left[\frac{\partial^2\phi}{\partial x \partial y}\right]_P + \cdots \right\} \right. + \cdots \tag{1.9}$$

The appropriate forms of $[\phi]_P (= \phi(P))$, $[\partial\phi/\partial x]_P$, etc. as derived from Eq. (1.5) can now be substituted. The quantities $\mathcal{Q}_b$, $\underline{p}_b$, $\underline{\underline{\mathcal{Q}}}_b$ can also be defined for molecule *b*. Finally, the potential energy V can be written in the form of a sum of terms.

The first term is $\mathcal{Q}_b \mathcal{Q}_a / 4\pi\varepsilon^\circ r$, describing simply the interaction between two charges, $V_{\mathcal{Q}\mathcal{Q}}$.

The next term is due to charge-dipole interaction:

$$V_{\mathcal{Q}p} = \frac{\mathcal{Q}_b}{4\pi\varepsilon^\circ r^2} \left\{ \frac{x}{r} p_{a,x} + \frac{y}{r} p_{a,y} + \frac{z}{r} p_{a,z} \right\} + \frac{\mathcal{Q}_a}{4\pi\varepsilon^\circ r^2} \left\{ \frac{x}{r} p_{b,x} + \cdots \right\}$$
$$= \frac{\underline{r} \cdot (\mathcal{Q}_a \underline{p}_b - \mathcal{Q}_b \underline{p}_a)}{4\pi\varepsilon^\circ r^3} \tag{1.10}$$

The contribution has also been written in vector notation, with the direction of $\underline{r}$ from the origin to P.

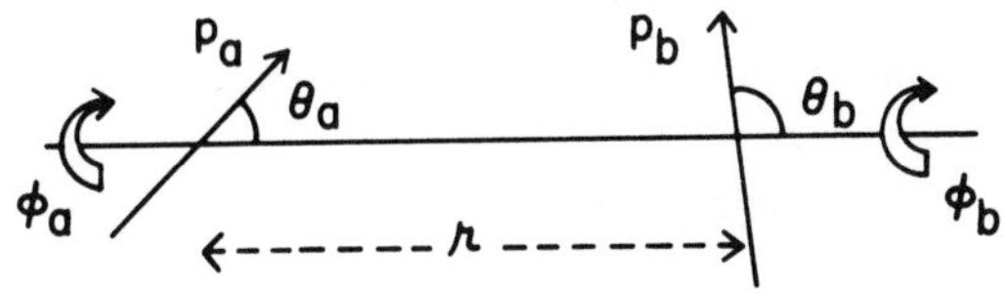

Fig. 1.2. Definition of the angles θ_a, θ_b, ϕ_a, ϕ_b.

These two terms, as well as the charge-quadrupole, charge-octopole, etc. terms, will be zero if ions are not involved. The first nonzero term is then the dipole-dipole contribution V_{pp},

$$V_{pp} = \frac{1}{4\pi\varepsilon^\circ r^3}\left\{\underline{p}_a\,\underline{p}_b - \frac{3(\underline{p}_a\cdot\underline{r})(\underline{p}_b\cdot\underline{r})}{r^2}\right\} \tag{1.11}$$

in the most general form. This will be considered in more detail.

A simpler expression can be obtained for (1.11) through introduction of the coordinate system shown in Fig. 1.2. When the z axis is chosen as the intermolecular line, then $p_{a,x} = p_a \sin\theta_a \cos\phi_a$, etc. Substitution of such forms into (1.11) leads to

$$V_{pp} = \frac{-p_a p_b}{4\pi\varepsilon^\circ r^3}\{2\cos\theta_a\cos\theta_b - \sin\theta_a\sin\theta_b\cos(\phi_a - \phi_b)\} \tag{1.12}$$

Equation (1.12) expresses the instantaneous contribution to the potential energy. Completely random mutual orientations of the molecule would give a time average contribution of zero. The mutual orientation is not random, however, as there is a weighing factor $\exp[-V_{pp}/kT]$ in the time average of orientations (Sec. 18.1)

The time (or ensemble) average potential energy arising from the preferential alignment can then be expressed as

$$\langle V_{pp}\rangle = \frac{\int V_{pp}\exp[-V_{pp}/kT]\,d\tau_a\,d\tau_b}{\int\exp[-V_{pp}/kT]\,d\tau_a\,d\tau_b} \tag{1.13}$$

The integration is over all orientations, with $d\tau_a = \sin\theta_a\,d\theta_a\,d\phi_a$.

For cases when $V_{pp} \ll kT$, then the exponential in 1.13 can be expanded as

$$\exp\left[-\frac{V_{pp}}{kT}\right] \simeq 1 - \frac{V_{pp}}{kT} + \cdots \tag{1.14}$$

and a contribution to the time average potential energy

$$\langle V_{pp}\rangle = -\frac{2p_a^2 p_b^2}{3kTr^6}\left(\frac{1}{16\pi^2\varepsilon^{\circ 2}}\right) \tag{1.15}$$

is predicted. The last factor converts the units to SI units.

Equation (1.15) predicts an attractive component in the intermolecular potential energy for polar molecules due to their preferential alignment. This is often referred to as the Keesom alignment effect and can be an appreciable part of the attraction. It is temperature-dependent, and has a $(1/r)^6$ dependence in agreement with the form of the 6-12 potential (1.1).

(c) Polarization and Induced Dipoles

When a charge distribution is in an electric field $\underline{E}$, it is distorted. This distortion (or polarization) can be described in terms of an induced dipole. In the simplest case, the induced dipole $\underline{p}_{in}$ is given by Eq. (20.8).

$$\underline{p}_{in} = \alpha\varepsilon^{\circ}\underline{E} \tag{1.16}$$

The constant of proportionality α is known as the polarizability. Values of α in the literature are usually given in cgs units (cm^3). To convert these to the SI units used in Equation (1.16) they must be multiplied by the factor $4\pi \times 10^{-6}$.

Equation (1.16) is not valid generally. For more accurate descriptions α must be considered as a tensor $\underline{\underline{\alpha}}$, not as a scalar [Sec. 12.1(f)]. The linearity of relationship (1.16) can also become invalid when the field strength is too great, and a hyperpolarizability term βE^2 must be introduced into (1.16).

The polarization in a molecule is primarily due to "electron polarization," where electronic charge density is displaced. Some "molecular polarization" can also occur due to distortion of the geometry of the molecule [11.1(b)]. An estimate of the polarizability of a polyatomic molecule can often be estimated by adding polarizabilities of the various bonds or functional groups present [1].

There will then be an induced contribution $V_{p,\text{ind}}$ to the intermolecular potential energy due to polarization effects. When $\underline{E}$ is the electric field at one molecule due to the permanent dipole of the other, then the magnitude of V_{ind} is given by

$$V_{\text{ind}} = -\int_0^E \underline{p}_{\text{ind}} \cdot d\underline{E}' = -\int_0^E \alpha\varepsilon^\circ \underline{E}' \cdot d\underline{E}' = -\frac{\alpha\varepsilon^\circ E^2}{2} \tag{1.17}$$

The electric field $\underline{E}$ due to a distribution is given by $-\underline{\nabla}\phi$. When only a dipole is assumed present the field at $\underline{r}$ is

$$\underline{E} = -\frac{\underline{p}}{4\pi\varepsilon^\circ r^3} + \frac{3\underline{r}(\underline{p}\cdot\underline{r})}{4\pi\varepsilon^\circ r^5} \tag{1.18}$$

Considering again the simple configuration shown in Fig. 1.2, V_{ind} can be shown to be

$$V_{\text{ind}} = -\frac{1}{2r^6(16\pi^2\varepsilon^\circ)}\left[p_a^2\alpha_b(3\cos^2\theta_a + 1) + p_b^2\alpha_a(3\cos^2\theta_b + 1)\right] \tag{1.19}$$

In (1.19), V_{ind} is again the instantaneous potential energy. The time average contribution is given by

$$\langle V_{\text{ind}}\rangle = \frac{\int V_{\text{ind}} \exp[-V_{\text{ind}}/kT]\, d\tau_a\, d\tau_b}{\int \exp[-V_{\text{ind}}/kT]\, d\tau_a\, d\tau_b} \simeq \frac{\int V_{\text{ind}}\, d\tau_a\, d\tau_b}{\int d\tau_a\, d\tau_b} \tag{1.20}$$

The simplification can be made as in this case $\int V_{\text{ind}}\, d\tau_a\, d\tau_b \neq 0$, while V_{ind} is assumed $\ll kT$.

The final result becomes

$$V_{\text{ind}} = -\frac{1}{r^6}(p_a^2\alpha_b + p_b^2\alpha_a)\cdot\frac{1}{16\pi^2\varepsilon^\circ} \tag{1.21}$$

This attractive energy has again a $(1/r)^6$ dependence. At least one of the molecules must be polar to have a nonzero contribution. It is often referred to as the Debye induction effect [see also Sec. 11.1(c)].

(d) Dispersion Forces

An attractive energy is present between molecules even if they are both nonpolar, so that V_{pp} and V_{ind} are zero. Such interactions are also greater than those expected from higher terms in Eq. (1.9) and

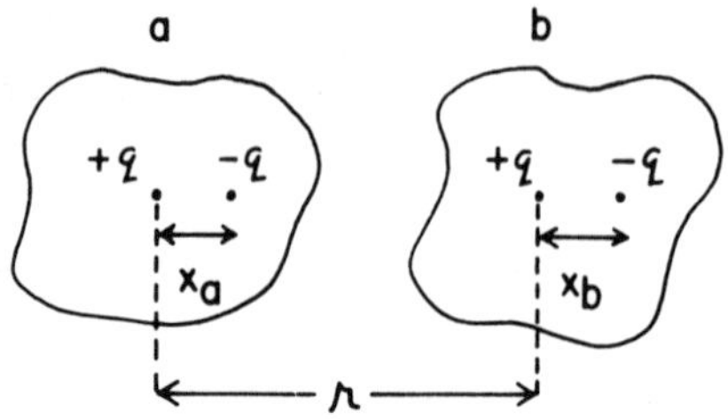

Fig. 1.3. Schematic diagram to illustrate dispersion forces.

have a $(1/r)^6$ dependence instead of the $(1/r)^8$ dependence expected from quadrupole-quadrupole interactions.

This additional contribution to V is due to "dispersion," or "London" or "induced dipole-induced dipole" interactions. It arises from a correlation in the zero-point fluctuation of the centers of charge in adjacent molecules. The origin of these forces will be illustrated by reference to a simple one-dimensional model as shown in Fig. 1.3.

Two molecules, a and b, are assumed to be a distance r apart. Due to zero-point motion, the centers of positive and negative charge in a molecule need not instantaneously be identical. Thus the centers of charge of molecule a are separated by a distance x_a and of molecule b by x_b at some instant.

Thus a will have an instantaneous dipole qx_a which, from the discussion in Sec. 1(c), would be expected to polarize molecule b, and vice versa. This would be expected to lead to an "induced dipole-induced dipole" interaction.

The zero-point motion of the centers of charge in a molecule is assumed to be simple harmonic. Thus, when a and b are of the same species, there is present an instantaneous potential energy $\frac{1}{2}\delta(x_a^2 + x_b^2)$. Interactions between charges on different molecules must be assumed to be coulombic.

When an amount of charge q is involved in both molecules, then the total potential energy is

$$V = \frac{1}{2}f(x_a^2 + x_b^2) + \frac{q^2}{4\pi\varepsilon^\circ}\left(\frac{1}{r} + \frac{1}{r - x_a + x_b} - \frac{1}{r - x_a} - \frac{1}{r + x_b}\right)$$

$$\simeq \frac{1}{2}f(x_a^2 + x_b^2) - \frac{2q^2 x_a x_b}{4\pi\varepsilon^\circ r^3} \qquad (1.22)$$

The simplification can be made as $x_a \simeq x_b$ and as $r \gg x_a$.

Equation (1.22) expresses the instantaneous total potential energy. The system must be considered in terms of quantum mechanics if changes in the zero-point energy due to intermolecular interactions are to be calculated. Thus, (1.22) is set into the Schrödinger wave equation (SWE) for the system [Eq. (21.4)]. The energy states for the two "harmonic oscillators" involved can then be obtained from the eigenvalues [Eq. (21.22)]. Finally the intermolecular interaction energy can be found by comparing these energies to the energies of two free oscillators.

When the variables x_a, x_b are changed to $x' = 1/\sqrt{2}\cdot(x_a + x_b)$ and $x'' = 1/\sqrt{2}\cdot(x_a - x_b)$, it is possible to separate the variables in the SWE to have $\psi(x', x'') = \psi'(x')\cdot\psi''(x'')$. The equation for $\psi'(x')$ and $\psi''(x'')$ become simply those for simple harmonic motion [Eq. (21.21)]. The total ground-state energy for the system is then found to be [2]:

$$E_0 = \frac{1}{2}h(\nu' + \nu'') = \frac{1}{2}h\nu_0\left\{\left(1 + \frac{2q^2}{4\pi\varepsilon^\circ f r^3}\right)^{\frac{1}{2}} + \left(1 - \frac{2q^2}{4\pi\varepsilon^\circ f r^3}\right)^{\frac{1}{2}}\right\} \qquad (1.23)$$

The substitution $\nu_0 = [1/(2\pi)]\cdot(f/\mu)^{\frac{1}{2}}$ has been made, where μ is the reduced mass.

Two isolated oscillators have a zero-point energy $h\nu_0$. When the binomial theorem is used to expand (1.23), then only the first nonzero term need be kept if $2q^2/(4\pi\varepsilon^\circ f r^3) \ll 1$. With this assumption, the interaction energy becomes

$$\langle V_{disp}\rangle = -\frac{h\nu_0 q^4}{2f^2 r^6}\left(\frac{1}{16\pi^2\varepsilon^{\circ 2}}\right) \qquad (1.24)$$

Equation (1.24) can be put into a more useful form. The force constant can be eliminated. From (1.17) the energy of the induced dipole is $\frac{1}{2}\alpha\varepsilon^\circ E^2$. This was assumed previously to be $\frac{1}{2}fx^2$. In this way the relation $f = q^2/\alpha\varepsilon^\circ$ is obtained.

The frequency ν_0 can in principle be calculated from measurements of dispersion of light. This is the origin of the term "dispersion force." As such data are seldom readily available, ν_0 is instead equated to the maximum frequency of radiation emitted by the molecule, $\nu_0 = \nu_m = Ie/h$. Here I is the ionization potential for the molecule and e is taken to be the electronic charge. Generalized to two different molecules in three dimensions, the result is (for q = e)

$$\langle V_{\mathrm{disp}} \rangle = -\frac{3}{2r^6}\frac{eI_aI_b\alpha_a\alpha_b}{I_a + I_b}\left(\frac{1}{16\pi^2}\right) \tag{1.25}$$

Again a $(1/r)^6$ dependence results.

(e) *Comparison of Magnitudes of Forces*

As seen from Eqs. (1.29), (1.21), and (1.15), the theoretical basis for the $(1/r)^6$ dependence in the 6-12 potential is reasonable, even in the case of nonpolar species. In most cases, values of ε in (1.1) are not calculated from α, p, etc., because accurate values of these molecular parameters are often as difficult to measure as values of ε itself.

The various methods of obtaining molecular parameters such as p, α, Q, ε, σ, etc. are not discussed here. Intermolecular pair potentials are considered more as a means to elucidating liquid structure and dynamics, rather than an end in itself. Nevertheless, considerable knowledge regarding these parameters can be obtained from studies of structure and dynamics in liquids (Chaps. 3, 11, 15, and 16). Methods of obtaining these parameters from gas-phase measurements are discussed in Ref. 1.

It is instructive to make a rough comparison between the magnitudes of $\langle V_{pp} \rangle$, $\langle V_{\mathrm{ind}} \rangle$ and $\langle V_{\mathrm{disp}} \rangle$. Table 1.1 shows such a comparison for a selection of molecular species. The units used in the table are those commonly found in the literature. SI units can be obtained through the conversion table at the end of this volume.

It should be noted that the contributions are quite sensitive to the magnitudes of α and p. The polarizability α increases with the size of the molecule and its volume. The values listed here, for

TABLE 1.1

Comparison of Magnitude of Forces

Species	$p/10^{-18}$ esu·cm	$\alpha/10^{-24}$ cm^3	$h\nu_0/V$	$\langle V_{pp}\rangle^a$	$\langle V_{ind}\rangle^b$	$\langle V_{disp}\rangle^c$
CO	0.12	1.99	14.3	0.003	0.057	67
H_2O	1.84	1.48	18	190	10	47
H_2	0	0.79	16.4	0	0	11
Cl_2	0	4.6	18.2	0	0	461
Ar	0	1.6	15.4	0	0	57

[a] $\langle V_{pp}\rangle = 2p^4/293k/10^{-60}$ erg^{-1} cm^{-6}.
[b] $\langle V_{ind}\rangle = 2p^2\alpha/10^{-60}$ erg^{-1} cm^{-6}.
[c] $\langle V_{disp}\rangle = 3\alpha^2 h\nu_0/4/10^{-60}$ erg^{-1} cm^{-6}.

all but Ar are averages, as the value of α depends on the orientation of the molecule in the electric field.

If the average distance between two water molecules is assumed to be 2.5 Å, then it is seen that at 293°K, $\langle V_{pp}\rangle \simeq 8 \times 10^{-13}$ erg. This is not $\ll kT$ which equals 4×10^{-14} erg, but is greater. Thus Eq. (1.15) is not valid in this case.

The 6-12 potential as given in Eq. (1.1) can be used for $V(r)$ (actually $\langle V(r)\rangle$) between identical or different species. When two different species are involved, σ is set equal to $\frac{1}{2}(\sigma_a + \sigma_b)$ and ε to $(\varepsilon_a \cdot \varepsilon_b)^{\frac{1}{2}}$. This substitution can be seen to be reasonable in the light of Eqs. (1.15), (1.21), and (1.25), and it has had empirical success. Often these relations are referred to as the Lorentz-Berthelot rules.

There are several other forms of potentials which attempt to take into account some of the phenomena neglected or approximated by the 6-12 potential. Quadrupole terms can be included, and a more realistic repulsion term can be substituted. Such models are discussed in some detail in Refs. 1, 3, and 4. They will not be covered here, even though some of the phenomena suggesting changes in the 6-12 potential will be discussed in the following sections.

(f) Perturbation Theory Treatment of Intermolecular Forces

Section 1(d) is an example of a very primitive quantum-mechanical calculation regarding intermolecular interactions. The other contributions, ($\langle V_{pp}\rangle$ and $\langle V_{\text{ind}}\rangle$), can also be described in terms of quantum-mechanical formalism. Such an approach is quite common in recent theoretical descriptions [3], and leads to a discussion of three-body and short-range forces. A quantum-mechanical perturbation treatment is outlined here. The reader is referred to Chap. 21 for the origin of the basic relationships assumed.

The molecules are here labeled a and b. An isolated a molecule has a ground-state wavefunction $\psi^{\circ}_{a,0}$ and excited states $\psi^{\circ}_{a,i}$, with corresponding energies $E^{\circ}_{a,0}$ and $E^{\circ}_{a,i}$. Analogous quantities are defined for b. In the case of no interaction, the total ground-state wavefunction is then $\psi^{\circ}_{0} = \psi^{\circ}_{a,0}\cdot\psi^{\circ}_{b,0}$, with an energy $E^{\circ}_{0} = E^{\circ}_{a,0} + E^{\circ}_{b,0}$.

The perturbation potential between the two molecules will be represented by V'. The interaction between two permanent charge distributions will then be given by the first-order perturbation term [Eq. (21.27)]

$$E' = \int \psi^{\circ *}_{0} V' \psi^{\circ}_{0}\, d\tau \;\; (= \langle a,0;b,0|V'|a,0;b,0\rangle) \tag{1.26}$$

Equation (1.26) is the formal quantum-mechanical equivalent of (1.8).

The second-order perturbation can be written as

$$E'' = \sum_{i,j} \frac{|\langle a,0;b,0|V'|a,i;b,j\rangle|^2}{(E^{\circ}_{a,0} + E^{\circ}_{b,0} - E^{\circ}_{a,i} - E^{\circ}_{b,j})} \tag{1.27}$$

This is a summation over all the states i of molecule a and j of molecule b, the ground state i = j = 0 excepted.

The sum (1.27) can be factored to give the formal quantum-mechanical analogs of induction and dispersion forces. Thus

$$E'' = \sum_{j\neq 0} \frac{|\langle a,0;b,0|V'|a,0;b,j\rangle|^2}{(E^{\circ}_{b,0} - E^{\circ}_{b,j})}$$

$$+ \sum_{i\neq 0} \frac{|\langle a,0;b,0|V'|a,i;b,0\rangle|^2}{(E^{\circ}_{a,0} - E^{\circ}_{a,i})}$$

$$+ \sum_{i,j\neq 0} \frac{|\langle a,0;b,0|V'|a,i;b,j\rangle|^2}{(E^\circ_{a,0} + E^\circ_{b,0} - E^\circ_{a,i} - E^\circ_{b,j})} \tag{1.28}$$

The first two sums represent the induction energy, i.e. the permanent charge of one molecule interacting with the distortion of the other molecule. The distortion is caused by the perturbation V'. The last sum represents the dispersion energy, i.e., the correlated composite distortion of both molecules.

More exact calculations can be made for $\langle V_{ind}\rangle$ and $\langle V_{disp}\rangle$, using the formalism in Eq. (1.28) for simple systems. Examples can be found in Ref. 3. The perturbation treatment can be continued to third-order to take account of "third-order forces."

(g) Many-Body Forces

Pairwise additivity of potential energies is not strictly valid. If there are three polar molecules a, b, and c close to each other, for example, then the orientation of a with respect to b is not independent of the presence of c. The potential energy in the Boltzmann (exponential) factor in Eqs. (1.13) and (1.20), for example, would be dependent on the position and orientation of c as well. Such an effect would also be present in the case of dispersion forces.

Such many-body effects are always present in liquids, but the previous discussion has always been based on a model of two molecules only. The effective pair potential between molecules in a liquid can be changed considerably by this effect. In carbon tetrachloride it is calculated to decrease by 32% [5]. The dispersion forces between lateral base pairs in the DNA double helix is also found to decrease by 14% due to the presence of the solvent (water), which acts in the correlating manner described above.

The quantitative treatment of many-body problems involves third-order perturbation theory. It begins with a total unperturbed wavefunction for three molecules, analogous to that for two molecules in Sec. 1.1(f), and assumes a perturbation consisting of three instantaneous dipole-dipole interaction terms, such as Eq. (1.11). The development of the formalism and its application to particular problems is, however, quite complex and beyond the scope of this book. Treatments of these problems can be found in Refs. 3 and 5.

1.2 SHORT-RANGE FORCES

(a) Origin of Repulsive Forces

The forces discussed in the previous section are all "long-range," in that the electron distributions of the molecules involved are not assumed to overlap. Such long-range forces give, in general, an attractive contribution to the pair potential. An obvious exception is the repulsion of two like-charged ions.

The repulsive forces occurring at short ranges can be treated as examples of chemical forces. Their origin is determined by the Pauli principle. This demands that the total wavefunction for the system (in this case two molecules) be antisymmetric to the exchange of two electrons, or, equivalently, that only one electron can occupy a specific energy state (spin included).

Thus an atom of a molecule will repel other atoms (both of the same and other molecules) if the atoms approach each other to distances where the wavefunction of the atoms start to overlap and if both atoms have a "closed-shell" structure. In terms of molecular orbital theory, repulsion occurs if there are no empty MOs present that lower the total potential energy of the system. When empty bonding orbitals are present, then such short-range forces can be strongly attractive and give rise to a chemical bond.

A quantitative discussion of short-range repulsive forces involves calculations relevant to chemical bonding. An outline of the approach is presented below to indicate how this differs from the quantum-mechanical treatment of long-range forces. Thorough discussions of chemical bonding (and repulsion) can be found in most quantum chemistry texts and in Refs. 1 and 5.

(b) Forms of the Repulsion Term

For the abovementioned calculations, the "adiabatic approximation" is usually made. The nuclei are assumed to move slowly with respect to the electrons, so that the wavefunction for the electrons in the system can be obtained, assuming a constant configuration for the nuclei.

The use of perturbation theory to obtain the electronic wavefunctions for the system, as in Sec. 1.1(f), is not valid in the case of short-range interactions. In Sec. 1.1(f), the electrons can be labeled as belonging to either one or the other of the molecules, but in this case they cannot. This indistinguishability of electrons must be taken account of in the electronic wavefunctions of the system. When this is done, large energy terms (called "exchange" terms in the valence bond approach) appear. When positive, they lead to a repulsion, when negative to an attraction (i.e., chemical bonding).

The valence-bond and MO methods are most commonly used for such calculations. These will not be discussed in detail here. Most quantum chemistry books have discussions of both approaches. To a first approximation, the repulsive term has a form

$$\langle V_{rep} \rangle = C_1 \exp[-C_2 r] \qquad (1.29)$$

This is obtained by fitting data to values calculated by various quantum-mechanical methods [3]. There is no formal justification for the form chosen, just as in the case of the $(1/r)^{12}$ term.

Numerical calculations of these repulsive terms are, of course, quite difficult, even for simple systems such as two He atoms. In the case of He, the repulsive energy as calculated by the LCAO-MO (linear combination of atomic orbitals) method, using Hartree-Fock atomic orbitals, has $C_1 \simeq 12.2 \times 10^{-10}$ erg and $C_2 = 2.5 \times 10^{-8}$ cm^{-1} [3]. The Lennard-Jones parameters for He are $\varepsilon = 1.4 \times 10^{-15}$ erg, $\sigma = 2.6 \times 10^{-8}$ cm.

(c) Charge-Transfer Forces

Intermolecular attraction arising from the formation of "charge-transfer" (CT) complexes is also a short-range phenomenon. The distinction between the formation of such complexes and of new molecules is not always clear, and the formalism can be extended to include the formation of species normally defined as "molecules" [6].

Such complexes arise between an acceptor molecule a and a donor molecule d. The wavefunction for the total system can then be approximated as

$$\psi_0 = c_0\psi_{a,d,0} + \Sigma c_i\psi_{a^-,d^+,i} \tag{1.30}$$

The c's are coefficients. Terms of the type where an electron is transferred from a to d are neglected here. In simple cases only some leading terms in the summation need be considered.

The intermolecular complex is thus stabilized by a net charge transfer from d to a. Excited states of such complexes often have as a main term an excited state of the a^-d^+ type. This can lead to an intense spectrum characteristic of CT complexes; for example, the case of benzene and iodine.

Benzene is a "sacrificial" donor, i.e., the electrons are donated from a bonding MO. Iodine is a "sacrificial" acceptor. Thus, on entering into the CT complex, the bond length of I_2 is expected to increase, indicating a weaker I-I bond. Although both benzene and iodine are in the CT complex individually in less stable states, there is, nevertheless, a net gain of stability in the CT complex as a whole. "Increvalent" donors and acceptors can also be present, where a lone pair is donated or obtained, e.g., NH_3 (donor) or $SnCl_4$ (acceptor).

The case of iodine:benzene (and halogen:π donors in general) is probably the "classical" case of CT complexes. However, a wide variety of phenomena, from ion pairing to Lewis acid-base pairing, to even covalent compound formation, can be treated under this formalism. A general discussion of the phenomenon is given in Ref. 6.

(d) Hydrogen Bonding

Hydrogen bonding can also be treated as an example of CT forces in some cases. The term "hydrogen bond" is usually used to characterize a strong interaction between the H of an OH or NH (in general, XH) group with O, N, F, or Cl atoms, which have an unshared pair of electrons, in some species Y. A CT contribution of the type ψ_{Y^+, XH^-} can be postulated to be present in some cases [7].

However, hydrogen bonds of a "weak" type are thought to be due predominantly to classical electrostatic effects [see Sec. 1.1(b)]. The X-H bond gives rise to a strong local electric field which polarizes the electrons on the Y species. As the H has no electrons to impede the approach of the Y, the distance H-Y is abnormally small, and a strong interaction results. The X-H bond distance is affected to an abnormal degree as well and becomes longer in the H-bonded form X-H---Y. The IR intensity [Sec. 12.3(g)] of the X-H stretching mode increases owing to the greater sensitivity of the dipole moment to the position of H. There is also a chemical shift of the H-bonded proton in NMR spectra [Sec. 13.3(b)].

"Strong" hydrogen bonds, with energies well above the typical 4 - 30 kJ mol^{-1} level, occur less often. In a case such as the hydrogen maleate ion, it is believed that the H moves across the bond, i.e., resonance stabilization takes place. This effect is unlikely to take place in the case of weak H bonds.

MO calculations for general cases of H-bonding are now available [8], and there are numerous calculations for H-bonding involving H_2O [Sec. 1.3(b)]. References 9 and 10 give a more thorough discussion of this phenomenon.

1.3 WATER

(a) Charge Distribution in the Water Molecule

The ultimate description of the charge distribution in a molecule is in terms of its wavefunction. As shown in Sec. 1.1(a), for many purposes the molecule can also be described in terms of multipoles.

The calculation of the total wavefunction for the water molecule has been done by a number of authors. Reference 11 gives a review of some more recent calculations, and an innovative calculation is given in Ref. 12. These are generally LCAO-MO self-consistent field calculations, and can involve a bases set of up to 30 functions.

The results of such a calculation expressed in terms of wavefunctions is quite complex and difficult to use in ordinary calculations. Yet a multipole description may not be valid for many calculations involving water. In such cases, the charge distribution can be described in terms of a set of point charges. Table 1.2 gives such a description of the water molecule in terms of 7-point charges [13]. This charge distribution is similar to the electrostatic component of an empirical potential energy function [14] for which the charge positions are given in parentheses. The empirical function [14] has, in addition, a repulsion and dispersion energy term $2.80 \times 10^5 \exp[-3.25r] - 1.19 \times 10^5 \times r^{-6}$, where r is given in angstroms and the energy in kilojoules per mole. As seen in Table 1.2 the skeleton of the H_2O is thus placed in the yz plane, with the xz plane bisecting the HOH angle. The dipole moment of water is then in the z direction with a magnitude of 1.84 D (10^{-18} esu·cm).

Another simpler combination of a Lennard-Jones and a point charge potential has also been used with success for water [15]. The simplest potential possible is desirable when many calculations are to be made,

TABLE 1.2

Charge Distribution in the Water Molecule

		Coordinates / Å		
Entity described	Charge	x	y	z
Oxygen nucleus with 2(1s) electrons	+6e	0(0)	0(0)	0(0)
Hydrogen nuclei	+e	0(0)	±0.764(±0.757)	0.586(0.586)
Bonding electrons	-2e	0(0)	±0.463(±0.360)	0.355(0.295)
Lone-pair electrons	-2e	±0.275(±0.144)	0(0)	-0.158(-0.100)

e.g., in molecular dynamics calculations [Sec. 3.3(b)]. Four charges (two +0.17e and two -0.17e) are placed tetrahedrally 1 Å from the center to make the interactions dependent on orientation. The Lennard-Jones parameters for neon (σ = 2.82 Å, ε = 5.01 x 10^{-15} erg) are used, as neon is isoelectronic with water.

The polarizability of the molecule as a whole (1.48 x 10^{-24} cm^3) can be used for electrostatic energy calculations. However, the polarizability of various parts of the molecule would be a more accurate representation. Often this can be done in terms of chemical bonds. Perpendicular ($\alpha_\perp$) and a parallel ($\alpha_\parallel$) components can be included for each bond. The lone-pair electrons must also be considered.

(b) Water-Water Interactions

Hydrogen bonding between water molecules can be described electrostatically on the basis of the simple model of water outlined in Sec. 1.3(a). A very simple model is shown in Fig. 1.4. Positive charges at the oxygen positions represent the remainder of the molecules (+2e at O_a and +e at O_b). The energy of the H bond calculated on such a simple model is calculated to be 24.9 kJ mol^{-1} [16]. This does not even take into account the contributions arising from polarization. Such calculations suggest that H bonds are essentially electrostatic in nature.

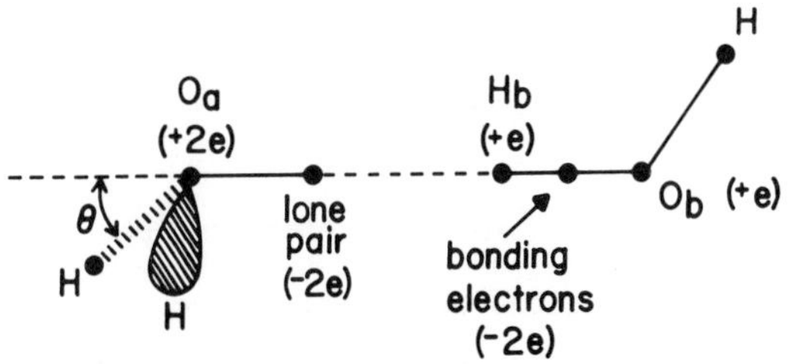

Fig. 1.4. Schematic diagram to illustrate H-bonding to form a water dimer.

Quantum-mechanical calculations have also been made of H-bonding between water molecules. A comparison of such calculations is in Ref. 17. In spite of the use of large sets of base functions and sophisticated techniques, there is a considerable deviation between various results. Five different calculations performed since 1968 have given a water-water pair potential energy ranging from 19.7 to 27.4 kJ mol^{-1}.

Three-body forces [Sec. 1.1(g)] in water interactions are of particular interest as it has been proposed that H bond formation in water is cooperative. Quantum-mechanical trimer calculations have been performed [17]. The correction necessary to allow for three-body interactions is dependent upon the H bond pattern involved, and is of a considerable magnitude.

Electrostatic calculations are not sufficient to explain the behavior of these three-body interactions. The calculations also predict a charge transfer of $\simeq -0.05e$ to the proton from the oxygen involved in the bond. Such charge-transfer effects are also not accounted for in classical calculations. Thus, for more accurate water calculations, quantum-mechanical effects must be considered.

The actual structure of an H-bonded water dimer can be determined from molecular beam electric resonance spectroscopy [18]. An O-O distance of 2.98 Å is found for the dimer, with the value of θ (Fig. 1.4) as $60° \pm 10°$ from the O-O axis. The dipole moment along the principal axis (essentially the O-O axis) is found experimentally to be 2.60 D, 0.49 D greater than the value 2.11 D obtained through vector addition of the monomer moments. Again some charge transfer effects must be postulated to be present, as electrostatic effects give an enhancement of only 0.44 D.

(c) Water-Ion Interactions

The use of the expressions developed in Sec. 1.1 is not justified when interactions between an ion and neighboring water molecules is considered. The electric field due to an ion is very great at such short distances, and it varies considerably within the dimensions of a molecule. Such conditions cannot be reproduced on a macroscopic level.

A point-charge model of the water molecule Sec. 1.1(a) is an improvement in such calculations. However, CT interactions and other effects needing a quantum-mechanical interaction are not included in such an approach.

Quantum-mechanical calculations have been performed on ion-water interactions [19, 20]. They are, however, of a semiempirical nature, using a CNDO method. This is in contrast to the "ab initio" approach for calculations on the water monomer and dimer [Sec. 1.3(a,b)]. Several water molecules were set into the ion hydration model, however. Ab initio studies of ion hydration have been made [21], but with only a single water molecule included. These ab initio studies give values in reasonable agreement with experimental values determined through mass spectrometry [22].

An especially important case of water-ion interaction is in the hydration of the proton. The most stable structure is an $H_9O_4^+$ species. As expected, the calculations show a considerable transfer of negative charge to the protons in the H_3O^+ ion. This structure is not likely to be rigid in aqueous solution, however, as the energy barrier for rotation about the hydrogen bond axis is below kT.

The discussion of ion-solvent interactions is continued in Chap. 5.

(d) Interaction of Water with Nonpolar Species

The term "hydrophobic interaction" is at times used in the discussion of aqueous solutions of nonpolar groups. This type of interaction is of importance in determining the conformation of nonpolar molecules in aqueous solution. The formation of micelles is the most obvious case of hydrophobic interaction. Another well-known example is the stability of the α-helix form of polyamino acids in aqueous solution [23, 24].

From the expressions in Sec. 1.1 it can be seen that the interaction between polar species should result in a lower energy than the interaction between a polar and a nonpolar species, all other things being equal. In the latter case, no contributions of the form of Eq. (1.15) are present. Polar groups are thus more stable when they are adjacent to each other rather than to nonpolar groups. There is therefore a tendency for the "hydrophobic" solute molecules to be in contact with each other, or perhaps separated by a single water molecule. The same type of interaction can occur in other solvents, so that the more general term "solvophobic interaction" is also used [25].

No actual repulsion need be present between the water and the nonpolar groups, as attractive forces exist due to polarization and dispersion effects. Thus the term "hydrophobic" is misleading. It is actually found that the transfer of the nonpolar group from the nonpolar environment to the aqueous environment is often exothermic [23].

To explain the exothermicity mentioned above, as well as volume and entropy effects, it is necessary to consider the environment of the polar-nonpolar interaction and, not just the groups directly involved. The water molecules around a nonpolar group are believed to be in a more structured "iceberg" form with both a lower enthalpy and entropy as compared to bulk water.

This increase in water structure near nonpolar groups is at times referred to as "hydrophobic structuring". Solutes are then classified as "hydrophobic," i.e., those increasing the structuring in water, and "hydrophilic," those decreasing the structuring. These effects will be discussed further in Chap. 4.

A reliable quantitative treatment of such phenomena is not yet available. Reference [26] gives an outline of a quantitative approach to a related simpler system, i.e., aqueous solutions of inert gases.

REFERENCES

Reference 1 contains a thorough discussion of theoretical approaches to intermolecular forces. It also contains many experimental data. Reference 3 gives an updating of the approaches in Ref. 1, and includes a thorough discussion based on quantum mechanical considerations.

References 6 and 8 are part of the summary of a meeting, "Interactions Moléculaires en Phase Liquide," Journal de Chimie Physique, Vol. 61, Nos. 1, 2(1964); therein are numerous articles of relevance to the topics in this book. Another such summary can be found in Discussions of the Faraday Society, No. 40 (1965) on "Intermolecular Forces." The properties of the water molecule and its interactions are reviewed in Refs. 10 and 13.

1. GR4.
2. F. London, Disc. Faraday Soc., *33*, 8 (1937).
3. H. Margenau and N. R. Kestner, Theory of Intermolecular Forces, Pergamon Press, London, 1969.
4. GR3.
5. N. R. Kestner and O. Sinanoglu, J. Chem. Phys., *38*, 1730 (1963).
6. R. S. Mulliken, J. Chim. Phys., *61*, 20 (1964).
7. H. Ratajczak, J. Phys. Chem., *76*, 3991 (1972).
8. J. E. DelBene, J. Am. Chem. Soc., *95*, 6517 (1973).
9. H. C. Longuet-Higgins, J. Chim. Phys., *61*, 1 (1964).
10. G. C. Pimentel and A. D. McClellan, The Hydrogen Bond, Freeman, San Francisco, Calif., 1960.
11. GR5.
12. T. H. Dunning Jr., R. M. Pitzer, and S. Aung, J. Chem. Phys., *57*, 5044 (1972).
13. GR4, based on the paper of A. Duncan and J. A. Pople, Trans. Faraday Soc., *49*, 217 (1953).
14. L. L. Shipman and H. A. Scheraga, J. Phys. Chem., *78*, 909 (1974).
15. A. Ben-Naim and F. H. Stillinger Jr., in GR6.
16. J. Lennard-Jones and J. A. Pople, Proc. Roy. Soc., London, *A 205*, 155 (1951).
17. D. Hankins, J. W. Moscowitz, and F. H. Stillinger Jr., J. Chem. Phys., *53*, 4544 (1970).
18. T. R. Dyke and J. S. Muenter, J. Chem. Phys., *60*, 2929 (1974).
19. R. E. Burton and J. Daly, Trans. Faraday Soc., *66*, 1281 (1970); *67*, 1219 (1971).
20. A. Gupta and C. N. R. Rao, J. Phys. Chem., *77*, 2888 (1973).
21. H. Kistenmacher, H. Popkie, and E. Clementi, J. Chem. Phys., *59*, 5842 (1973).

22. M. Arshadi, R. Yamdagni, and P. Kebarle, J. Phys. Chem., *74*, 1475 (1970).

23. W. Kauzmann, Adv. Protein Chem., *14*, 1 (1959).

24. G. Némethy, Angew. Chem., *79*, 260 (1967).

25. M. Yaacobi and A. Ben-Naim, J. Sol. Chem., *2*, 425 (1973). J. Phys. Chem., *78*, 175 (1974).

26. A. Ben-Naim, in GR6.

Further Recent References

A. Koide and T. Kihara, "Intermolecular Forces for D_2, N_2, O_2, F_2, and CO_2", Chem. Phys., *5*, 34 (1974).

T.B. MacRury, W. A. Steele and B. J. Berne, "Intermolecular Potential Models for Anisotropic Molecules, with Applications to N_2, CO_2, and Benzene", J. Chem. Phys., *64*, 1288 (1976).

S. Green, "Comment on Determination of the Interaction Potential Between Ar and HCl", J. Chem. Phys., *60*, 2654 (1974).

D. J. Evans and R. O. Watts, "Interactions Between Benzene Molecules II. Static Lattice Energy and Structure", Molec. Phys., *31*, 83 (1976).

B.F. Levine and C. G. Bethea, "Second and Third Order Hyperpolarizabilities of Organic Molecules", J. Chem. Phys., *63*, 2666 (1975).

S. F. O'Shea and W. J. Meath, "Charge-Overlap Effects in the Non-Additive Triple-Dipole Interaction", Mol. Phys., *28*, 1431 (1974).

M-J. Huron and P. Claverie, "Calculation of the Interaction Energy of One Molecule with its Whole Surrounding III. Application to Pure Polar Compounds", J. Phys. Chem. *78*, 1862 (1974).

L. L. Shipman, J. C. Owicki, and H. A. Scheraga, "Structure, Energetics, and Dynamics of the Water Dimer", J. Phys. Chem. *78*, 2055 (1974).

O. Matsuoka, E. Clementi, and M. Yoshime, "CI Study of the Water Dimer Potential Surface", J. Chem. Phys., *64*, 1351 (1976).

F. A. Momany, L. M. Carruthers, and H. A. Scheraga, "Intermolecular Potentials from Crystal Data IV. Application of Empirical Potentials to the Packing Configurations and Lattice Energies in Crystals of Amino Acids", J. Phys. Chem., *78*, 1621 (1974).

B. S. Ault, E. Steinback, and G. C. Pimentel, "Matrix Isolation Studies of Hydrogen Bonding. The Vibrational Correlation Diagram", J. Phys. Chem. *79*, 615 (1975).

G. van Hooydonk, "On an Ionic Approximation to Donor-Acceptor and Ion-Molecule Bonding, with References to Solvation Effects", Z. Naturforsch., *30a*, 845 (1975).

Chapter 2

MODELS DESCRIBING LIQUIDS

Chapters 2 and 3 deal, in different ways, with the problem of the description of the structure of pure liquid. The various approaches are attempts to describe the macroscopic (thermodynamic) properties of liquid in terms of the microscopic parameters describing individual molecules. In Chap. 2, the problem is approached by visualizing physical models of the liquid and then calculating its properties from these models. In Chap. 3, the problem is approached in a rigorous "ab initio" way.

In this chapter we will introduce radial distribution; a rigorous description of it is given in Chap. 3. The radial distribution function $g(r)$ can be thought of as describing the deviation of the local density from the mean density as a function of the distance from a molecule. In liquids it is typically of the shape shown in Fig. 2.1, approaching a value 1 for r greater than a few molecular diameters. It is zero for small r due to the repulsion term in the intermolecular potential (Fig. 1.1). It then shows a maximum when r is of the order of nearest-neighbor distances, a smaller maximum at next-nearest-neighbor distances, etc. until the ordered structure of the liquid disappears.

After introducing some thermodynamic considerations regarding liquids in Sec. 2.1, some models of liquids are outlined in Sec. 2.2.

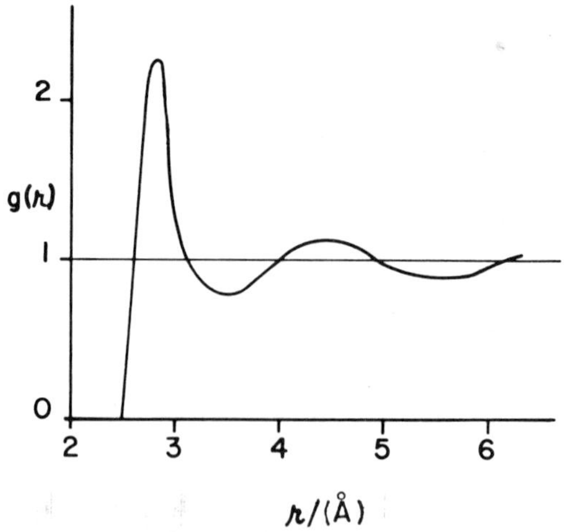

Fig. 2.1. An example of a radial distribution function for a liquid.

With recent advances in approaches to distribution function theories (Sec. 3.2) and computer simulation (Sec. 3.3), such model theories are not being developed further to any great extent. There is a substantial literature built up around them, however, and they are useful in introducing visual models of liquids. Some such models are also used for description of transport phenomena.

A summary of approaches to the elucidation of the structure of liquid water is included at the end of this chapter. It shows examples of the model approaches discussed in this chapter using water as a comparison substance.

2.1. THERMODYNAMICS OF PURE LIQUIDS

(a) Phase Changes

A liquid can be described as material which conforms to the shape of a container, without necessarily filling its whole volume, when placed in it. Some of the characteristic thermodynamic properties of a liquid are outlined below (see also Sec. 8.1).

The freezing (or melting) point of a substance is the temperature at which solid and liquid can coexist in equilibrium. This means that $\mu_s = \mu_l$ [Eq. (17.23)]. The melting point is a function of the applied pressure, but not a sensitive one; it also does not exist at all pressures. At sufficiently low pressures, a gas-solid equilibrium exists, and the liquid phase is nonexistent (see schematic phase diagram in Fig. 2.2). Only at the triple point (tp) can a liquid exist in equilibrium with both the solid and the gaseous phases.

In a liquid→solid transition, the entropy, enthalpy, and volume of the system are generally decreased. Water is an exception, as there the volume increases. These changes are discontinuous, and are referred to as the entropy, enthalpy, volume, etc. of fusion. Other properties such as heat capacity, refractive index, etc. also change discontinuously, but the free energy is continuous (see Fig. 8.1).

A liquid has a vapor pressure at all temperatures. This is the pressure of the gaseous phase in equilibrium with the liquid. The boiling point is reached when the vapor pressure of the liquid equals

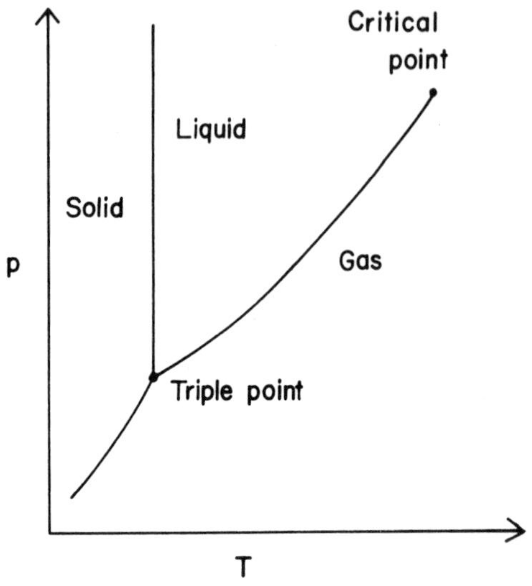

Fig. 2.2. Schematic phase diagram for a pure substance.

the external pressure. The boiling point is quite sensitive to pressure, as the vapor pressure is quite temperature-dependent. The relation between p and T is often adequately described by the Clausius-Clapeyron equation,

$$\frac{\partial \ln p}{\partial (1/T)} = -\frac{\Delta H_{vap}}{nR} \qquad (2.1)$$

where ΔH_{vap} is the heat of vaporization.

In a transition liquid→vapor, the volume, enthalpy, and entropy all increase. Such an increase is discontinuous, except at the critical point. Here the molar volumes of the gas and liquid become identical and the meniscus disappears. From Fig. 2.3, it can be seen that both $(\partial p/\partial V)_T$ and $(\partial^2 p/\partial V^2)_T$ must be zero there.

The behavior of thermodynamic properties in approaching the critical point is difficult to describe. It is currently done through a system of indices [1]. Thus, for example, the approach of p to p_c as a function of $|V - V_c|$ is described by an index δ. The approach is along the critical isotherm.

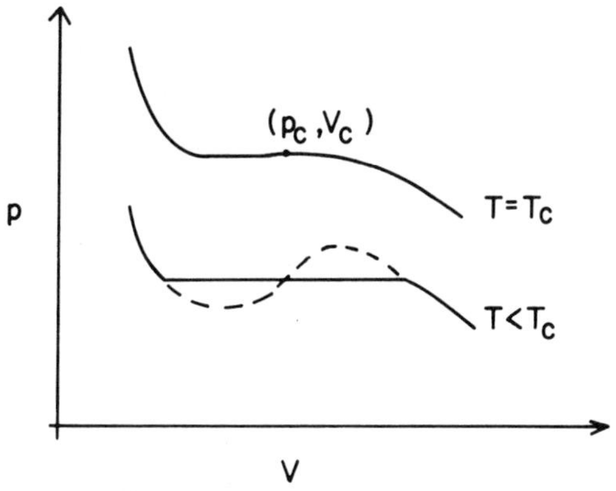

Fig. 2.3. Schematic pV isotherms at and below the critical temperature.

$$\delta = \lim_{V \to V_c} \left(\frac{\ln|p - p_c|}{\ln|V - V_c|} \right) \tag{2.2}$$

For a van der Waals fluid [Eq. (2.4)], the critical index should equal 3. Experimentally it appears to be 4.8 ± 0.4. Such index notation is used for critical phenomena in general, not only for liquids of one component.

(b) Law of Corresponding States

The critical constants T_c, p_c, V_c are at times used to introduce dimensionless reduced variables; $p_{red} = p/p_c$, $T_{red} = T/T_c$, $V_{red} = V/V_c$. The term "reduced variables"is also used for another set of variables, $p^* = p\sigma^3/\varepsilon$, $T^* = kT/\varepsilon$, $V^* = V/L\sigma^3$, where ε and σ are parameters in the 6-12 potential [Eq. (1.1)].

Such reduced variables can be used to formulate a universal equation of state in the form

$$\frac{pV}{nRT} = f(V^*, T^*) \tag{2.3}$$

The function f is universal, i.e., independent of the substance considered. Equation (2.3) is a statement of the law of corresponding states [see Sec. 18.4(c)].

This law is valid only if the total potential energy in the liquid can be expressed as a sum of pairwise intermolecular interactions. The form of the interactions must also be the same for all the species. considered. The 6-12 form is assumed valid in the previous discussion.

By making use of this law, it is not necessary to perform the numerical calculations pertinent to arriving at an equation of state for each individual species. Instead, it needs to be done only once to arrive at the universal equation.

(c) Van der Waals Equation of State

The very earliest model of liquids is that suggested by van der Waals in 1873. The equation itself is inadequate for reasonably accurate descriptions, but the physical basis of the model used by van der Waals seems quite adequate in the light of recent work [2].

A liquid in this model is an extreme case of an imperfect gas. The equation is thus in a form analogous to the ideal gas law,

$$\left(p + \frac{n^2 a}{V^2}\right)\left(\frac{V}{n} - b\right) = RT \tag{2.4}$$

where a and b are parameters which are related to the attractive forces and the sizes of the species involved. Equation (2.4) is not written as an universal equation of state [see Eq. (2.6)].

The physical basis of the model implies that a liquid may be regarded as a system of hard spheres, with attractive forces providing a uniform background energy. Similar models have recently had success in describing the liquid state [Sec. 3.3(c)].

Equation (2.4) predicts the existance of a critical point. The critical constants can be obtained in terms of a and b by setting $(\partial p/\partial V)_{T=T_c} = 0$, $(\partial^2 p/\partial V^2)_{T=T_c} = 0$. The results are

$$p_c = \frac{a}{27b^2} \qquad \frac{V_c}{n} = 3b \qquad T_c = \frac{8a}{27bR} \qquad \frac{p_c V_c}{nRT_c} = 0.375 \tag{2.5}$$

The compressibility factor pV/nRT is a universal function of reduced variables, and should thus be a constant at the critical point (Table 2.1).

Using the expressions for p_c, T_c, V_c from Eq. (2.5), the van der Waals equation can be written in the form of a universal equation of state:

$$\left(p_{red} + \frac{3n}{V_{red}}\right)\left(\frac{3V_{red}}{n} - 1\right) = 8T_{red} \qquad (2.6)$$

Equation (2.6) contains no parameters such as a and b which refer to a specific substance.

2.2. CELL THEORIES

(a) Basic Relationships for Cell Theories

In cell theories, the structure of a liquid is assumed basically to be that of a solid. Thus a volume V is divided up into N cells, each containing one molecule. Each molecule is assumed to move about in its cell independent of the motion of its neighbors.

The above model is essentially the same as a simple model of a solid, e.g., the Einstein model (Sec. 18.2). A difference between a solid and a liquid is that, whereas in a solid the molecules are essentially confined to the cells, in a liquid they have some possibility of movement from cell to cell (Chap. 6). In a dilute gas, molecules are free to move throughout the volume V.

The entropy of a gas is larger than the entropy of a solid because of this greater freedom of movement. This added entropy is called the "communal entropy," and has a magnitude Nk. It is the difference in entropy between N indistinguishable molecules free to move in a volume V, and N distinguishable molecules, each free to move in a volume V/N. A liquid would thus have at least part of this communal entropy.

The basic statistical mechanical relationships will be presented here first. The meaning of each of the terms will then be discussed in turn. The Helmholtz free energy A for the system can be written in the form (see Chap. 18)

$$A = -kT \ln Q = -NkT \ln\left(\frac{V_f}{\Lambda^3}\right) - NkT + \frac{N\upsilon(0)}{2} \qquad (2.7)$$

Q is the canonical partition function for the system, V_f the "free" or "effective" volume of a molecule in its cell, Λ the thermal de Broglie wavelength [Eq. (18.22)] and $\nu(0)$ the potential energy of a molecule at the middle of the cell.

V_f is defined in terms $\nu(\underline{r})$ as

$$V_f = \int_{\text{cell}} \exp\left[-\frac{\nu(\underline{r}) - \nu(0)}{kT}\right] d\underline{r} \tag{2.8}$$

Even for hard spheres, V_f will be less than V/N, and will have a complicated geometrical shape. In this case, however, $\nu(\underline{r})$ is uniform throughout the volume not excluded by neighboring molecules. For a more realistic potential, $\nu(\underline{r})$ will not be uniform inside the cell. Equation (2.8) can be considered to be the configuration integral for a molecule [Eq. (18.30)].

The first term on the right-hand side of Eq. (2.7) represents the contribution of N molecules (assumed monoatomic) in N distinguishable volumes V_f. The second term is the contribution to A of the total communal entropy. The third term is the contribution of the potential energy of the system with molecules at rest at their cell centers.

(b) Hard-Sphere Model

An equation of state can be obtained from the cell theory which very much resembles the van der Waals equation. In a cubic lattice, the distance between lattice points (cell centers) is $(V/N)^{1/3}$. The available volume per molecule is then approximately

$$V_f = \left[2\left(\frac{V}{N}\right)^{1/3} - 4a\right]^3 = 8\left[\left(\frac{V}{N}\right)^{1/3} - 0.78\left(\frac{b}{L}\right)^{1/3}\right]^3 \tag{2.9}$$

where a is the hard-sphere radius, b the van der Waals parameter, and L Avogadro's number.

The potential energy $\nu(0)$ is related to the internal energy of vaporization, ΔU_{vap}, as

$$\frac{L\nu(0)}{2} = -\frac{\Delta U_{vap}}{n} = -\frac{a(T)\cdot n}{V} \tag{2.10}$$

Equation (2.10) is written in the above form to make the resultant equation of state comparable to the van der Waals equation. Thus $a(T)$ is a "temperature-dependent" van der Waals parameter.

When Eqs. (2.9) and (2.10) are substituted into (2.7), then the equation of state can be obtained from $p = -(\partial A/\partial V)$ [Eq. (17.7)]. It is

$$\left[p + \frac{a(T)n^2}{V^2}\right]\left[\frac{V}{n} - 0.78b^{1/3}\left(\frac{V}{n}\right)^{2/3}\right] = RT \tag{2.11}$$

This is identical to Eq. (2.4) except that the excluded volume is not a constant. Equation (2.11) is a refinement of (2.4) when overlapping is considered at high densities. Reference 3 gives a more thorough discussion.

(c) Lennard-Jones-Devonshire (LJD) Model

The LJD cell theory uses the 6-12 potential [Eq. (1.1)] to calculate the free volume V_f. The calculation of $\upsilon(\underline{r}) - \upsilon(0)$ would be quite difficult if the neighbors were considered as discrete molecules. The approximation is therefore made that the c nearest neighbors are uniformly smeared out over a spherical surface a distance a from the center. This makes $\upsilon(\underline{r}) = \upsilon(r)$.

Even with this approximation, the calculation of $\upsilon(\underline{r}) - \upsilon(0)$, and thus V_f, A etc. is complicated and numerical methods must be used. The necessary numerical integrations [3] need be performed only once, however. The equation of state when written in terms of reduced quantities is a universal one. It is of the form:

$$\frac{pV}{NkT} = 1 + \frac{24}{T^*}\left[\frac{1}{V^{*4}}\left(1 + \frac{2g'}{g}\right) - \frac{1}{V^{*2}}\left(1 + \frac{2g''}{g}\right)\right] \tag{2.12}$$

where g', g'', and g are integrals dependent on c, T*, and V*.

Results from the LJD theory are shown in Table 2.1 in comparison with other theories. The comparison is in the form of reduced values for the critical constants. The LJD theory does not describe a liquid well near the critical point. It is in reasonable agreement with experiment at high densities, however, as expected on the basis of the underlying model.

(d) Variations of the Cell Theory

The LJD theory has been extended to take account of interaction of a molecule with its next-nearest neighbors as well (at $2a\sqrt{2}$ and $2a\sqrt{3}$). Double occupancy of cells has also been allowed for in later versions. There is no significant improvement in agreement with experiment, however.

Instead of describing the possibility of motion of molecules in a liquid through introduction of a communal entropy, it is also possible to introduce it by allowing cells to be unoccupied, i.e., "holes" to be present. The introduction of holes in the model seems natural in the light of the excess volume of liquids over solids.

In such hole theories, the number of cells is greater than the number of molecules. The cells are assumed to be of a size such that double occupancy is impossible, but that interaction over distances greater than nearest-neighbor can be neglected. The value of V_f in such theories is in principle dependent on the fraction of nearest-neighbor sites which are vacant. Some versions assume it to be a constant, however. Also, distribution of holes in the liquid model cannot be treated exactly. It is often assumed to be random, i.e., independent of energy considerations [Bragg-Williams approximation, Sec. 4.2(a)].

The hole theories do not show much improvement over the LJD theory as seen in Table 2.1, where two different hole (free volume) theories are shown. References 3 and 4 discuss several. An extra adjustable parameter is used in some hole theories, as the cell size is varied to minimize the free energy.

"Worm" or "tunnel" models [5] are other examples which are essentially variations of cell theory. Here the space is partitioned into cells which are long narrow tubes. The radii of the tubes is of the order of the mean molecular spacing, but each cell is capable of accommodating a large number of molecules in a row. The motions of the molecules are then assumed to be resolvable into independent transverse and longitudinal modes. This makes it possible to include cooperative motions of molecules into the model.

(e) Comparison of Results

The values of ε, σ used to calculate the reduced variables presented in Table 2.1 can be obtained by various means [3]. It can be seen that T_c^*, p_c^*, V_c^* are reasonably constant for nonpolar species where quantum-mechanical effects are unimportant. Thus ε and σ can also be estimated simply by noting the critical constants of a liquid. Empirical rules also relate them to melting and boiling points, molar volumes of solids, etc.

TABLE 2.1

Comparison of Theories with Experimental Results

Substance or theory	T_c^*	V_c^*	p_c^*	p_cV_c/nRT_c
He	0.52	5.75	0.027	0.30
Ar	1.26	3.16	0.116	0.29
N_2	1.33	2.96	0.131	0.29
CH_4	1.29	2.96	0.126	0.29
VDW	0.23	8.9	0.013	0.35
LJD	1.30	1.77	0.43	0.59
Hole [(a)]	2.74	2.0	0.47	0.34
Hole [(b)]	1.18	3.25	0.26	0.72
Tunnel [(c)]	1.07	1.8	0.37	0.62
Worm [(d)]	1.5	2.8	0.44	0.82

[(a)] Cernuschi and Eyring (see Refs. 3 or 4).

[(b)] Peek and Hill (see Refs. 3 or 4).

[(c)] Barker (see Ref. 5).

[(d)] Dahler (see Ref. 5).

2.3. SIGNIFICANT STRUCTURE THEORY

(a) Description of the Model

The significant structure theory is a model theory with a wide range of application. The parameters introduced into it are not the 6-12 pair-potential parameters, but experimental quantities such as the sublimation energy ΔU_{sub}, volume of the solid V_s, and Einstein characteristic terperature θ_e of the solid, and the liquid volume at the melting point. The last datum is not required if a method of successive approximations is used.

The preceding discussion, especially regarding hole theories, implies that at extreme limits a liquid resembles a solid or a gas. The significant structure theory pursues this feature of the liquid state [4].

Instead of the immobile holes introduced in the hole theory, the excess volume of a liquid over a solid, $(V - V_s)$ is pictured to be in the form of "fluidized vacancies" [for water see Sec. 2.4(d)]. A molecule beside such a vacancy or hole has conferred on it greater translational freedom. The increase in translational freedom of molecules can equivalently be expressed as having the holes behave as gas-like molecules.

No vacancies are assumed present in the solid. Thus there are $(V - V_s)/V_s$ moles of vacancies per mole of molecules. A fraction V_s/V of the positions around a hole are occupied. As it is the molecules around the hole which give the hole its properties (i.e., which result in an increase in the translational degrees of freedom), then the fraction of holes which have gas-like properties is given by $(V - V_s)/V_s \cdot (V_s/V)$. The remaining fraction of a mole, V_s/V, is associated with solid-like molecules.

A vacancy in the liquid moves about as freely as a molecule in the gas phase, and the concentration of vacancies in the liquid will equal the concentration of molecules in the "equivalent" gas. This equivalence of the vacancies in a liquid to molecules in a gas is basic to significant structure theory.

(b) Formulation of the Partition Function

In this section we will discuss the partition function for significant structure theories. For a mole of monatomic liquid, the partition function is given by Eq. (18.13).

$$Q = (q_s)^{LV_s/V} (q_g)^{L(V - V_s)/V}$$
$$= \left\{ \frac{\exp[\Delta U_{sub}/RT]}{(1 - \exp[-\theta_e/RT])^3} \cdot \left[1 + \frac{h(V - V_s)}{V}\right] \exp\left[\frac{-a \cdot \Delta U_{sub} \cdot V_s}{(V - V_s)RT}\right]\right\}^{LV_s/V}$$
$$\left\{ \frac{(V - V_s)}{\Lambda^3} \cdot \frac{eV}{L} \right\}^{L(V - V_s)/V} \tag{2.13}$$

The terms within the curly brackets represent the portion of the partition function due to the solid-like aspect of liquids. The factor $\exp[\Delta U_{sub}/RT]/(1 - \exp[-\theta_e/RT])^3$ is the partition function for an atom in an Einstein solid [Eq. (18.15)]. As ΔU_{sub} is the sublimation energy, the reference energy is for atoms in the framework.

The factor $[1 + h(V - V_s)/V]$ is a geometrical degeneracy factor. Additional sites become available for a molecule if it has sufficient energy to push neighbors aside. Thus the number of sites will be 1 plus the number of neighboring positions $h(V - V_s)/V$ which the molecule can occupy, times the probability that it can occupy the site. h and a are dimensionless proportionality parameters. h is V_s/V times the number of neighboring positions. It is approximately equal to 10.8. The energy required to occupy a neighboring site is assumed to be proportional to ΔU_{sub} and to $V_s/(V - V_s)$. The constant of proportionality a has a value of ~0.005, but it is often used as an adjustable parameter in the theory.

The terms within the second curly brackets is the partition function for the gas-like part of the liquid [Eq. (18.23)]. The factor eV/N is included here; it is the Stirling approximation equivalent to the term $[(L(V - V_s)/V)!]^{-1}$, which would otherwise appear in the total gas-like portion of the partition function. It is present because of the indistinguishability of the gaseous molecules.

(c) Refinements for Polyatomic Molecules

Equation (2.13) has been written for monatomic species. In the case of polyatomics, rotational motion and internal vibrations of the molecules must be considered. The molecules may not be able to rotate freely in the liquid or solid states. In such a case, a rotational degree of freedom goes over into a "librational" degree of freedom (Chap. 7).

When rotation is hindered in the solid, the number of degrees of freedom assigned to "Einstein" oscillators in q_s is increased from 3 to 6 (5 for linear molecules). The "freezing" of rotational into librational degrees of freedom is generally occompanied by a high entropy of fusion. Internal rotations [6] and vibrations must also be included in the partition function.

In the gas-like portion of the partition function, free rotation is assumed. In some cases a dimer term is included in the gas-like portion. An example is the case for molten metals, where dimer concentrations in the actual vapor are quite high.

Once the partition function is available, then the free energy of the liquid can be calculated, and from this, other thermodynamic properties for the liquid [Eq. (17.2)]. The significant structure theory can also be used for calculation of transport properties, surface tension, etc. and can be applied to liquid mixtures. An example of the results is shown in Sec. 2.4(d) for the special case of water. It should be noted that this is an empirical theory, introducing a considerable amount of experimental information of properties of the substance in order to predict some further properties.

2.4. COMPARISON OF MODEL THEORIES FOR LIQUID WATER

(a) Introduction

The structure of water has been described by a large number of models and theoretical approaches. Reviews with more complete references can be found in Refs. 7, 8, and 9. In this section a sampling of the theoretical approaches will be outlined to illustrate some of these approaches.

There are a large number of two-state theories of water. In such theories liquid water is assumed to be a mixture of two forms of water molecules. Often one form is unassociated water, i.e., water in the "monomer" form. The other form is then an associated, structured form. It has been assumed by various authors to be a quartz-like hydrogen-bonded species, a clathrate structure, etc.

Other two-state theories assume two types of hydrogen-bonded structures, one more dense than the other. Two-state theories can best be illustrated by a discussion of "multistate" theories as presented in Sec. 2.4(b).

There has been some controversy as to whether a "continuum" or a "two-state" model is appropriate for liquid water (see, e.g., Ref. 10). An outline is therefore given in Sec. 2.4(c) of a continuum model. Section 2.4(d) contains an outline of the application of the significant structure theory to liquid water. It is somewhat more complex than application of this theory to other liquids because $V_s > V$ in the case of water. The use of cell theory to describe liquid water is outlined in Sec. 2.4(e). In this system adjustable parameters are not used, and a realistic intermolecular potential energy function is assumed.

Descriptions of liquid water using Monte Carlo and molecular dynamics methods are given in Sec. 3.3(c). A comparison of the results from all these theories with experimental results is postponed to later chapters when the experimental techniques have been discussed.

(b) Multistate Theories

The Nemethy-Scheraga model of liquids is probably the best-known multistate theory [11]. The formation of hydrogen bonds can be thought of as being "cooperative" [Sec. 1.3(b)]. Thus it is postulated that H bonds are not made or broken singly, but several at a time. This produces clusters of highly hydrogen-bonded regions. Local energy fluctuations then govern the formation and dissolution of the clusters. They are often referred to as "flickering clusters" and the model as the Frank and Wen model.

Five species of water are postulated to exist in the theory, corresponding to water molecules with 0, 1, 2, 3, and 4 H bonds. The model can also be viewed as the "two-state" model, with water either in the form of monomers (no H bonds) or in clusters (1, 2, 3, or 4 H bonds). The five species are assumed to have equally spaced energy levels, $E_0 \cdots E_5$ with $\Delta E = 2.76$ kJ mol^{-1}. This rather low value of ΔE is arrived at by allowing ΔE to be an adjustable parameter and noting the value for the best fit.

The fractions of species present, $x_0 \cdots x_5$, can be described by relationships containing three variables: x_0, the average number of molecules in a cluster n, and the fraction of molecules in a cluster with only one H bond, y_1. For a cluster of specific size and structure, the fractions y_2, y_3, and y_4 are related to each other.

The partition function Q is then written as

$$Q = \Sigma \left\{ \frac{N!}{N_0!N_1!N_2!N_3!N_4!} \left(q_4 \exp\left[- \frac{E_4}{RT} \right] \right)^{Nx_4} \left(q_3 \exp[\ ] \right)^{Nx_3} \right.$$

$$\left. (q_2 \exp[\ ])^{Nx_2} (\ )^{Nx_1} (\ )^{Nx_0} \right\} \qquad (2.14)$$

The summation is over all values x_0, n, and y_1. However, Q is assumed to equal only the maximum term of Eq. (2.14). This can be found by solving the simultaneous equations $\partial \ln Q/\partial n = \partial \ln Q/\partial x_0 = \partial \ln Q/\partial y_1 = 0$.

The "molecular" partition functions $q_0 \cdots q_5$ include only the translational, rotational, and vibrational parts. q_0 is taken as the product $q_t q_r q_v$, i.e. (see Chap. 18),

$$q_0 = q_t q_r q_v = \left(\frac{V_f}{\Lambda^3} \, \frac{2\pi}{\sigma} (2\pi I kT)^{1/2} \left\{ \prod_{j=1}^{5} \left(1 - \exp\left[- \frac{h\nu_j}{kT} \right] \right)^{-1} \right\} \right. \qquad (2.15)$$

V_f denotes the free volume as defined in Eq. (2.8). Only one rotation is assumed allowed, along the dipole axis of the nonbound molecule. The remaining two degrees of freedom are assumed to be librational (i.e., hindered rotations).

The q_1, q_2, q_3, q_4 are assumed each to contain six vibrational (or librational) degrees of freedom. The frequencies used in the expressions are obtained from assignments of Raman and infrared spectra of liquid water.

The free volume V_f was used as an adjustable parameter in the theory. A value 4.4×10^{-25} cm^3 mol^{-1} gave the best results. Thus a number of adjustable parameters and pieces of experimental data are used in the theory.

From Q, the free energy A and thermodynamic parameters can be obtained. There is good agreement between this theory and experimental values of A, S, and U over a range 0 to 100°C. The agreement between theoretical and experimental values of C_V is not good, however. The actual calculations are quite complex, and have been done numerically with the aid of computers.

Instead of formulating a partition function in terms of numbers of H bonds as in Eq. (2.14), recent extensions of "multistate" theories [12] have the Q formulated in terms of clusters of different sizes. Cluster sizes from 1 to 9 have been included. A cooperative H-bonding effect [Sec. 1.3(b)] has been taken into account by assuming energies of 8.6, 17.1, 11.7, and 18.4 kJ mol^{-1} for the first, second, third, and fourth H bonds on a water molecule. The results indicate that water molecules would be predominantly in clusters of 5 or 6, with essentially none in clusters of >7 molecules. As T increases, the number of molecules in smaller clusters increases. The results resemble the "continuum" model results [Sec. 2.4(c)] in several aspects.

(c) Continuum Theory

In the previous model, a considerable fraction of the H bonds present in ice are assumed broken when the liquid is formed. In the continuum approach, the bonds are assumed to bend in the liquid.

The continuum theory of Pople [13] assumes that, as the temperature of ice rises, the H bonds become increasingly bent. This eventually leads to a breakdown in long-range order of fusion. After fusion, the 4 H bonds are assumed to be able to bend independently; before fusion (i.e., in ice) they can bend only in a manner which maintains lattice order.

An H bond bending force constant f is introduced. Thus the probability $w(\theta)\,d\theta$ that the intermolecular line makes an angle between θ and $\theta + d\theta$ with the bond-forming direction (linear O...H-O configuration) is written as

$$w(\theta)\,d\theta = \frac{\exp[-f\cos\theta/kT]\sin\theta\,d\theta}{\int\exp[-f\cos\theta/kT]\sin\theta\,d\theta} \tag{2.16}$$

The average distortion can then be expressed by $\langle\cos\theta\rangle$. This is

$$\langle\cos\theta\rangle = \coth\left(\frac{f}{kT}\right) - \left(\frac{kT}{f}\right) \tag{2.17}$$

Equation (2.16) is strictly valid only if the librational frequencies corresponding to changes in θ are small as compared to kT/h. This is not strictly valid.

A numerical value for f is chosen to give the best fit of the calculated radial distribution function to an experimental one. It has a value $10kT$ for the best fit at 1.5°C. In fitting experimental distribution functions with this theory, some other parameters are also chosen to give the best fit.

There are four nearest neighbors for a specific water molecule. The system is continually branching; thus the second shell should have 12 and the third 36 water molecules. It is assumed, however, that molecules in the third shell can be connected to the central molecule by more than one bonding sequence. Thus the number set 4, 12, 36 is adjusted to 4, 11, 12 to give the best results.

With the above adjustable parameters, the theory can be made to fit radial distribution functions in a satisfactory manner. It can also be used to explain the increase in density on fusion. This is due to an increase in the density of molecules in the shells around a central molecule due to the bending of H bonds. The average distortion is calculated to be considerable, with $\cos^{-1}(\langle\cos\theta\rangle) \simeq 30°$. The calculated static dielectric constant on this model is also in good agreement with the experimental [Sec. 11.3(b)].

(d) Significant Structure Theory (SST)

The partition function for liquid water is in terms of the SST written as [14]

$$Q = (q_{sI})^{N_I} \cdot (q_{sIII})^{N_{III}} \cdot (q_g)^{N(V - V_s)/V_s} \qquad (2.18)$$

As shown in Sec. 2.3(b), q_g is the molecular partition function for water in the gaseous state. q_{sI} and q_{sIII} are partition functions for ice I-like and ice III-like molecules.

Thus, in addition to "fluidized vacancies," liquid water is assumed to have an equilibrium between two types of icelike molecules. The ice I-like molecules are in cagelike (clathrate) structures of about 46 molecules each with the density of ice I. These clusters are assumed distributed in an ice III-like structure, which is more dense than ice-I.

V_s here is not the molar volume of real ice, but of a mixture of ice I and ice III. The equilibrium constant for the ice I-ice III equilibrium is obtained by introducing the ΔS, ΔH, and ΔV between these forms. The parameters ΔU_{sub}, θ_e, h, a and the vibrational frequencies are assumed to be the same for ice I and ice III molecules. There are thus a large number of parameters which are introduced into the theory.

Although the model predicts a maximum density for H_2O at 4°C and for D_2O at 11°C, it is in considerable error in predicting the critical constants. The authors [14] believe the use of perfect gas theory (Sec. 18.3) may be responsible for this descrepancy. The holes in the liquids should cluster in the liquid in the same manner as molecules begin to cluster in the vapor near the critical point.

(e) Cell Theory

In distinction to the empirical theory in Sec. 2.4(d) which introduces many experimental parameters, the cell theory outlined below [15] uses more basic information. An intermolecular pair potential and the basic geometry of the cells are assumed, but no adjustable parameters are used.

The basic cell theory equations (2.7) and (2.8) are applicable in this case. The potential energy function $v(\underline{r})$ arises because of the complex intermolecular potential [Sec. 1.3(a)]. The intermolecular potential energy $v(\underline{r})$ is computed assuming each water molecule as a system of 7-point charges, corresponding to the entities in Table 1.2. The directions of the H's and the lone pairs are assumed to be tetrahedral. The H's are 0.96 Å from O, the lone pairs 0.29 Å and the bonding electrons 0.62 Å along the OH axis. Superposed on this is a repulsive potential $c_1 \exp[- c_2 r]$ adjusted so that the minimum in $v(r)$ occurs at $r = 2.76$ Å.

The cells were arranged according to an expanded ice lattice. The integration for V_f was then carried out by choosing the position and orientation of an H_2O in its cell randomly many times and numerically calculating the integral. Although the angle variables were sampled from a uniform distribution, a Gaussian distribution was used for the space variables. Thus V_f can be obtained as a function of and the size of the cell, as determined by the lattice assumed.

The results of the calculations are not in very good agreement with experiment. However, in this theory there are no adjustable parameters, and relatively few input parameters. The presence of "interstitial" molecules in the lattice was also neglected. Approximately 20% of the molecules should be placed in interstitial positions if the experimental density is to be obtained.

A more recent model of water based primarily on the cell theory has recently been suggested [16]. A simpler intermolecular potential energy function is used, comprised of 4-point charges and a neon 6-12 potential [Sec. 1.3(a)]. The necessity of including quantum effects to describe orientation is pointed out as the differences between rotational energy levels for H_2O are not $\ll kT$ in the normal liquid range.

REFERENCES

A thorough discussion of the equilibrium thermodynamic properties of liquids is given in Ref. 1. Both Refs. 3 and 4 give a discussion of various model theories of liquids, and Ref. 4 gives a thorough account of significant structure theory.

1. GR3.
2. M. Rigby, Quart. Rev., *24*, 417 (1970).
3. GR4.
4. H. Eyring and M. S. Jhon, Significant Liquid Structures, Wiley, New York, 1969.
5. H. S. Chung and J. S. Dahler, J. Chem. Phys., *43*, 2610 (1965) and preceding papers.
6. G. L. Faerber, S. M. Breitling, A. MacKnight, and H. Eyring, J. Phys. Chem., *76*, 731 (1972).
7. GR6.
8. H. S. Frank in GR7.
9. GR5.
10. J. Schiffer, J. Chem. Phys., *50*, 566 (1969); G. E. Walrafen, ibid., p. 567.
11. G. Némethy and H. A. Scheraga, J. Chem. Phys., *36*, 3382 (1962).
12. B. R. Lentz, A. T. Hagler, and H. A. Scheraga, J. Phys. Chem., *78*, 1531 (1974).
13. J. A. Pople, Proc. Roy. Soc., *A205*, 163 (1951).
14. M. S. Jhon, J. Grosh, T. Ree, and H. Eyring, J. Chem. Phys., *44*, 1465 (1966).
15. M. Weissmann and L. Blum, Trans. Faraday Soc., *64*, 2605 (1968).
16. O. Weres and S. A. Rice, J. Am. Chem. Soc., *94*, 8983 (1972).

Further Recent References

G. M. Bell and H. Sallouta, "An Interstitial Model for Fluid Water. Accurate and Approximate Results", Mol. Phys., *29*, 1621 (1975).

P. Boutron and R. Alben, "Structural Model for Amorphous Solid Water", J. Chem. Phys., *62*, 4848 (1975).

B. R. Lentz, A. T. Hagler, and H. A. Scheraga, "Structure of Liquid Water. II. Improved Statistical Thermodynamic Treatment and Implications of a Cluster Model", J. Phys. Chem., *78*, 1531 (1974).

G. S. Kell, "Distribution Function and Angular Deformations of a Model Related to Vitreous Ice and Liquid Water", Can. J. Chem., *52*, 1945 (1974).

Chapter 3

LIQUID THEORIES BASED ON DISTRIBUTION FUNCTIONS

In this chapter no model of a liquid is assumed. Instead, attempts are made to obtain the structural, and in some cases dynamical, properties of liquids starting only with an intermolecular potential energy function. Such a "fundamentalist" approach cannot be carried through to a final description of the properties of bulk liquids, because the mathematical and/or computational problems involved are at present insurmountable. Thus, approximations must be made in the course of developing the theory. Such simplifications can occur through, e.g., assuming the potential energy pairwise additive, choosing a simple pair-potential energy function, neglecting terms in expansions, restricting the size of computer simulation models, etc.

After an introduction to distribution functions in Sec. 3.1, relationships between $g(r)$ and $v(r)$ are examined in Sec. 3.2. To a first approximation, attempts to relate $g(r)$ with $v(r)$ can be thought to follow either from a "series expansion method" [Sec. 3.2(b)] or a "perturbation method" [Sec. 3.2(c)]. It is not possible to clearly resolve all theoretical approaches into one or the other, however, as either approach can be taken to arrive at a particular final result. Examples mentioned in the last paragraphs in Secs. 3.2(b) and (c) show the difficulty in classifying a theoretical approach uniquely.

The validity of the various theories can be tested by comparison to experiment. A more valid test of the theoretical approach is actually through comparison with good computer simulation results. The computer simulation (CS) results may not agree fully with the experimental results for real liquids. However, if a sufficiently large number of configurations are chosen, then the CS results converge to the correct results for the liquid under the assumptions made in their input. If other theoretical approaches begin with the same assumptions as the CS, then the results can meaningfully be compared to CS results. If some such other approach (e.g., a cell theory, a perturbation theory, etc.) produces results very different from the CS results, then that theoretical approach cannot give an accurate description. Whether the assumptions made are valid for a real liquid is not relevant here; it is the approach rather than the model which is tested by such comparisons.

Section 3.3 on computer simulation could, in a sense, be set under Part B, "Experimental Techniques." Such simulations can be viewed as numerical experiments rather than theoretical approaches. In setting up such a simulation, assumptions must be made regarding the type of intermolecular potential energy function used, the type of interactions to be included etc., so that the results cannot be completely valid for a real liquid. Results of such "numerical experiments" are referred to in later chapters, as well as in Sec. 3.2.

3.1. TYPES OF DISTRIBUTION FUNCTIONS

(a) Definitions

The simplest distribution function is simply the particle or number density $n = N/V$. In liquids it can be equated to the distribution function $n^{(1)}(\underline{r})$, where $n^{(1)}(\underline{r})\ d\underline{r}$ gives the probability of finding a molecule in $d\underline{r}$ at $\underline{r}$ irrespective of the positions of the other molecules. Higher order distribution functions $n^{(2)}$, $n^{(3)}$ ... $n^{(i)}$ ... can also be formulated

Thus the pair distribution function $n^{(2)}\ (\underline{r}_1, \underline{r}_2)$ is difined in analogy as the probability of simultaneously finding molecules at $\underline{r}_1$ and $\underline{r}_2$, irrespective of the positions of the other molecules (differential volumes $d\underline{r}_1$, $d\underline{r}_2$ are understood). Such distribution functions are interrelated by equations such as (3.1). The integration is only wrt. $\underline{r}_2$.

$$\int_V n^{(2)}(\underline{r}_1, \underline{r}_2)\ d\underline{r}_1\ d\underline{r}_2 = n^{(1)}(\underline{r}_1)\ d\underline{r}_1 \cdot (N - 1) = \frac{N(N - 1)}{V} \quad (3.1)$$

The distribution functions can be formally related to the potential energy $V\{N\}$ of the system. The symbol $\{N\}$ indicates that V is a function of the coordinates of the N molecules. For $n^{(2)}$ the relation is

$$n^{(2)}(\underline{r}_1, \underline{r}_2)\ d\underline{r}_1\ d\underline{r}_2 = \frac{N!}{(N - 2)!} \int \cdots \int_V \frac{\exp[-V\{N\}/kT]}{Z_N}\ d\{N - 2\} \quad (3.2)$$

Here Z_N is the configuration integral [Sec. 18.4(a)]. The symbol $\int\cdots\int\cdots d\{N - 2\}$ indicates integration over the volume with respect to the coordinates of N - 2 of the molecules. The first factor accounts for the number of ways of placing 2 of the N molecules in the volume elements $d\underline{r}_1$ and $d\underline{r}_2$. The second is the sum of the probabilities of finding the remaining (N - 2) molecules in all possible configurations.

A closed system has been assumed here, i.e., N fixed. For many cases, it is necessary to consider an open system, where μ and not N is fixed. This leads to considerations of the grand canonical ensemble, where all possible numbers of molecules N are considered. Reference 1 considers these aspects in detail. They will not be covered here, even though some results from such treatments are used.

When the total intermolecular potential energy V is considered to be the sum of pairwise interactions v, then the pair distribution $n^{(2)}$ is the most important one. It is often more convenient to consider normalized distribution functions. Thus a "radial distribution function," $g(r)$, is introduced as

$$n^{(2)}(\underline{r}_1, \underline{r}_2) = n^{(1)}(\underline{r}_1)n^{(1)}(\underline{r}_2)g(\underline{r}_1, (\underline{r}_1 - \underline{r}_2)) \tag{3.3}$$

For an isotropic fluid Eq. (3.3) simply reduces to

$$n^{(2)}(r) = n^2 g(r) \tag{3.4}$$

$g(r)$ is also at times defined in terms of δ functions. Thus

$$n g(r) = \frac{1}{N}\langle \sum_{i \neq j} \delta(\underline{r} + \underline{r}_i - \underline{r}_j)\rangle \tag{3.5}$$

The δ function will have nonzero values only for $\underline{r} + \underline{r}_i - \underline{r}_j = 0$; i.e., for $\underline{r} = (\underline{r}_j - \underline{r}_i)$, where $\underline{r}_i$ and $\underline{r}_j$ are the positions of the ith and jth molecules. The sum is over all the molecules in a configuration. The symbol $\langle \cdots \rangle$ then indicates that the ensemble average of all configurations is taken.

When departures of the distribution from random values is considered (Sec. 3.2), then it is convenient to introduce a "total correlation function," $h(r)$. It is defined as

$$h(r) = g(r) - 1 \tag{3.6}$$

Another correlation function, the "direct" correlation function, is introduced through the Ornstein-Zernike relation. This is of the form of an integral equation:

$$h(r_{12}) = c(r_{12}) + n\int c(r_{13})h(r_{23})\, d\underline{r}_3 \quad (3.7)$$

$c(r)$ has a range shorter than $h(r)$, comparable to the range of the pair potential $v(r)$. The physical meaning of $c(r)$ can best be described by substitution of Eq. (3.7) for $h(r_{23})$ in the integral in (3.7). This leads to the expression

$$h(r_{12}) = c(r_{12}) + n\int c(r_{13})c(r_{23})\, d\underline{r}_3 + n^2\int\int c(r_{13})c(r_{34})c(r_{42})\, d\underline{r}_3\, d\underline{r}_4 + n^3\int\int\int\cdots \quad (3.8)$$

These distribution and correlation functions will be used in the discussion in the following sections. They are incomplete descriptions of the relative positions of the molecules. The distribution of orientations, velocities, internal vibrations, etc. are not considered. They are also time-independent; time-dependent distribution functions are discussed in Chap. 7.

(b) Relationships with Thermodynamic Properties

The internal energy U of a system of monatomic species can be written as

$$U = \frac{3}{2}NkT + \langle V \rangle \quad (3.9)$$

Here $\langle V \rangle$ is the average potential energy of the system

$$\langle V \rangle = \frac{\int\cdots\int V\{N\} \exp[-V\{N\}/kT]\, d\{N\}}{Z_N} \quad (3.10)$$

When the total potential energy can be written as a sum of pair interactions, i.e., $V\{N\} = \sum_{i>j} v(r_{ij})$, then for large N, $\langle V \rangle$ can be written as

$$\langle V \rangle = \frac{Nn}{2} \int_V v(r)g(r)\, d\underline{r} \quad (3.11)$$

Equation (3.11) can be obtained either formally or by simple interpretation of the distribution function $g(r)$. The potential energy of interaction of a molecule with neighbors at a distance r to

$r + dr$ is given by $\{4\pi r^2\ dr\}\{ng(r)\}\{v(r)\}$. The first curly bracket gives the volume of the shell, the second the number density in the shell, and the third the potential energy of interaction per pair. The total potential energy is N/2 times the $\int dr$ of this expression, or Eq. (3.11), as $d\underline{r} \equiv 4\pi r^2\ dr$.

The pressure is given by $p = -\partial A/\partial V$. The configurational part of Q can be related to $g(r)$ and $v(r)$. Then A can be expressed in terms of Q. The appropriate differentiation then gives

$$p = \frac{N}{V} kT \left[1 - \frac{n}{6kT} \int r \frac{dv(r)}{dr} \cdot g(r)\ d\underline{r}\right] \qquad (3.12)$$

In order to get an expression for the compressibility, the grand canonical partition function must be considered, although it can also be obtained through consideration of fluctuations [Eq. (19.32)]. The result is written in the form

$$\left(\frac{\partial n}{\partial p}\right)_{V,T} kT = n\int (g(r) - 1)\ d\underline{r} + 1 = nkT\kappa_T \qquad (3.13)$$

where κ_T is the isothermal compressibility.

(c) Properties of Fourier Transforms

It is of interest to consider the physical significance of the Fourier transform of $g(r)$. It is usually written in the form

$$S(q) = 1 + n\int \exp[i\underline{q}\cdot\underline{r}](g(r) - 1)\ d\underline{r} \qquad (3.14)$$

The function $S(q)$ is often referred to as the "structure factor." For isotropic systems it is a function only of the magnitude of the wave vector q.

$S(q)$ can be shown to describe the wavelength (Fourier) distribution of the mean square of the density variations. Although the mean value $\langle n(\underline{r}_1) - n\rangle$ equals zero,

$$\langle (n(\underline{r}_1) - n)(n(\underline{r}_2) - n)\rangle \qquad (3.15)$$

is nonzero, if there are correlations present between the positions of particles. Here $n(\underline{r}_1)$ is the instantaneous particle density at $\underline{r}_1$, while n is the mean value N/V.

When (3.15) is expanded, it becomes

$$\langle (n(\underline{r}_1) - n)(n(\underline{r}_2) - n)\rangle = \langle n(\underline{r}_1)n(\underline{r}_2)\rangle - n^2 \tag{3.15a}$$

From the definition of $g(r)$, it can be seen that for $r = |\underline{r}_2 - \underline{r}_1|$

$$\langle n(\underline{r}_1)n(\underline{r}_2)\rangle = n^2 g(r) + n\,\delta(\underline{r}_2 - \underline{r}_1) \tag{3.16}$$

The δ function in Eq. (3.16) accounts for the fact that when $\underline{r}_1 = \underline{r}_2$, the molecule in $d\underline{r}_1$ is also in $d\underline{r}_2$. This is not accounted for by $g(r)$.

Thus Eq. (3.15a) can be written as

$$\langle (n(\underline{r}_1) - n)(n(\underline{r}_2) - n)\rangle = n\delta(\underline{r}_2 - \underline{r}_1) + n^2(g(r) - 1) \tag{3.17}$$

The Fourier components of the mean square density variations is then given by

$$\langle \int\int (n(\underline{r}_1) - n)(n(\underline{r}_2) - n)\exp[i\underline{q}\cdot(\underline{r}_2 - \underline{r}_1)]\,d\underline{r}_1\,d\underline{r}_2\rangle$$

$$= \langle |\int (n(\underline{r}) - n)\exp[i\underline{q}\cdot\underline{r}]\,d\underline{r}|^2\rangle$$

$$= nV(1 + n\int (g(r) - 1)\exp[i\underline{q}\cdot\underline{r}]\,d\underline{r}$$

$$= nVS(q) \tag{3.18}$$

The typical shape of the $S(q)$ curve is shown in Fig. 3.1. The limiting value is related to the compressibility (3.13), as

$$S(0) = nkT\kappa_T \tag{3.19}$$

Near the critical point of a liquid, where κ_T is large, $S(0) \gg 1$ and the small q (long wavelength) part of the $S(q)$ curve dominates [Sec. 3.4(b)].

A large peak is present near $q \simeq 2\pi/d$, where d is approximately equal to the atomic spacing. Oscillations in $S(q)$ usually continue up to values of $q \approx (20\ \text{Å})^{-1}$. This is to be expected on the basis of short-range order in liquids, as $S(q)$ is a measure of the statistical weight of distribution of wavelengths present in the density variations.

It will later be shown [Secs. 14.1(d), 15.1(b), 16.1(c)] that $S(q)$ is also simply related to various scattering cross sections at a scattering angle θ such that

$$q = \frac{4\pi}{\lambda}\sin\left(\frac{\theta}{2}\right) \tag{3.20}$$

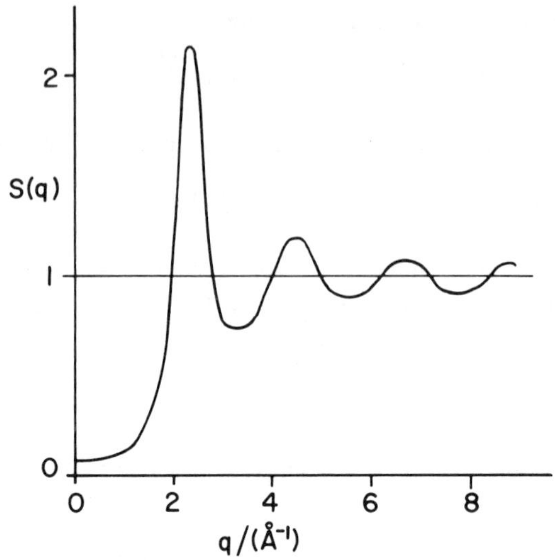

Fig. 3.1. Typical shape of the structure factor $S(q)$ for a liquid.

Equation (3.20) assumes that energy transfer can be neglected. This is valid in light and x-ray, but not in thermal neutron scattering.

3.2. RELATIONSHIP OF DISTRIBUTION FUNCTIONS TO PAIR POTENTIALS

(a) Superposition Approximation

There is no exact relation between $g(r)$ and $v(r)$ for liquids which can be solved in practice. This is true even for simple potentials such as the hard-sphere potential. Thus various approximations must be used to get relationships between $g(r)$ and $v(r)$ which can be solved exactly or even numerically. The approach described in this section uses the Kirkwood superposition approximation, and leads to the Yvon-Born-Green (YBG) equation relating $g(r)$ and $v(r)$.

Consider a molecule (labeled 1) at $\underline{r}_1$ in a liquid, and another molecule at $\underline{r}_2$, where $|\underline{r}_1 - \underline{r}_2| = r_{12} = r$. In such a case, the mean force acting on 1 can be expressed as shown in Eq. (3.21). This can be seen on referring back to Eqs. (3.2) and (3.4).

$$\frac{\int \exp[-V\{N\}/kT] \, \frac{\partial V\{N\}}{\partial \underline{r}_1} \, d\{N-2\}}{\int \exp[-V\{N\}/kT] \, d\{N-2\}} = \frac{kT}{g(r)} \frac{\partial g(r)}{\partial \underline{r}_1} \tag{3.21}$$

The force in Eq. (3.21) is sometimes written as $-\partial\phi_{me}/\partial\underline{r}_1$ where $\phi_{me}(r)$ is the "potential of mean force,"

$$\phi_{me}(r) = -kT \ln g(r) \tag{3.22}$$

For a dilute gas, $\phi_{me}(r) \to v(r)$.

Such a force can be evaluated in another way, however. The force on 1 due to a second molecule at $\underline{r}_2$ is $-\partial v(r)/\partial\underline{r}_1$, where $r = |\underline{r}_2 - \underline{r}_1|$. A third molecule is then positioned in $d\underline{r}_3$ at $\underline{r}_3$. The probability that it is at $\underline{r}_3$ while 1 is at $\underline{r}_1$ and 2 at $\underline{r}_2$ is given by

$$w(\underline{r}_1, \underline{r}_2, \underline{r}_3) \, d\underline{r}_3 = \frac{n^{(3)}(\underline{r}_1, \underline{r}_2, \underline{r}_3) \, d\underline{r}_3}{n^{(2)}(\underline{r}_1, \underline{r}_2)} \tag{3.23}$$

Equation (3.23) follows from a generalization of the definition of a pair distribution function to a triplet distribution function $n^{(3)}$.

The force on 1 due to 3 is then

$$-\frac{\partial v(r_{13})}{\partial \underline{r}_1} \cdot w(\underline{r}_1, \underline{r}_2, \underline{r}_3) \, d\underline{r}_3 \tag{3.24}$$

Now the position of 3 is varied throughout the whole volume, i.e., (3.24) is integrated over the volume. In this case the total force on 1 is given by

$$-\frac{\partial v(r)}{\partial \underline{r}_1} - \int \frac{\partial v(r_{13})}{\partial \underline{r}_1} \cdot \frac{n^{(3)}(\underline{r}_1, \underline{r}_2, \underline{r}_3) \, d\underline{r}_3}{n^{(2)}(\underline{r}_1, \underline{r}_2)} \tag{3.25}$$

This can be equated to (3.21).

The resultant relationship contains $v(r)$, $g(r)$ (or $n^{(2)}$) and $n^{(3)}$. It cannot be solved explicitly unless another relationship is obtained between these three quantities.

The YBG equation is obtained when $n^{(3)}$ is eliminated by using the Kirkwood superposition approximation. This states that the probability of finding 3 at $\underline{r}_3$, 2 at $\underline{r}_2$, and 1 at $\underline{r}_1$ is the product of finding the three separate pairs, i.e.,

$$n^{(3)}(\underline{r}_1, \underline{r}_2, \underline{r}_3) = \frac{n^{(2)}(\underline{r}_1, \underline{r}_2)\cdot n^{(2)}(\underline{r}_2, \underline{r}_3)\cdot n^{(2)}(\underline{r}_3, \underline{r}_1)}{n^3} \quad (3.26)$$

It is obviously a good approximation if at least one of the three particles is far away, i.e., at low densities.

The resultant YBG equation is

$$\ln g(r) + \frac{v(r)}{kT} = -n\int F(|r_1 - r|)(g(\underline{r}_1) - 1)\, d\underline{r}_1 \quad (3.27)$$

where

$$F(r) = \frac{1}{kT}\int_{\infty}^{r} g(x)\frac{\partial v(x)}{\partial x}\, dx$$

Equation (3.27) contains $g(r)$ and $v(r)$ only. One of these functions can then be solved in terms of the other, if not explicitly, then at least numerically.

(b) HCN and Percus-Yevick Theories

The hypernetted chain (HNC) and Percus-Yevick(PY) equations can best be described by expanding (3.2) in terms of Mayer f functions [Sec. 4.4(b)]. Thus

$$\exp\left[-\frac{V\{N\}}{kT}\right] = \prod_{i>j} \exp\left[-\frac{v(r_{ij})}{kT}\right] = \prod_{i>j} (1 + f_{ij}) \quad (3.28)$$

$g(r)$, $h(r)$, and $c(r)$ can then all be expressed as sums of graphs representing integrals over f functions. Reference 3 gives a summary.

In particular, the direct correlation function $c(r)$ can be shown [1] to be given by a sum of irreducible clusters as

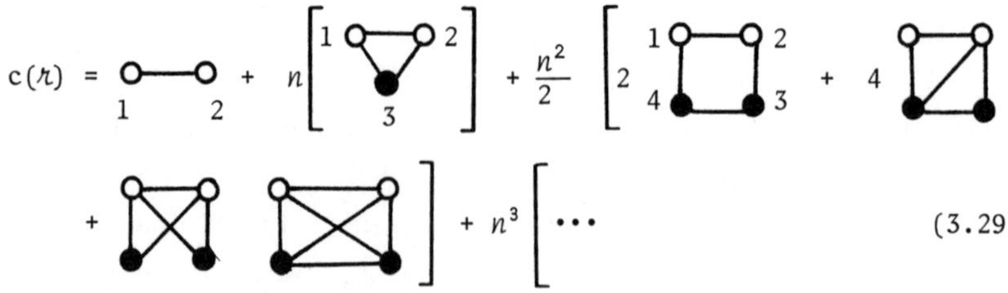

(3.29)

The first term  is simply $f_{12} = \exp[-v(r_{12})/kT] - 1$; the second, $\int f_{12} f_{23} f_{31}\, d\underline{r}_3$; the third, $\int\int f_{12} f_{23} f_{34} f_{41}\, d\underline{r}_3\, d\underline{r}_4$; etc. Each line in a graph indicates a Mayer f function in the product, and a filled circle, an integration.

The HNC equation is equivalent to an equation for $c(r)$ which contains the first two terms of (3.29), but truncates the n^2 term to

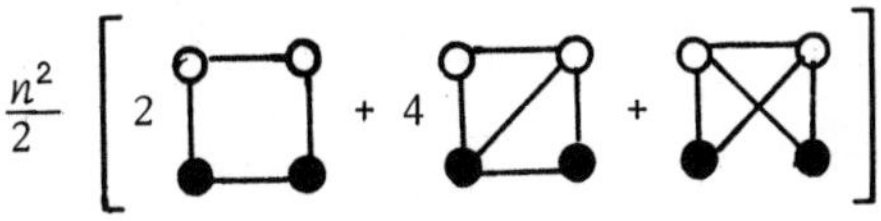 (3.30)

This allows (3.29) to be summed, giving

$$c(r) = h(r) - \ln g(r) - \frac{v(r)}{kT} \tag{3.31}$$

As $c(r)$, $h(r)$, and $g(r)$ are related by other equations, then (3.31) gives a relationship for the two functions $g(r)$ and $v(r)$. The HNC equation was derived by examining the cluster expansion and excluding terms which made summation impossible.

The PY theory was not originally formulated from an examination of cluster expansions, but can be expressed also as a truncation of the n^2 term. In it, the third term in $c(r)$ is truncated to be

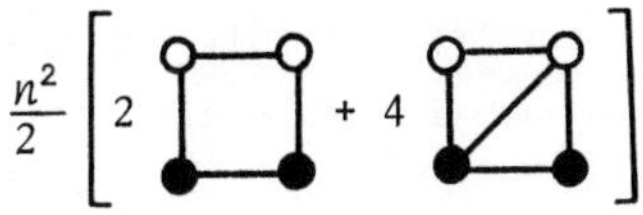 (3.32)

This leads to an equation

$$c(r) = g(r)(1 - \exp[v(r)/kT]) \tag{3.33}$$

The PY equation gives better results than the HNC equation [Sec. 3.2(d)] even though it contains fewer terms than the HNC equation. The two diagrams dropped in the PY equation tend to cancel each other. The PY equation has also been solved exactly for a hard-sphere liquid, while only numerical solutions have been obtained for the HNC equation.

The basic PY and HNC equations have been improved by various sophistications. Reference 3 contains a summary. Some of these extensions are included in the comparison in Sec. 3.2(d). They can be considered to be other cases of "cluster expansion" theories, starting with distribution functions written as in (3.29) and summing over selected graphs. Interrelations between these and other related theories, are discussed in Ref. 4.

Other related approaches start with the Ornstein-Zernike relation (3.7), and make assumptions about the forms of $c(r)$ and $h(r)$. Thus, in the "hard-core mean spherical model" (MSM), (3.7) is used with the approximations

$$c(r) = -\frac{1}{kT} v(r) \qquad \text{for } r \geqslant r_c$$

$$h(r) = -1 \qquad \text{for } r < r_c \qquad (3.34)$$

where r_c is the "hard-core radius." In the soft-core MSM, the Percus-Yevick equation (3.33) is used for $r < r_c$. The MSM gives results for $g(r)$ for neon, argon, krypton, and xenon in good agreement with neutron diffraction measurements and molecular dynamics calculations [5]. In these calculations, the value of r_c was chosen so that $h(r_c) = 0$, and a variational procedure [Sec. 3.2(c)] was used to obtain $c(r)$ inside the core.

Theories starting from an Ornstein-Zernike-like equation involving Fourier transforms of h and c have also been developed. Computations for $S(q)$ for hard-shpere diatomic molecules [6], again using a variational procedure, show good agreement with molecular dynamics results [see also Sec. 5.2(e)].

The approach in Ref. 6 differs also from most theories in that it makes a treatment of molecular fluids possible. Most theories starting with the Ornstein-Zernike equation or series expansion are applicable only to monatomic fluids, Another approach to treatments of molecular fluids is given in Ref. 7, where the MSM theory is extended to cover polarizable hard spheres each with a point dipole.

(c) Perturbation Techniques

With the realization that the structure of liquids is primarily determined by repulsive forces, perturbation expansions have been developed. In such calculations, the effect of the attractive portion of $v(r)$ is obtained by a perturbation expansion in the strength of the attractive potential. Reference 8 gives a review of recent developments in such treatments.

Especially at high temperatures, the repulsive forces are largely responsible for determining the structure of a fluid. Thus when the reference (unperturbed) system is one with simple repulsive forces only (e.g., hard spheres), then the free energy can be expanded in powers of $1/kT$. Thus

$$A - A_0 = \frac{N^2}{2V} \int v_1(r) g_0(r) \, d\underline{r} + \frac{\text{terms}}{T} + \frac{\text{terms}}{T^2} + \cdots \tag{3.35}$$

In Eq. (3.35), $v_1(r)$ is the difference between the pair potential function of the actual and the reference systems. A_0 and $g_0(r)$ refer to the reference system (e.g., hard spheres). Terms with $1/T$ dependence already involve the three- and four-body distribution functions.

The perturbation $v_1(r)$ need not be restricted to include only attractive forces. A perturbation treatment can also be made to account for the less than infinite steepness of the repulsion. In addition, the second term in (3.35), including three- and four-body interactions has been taken into account [9].

Perturbation calculations have also been developed for polar molecules in the form of hard spheres with central point dipoles. Such a theory is compared with a mean spherical model approach for the same type of system in Ref. 10. The results from the two approaches differ considerably, but a preliminary form of the MSM theory was used, which does not include polarizability effects [7].

A variational approach has also been developed [8]. This is based on the observation that expansion (3.35) is of such a form that

$$A - A_0 \leqslant \frac{N^2}{2V} \int v_1(r) g_0(r) \, d\underline{r} \tag{3.36}$$

Thus by varying the properties of the reference system, the inequality can be minimized.

The hard-sphere system is the only one where A and $g(r)$ are known as a function of the intermolecular potential parameters (i.e., of the hard-sphere diameter 2a). The inequality can then be minimized by varying the ratio a/σ, where σ is the 6-12 distance parameter. Calculations have generally been made with a hard-sphere system as the reference system. Properties of other reference systems are as yet not well known. A real reference system such as argon could also be used for more practical calculations.

The variational method need not be used for the theory as a whole. A variational procedure can be used as a general tool for finding solutions to any kind of theory. The procedure generally [Sec. 21.3(b)] is to take a variational function $\phi(\gamma_1, \gamma_2 \cdots)$ where the γ_i are adjustable parameters. The γ_i are then varied until $\partial\phi/\partial\gamma_i = 0$ for $i = 1, 2, \ldots$. The problem then is reduced to finding a proper variational function. In Ref. 5 ϕ is a function involving $c(r)$ and $v(r)$, with the parameters γ_i introduced by setting $c(r) = \Sigma\gamma_i r^i$.

The basic problem remaining in nearly all these theories and computer simulations is that the total potential energy is assumed to be a sum of pair potentials. As seen in Sec. 1.1(g), this is not always a valid assumption.

(d) Comparison of Theories

In this comparison the form of the theory is tested. Thus the Monte Carlo and molecular dynamics results can be viewed as "exact" results for the pair potentials assumed (rigid spheres or 6-12). A comparison to a real liquid is also given. It should be used in conjunction with Table 2.1.

These critical constants can be obtained either from the pressure equation (3.12) or the compressibility equation (3.13). The two sets of values differ somewhat. Those quoted in Table 3.1 are obtained from the compressibility equation.

The data in Table 3.1 have been obtained by numerical calculations. The values of T_c^* and p_cV_c/nRT_c are all higher than for the real liquid, even though close to the exact values of a 6-12 liquid. This is an indication that the description of the potential energy of liquid argon in terms of sums of 6-12 pair potential interactions is not fully satisfactory.

TABLE 3.1

Critical Constants for 6-12 Fluid

System	T_c^*	V_c^*/n	$\frac{p_c V_c}{nRT_c}$	Ref.
Argon (real)	1.26	3.16	0.29	3
MC or MD	1.32-1.36	2.8-3.1	0.30-0.36	3
HNC	1.32	3.6	0.36	8
PY	1.39	3.6	0.30	8
PY II	1.33	3.0	0.34	8
Perturbation	1.35	3.3	0.34	8
Variation	1.36	3.1	0.37	8
YBG	1.58	2.5	0.48	11

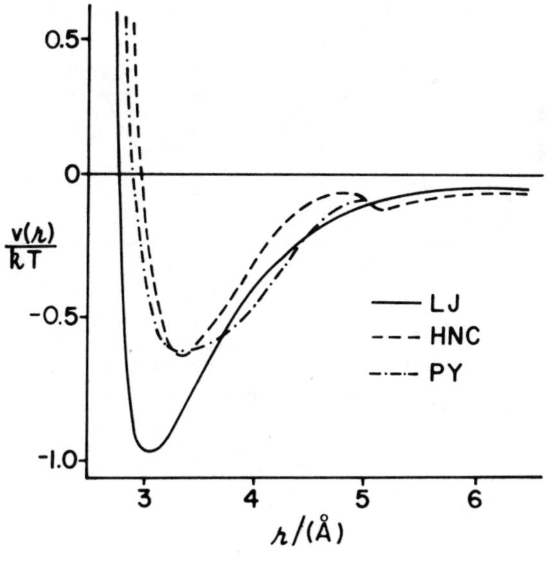

Fig. 3.2. Comparison of pair potentials $v(r)$ for argon obtained from experimental $g(r)$. (After Ref. 12.)

This aspect also shows up when the effective pair potential for neon is considered. Figure 3.2 shows the 6-12 potential derived from gas phase measurements compared to pair potentials derived by analyzing the experimental radial distribution function be various theories. The $v(r)$ are obtained by applying the PY and HNC theories to the $g(r)$ for neon at 35.0 K as determined from neutron scattering [12]. The PY and HNC theories are both unsatisfactory.

Finally, Fig. 3.3 shows a comparison of the $g(r)$ obtained for a hard-sphere fluid from various theories. They are again compared to the "exact" MC solutions.

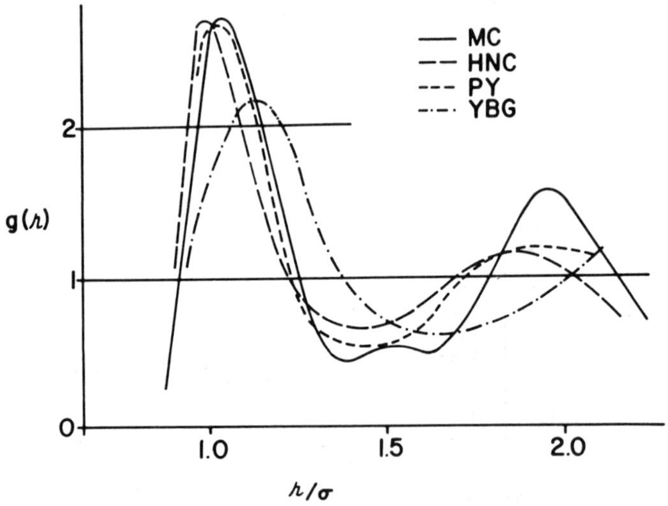

Fig. 3.3. Comparison of pair distribution functions $g(r)$ for a hard sphere liquid calculated through various theories. (After Ref. 1.)

3.3. COMPUTER SIMULATION OF LIQUIDS

(a) Monte Carlo Method

In both the Monte Carlo (MC) and molecular dynamics (MD) methods, the system is composed of N particles placed in a cell of volume V. If no phase changes take place, then a sample of several hundred particles is sufficient. The actual liquid is visualized to consist of an array of such identical cells. Surface effects are thus minimized by assuming that if a particle leaves the cell on one side, then it reenters on the other side.

In the MC method it is necessary to initially specify N, V, T, the coordinates of the particles, and the interparticle potential energy. The canonical ensemble average of properties could then in principle be obtained in a manner such as pictured in most derivations of basic statistical mechanical relationships.

The coordinates of the N particles are chosen randomly, and the potential energy V_i and the value P_i of some property P are calculated. This is repeated for a large number of randomly chosen configurations i. The ensemble average value of the property P can then be obtained from Eq. (18.5).

$$\langle P \rangle = \frac{\Sigma P_i \exp[-V_i/kT]}{\Sigma \exp[-V_i/kT]} \tag{3.37}$$

The summation is over all the random configurations chosen.

Such an approach is not feasible in practice for close-packed systems, as there is a large probability that in choosing the coordinates randomly, a high-energy, low-probability configuration is chosen. Instead of choosing configurations randomly and weighting them with $\exp[-V_i/kT]$, it is possible to choose configurations with a probability $\exp[-V/kT]$ and weight them equally. The two procedures give identical results (13), but the latter is computationally far more favorable.

In the typical MC calculation, a particle is thus given a random displacement. The particle can be chosen randomly or serially. The potential energy for the new configuration is calculated. If the change, ΔV, from the previous configuration is negative, then the move is accepted. If $\Delta V > 0$, then the move is accepted with a probability $\exp[-\Delta V/kT]$.

This can be done by choosing a random number between 0 and 1. If the random number is $<\exp[-\Delta V/kT]$, then the new configuration is accepted. The procedure is particularly simple for the case of a hard-sphere potential. In this case ΔV is either 0 or $+\infty$, and a move is accepted or outright rejected.

Repetition of this procedure generates a chain of configurations. The overall average of a property then converges to the canonical ensemble average as the chain increases in length. In this chain, a configuration is counted again if the subsequent move is rejected. A typical MC calculation involves the generation of hundreds of thousands of configurations for a model of hundreds of particles.

In addition to MC calculations on hard-sphere liquids, the 6-12 potential has been used, as well as point-charge descriptions [14]. Triple dipole three-body interactions [Sec. 1.1(g)] have also been taken into account in systems with small (50) numbers of particles [15].

The MC method cannot be used to examine transport properties, as can the MD method. It has the advantages of having a predetermined value of T. It can also be applied to constant pressure as well as constant volume systems, and is thus more suitable for examination of phenomena such as phase equilibria.

(b) Molecular Dynamics Method

The MD method describes essentially a microcanonical ensemble. Here both the velocity and the position of each particle must initially be specified. The motions of the particles are then followed by numerically solving the classical equations of motion assuming a given interparticle potential energy.

The number of particles involved is generally in the hundreds, the time interval in the numerical calculations about 10^{-16} to 10^{-14} sec, and the number of time intervals in the thousands. This requires considerable computer time, especially when a complex intermolecular potential is used and orientation coordinates are included [16].

The total energy of the system remains constant except for fluctuations arising from the finite nature of the time increments. The temperature as calculated from the mean kinetic energy can change considerably in the early stages of the computation. The velocity distribution equilibrates quite quickly, however, typically in the time required for two to four collisions per particle.

Thermodynamic properties such as pressure, internal energy, etc. and the radial distribution function $g(r)$ sec. 3.1(a)]] can be determined by both the MC and MD methods. The MD method can also be used to determine the velocity correlation functions, van Hove functions and orientational correlation functions (Secs. 7.1, 2). Diffusion constants and relaxation times can thus subsequently be obtained for the systems.

(c) Comparison of Results

MC and MD results for various liquids have been used for the testing of various theoretical approaches in Sec. 3.2. Here the results of computations for water are briefly discussed in order to illustrate the methods in more detail and to indicate advantages and disadvantages of the methods.

A MC simulation of liquid water has been carried out for a system of 64 molecules in three dimensions [14]. There are no adjustable parameters in the theory. The input parameters consist of the experimental density at 25°C and a pair potential function $\upsilon(r)$.

The pair potential used is the sum of a 6-12 potential (ε = 2.96 kJ mol^{-1},σ = 2.725 Å), and the interaction of 4 charges on one molecule with 4 on another. The charges make $\upsilon(r)$ orientation-dependent. A hard-sphere cutoff was set at 2 Å, and $\upsilon(r)$ was assumed to be 0 for $r > 6.2$ Å.

Configurations were generated by choosing a molecule of the 64 at random; next, three random displacements from a sample uniformly distributed inside a range ±0.25 Å were selected; then, an angle from a sample uniformly distributed in a range ±10° was selected. The change in potential energy was calculated. If $\exp[-\Delta V/kT]$ < a randomly chosen number between 0 and 1, then the next configuration was assumed to be the same as the previous. If >, the move is accepted.

After 120,000 configurations at 25°C to equilibrate the system, 110,000 configurations were generated. The potential energy average $\langle V \rangle$, $\langle V^2 \rangle$ and the radial distribution function were obtained from these 110,000 configurations.

From these data, the calculated value of U is -35.0 kJ mol^{-1} as compared to the experimental value -34.0; the calculated value of C_V is 85.6 J K^{-1} mol^{-1} as compared to 75.1. The radial distribution function does not agree well with the experimental one, however. The $g(r)$ used seems to allow molecules to approach each other too closely.

Another MC study of water with a different potential energy function [17] gave a value of U for 27°C of -40.4 kJ mol^{-1}. There is a variation ±1 kJ mol^{-1} in U depending on the initial configuration chosen, even though up to 60,000 configurations were generated in each case. The configurations obtained correspond more to the continuum model of water [Sec. 2.4(c)]. Results of such calculations are completely dependent on the potential energy function chosen.

A very extensive MD study of water has been carried out [16]. In the most recent version, an intermolecular potential (ST2) was used which had a Lennard-Jones potential between oxygens [Sec. 1.3(a)] together with negative charges 1 Å from the O and equal, opposite positive charges 0.8 Å form the O. The charge-oxygen-charge angles were all tetrahedral.

Classical Newton-Euler equations were used to follow the dynamics of the system. The time increment Δt for numerical integration of these equations was initially chosen to be 4.4×10^{-16} sec. To advance the system of 216 molecules by this amount of time requires 40 sec of computing time. Thus there is a time dilation of approximately 10^{17}.

The molecules were initially placed randomly with no translational or orientational velocities. The density was equivalent to 1 gm cm^{-3}. Such a random configuration in liquids has an extremely high potential energy. Thus after several Δt, the temperature was > 10^{40} K. A change in T is possible in a MD simulation as the model is a constant energy, not a constant T system.

After removing energy from the system several times by "freezing" the motion of the molecules, a temperature 34.3°C was obtained. After 5000 steps to age the system at this temperature, another 5000 steps were simulated, during which several averages were obtained.

The latest calculations give U = -34.1 kJ mol^{-1} and C_V = 87.6 JK^{-1} mol^{-1}. A density maximum is even predicted at 27°C. The agreement of the calculated x-ray scattering intensity with the experimental [Sec. 15.3(c)] is reasonably good.

Stereoscopic slides were made of the system at 500 Δt intervals. A sequence of such pictures gives the impression of liquid water as a highly disordered substance [16]. Molecules seem to have a tendency to be oriented into approximations of tetrahedral bonds, but there is considerable bending in these H bonds. No clusters of anomalous density or patterns characteristic of ice structures appear, and no obvious separation between "interstitial"- and "network"-type molecules appears. There is evidence that non-H-bonded OH bonds exist which have a lifetime greater than the period of water molecule vibrations.

Although the above description supports a continuum structure for liquid water, it cannot be considered as a proof that two-state structural models are incorrect. The cooperative aspect of H-bonding is not included in this model, and it is this property of interactions between water molecules which suggests the existance of "flickering clusters."

Besides static properties of the system, such as the radial distribution function, it is also possible to obtain time-correlation functions (Chap. 7) from a MD simulation. These can be related to results obtained from various experimental techniques.

3.4. THE CRITICAL REGION

(a) Fluctuations

In Sec. 2.1(a) the critical point was introduced so that reduced parameters could be referred to. At the cirtical point, $(\partial p/\partial V) = (\partial^2 p/\partial V^2) = 0$. Thus the isothermal compressibility $\kappa_T \to \infty$, i.e.,

$$\kappa_T = -\frac{1}{V}\left(\frac{\partial V}{\partial p}\right)_T = \frac{1}{n}\left(\frac{\partial n}{\partial p}\right) \to \infty \tag{3.38}$$

The divergence of κ_T near the critical point is usually described by the equation

$$\kappa_T = \text{constant x } |T - T_c|^{-\gamma} \tag{3.39}$$

The experimental value for γ is $\simeq 1.1$. Equation (3.39) is of a form equivalent to (2.2).

This divergence of κ_T near the critical point is due to the possibility of large fluctuations of the density $n(r)$. These fluctuations can be described by the radial distribution function.

The temperature may be considered constant in considering density fluctuations, as fluctuations of temperature and density (or volume) can be shown to be statistically independent (Sec. 19.3) [3], i.e.,

$$\langle \delta T \cdot \delta V \rangle = 0 \tag{3.40}$$

Pressure and entropy fluctuations can similarly be shown to be statistically independent, i.e.,

$$\langle \delta S \cdot \delta p \rangle = 0 \tag{3.41}$$

The mean square fluctuations of all these quantities $\langle \delta S^2 \rangle$ etc. are all nonzero.

The symbol δS indicates the change in entropy in a fluctuation in a small part of the system. For a nonmechanical variable such as S or T, it should be interpreted as the change in S as a function of U and V due to the fluctuations in the mechanical variables, U and V.

When V and T are considered to be constant, then the probability of a fluctuation, w, can be written as

$$w \propto \exp\left[-\frac{\delta A}{T}\right] \tag{3.42}$$

This relationship can be derived from statistical thermodynamics [Eq. (19.25)]. It can be thought of as a generalization of the equilibrium constant relation under constant p, T conditions, where (Sec. 17.4)

$$K = \exp\left[-\frac{\Delta G^{\theta}}{kT}\right] \tag{3.43}$$

Equation (3.43) compares the probability of the system being in two states differing in free energy by ΔG^{θ}

The symbol δA in (3.42) represents the change in free energy in the body considered during the fluctuation. It can be written as

$$\delta A = \int_V (A(\underline{r}) - A)\, d\underline{r} \tag{3.44}$$

where A is the mean free energy per unit volume in the whole body, and $A(\underline{r})$ is the instantaneous free energy at $\underline{r}$ per unit volume. It will vary from point to point just as the density $n(\underline{r})$ [Sec. 3.1(a)].

(b) Fourier Analysis of Density Fluctuations

The quantity $(A(\underline{r}) - A)$ in (3.44) can be expanded in terms of number density $(n(\underline{r}) - n)$. The first term gives a zero contribution to δA, as the number of particles in the volume is assumed constant. The second term is of the form

$$\frac{1}{2}a(n(\underline{r}) - n)^2 \tag{3.45}$$

The coefficient a is

$$a = \left(\frac{\partial^2 A}{\partial n^2}\right)_T = \left(\frac{\partial \mu}{\partial n}\right)_T = \frac{1}{n}\left(\frac{\partial p}{\partial n}\right) \tag{3.46}$$

It is thus positive, decreasing to zero at the critical point. As $(\partial^2 p/\partial n^2)$ also approaches zero near the critical point, the third term can be neglected.

In an inhomogeneous body such as that considered, $(A(\underline{r}) - A)$ can also contain terms containing the derivatives of $n(\underline{r})$ with respect to space coordinates. For an isotropic system, the contribution to $A(\underline{r}) - A$ from this can be written as

$$\frac{1}{2}b\left|\frac{\partial n(\underline{r})}{\partial \underline{r}}\right|^2 = \frac{1}{2}b|\nabla n(\underline{r})|^2 \tag{3.47}$$

To have a minimum in A corresponding to $n(\underline{r}) = n$, the constant b must be positive. Thus

$$A(\underline{r}) - A = \frac{1}{2}\,a(n(\underline{r}) - n)^2 + \frac{1}{2}\,b|\nabla n(\underline{r})|^2 \tag{3.48}$$

Now $n(\underline{r}) - n$ can be expanded in terms of a Fourier series as

$$n(\underline{r}) - n = \sum_q c(\underline{q})\,\exp[-i\underline{q}\cdot\underline{r}] \tag{3.49}$$

where the coefficients are

$$c(\underline{q}) = \frac{1}{V}\int(n(\underline{r}) - n)\,\exp[i\underline{q}\cdot\underline{r}]\,d\underline{r} \tag{3.50}$$

$c(-\underline{q})$ must equal $c^*(\underline{q})$ as $(n(\underline{r}) - n)$ is real.

Substitution of (3.49) into (3.48) gives through (3.44)

$$\delta A = \frac{1}{2}\,V\sum_q(a + bq^2)|c(\underline{q})|^2 \tag{3.51}$$

Equation (3.51) indicates that the fluctuations of the various Fourier components $|c(\underline{q})|$ are statistically independent, as there are no cross terms present. The probability of a fluctuation with wave vector $\pm\underline{q}$ is then given by

$$w \propto \exp\left[-\frac{V}{kT}(a + bq^2)|c(\underline{q})|^2\right] \tag{3.52}$$

The mean square fluctuation can be obtained by noting that the probability w must be in the form of a Gaussian distribution (19.23)

$$w(x)\,dx = (2\pi\langle x^2\rangle)^{-1/2}\exp\left[-\frac{x^2}{2\langle x^2\rangle}\right]dx \tag{3.53}$$

Thus

$$\langle|c(\underline{q})|^2\rangle = \frac{kT}{V(a + bq^2)} \tag{3.54}$$

The factor 2 disappears as $|c(\underline{q})|^2$ is the sum of two independent quantities due to the complex nature of $c(\underline{q})$.

From (3.18), the following relationship can then be obtained:

$$n\int (g(r) - 1) \exp[i\underline{q}\cdot\underline{r}]\, d\underline{r} + 1 = S(q)$$
$$= \frac{V}{n}\langle |c(\underline{q})|^2\rangle$$
$$= \frac{kT}{n(a + bq^2)} \tag{3.55}$$

Because a and b are both small, the right-hand side of (3.55) is >>1, thus (3.55) can be written as

$$n^2\int (g(r) - 1) \exp[i\underline{q}\cdot\underline{r}]\, d\underline{r} = \frac{kT}{(a + bq^2)} \tag{3.56}$$

or

$$(g(r) - 1) = h(r) = \frac{kT}{4\pi n^2 b} \cdot \frac{1}{r} \cdot \exp[-\sqrt{\frac{a}{b}} \cdot r] \tag{3.57}$$

(c) Ornstein-Zernike Model

At the critical point, $a = 0$ and the correlation function $h(r)$ is given by

$$h(r) = \frac{kT}{(4\pi n^2 b r)} \tag{3.58}$$

Thus the correlations between molecules in the system decreases very slowly with increasing distance. Equation (3.58) is the classical result of Ornstein and Zernike. It can also be derived from consideration of Eq.((3.7) [11].

A "persistence length" L is often used in discussions. It is temperature-dependent and defined by

$$L^2 = \frac{\int r^2 h(r)\, d\underline{r}}{\int h(r)\, d\underline{r}} \tag{3.59}$$

In the O-Z model, it can be related to the constants a and b, and a temperature-independent distance parameter ℓ. Thus

$$L^2 = \frac{\ell^2 T_c}{|T - T_c|} = \frac{6}{\kappa^2} \tag{3.60}$$

where $\kappa^2 = a/b$. These distance parameters can be obtained experimentally by various means [see Secs. 10.3(f), 14.3(f), 15.3(d)].

REFERENCES

Reference 1 gives a thorough description of relationships between distribution functions, pair-potential functions, etc. A briefer version can be found in Ref. 3.

1. S. A. Rice and P. Gray, Statistical Mechanics of Simple Liquids, Wiley, New York, 1965.
2. L. D. Landau and E. M. Lifshitz, Statistical Physics, 2nd ed., Pergamon, London, 1969.
3. GR3.
4. H. C. Andersen and D. Chandler, J. Chem. Phys., *57*, 1918 (1972).
5. A. H. Narten, L. Blum, and R. H. Fowler, J. Chem. Phys., *60*, 3378 (1974).
6. L. J. Lowden and D. Chandler, J. Chem. Phys., *59*, 6587 (1973).
7. M. S. Wertheim, Mol. Phys., *26*, 1425 (1973).
8. G. A. Mansoori and F. B. Canfield, Ind. Eng. Chem., *62*, 12 (1970).
9. J. A. Barker and D. Henderson, Account Chem. Res., 303 (1971).
10. G. S. Rushbrooke, G. Stell, and J. S. Høye, Mol. Phys., *26*, 1199 (1973).
11. GR2.
12. L. A. de Graaf and B. Mozer, J. Chem. Phys., *55*, 4967 (1971).
13. N. Metropolis, A. W. Rosenbluth, M. N. Rosenbluth, A. H. Teller, and E. Teller, J. Chem. Phys., *21*, 1087 (1953).
14. J. A. Barker and R. O. Watts, Chem. Phys. Lett., *3*, 144 (1969).
15. I. R. McDonald and K. Singer, Quart. Rev., *24*, 238 (1970).
16. A. Rahman and F. H. Stillinger, J. Chem. Phys., *55*, 3336 (1971); *57*, 1281 (1972); *60*, 1545 (1974).
17. G. N. Sarkisov, G. G. Malenkov, and V. G. Dashevskii, Zh. Strukt. Khim., *14*, 6 (1973).

Further Recent References

M. S. Ananth, K. E. Gubbins, and C. G. Gray, "Perturbation Theory for Equilibrium Properties of Molecular Fluids", Mol. Phys., *28*, 1005 (1974).

L. J. Lowden and O. Chandler, "Theory of Intermolecular Pair Correlations for Molecular Liquids. Applications to the Liquids Carbon Tetrachloride, Carbon Disulfide, Carbon Diselenide, and Benzene", J. Chem. Phys. *61*, 5228,(1974).

B. M. Ladanyi and D. Chandler, "New Type of Cluster Theory for Molecular Fluids: Interaction Site Cluster Expansion", J. Chem. Phys. *62*, 4308 (1975).

D. Henderson, W. G. Madden and D. D. Fitts, "Monte Carlo and Hypernetted Chain Equation of State for the Square-Well Fluid", J. Chem. Phys., *64*, 5026 (1976).

H. J. Raveché, R. D. Mountain, and W. B. Streett, "Freezing and Melting Properties of the Lennard-Jones System", J. Chem. Phys., *61*, 1970 (1974).

G. N. Patey and J. P. Valleau, "Dipolar Hard Spheres: A Monte Carlo Study", J. Chem. Phys., *61*, 534 (1974).

J. S. Høye and G. Stell, "Statistical Mechanics of Polar Systems. II", J. Chem. Phys., *64*, 1952 (1976).

J. Kushick and B. J. Berne, "Computer Simulation of Anisotropic Molecular Fluids", J. Chem. Phys., *64*, 1362 (1976).

F. H. Stillinger and A. Rahman, "Molecular Dynamics Study of Liquid Water under High Pressure", J. Chem. Phys., *61*, 4973 (1974).

G. C. Lie, E. Clementi, and M. Yoshimine, "Study of the Structure of Molecular Complexes. XIII. Monte Carlo Simulation of Liquid Water with a Configuration Interaction Pair Potential", J. Chem. Phys., *64*, 2314 (1976).

R. O. Watts, "Monte Carlo Studies of Liquid Water", Mol. Phys., *28*, 1069 (1974).

H. L. Lemberg and F. H. Stillinger, "Central-force Model for Liquid Water", J. Chem. Phys., *62*, 1677 (1975).

Chapter 4

LIQUID MIXTURES

Chapters 4 and 5 deal with systems which are composed of at least two components. The difference is that in the case of nonelectrolyte solutions (Chap. 4), the forces between the particles in the mixture are of a relatively short range, varying approximately as $1/r^7$ (Chap. 1). Thus, for the purpose of most calculations, it is sufficient to consider only nearest-neighbor interactions.

When ions are present, longer-range ($1/r^2$) forces exist between the ions. It is thus no longer adequate to consider simply nearest-neighbor interactions. In addition, the electric fields next to ions are very strong. Therefore, the interaction of the ions with the neighboring solvent molecules must also be considered in some detail.

Some of the discussion is applicable to both electrolyte and nonelectrolyte solutions. In particular, much of Sec. 4.1 is relevant to the discussions in Chap. 5.

Section 4.2 outlines some of the statistical mechanical approaches that have been used to describe liquid mixtures. Both theories which treat the problem from a model-building approach (analogous to Chap.2) and those starting with a "fundamentalist" approach are included. As in the case of single-component systems (Sec. 3.2) it is attempted to classify theoretical approaches under major types. However, as shown in Sec. 3.2, such a classification is by no means unique. An exhaustive list of approaches used is not presented in Sec. 4.2 but simply a sampling of the major types of approaches.

For simplicity, only mixtures involving two components (A and B) are considered. The theories can be generalized to multicomponent mixtures. (See references at the end of this chapter.)

There seems to be considerable variation regarding nomenclature in the various theoretical approaches introduced here. Thus, there may be some difficulty in following a discussion when several references are used.

4.1. THERMODYNAMICS

(a) Ideal and Real Mixtures

An ideal mixture can be defined [1] as that in which the chemical potential of a component A is given as in Eq. (4.1). The other component, B, would have an analogous expression

$$\mu_a^{id} = \mu_a^{\bullet} + RT \ln X_a \qquad (4.1)$$

The chemical potential of pure component A is given by $\mu_a^{\bullet}$ and is a function of T and p (or V). The superscript ^{id} implies an ideal solution. Chapter 17 can be consulted for definitions of the symbols used.

At equilibrium the chemical potential of a component in the mixture must equal that in the gas phase. If the vapor in equilibrium with the mixture is ideal, then Eq. (4.1) leads to Raoult's law,

$$p_a = p_a^\bullet X_a \tag{4.2}$$

The Gibbs free energy of mixing for a mixture is defined as

$$\Delta G_m = n_a(\mu_a - \mu_a^\bullet) + n_b(\mu_b - \mu_b^\bullet) \tag{4.3}$$

For ideal mixtures,

$$\Delta G_m^{id} = -T\Delta S_m = RT(n_a \ln X_a + n_b \ln X_b) \tag{4.4}$$

Here n_a, n_b refer to the number of moles of A, B present. The symbol G_a can also be used for μ_a, i.e., the partial molar Gibbs free energy of A. The other mixing functions for an ideal solution are all zero, i.e.,

$$\Delta V_m^{id} = \Delta U_m^{id} = \Delta H_m^{id} = 0 \tag{4.5}$$

For real mixtures, (4.1) must be replaced by

$$\mu_a = \mu_a^\bullet + RT \ln a_a = \mu_a^\bullet + RT \ln f_a X_a \tag{4.6}$$

The activity coefficients f introduced here are defined with a different reference state ($X_a = 1$) than the γ usually used in discussion of electrolyte solutions, where the reference is a 1 molal ideal solution. In ideal mixtures, $f_a = f_b = 1$ for the whole range of composition. The thermodynamic mixing functions for real systems are then divided up as, e.g., $\Delta G_m = \Delta G_m^{id} + \Delta G_m^e$, where ΔG_m^e is the excess free energy of mixing. In terms of activity coefficients it is

$$\Delta G_m^e = RT(n_a \ln f_a + n_b \ln f_b) \tag{4.7}$$

Other excess functions can be expressed in terms of derivatives of f, e.g.,

$$\Delta S_m^e = -RT\left(n_a \frac{\partial \ln f_a}{\partial T} + n_b \frac{\partial \ln f_b}{\partial T}\right) \tag{4.8}$$

Such excess functions are related by the usual thermodynamic relationships such as

$$\Delta G_m^e = \Delta H_m^e - T\ \Delta S_m^e = \Delta U_m^e + p\ \Delta V_m^e - T\ \Delta S_m^e \tag{4.9}$$

Because of Eq. (4.5), $\Delta V_m^e = \Delta V_m$; $\Delta U_m^e = \Delta U_m$; $\Delta H_m^e = \Delta H_m$. The excess functions are useful especially for systems which deviate only slightly from ideality.

Solutions which show no sign of solvation or association effects, i.e., of specific chemical or association effects, have small ΔS_m^e, as they have virtually random mixing. Often such solutions are referred to as "regular" solutions [2].

(b) Miscibility

Two components are miscible in all proportions only if the curve of ΔG_m vs X_a is concave upward in the whole range of composition at the T, p considered. Thus $(\partial^2\Delta G_m/\partial X_a^2) > 0$. Curve (i) in Fig. 4.1 shows such a case.

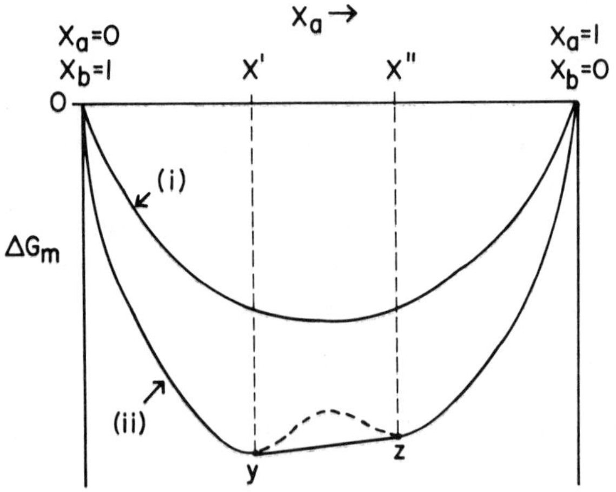

Fig. 4.1. Schematic curves of ΔG_m for a (i) totally mixcible system, and (ii) one showing a miscibility gap.

The ΔG_m vs X curve can however also have a shape of the type shown in curve (ii). At $X_a = X'$ and X'', the slope of ΔG_m vs X_a is the same. Thus $\mu'_a = \mu''_a$, and two phases with compositions X'_a and X''_a can exist in equilibrium. The Gibbs-Duhem relation (17.14) ensures that μ_b is the same in the two phases as well.

Such a two-phase system would have a lower total free energy than any one-phase system with X in the range X' to X''. The net ΔG_m for the two-phase system with an overall composition X is given by the straight line yz. This is lower than the ΔG_m of the (unstable) one-phase system as given by the dashed curve.

The curve of ΔG_m vs X for a system varies with temperature. At some temperature T_c, the festoon shape shown in curve (ii) of Fig. 4.1 may disappear, so that the ΔG_m vs X curve is again concave upwards everywhere. At this critical solution point,

$$\frac{\partial^2(\Delta G_m)}{\partial X^2} = \frac{\partial^3(\Delta G_m)}{\partial X^3} = 0 \qquad (4.10)$$

The fourth derivative must be positive.

Liquid mixtures can thus show solubility curves such as those in Fig. 4.2. The horizontal lines indicate the regions in which the system exists in two phases. Points X' and X'' in Fig. 4.2(a) can for example correspond to X = X' and X'' in Fig. 4.1, curve (ii) if that figure is drawn for T = T'.

The system represented in Fig. 4.2(a) shows an upper critical solution temperature (UCST), or "consolute point," while (b) shows one with a LCST (lower). It can be shown [1] that in a system at the UCST,

$$\left(\frac{\partial^2 \Delta H_m}{\partial X^2}\right)_{X_c} < 0 \qquad \text{and} \qquad \left(\frac{\partial^2 \Delta S_m}{\partial X^2}\right)_{X_c} < 0 \qquad (4.11)$$

while for a LCST they are both >0. The derivatives are evaluated at the critical composition X_c. When ΔH_m vs X and ΔS_m vs X curves have no points of inflection, then the signs of the derivatives in (4.11) are determined by the signs of the functions ΔH_m, ΔS_m themselves. In

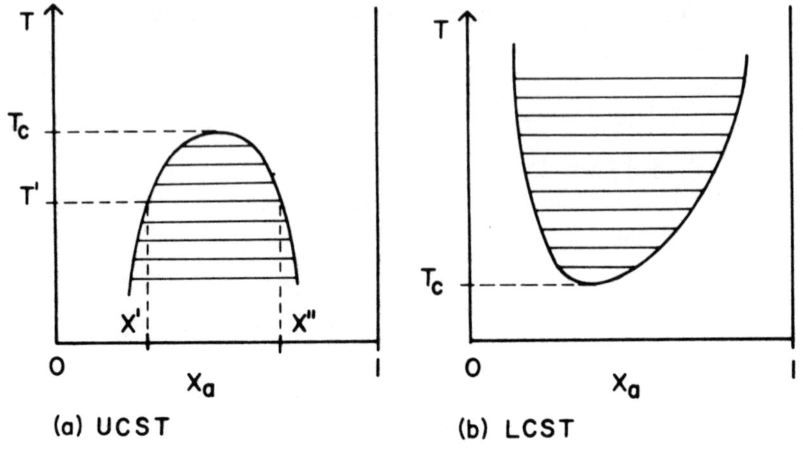

Fig. 4.2. Schematic curves for systems showing (a) an upper critical solution temperature, and (b) a lower critical solution temperature.

practice, a LCST occurs only when ΔS_m^e is large and negative, while for an UCST, ΔH_m is large and positive.

There is an analogy between a one-component and a two-component system. Thus the indices introduced in Sec. 2.1(a) for description of the one-component critical region are also applicable here. The compressibility in a one-component system ($\sim\partial p/\partial V$ or $\partial^2 G/\partial V^2$) is thus analogous to $\partial^2 G/\partial X^2$ in the two-component system, etc. Evidence suggests that the critical indices are the same for a liquid-liquid critical point in a two-component system as for a gas-liquid critical point in a one-component system.

(c) Solubility of Solids and Gases

Solutions of solids can be considered in the same framework as liquid-liquid mixtures. However the standard state of the solid must be taken as that of a hypothetical supercooled liquid. If the heat of fusion, ΔH_f^θ, is assumed constant, then

$$\left(\frac{\partial \ln a_s}{\partial T}\right)_p = \frac{\partial[(G_s - G^\bullet)/RT]}{\partial T} = \frac{\Delta H_f^\theta}{RT^2} \tag{4.12}$$

On integration of (4.12) from T to T_f, the activity of the solid referred to its new standard state is

$$\ln a_s = -\frac{\Delta H_f^\theta}{R}\frac{(T_f - T)}{TT_f} \tag{4.13}$$

The solubility is reached at the concentration of the solute X_b where a_b (the activity of the solute) equals a_s. In the case of an ideal solution, $a_b = X_b$. Thus the solubility is given by

$$\ln X_{b,sat} = -\frac{\Delta H_f^\theta}{R}\frac{(T_f - T)}{TT_f} \tag{4.14}$$

where $X_{b,sat}$ is the mole fraction of solute present in a saturated solution. Improvements can be made in (4.14) by considering heat capacity differences etc. [2].

A corresponding equation can be obtained for the solubility of a vapor above its normal boiling point. In this case T_f is replaced by T_B and ΔH_f^θ by $-\Delta H_{vap}^\theta$ in (4.14). Gaseous solutions are often quite dilute. In such cases, Henry's law gives to a good approximation

$$a_b = p_b = \text{constant}\cdot X_b \tag{4.15}$$

Solubility of solids and gases can also be considered from the point of view of phase diagrams.

The schematic freezing point diagram Fig. 4.3(a) shows a system with a "eutectic" point E. The horizontal lines show regions where two phases coexist (a one component solid and a liquid mixture). Point z gives then the solubility of A in B at a temperature T_z. Such a diagram is relatively insensitive to pressure.

Figure 4.3(b) shows a boiling point diagram with an "azeotrope" Z. Not all mixtures have azeotropes, and azeotropes can be ones which exhibit a minimum boiling point as well as a maximum as shown in Fig. 4.3(b). The composition of the vapor and the liquid in equilibrium with it at T_B is identical only in the case of the pure components and the azeotrope mixture. Boiling point diagrams are quite sensitive to pressure. From a series of constant pressure curves such as in Fig.

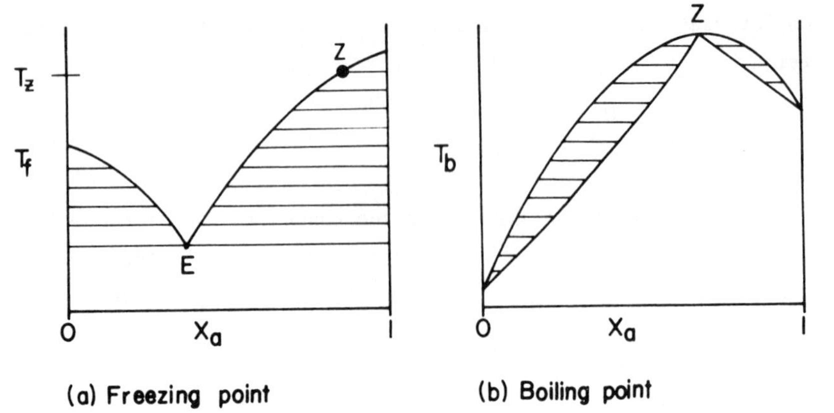

Fig. 4.3. Schematic diagram showing (a) the freezing point and (b) the boiling point of a system as functions of composition.

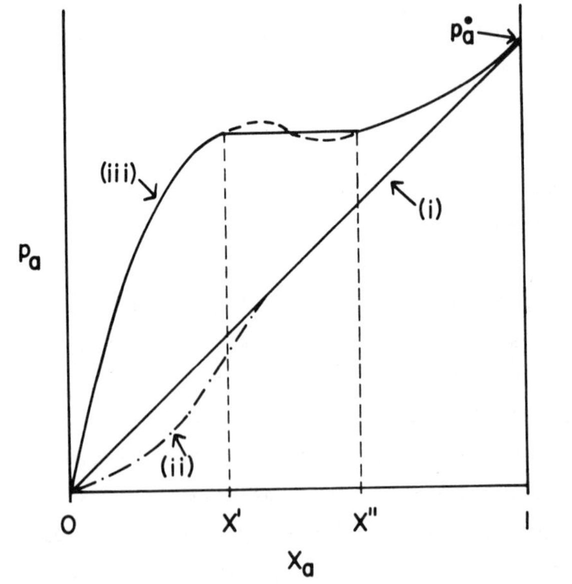

Fig. 4.4. Schematic vapor pressure diagram for a 2 component system: (i) $\nu = 0$ (ii) $\nu > 0$ (iii) $c\nu/kT < -4$.

4.3(b) drawn for different pressures, it is possible to construct vapor pressure curves such as those shown in Fig. 4.4.

Curve (i) in Fig 4.4 is for an ideal solution, while curve (iii) is for a solution at a temperature below the UCST [Fig. 4.2(a)]. The coexistence of two phases with compositions X' and X" is shown. The phases can coexist as they have the same vapor pressure, i.e., the same chemical potential (curve (ii) in Fig. 4.1).

(d) Empirical Rules for Excess Functions

Before going on to outlining some statistical mechanical approaches to liquid mixtures, some equations for estimating ΔU_m and ΔV_m for mixtures from thermodynamic data of pure liquids will be considered.

The energy of mixing ΔU_m can be estimated through the Scatchard equation [2],

$$\Delta U_m = (X_a V_a + X_b V_b)(\delta_a - \delta_b)^2 \phi_a \phi_b \tag{4.16}$$

Here ϕ_a is the volume fraction of A and δ_a the "solubility parameter",

$$\delta_a = (\Delta U_{V,a}/V_a)^{1/2} \tag{4.17}$$

where $\Delta U_{V,a}$ is the energy of vaporization of A.

Equation (4.17) is obtained only as a number of assumptions are made: (i) $\Delta S_m^e = 0$, i.e., the mixing of molecules is assumed random; (ii) $\Delta V_m = 0$; (iii) the energy can be expressed in the form of pair interactions; (iv) the cohesive energy density for component A is $e_{aa} = \Delta U_{V,a}/V_a$; (v) e_{ab} can be written as $e_{ab} = (e_{aa}, e_{bb})^{1/2}$ [Sec. 1.1(e)]. With these assumptions, (4.17) can be obtained starting from

$$-\Delta U_m = \frac{e_{aa}V_a^2X_a^2 + 2e_{ab}V_aV_b + e_{bb}V_b^2X_b^2}{X_aV_a + X_bV_b} \tag{4.18}$$

An estimate can also be made for ΔV_m. When ΔS_m^e is assumed = 0 and $\Delta A_m^e \approx \Delta G_m^e$, then, very roughly,

$$\Delta V_m = -\frac{\partial \Delta G_m^e}{\partial p}_T \simeq -\kappa V \frac{\partial \Delta U_m}{\partial V} \simeq -\kappa V \frac{\Delta U_m}{V} \simeq \kappa \Delta G_m^e \tag{4.19}$$

Here κ is the compressibility calculated for the unmixed system.

Experimental data are most often obtained at constant p conditions, while theoretical calculations are more often for constant V conditions. In the correlation of experiment with theory, the data must be corrected for this difference. Thus

$$\Delta A_m^e - \Delta G_m^e = -\frac{1}{2}\frac{1}{V\kappa}\cdot\Delta V_m^2 + \cdots$$
$$(\Delta S_m^e)_V - (\Delta S_m^e)_p = \frac{1}{T}(\Delta U_m - \Delta H_m) = -\frac{\alpha}{\kappa}\cdot\Delta V_m \tag{4.20}$$

Here α is the coefficient of thermal expansion (Sec. 17.2). While differences between ΔA_m^e and ΔG_m^e are usually negligible (for $\Delta V_m < 1$ $cm^3\ mol^{-1}$), changes in ΔS_m^e, and differences between ΔU_m^e and ΔH_m^e can be considerable, with even changes in sign occurring [2].

4.2. STATISTICAL MECHANICS OF MIXTURES

(a) Lattice Theory

The lattice theory outlined below is based on a rather restricted model. It is thus not of much use for practical calculations on real liquids, although it is of more use for solid solutions. It is nevertheless discussed here as it illustrates many of the phenomena present in liquid mixtures in a simple way.

The model is quite similar to the cell theories (Sec. 2.2). There are N_a molecules of A and N_b of B distributed on sites in a regular lattice, each with c nearest neighbors, and with no vacant sites. Each molecule has a molecular partition function q_a or q_b due to movement about the lattice sites, i.e., with potential energy terms from intermolecular interaction not included.

A partition function for the system can be written right away if the molecules are assumed distributed randomly among the sites (i.e., $\Delta S_m^e = 0$). Nearest neighbor interaction energies are written as υ_{aa}, υ_{ab}, υ_{bb}, where, for example, υ_{ab} represents the energy between an A and a B molecule on neighboring sites. With the further definitions $\upsilon = \upsilon_{aa} + \upsilon_{bb} - 2\upsilon_{ab}$ and N_{ab} = number of nearest neighbor AB pairs = $cN_aN_b/(N_a + N_b)$,

$$Q = (q_a)^{N_a} \cdot (q_b)^{N_b} \frac{(N_a + N_b)!}{N_a! N_b!} \exp\left[- \frac{(N_{aa}\nu_{aa} + N_{ab}\nu_{ab} + N_{bb}\nu_{bb})}{T}\right]$$

$$= \left(q_a \exp\left[- \frac{c\nu_{aa}}{2kT}\right]\right)^{N_a} \cdot \left(q_b \exp\left[- \frac{c\nu_{bb}}{2kT}\right]\right)^{N_b} \frac{(N_a + N_b)!}{N_a! N_b!}$$

$$\left(\exp\left[+ \frac{\nu}{2kT}\right]\right)^{N_{ab}} \tag{4.21}$$

When $\nu = 0$, then two AB interactions have the same energy as an AA plus a BB. All the results for the ideal mixture [Sec. 4.16] can then be derived from (4.21). The assumption of random distribution is in this case also valid.

However, when $\nu \neq 0$, the "Bragg-Williams" approximation of random distribution is not valid. Intermolecular interactions are then not uniform, and either unlike ($\nu > 0$) or like ($\nu < 0$) nearest neighbor pairs would be favored. Thus (4.21) should be looked on as a first approximation to a more realistic partition function.

When (4.21) is used, then $\Delta S_m = \Delta S_m^{id}$ even for $\nu \neq 0$. However, ΔA_m^e and $\Delta U_m \neq 0$. This can be seen by setting

$$\mu_a = -kT \frac{\partial \ln Q}{\partial \ln N_a}$$

$$= \ln X_a - \ln q_a \exp\left[- \frac{c\nu_{aa}}{2kT}\right] - \frac{c\nu(1 - X_a)^2}{2kT} \tag{4.22}$$

An analogous expression is valid for μ_b. Thus

$$\Delta A_m = N_a(\mu_a - \mu_a^\bullet) + N_b(\mu_b - \mu_b^\bullet) = \Delta A_m^{id} + \Delta A_m^e$$

$$= -kT(N_a \ln X_a + N_b \ln X_b) - (N_a + N_b) \frac{c\nu X_a X_b}{2kT} \tag{4.23}$$

The last term is equal to ΔU_m. A critical solution temperature is predicted by (4.23) from relations (4.10) when $X_a = X_b = 0.5$, $c\nu/kT = -4$.

Vapor pressure curves such as those shown in Fig. 4.4 (page 86) can also be obtained from (4.23). Thus

$$p_a = p_a^\bullet X_a \exp\left[- \frac{c\nu(1 - X_a)^2}{2kT}\right] \tag{4.24}$$

In real systems where $S_m^e \neq 0$, it is not solely the energy term which determines the type of deviation from Raoult's law. In the case of curve (iii) in Fig. 4.4, the system can exist in two phases, as the partial pressure of A can be the same for a liquid mixture of compositions X_a' and X_a'', for example. Note the similarity to the one-component vapor pressure diagram (Fig. 2.3). In a one-component system, concentration is proportional to 1/V.

More sophisticated developments of the lattice theory are available [3] where a certain amount of ordering is introduced into the mutual distribution of molecules. Thus ΔA_m^e can be expressed as a series

$$\Delta A_m^e = \frac{a_1}{kT} + \frac{a_2}{(kT)^2} + \cdots \tag{4.25}$$

where (4.23) gives the first term $(a_1 = (N_a + N_b)c\upsilon X_a X_b/2)$. Examples of such refinements is the use of the "quasi-chemical" approximation for distribution of molecules on lattice sites. When the sizes of the components are very different (e.g., polymer solutions), then one of the components can be thought to occupy several lattice sites. An exact solution for this problem is also available for the two-dimensional square plane lattice.

(b) Approaches Using the Law of Corresponding States

Many theoretical treatments of liquid mixtures begin by making use of the law of corresponding states [Sec. 18.4(c)]. In such cases the intermolecular pair potential is considered to be of the form [Eq. (18.37)]

$$\upsilon_{ij} = \varepsilon_{ij}\phi\left(\frac{r}{\sigma_{ij}}\right) \tag{4.26}$$

where ϕ is a universal function. In the case of the 6-12 potential (1.1) $\phi(y) = 4(y^{-12} - y^{-6})$.

Such theories usually begin in the first approximation by introducing a hypothetical pure liquid which represents the liquid mixture.

This liquid would have a pair potential of the form of (4.26), but the parameters ε and σ would be functions of the composition of the mixture.

The configurational partition function for the mixture can be represented by

$$Z = \frac{(N_a + N_b)!}{N_a!N_b!} (\sigma^3 \cdot z_{red}(T^*, V^*))^{N_a + N_b} \tag{4.27}$$

Here $z_{red}(T^*, V^*)$ is a universal function of the reduced temperature and volume (18.40). Equation (4.27) differs from Z of a pure substance as it also contains a statistical factor.

The configurational free energy A_{con} can then be obtained from (4.27) as $A_{con} = -kT \ln Z$. The value of G_{con} is often preferred for comparison with experiment. This can be obtained as

$$G_{con} = A_{con} + pV = A_{con} - V^*\left(\frac{\partial A_{con}}{\partial V^*}\right)_T \tag{4.28}$$

Equation (4.28) gives G_{con} as a universal function of V*, T*.

(1) Average Potential Model

An approach developed extensively by Prigogine [3] is often referred to as "average potential model." It notes that (4.28) is a universal function valid for the pure components as well as the mixture itself. It can thus be obtained either experimentally, or through a theory for single-component liquids (e.g., Chaps. 2 and 3). The excess mixing functions are then available if the dependence of the average potential parameters ε, σ is known in terms of parameters of the pure components ε_{aa}, σ_{aa}, etc.

In order to express ε, σ in terms of the other intermolecular potential parameters, three parameters δ, θ, and ρ are often used. When pure A is considered as the "reference" fluid, then

$$\delta = \frac{1}{\varepsilon_{aa}}(\varepsilon_{bb} - \varepsilon_{aa}) \qquad \theta = \frac{1}{\varepsilon_{aa}}\left(\varepsilon_{ab} - \frac{\varepsilon_{aa} + \varepsilon_{bb}}{2}\right)$$
$$\rho = \frac{\sigma_{bb} - \sigma_{aa}}{\sigma_{aa}} \tag{4.29}$$

The Lorentz-Berthelot rule [Sec. 1.1(e)] is usually assumed for σ, i.e., $\sigma_{ab} = (\sigma_{aa} - \sigma_{bb})/2$, but often not for ε. Thus ε_{ab} is introduced as a new parameter. With the use of the parameters defined in (4.29), the average potential parameter ε is, for example,

$$\varepsilon = \varepsilon_{aa}(1 - \delta X_b - 2\theta X_a X_b + \frac{3}{2} c\rho^2 X_a X_b) \tag{4.30}$$

To get (4.30), it has been assumed that v is given in a form assuming random mixing, i.e.,

$$v(r) = X_a^2 v_{aa}(r) + 2X_a X_b v_{ab}(r) + X_b^2 v_{bb}(r) \tag{4.31}$$

The above is only a very brief outline giving the essence of the average potential approach. A detailed version with many extensions is given in Ref. 3.

(2) Conformal Solutions

All the approaches described in Sec. 4.2(b) are at times called "conformal theories." The name is more specifically applied to approaches in which pair potential parameters are given in terms of reference state parameters ε_0, σ_0 as

$$\varepsilon_{ij} = f_{ij}\varepsilon_0 \qquad \sigma_{ij} = \frac{\sigma_0}{g_{ij}} \tag{4.32}$$

The parameters ε and σ can then be expressed as an expansion in $(f_{ij} - 1)$ and $(g_{ij} - 1)$

$$\begin{aligned} \sigma &= \sigma_0 \Sigma \frac{X_i X_j}{g_{ij}} = \sigma_0\{1 - \Sigma X_i X_j (g_{ij} - 1) + \cdots\} \\ \varepsilon &= \varepsilon_0\{1 + \Sigma X_i X_j (f_{ij} - 1) + \cdots\} \end{aligned} \tag{4.33}$$

The summation is over AA, BB, AB, and BA.

The difference in configurational free energy between the real and the reference system can then be expressed as [4]

$$A_{con} - A_{con,\,0} = \Sigma X_i X_j \{V_0(f_{ij} - 1) + 3((N_a + N_b)kT - p_0 V)(g_{ij} - 1) + \cdots\} \tag{4.34}$$

Here V_0 is the intermolecular potential energy of the reference system, and p_0 the pressure.

This treatment has been extended to take into account second-order terms [1]. It can be thought of as a type of perturbation method where the expansion is in terms of $(f_{ij} - 1)$ and $(g_{ij} - 1)$ instead of 1/T as in Eq. (3.35).

(3) van der Waals

The theory originally suggested by van der Waals for fluid mixtures also represents an example of the use of corresponding states. The van der Waals equation (2.4) for a mixture is simply written as

$$p = \frac{T}{(V/n - b)} - \frac{an^2}{V^2} \tag{4.35}$$

Now a and b are composition dependent, with

$$\begin{aligned} a &= X_a^2 a_a + 2X_a X_b a_{ab} + X_b^2 a_b \\ b &= X_a^2 b_a + 2X_a X_b b_{ab} + X_b^2 b_b \end{aligned} \tag{4.36}$$

The critical constants T_c, V_c can be determined from a and b, so that these parameters can be obtained in terms of pair potential parameters [Sec. 2.2(e)].

The results of more sophisticated treatments, but with the basic form (4.36) used for determining f_{ij} and g_{ij} [5] have led to results which are in good agreement with more exact treatments (e.g., the Percus-Yevick equation), and computer simulation.

There are several other theories of the same general type which will not be outlined here. Examples are Guggenheim's theory [6] and the HSE (hard-sphere excess) conformal solution theory [7].

(c) Distribution Functions

In the case of binary liquid mixtures, there are three radial distribution functions present, g_{aa}, g_{bb}, and g_{ab}. The Percus-Yevick equation (3.33) can be solved exactly for a system composed of a mixture of hard spheres of different sizes when the diameters are additive.

The PY solution for such a system is in good agreement with computer simulation methods. ΔU_m is of course 0, but there is a small negative ΔG_m^e giving a small negative ΔV_m. This implies that the smaller spheres occupy in part gaps between the larger, and that the common assumption of random mixing is not very good. As in the case of pure liquids, the hard-sphere results are important for real liquids, as the repulsive forces seem in many cases to be predominant in determining structure. Such a solution can also be used as a reference system for more realistic models.

Radial distribution functions and excess thermodynamic functions have also been calculated for a 6-12 potential using the PY equation. The Lorentz-Berthelot rules were used for ε_{ab} and σ_{ab}. The results indicate that deviations from the rule for ε_{ab} have little effect on the distribution functions, but that deviations from the rule for σ_{ab} have a large effect. The radial geometry is quite similar to that of a hard-sphere fluid. The ΔV_m in this mixture is also negative at higher densities. The densities were not high enough to be in the liquid range, however.

The solution of the PY equation for the case of hard spheres with nonadditive diameters [i.e., $\sigma_{ab} = 1/2(\sigma_{aa} + \sigma_{bb} + \alpha)$] has also been solved [8]. The extreme case of this is the "Widom-Rowlinson" model, where $\sigma_{ab} = \alpha$, $\sigma_{aa} = \sigma_{bb} = 0$. For this model, the PY equation predicts a phase transition [Sec. 4.1(b)]. The critical indices for this phase transition of this model have also been calculated.

(d) Use of Cluster Expansions

In the case of dilute solutions of nonelectrolytes, an approach can be used which is similar to the virial expansion for a dilute gas. In analogy with the equation of state for gases (18.36), the osmotic pressure π of the solution is given

$$\frac{\pi}{\rho_b RT} = 1 - \sum_j \frac{j}{j+1} \beta_j \rho^j = 1 + \sum_{j>2} B_j \rho_b^{j-1} \qquad (4.37)$$

Here the β_j are the irreducible cluster integrals, B_j the virial coefficients and ρ_b the concentration of B.

The calculation of the β can be more complicated in this case than for the gas, as the solvent (component) has some influence. If a hard-sphere model is assumed for the solute, then, however, $B_2 = 2\pi(2a)^3/3$ as for the gas.

A more detailed discussion of this approach is given in Ref. 9, while Ref. 4 gives another description. The approach can give good results at low concentrations only, just as a virial equation is most accurate at low densities.

The excess thermodynamic functions for this system can also be calculated. The activity of B can be obtained from the osmotic pressure equation, and then the excess functions can be obtained through (4.7).

(e) Fluctuations and Ordering

Much of the discussion on density fluctuations in Sec. 3.4 is relevant to concentration fluctuations in mixtures. Just as in Sec. (d) above, concentration is here the variable instead of density.

When the change δA in A (or δG in G) is small for a local concentration change δX_a, then the probability of such a fluctuation in concentration is large. This occurs when $\partial^2(\Delta A_m)/\partial X_a^2$ is very small, for example close to the critical solution region.

Either by analogy to the density variations in a single-component liquid [Sec. 3.4(b)], or from other approaches [10], the difference in A between a homogeneous (random) solution and a real solution can be described by [see Eq. (3.51)]:

$$\delta A = A(\underline{r}) - A = \frac{1}{2}\sum_q (a + bq^2)\cdot|C_q|^2 \qquad (4.38)$$

The average fluctuation amplitude $<|C_q|^2>$ is then given by

$$<|C_q|^2> = \frac{kT}{a + bq^2} \qquad (4.39)$$

in analogy with (3.51). Thus (4.38) describes the concentration fluctuations present in terms of Fourier components of the wave vectors of these fluctuations.

Another way of describing nonrandomness in liquid mixtures is by models where there is self-association between molecules of a species or complexing of molecules between two species. Several such models are outlined in Ref. 11, while Ref. 12 treats one in some greater detail.

The excess functions of mixing can be obtained from ΔG_m^e through the usual thermodynamic relationships. ΔG_m^e can be obtained from (4.23) written in the form

$$\Delta G_m^e = (n_a + n_b)RT \left\{ X \ln \frac{X_a}{X} + (1 - X) \ln \frac{X_b}{(1 - X)} \right\} \tag{4.40}$$

Here X is the stoichiometric concentration of A, and (1 - X) of B, while X_a and X_b are the actual concentrations. The activity coefficients are then $f_a = X_a/X$, $f_b = X_b/(1 - X)$.

The concentration X_a is not equal to X if some association or complexing takes place. As some of A and/or B are taken up in formation of the complex, $X_a \neq X$ and $(X_a + X_b) \neq 1$. The proper expressions for X_a and X_b in terms of X can be obtained assuming a model of some association. The larger the value of the equilibrium constant for the association, the greater ΔG_m^e.

ΔH_m, ΔS_m^e, ΔV_m can be obtained formally from ΔG_m^e. This is equivalent to knowledge of ΔH^θ, ΔS^θ, and ΔV^θ for the association equilibrium, i.e., the temperature and pressure dependence of K or ΔG^θ.

For an equilibrium of the type

$$A + 2B \rightleftarrows AB_2 \tag{4.41}$$

the excess mixture curves show an extremum at X = 0.33 as shown in Fig. 4.5. ΔH_m is negative indicating an exothermic association. ΔS_m^e would also be negative as the association decreases randomness, but $\Delta S_m = \Delta S_m^{id} + \Delta S_m^e$ need not be negative. As in many cases, there would be a compensating effect between ΔH_m and $T\Delta S_m^e$.

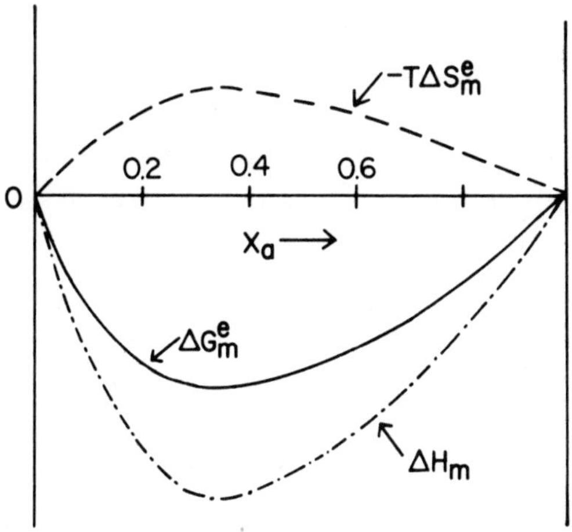

Fig. 4.5. Schematic curves of excess functions assuming the presence of AB_2 complexes.

(f) Other Approaches

Several theoretical approaches to description of liquid mixtures have not been covered in the previous sections and will be briefly mentioned here. They are in all cases extensions of approaches covered in Chaps. 2 and 3 for single-component systems.

The significant structure theory (Sec. 2.3) has been extended to liquid mixtures [13]. Even a greater number of experimental parameters are needed to apply the theory to mixtures than for single-component systems, so that the real usefulness of this approach is doubtful.

Mixtures of polar liquids have been treated [14] with the mean spherical model [Sec. 3.2(c)]. The components are taken to be hard spheres with the same diameter, but with point dipoles of different magnitude embedded in them. Analytical mathematical solutions are possible for the pair correlations functions and the dielectric constant. Several expected effects are not predicted by the theory, e.g., the aggregation of nonpolar molecules in a mixture containing strongly polar molecules.

The variational technique mentioned in the case of single-component liquids [Sec. 3.2(c)] has also been extended to the case of mixtures [15]. Calculations of excess functions have been carried out for mixtures of simple liquids assuming the 6-12 potential. Agreement with Monte Carlo simulation results is good, but the computational time is quite considerable.

Other computer simulation results for liquid mixtures are given in Ref. 16, where molecular dynamics results for 6-12 liquids are compared to conformal solution theory [Sec. 4.2(b)] results. The radial distribution functions obtained from the two approaches are in fair agreement. Further comparison of computer simulation, experimental and theoretical results for simple nonpolar systems can be found in Ref. 17.

4.3. SPECIAL CONSIDERATIONS FOR AQUEOUS SYSTEMS

Some types of mixtures, especially those involving water, are too complex and specific to be described adequately by any of the previous approaches. Figure 4.6 gives an idea of the complexity of water-alcohol systems. The diagram is drawn schematically for the t-butanol-water system. Other alcohol-water systems have similar curves for excess functions. ΔV_m is also negative for these systems.

It is noteworthy that, although the ΔS_m^e and ΔH_m curves are highly asymmetric, the resultant ΔG_m^e shown is a reasonably symmetric shape. The total entropy contribution to ΔG_m is $T\Delta S_m$. It can be obtained by adding $T\Delta S_m^{id}$ [Eq. (4.4)] to $T\Delta S_m^e$ and indicates that in the low alcohol concentration region, ΔS_m is actually negative, i.e., $|\Delta S_m^e| > |\Delta S_m^{id}|$.

A review of water-alcohol mixtures is given in Ref. 18. The model proposed to explain the behavior shown in Fig. 4.6 and related phenomena is as follows:

The structure of liquid water is assumed to be partially of an open, structured form [Sec. 2.4(a)]. This open form would have in it interstitial cavities. Some of these cavities would be occupied by "monomeric" water molecules. At low concentrations of alcohol,

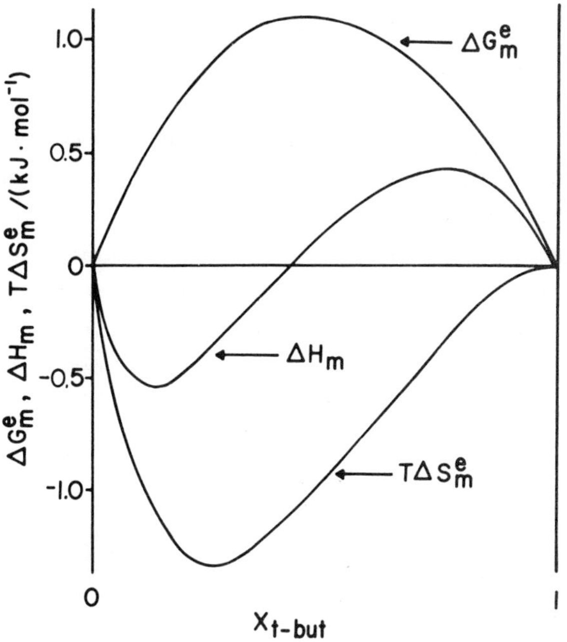

Fig. 4.6. Schematic curves of excess functions for the system t-butanol-water. After Ref. 18.

the alcohol molecules can be accomodated in these cavities. This brings about a negative ΔV_m, and a negative ΔS_m. The order of the water is preserved, while the alcohol is in a more ordered form in the mixture than in the pure alcohol.

At higher concentrations, the water structure is disrupted by the presence of alcohol. ΔH_m can become positive as the endothermic disruption of water is greater than the exothermic effect of more favorable H-bonding for the alcohol molecules in the aqueous mixture.

This model suggests that clathrate hydratelike structures exist in such aqueous solutions. Many instances of clathrate hydrates in the solid form have been reported [19]. Solid forms have been identified where guest molecules such as monatomic gases, hydrocarbons with up to 6 carbons, and other polyatomic species are situated in the holes of an ice-like lattice of H-bonded water molecules. Larger molecules, with a diameter between 5.6 and 6.6 Å can fit into a structure which gives a favorable overall composition of 1:17 (mol fraction 0.055).

Extensive theoretical consideration has also been given to aqueous solutions of the monatomic gases [20]. The anomalously high partial molar heat capacities in such solutions have been explained by the following model. The introduction of non-polar molecules increases the amount of water present in the structured form due to "hydrophobic interactions" as described in Sec. 1.3(d). As the highly H-bonded, structured form can absorb more energy through breaking of H-bonds, then the heat capacity is higher than expected.

REFERENCES

The major reference for this chapter is [1], which gives a thorough coverage of thermodynamics and most statistical-mechanical approaches. Mixtures made up of a liquid and a gas or solid (i.e., solutions) are covered more thoroughly in [2].

1. GR3.
2. J. H. Hildebrand and R. L. Scott, Regular Solutions, Prentice-Hall, Englewood Cliffs, 1962.
3. I. Prigogine, The Molecular Theory of Solutions, North-Holland, Amsterdam, 1957.
4. T. L. Hill, An Introduction to Statistical Thermodynamics, Addison-Wesley, Reading, 1960.
5. T. W. Leland, J. S. Rowlinson, G. A. Sather, and I. D. Watson, Trans. Farad. Soc., *65*, 2034 (1969).
6. E. A. Guggenheim, Mol. Phys., *9*, 199 (1965).
7. G. A. Mansoori and T. W. Leland, J. Chem. Soc. Faraday Trans. II, *68*, 320 (1972).
8. S. Ahn and J. L. Lebowitz, J. Chem. Phys., *60*, 523 (1974).
9. H. L. Friedman, Ionic Solution Theory, Interscience, New York, 1962.
10. V. P. Romanov and V. A. Solov'ev, in Water in Biological Systems (M. F. Vuks and A. I. Sidorova, eds.), Vol. II, 1, Consultants Bureau (1971).
11. J. H. Andreae, P. D. Edmonds, and J. F. McKellar, Acustica, *15*, 74 (1965).

12. A. Apelblat, J. Phys. Chem., *74*, 2214 (1970).

13. H. Eyring and M. S. Jhon, Significant Liquid Structures, Wiley, New York, 1969.

14. S. A. Adelman and J. M. Deutch, J. Chem. Phys., *59*, 3971 (1973).

15. G. A. Mansoori, J. Chem. Phys., *56*, 5335 (1972).

16. K. C. Mo, K. E. Gubbins, G. Jacucci, and I. R. McDonald, Molecular Phys., *27*, 1173 (1974).

17. I. R. McDonald, Ann. Rep. Chem. Soc. Sec. A, *69*, 75 (1972).

18. F. Franks and D. I. G. Ives, Quart. Rev., *27*, 1 (1965).

19. D. W. Davidson in GR8.

20. A. Ben-Naim in GR6.

Further Recent References

J.-L. Gustin and H. Renon, "Application de la Thermodynamique Statistique a l'Elaboration d'un Modèle de Réprésentation des Propriétes d'Excès des Mélanges Liquides", J. Chim. Phys., *70*, 1237 (1973).

W. Schröer, Nahordnung in Flüssigkeiten I. Ein Statistisch-Thermodynamisches Flüssigkeitsmodell auf der Basis von Kontaktwahrscheinlichkeiten", Ber. Bunsenges. physik. Chem., *78*, 626 (1974).

D. Isbister and R. J. Bearman, "Solution of the Mean Spherical Model for Dipolar Mixtures", Mol. Phys., *28*, 1297 (1974).

M. Flytzani-Stephanopoulos, K. E. Gubbins, and C. G. Gray, "Thermodynamics of Mixtures of Non-Spherical Molecules II. Strong Polar, Quadrupolar, and Overlap Forces", Mol. Phys., *30*, 1649 (1975).

M. L. Huggins, "Thermodynamic Properties of Liquids, Including Solutions. 12. Dependence of Solution Properties on Properties of the Component Molecules", J. Phys. Chem., *80*, 1317 (1976).

S. P. McAlister and E. D. Crozier, "The Concentration-Concentration Correlation Function in the Long-Wavelength Limit for Binary Liquid Alloys", J. Phys. C: Solid State Phys., *7*, 3509 (1974).

C. P. Hicks and C. L. Young, "The Gas-Liquid Critical Properties of Binary Mixtures", Chem. Rev., *75*, 119 (1975).

A. Ben-Naim, "Structure-Breaking and Structure-Promoting Processes in Aqueous Solutions", J. Phys. Chem., *79*, 1268 (1975).

Chapter 5

THEORETICAL APPROACHES TO ELECTROLYTE SOLUTIONS

This chapter first looks at the interaction of a single ion with the solvent in steps of increasing sophistication. Only cases where "physical" forces are present are considered. Thus ion-molecule interactions are assumed to be affected to a negligible degree by overlapping of the electronic distributions of the ions and the solvent molecules. However, no sharp distinction can be made between an ion interacting very strongly with solvent molecules in its primary solvation shell through "physical" forces, and a complex ion where the solvent is considered as a "ligand."

Ion-ion interaction is discussed next. Cases where "chemical" effects predominate are not included. Thus aspects of dissociation of weak acids are not discussed, even though ion pairing itself is covered.

The separation of the discussion into these two main parts is convenient, but not completely realistic. Ion-ion interactions are certainly quite dependent upon the specific ion-solvent interactions present, as illustrated in parts of Sec. 4.2. Ion-solvent interactions also never occur for the idealized case where the ion considered does not interact with other ions as well as the solvent. It is not possible to measure directly single-ion thermodynamic properties such as the heat of solvation, ΔH_{solv}, as ions of the opposite sign must be present for electrical neutrality.

Discussion of ion-solvent and ion-ion interactions for the most part is assumed to refer to aqueous solutions. Thus some phenomena in nonaqueous electrolyte solutions are discussed in Sec. 4.3 to indicate the specificity of parts of the previous discussion to aqueous solutions.

5.1. ION-SOLVENT INTERACTIONS

(a) Continuous Solvent Model

The simplest model of an electrolyte solution for predicting ion-solvent interaction effects is what is often called the "primitive" model. It pictures the ions as hard spheres of diameter 2a and a charge Ze. The solvent is assumed to be a continuous medium with dielectric constant ε.

A knowledge of the free energy of solvation for a species, ΔG_{solv}, as a function of T gives also ΔS_{solv} and ΔH_{solv}. To calculate ΔG_{solv}, i.e., the ΔG for the reaction ion (gas) $\rightleftarrows$ ion (solution), it is convenient to divide the reaction into three steps: (i) discharging of the ion in the gas; (ii) introduction of the "neutral ion" into the solvent; (iii) charging of the ion in the solvent.

The charging of an ion can be pictured as bringing charge from infinity to its surface. The potential at the surface with respect to infinity is $q/4\pi\varepsilon^{\bullet}\varepsilon a$, where q is the total charge on the sphere (Sec. 1.2). Thus the energy required to charge the sphere in a dielectric medium from 0 to ze is

$$\Delta G_{(iii)} = \int_0^{ze} \frac{q}{4\pi\varepsilon\varepsilon^{\bullet}a}\, dq = \frac{(ze)^2}{8\pi\varepsilon\varepsilon^{\bullet}a} \tag{5.1}$$

As $\varepsilon = 1$ in vacuum, then $\Delta G_{(i)} = -(ze)^2/8\pi\varepsilon^{\bullet}a$. No electrostatic work is done in step ii. Thus if only ion-solvent interactions arising from electrostatic effects are considered, then $\Delta G_{(ii)} = 0$. Thus

$$\Delta G_{solv} = \Delta G_{(i)} + \Delta G_{(ii)} + \Delta G_{(iii)} = -\frac{L(ze)^2}{8\pi\varepsilon^{\bullet}}(1 - 1/\varepsilon) \tag{5.2}$$

By including Avogadro's number L in the expression, Eq. (5.2) gives the free energy per mole rather than per ion. It is often called the Born equation.

The entropy of solvation, ΔS_{solv}, can be found from Eq. (17.7) as $\Delta S_{solv} = -(\partial \Delta G_{solv}/\partial T)$ and ΔH_{solv} from $\Delta G_{solv} = \Delta H_{solv} - T\Delta S_{solv}$ [Eq. (17.33)]. The values of these quantities vary from species to species only through variation of the ionic radius a. In general, this model gives values of ΔH_{solv} which are too high if the crystallographic radii of the ions are used. To obtain reasonable agreement with experiment, a value of a must be used, which is about 0.85 Å greater than the crystallographic radius for positive ions and 0.1 Å greater for negative.

It is not possible experimentally to determine ΔH_{solv} for a specific ionic species. To preserve electroneutrality, such thermodynamic measurements can be carried out only for pairs of oppositely charged ions. Single ion thermodynamic properties can be obtained only on a relative acale, e.g., by assuming ΔH_{solv} for $H^+ = 0$, or by assuming some other relationship. The Born equation predicts ΔH_{solv} equal for K^+ and F^-, as these ions have approximately the same radius. On the relative scale, however, they turn out to have a considerably different ΔH_{solv} in water (i.e., heat of hydration, ΔH_{hyd}). This indicates dificiencies in the Born model.

(b) Structured Solvent Models

The assumption of a structureless, continuous solvent with a bulk dielectric constant ε is quite crude. In the strong electric fields close to the ion, the dielectric constant would be expected to be smaller than the bulk value ε. Here the solvent molecules would be so fully oriented by the ion's field that the orientational contribution to ε would no longer be present. This effect seems to take place only in the primary solvation shell. It thus suggests that the molecular structure of the molecules present in the primary shell be taken into account.

As seen in Sec. 1.1(a), the electrical distribution in a molecule can be described in terms of multipoles. To a first approximation, the c molecules in the primary solvation shell can be considered as dipoles, and the following cycle [1] can be thought to represent solvation of an ion: (i) a cluster of c + 1 molecules is removed from the bulk of the solvent; (ii) the cluster is broken up; (iii) c of the molecules are set about the ion in their lowest-energy form; (iv) the ion and its primary solvation shell is reintroduced into the hole made in (i); (v) some restructuring of the solvent molecules in the secondary shell takes place; and (vi) the remaining solvent molecule is condensed into the liquid.

The energy changes of steps i, ii, and vi depend on the properties of the solvent, and can be estimated from its properties. For step iii, the standard ion-dipole interaction relations from Chap. 1 can be used. The thermodynamics of this step, i.e., gas-phase solvation of the ion, has also been studied experimentally [2]. The energetics of step v are difficult to estimate; often it is considered together with step i.

Step iv can be treated essentially the same way as the continuous solvent model in Sec. (a) above. This time, a distance $a + 2a_s$ is used instead of a for the charging and discharging, as the primary shell is included (a_s is the radius of the solvent).

Such an ion-dipole model still does not predict a difference in solvation enthalpy for negative and positive ions of the same size.

If, however, the solvent molecules are each described by a dipole and a quadrupole, then energies for step iii are different for positive and negative ions of the same size. Induction effects can also be included by considering the polarizability of the molecules.

For an even more detailed model, the solvent molecules can be modelled by sets of point charges and polarizable bonds [3]. Quantum mechanical calculations have also been performed on ion-solvent interactions. References to such calculations are given in Sec. 1.3(c). A thorough discussion is also given in Ref. 4.

(c) Solvation Numbers

In the previous section, the number of solvent molecules which are in the primary solvation shell, i.e., which are nearest neighbors of the ion, was given the symbol c. This is referred to at times as the "coordination" or "solvation" number. Another definition of solvation number would be the effective number of solvent molecules bound to the ion with sufficient strength to follow its motion. This latter definition would seem to be more proper, but there does not seem to be a consensus on the definition.

There are various methods available to determine the solvation (hydration) number, e.g., mobility, compressibility, and entropy measurements. Generally, the greater the charge on the ion, and the smaller the ion, the greater the hydration number. In such cases, the electric field close to the ion is strong, resulting in strong ion-solvent interactions. Conversely, the hydration numbers for large monovalent ions, e.g., Cs^+, I^- are low, close to 0.

In some cases there is considerable discrepancy in the hydration numbers determined by various methods. This is partly because the concept is not exactly defined. Individual solvent molecules in the primary solvation shell have a finite residence time τ_{solv} before they exchange with molecules outside this shell. Thus the hydration number expresses only an effective average number. The concept is nevertheless useful in simplifying various models.

The mean time that a water molecule is a nearest neighbor of the ion, τ_{solv}, depends on the energy required by a molecule to escape from the ion. This energy can be greater or smaller than that necessary for a water molecule to replace its nearest neighbor in bulk water. If the difference, ΔE, is <0, then

$$\frac{\tau_{solv}}{\tau_w} \simeq \exp\left[\frac{\Delta E}{kT}\right] \tag{5.3}$$

is <1, i.e., a water molecule next to an ion is in a less rigid environment than in bulk water. (τ_w is the mean residence time in bulk water).

Cases where $\tau_{solv}/\tau_w < 1$ (i.e., $\Delta E < 0$) are usually referred to as "negative hydration" or "structure breaking." There are other ways of defining these terms, e.g., through entropy rather than residence time differences. Negative hydration would be expected for large ions where ion-water interactions are smaller. Conversely, positive hydration occurs for small ions, where $\Delta E > 0$ and where hydration numbers are therefore greater [5].

The existance of cases where $\tau_{solv} < \tau_w$ can be explained as follows. If the field of the ion is not too strong, as, for example, at the surface of a large ion, then the ion-water interactions are not strong enough to restrict seriously the motion of solvating molecules. Yet the presence of the ion disrupts the regularity of the water structure enough so that $\tau_{solv} < \tau_w$ becomes possible. Such a zone of disrupted water structure is also thought to exist about small and highly charged ("structure making") ions. However, here the zone is further out, past the primary solvation shell.

In the case of large organic ions such as tetraalkylammonium ions, there can be a net "structure-making" effect [6], at least for $(C_3H_5)_4N^+$ and higher alkyls. Structure-making in these cases can be explained in terms of the hydrophobic interactions Sec. 1.3(d) of the alkyl groups. There is also evidence that these ions are solvated by the same type of clathrate structures as are present in their crystalline hydrates (Sec. 4.3).

5.2. ION-ION INTERACTIONS

(a) Debye-Hückel Model

Many attempts at interpreting the properties of electrolyte solutions start with the D-H model. It is essentially the same model as that introduced in Sec. 5.1(a), i.e., the "primitive" model with charged spheres in a continuous dielectric medium.

In Chap. 4, macroscopic properties of a solution were expressed for the most part in terms of excess thermodynamic functions. In electrolyte solutions, it is customary to express these in terms of the molal activity coefficient γ [Eq. (17.22)].

In the D-H model, the distribution of charge due to other ions about a central ion species i is given by the charge density $\rho_i(r)$. It can be expressed as

$$\rho_i(r) = \Sigma n_j z_j e g_{ij}(r) \tag{5.4}$$

where n_j is the mean number density of ionic species j, $z_j e$ the charge and $g_{ij}(r)$ the radial distribution function for species j with i the central ion (Sec. 4.2(c)]. If the species of the central ion is k, then $g_{ij}(r) \neq g_{kj}(r)$ in general.

There will be an electrostatic potential $\phi_i(r)$ about the central ion. This potential must satisfy Poisson's law [Eq. (20.5)]:

$$\Delta\phi_i(r) = \underline{\nabla}\cdot\underline{\nabla}\phi_i(r) = -\frac{\rho_i(r)}{\varepsilon^\bullet\varepsilon} \tag{5.5}$$

where $\rho_i(r)$ if difined by (5.4) for $r \geqslant a_i$, the radius of the central ion.

The distribution functions for the various ions are now assumed to be of the form

$$g_{ij}(r) = \exp\left[-\frac{z_j e\phi_i(r)}{kT}\right] \tag{5.6}$$

This is equivalent to assuming "the potential of mean force" (Sec. 3.22) to be the electrostatic potential energy.

Equations (5.4) - (5.6) form a set of equations which can, in principle, be solved to obtain $\phi_i(r)$. A nonnumerical solution is, however, not possible for the resultant differential equation. Thus the exponential term in (5.6) is usually expanded and the expansion terminated after two terms to give

$$\nabla^2\phi_i = \frac{1}{r}\frac{d^2(r\phi_i)}{dr^2} = -\frac{e}{\varepsilon^\bullet\varepsilon}\sum_j z_j n_j\left(1 - \frac{z_j e\,\phi_i}{kT}\right)$$

$$= \kappa^2\phi_i - \frac{e}{\varepsilon^\bullet\varepsilon}\sum z_j n_j \qquad (5.7)$$

The last term on the right-hand side drops out due to electroneutrality requirements. Here the parameter κ has been introduced as

$$\kappa^2 = \frac{e^2}{\varepsilon\varepsilon^\bullet kT}\sum n_j z_j^2 = \frac{2e^2}{\varepsilon^\bullet\varepsilon kT}I' \qquad (5.8)$$

where I' is related closely to the "ionic strength." The actual ionic strength I is defined in temms of molality rather than number concentration. Thus

$$I = \frac{1}{2}\sum m_j z_j^2 \qquad \left(\simeq \frac{1}{2}\sum c_j z_j^2 \text{ for aqueous solutions}\right) \qquad (5.9)$$

Relation (5.8) is written in terms of SI units. These are not the most commonly used units for practical calculations as indicated in Refs. 7 - 10. The quantity $1/\kappa$ is at times considered as the thickness of the "ionic atmosphere" or "ionic cloud" belonging to the central ion.

Equation (5.7) can be solved as a boundary value problem to give the solution for $r > a_i$

$$\phi_i(r) = \frac{z_i e \exp[-\kappa(r - a_i)]}{4\pi\varepsilon^\bullet\varepsilon r(1 + \kappa a_i)} \qquad (5.10)$$

Now the differential charging process as described in Sec. 5.1(a) can be carried out. This gives the contribution to the free energy due to ion-ion interaction. In the case of one molecule it is by analogy to Eq. (4.7) equal to

$$kT \ln \gamma_i = -\frac{(z_i e)^2}{8\pi\varepsilon^\bullet\varepsilon}\frac{\kappa}{1+\kappa a_i} \qquad \ln \gamma_i = \frac{-\kappa e^2 z_i^2}{8\pi\varepsilon^\bullet\varepsilon kT(1+\kappa a_i)} \tag{5.11}$$

In the case of infinite dilution, $\kappa a_i \ll 1$, and the limiting law (DHLL) is obtained,

$$\ln \gamma_i = -\frac{(z_i e)^2}{8\pi\varepsilon^\bullet\varepsilon kT}\kappa = -\frac{z_i^2}{8\pi}\frac{\kappa^3}{\Sigma n_j z_j^2} \tag{5.12}$$

Thus $\ln \gamma_i$ is expected (5.9) to vary approximately as $\sqrt{I}$ as $c \to 0$.

It is not possible to measure experimentally the activity coefficient for a single species (Sec. 17.3). Only mean activity coefficients of the type $\gamma_\pm$ can be measured, where $\gamma_\pm = \sqrt{\gamma_+\gamma_-}$ for a 1:1 electrolyte. The total excess free energy in the system due to ion-ion interactions can be found by summing $kT \ln \gamma_i$ over all particles [Eq. (4.7)]. It becomes from (5.12)

$$\Delta G^e = -\frac{\kappa^3 V}{8\pi} \tag{5.13}$$

Other thermodynamic properties can also be derived through (5.13)

(b) Extensions to the DH Model

Various extensions of the D-H model have been proposed. Some of these are of an empirical nature with little theoretical basis. A term linear in I is usually added to the expression for $\log \gamma_\pm$ to take account of ion-solvent and other short-range interactions [7].

The ion-size parameter a_i can also be considered as an adjustable parameter instead of the crystallographic radius. Its value for the best fit of (5.11) to experimental data is of the order of 4 Å [1].

The D-H model can also be extended by including more terms in the expansion of the exponential in (5.6). Numerical solutions of the complete Poisson-Boltzmann equation are also available [11]. Such nonlinear forms of the PB equation can give more reasonable results, but still contain the assumptions inherent in the D-H model.

Ion-solvent interactions can be included in the model in a simple way. Strongly solvated ions can be considered to interact so strongly with some of the solvent molecules that these molecules are effectively prevented from being solvent molecules with respect to other ions. Thus the effective concentration of the ions is raised and that of the solvent lowered. The solvation number is often included in such extensions as an adjustable parameter [7]. The values obtained for it are in reasonable agreement with values obtained through other methods [Sec. 5.1(c)].

(c) Ion Pairing

A plot of $4\pi r^2 g_{ij}(r) n_j \, dr$ vs. r gives the number of ions of species j about an i ion in a shell thickness dr at r as shown schematically in Fig. 5.1. This assumes (5.6) to hold, but with $\phi_i(r)$ given by a coulomb potential. The minimum of this curve appears at a distance q such that

$$\frac{z_i z_j e^2}{4\pi\varepsilon^{\bullet}\varepsilon q} = 2kT \qquad (5.14)$$

Equation (5.14) defines the Bjerrum distance q. If two ions are closer than q, then they are considered to form an "ion pair."

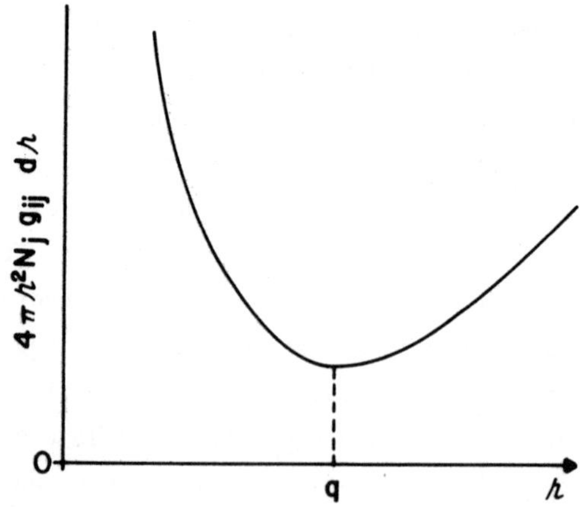

Fig. 5.1. Schematic curve giving the total number of ions of species about an ion of species j as a function of distance from i.

The degree of association of ions can then be found as

$$(1 - \alpha) = 4\pi n_i \int_a^q \exp\left[- \frac{z_i z_j e^2}{4\pi\varepsilon^\bullet \varepsilon k T r} \right] r^2 \, dr \tag{5.15}$$

Subsequently, the equilibrium constant for dissociation of ion pairs (i.e., ion pairs $\rightleftarrows$ free ions) is

$$K = \frac{\alpha^2 y_\pm^2 c}{(1 - \alpha)} = \frac{k_{diss}}{k_{assoc}} \tag{5.16}$$

Here $y_\pm$ is the molar activity coefficient [Eq. (17.22)]. The activity coefficient for the ion pair is assumed to be 1, as it is overall assumed to be a neutral species.

The ionic strength will also be affected by ion pairing. For a 1:1 electrolyte, I will no longer equal c but αc. Thus to obtain K from measured values of y, it is necessary to use approximations combining (5.16) with (5.11).

Another definition of ion pairs is given by Fuoss. In this case two ions are assumed to form a pair only if there is no solvent molecule between them. A form for the equilibrium association constant for Fuoss ion pairs can most readily be obtained by considering the rates of ion association and dissociation. This is done in Sec. 6.3 (d) with the result given in Eq. (6.83) for the general case of any potential $v(r)$. For a coulombic potential,

$$K = \frac{3000}{4\pi L d_{ab}^3} \exp\left[\frac{z_a z_b e}{4\pi\varepsilon\varepsilon^\bullet d_{ab} kT} \right] \tag{5.17}$$

This constant K varies with d_{ab} in such a way that it has a maximum at $d_{ab} = 2q/3$, where q is given by Eq. (5.14) [7].

It seems in cases to be necessary to postulate the existance of various types of ion pairs. In aqueous solutions of 2:2 electrolytes the following types of ion pairs can be distinguished experimentally [12],

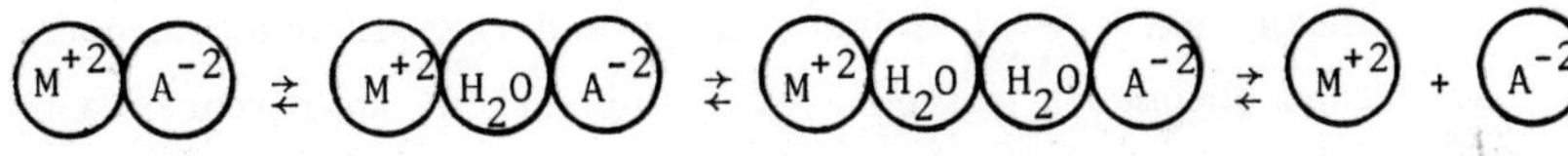

(5.18)

(contact ion pairs, solvent shared ion pairs, and solvent separated ion pairs).

Besides using the concept of ion pairs to extend the DH law to include ion association, it has also been used to calculate the complete ion-ion interaction term [13]. The primitive model is still assumed, but the problem is changed to one where there exist dipolar molecules instead of ions. In a symmetrical electrolyte, all ions are assumed to be paired to form dipoles.

The advantage of such an approach is that some of the problems resulting from the very long range of ion-ion forces are lessened. The model can also potentially better describe aspects of solvation behavior in solutions with finite concentrations. As seen from (5.18), the solvent molecules will be acted on by both members of an ion pair when the mean distance between ions is not too great.

(d) Lattice Theories and Molten Salts

The introduction of ion pairing allows the construction of models for larger concentrations. At high concentrations, it is possible to consider the electrolyte solution as being like a salt in the form of an ionic lattice with solvent molecules coming into the lattice and expanding it.

In such a regular expanded lattice, the electrostatic potential energy would vary as $1/\ell$, where ℓ is the mean ion-ion distance. As $1/\ell$ would vary as $c^{1/3}$, then the electrostatic energy and hence $\log \gamma_\pm$ would be proportional to $c^{1/3}$.

Plots of $\log \gamma_\pm$ vs $c^{1/3}$ do show a linear region in the medium concentration range. In the low concentration range the lattice arrangement would be so disturbed that the DH model is more appropriate. A lattice-like model would also predict an oscillating form for $g_{ij}(r)$ instead of the exponential form assumed in the DH model. Such oscillatory behavior has been found in both calculations and MC simulations [11].

In the extreme of concentration and temperature, an electrolyte solutions becomes a molten salt. Theoretical approaches to molten salts are reviewed in Ref. 14. Many of the approaches discussed in

Chaps. 2 - 4 are applicable. The presence of extra volume in the fused salt over the solid plays a prominent part in many of these approaches.

(e) Evaluation of the Configuration Integral

As in the case of imperfect gases [Sec. 18.4(b)] and the McMillan-Mayer approach to nonelectrolyte solutions [Sec. 4.2(d)], electrolyte solutions can be treated by expanding the osmotic pressure in the form of a virial equation of state. In this way, an expansion is obtained:

$$-\ln \gamma_j = \frac{(z_j e)^2}{8\pi\varepsilon^\bullet \varepsilon k T}\kappa + \frac{d}{dc_j}\sum_{n>2} B_n(\kappa)c^n \tag{5.19}$$

The coefficients $B_n(\kappa)$ are given in terms of integrals over Mayer cluster functions [Sec. 18.4(b)].

The first term in this cluster expansion theory gives simply the DHLL expression. The following terms do not give simple powers in c, as the B_n are also functions of c. There are difficulties in calculating the higher virial coefficients when coulomb potentials are used as the integrals can diverge [15]. Nevertheless, the calculations have been performed, and the "DHLL + B_2" form is often used to interpret experimental data,

Another way of approaching the calculation of the configurational integral is to use a "mode expansion" theory. This is equivalent to the cluster expansion theory, but avoids some mathematical problems [16]. In this case the Fourier transforms of the particle density are used (i.e., "collective variables") instead of $g_{ij}(r)$ [see also Sec. 3.2(b)]. The interparticle potential energy function is not used directly, but in the form of its Fourier transform.

The configurational integral is then expanded in terms of a product of averages of products of a finite number of modes. The qth mode is given by

$$S(\underline{q}) = \exp\left[-\frac{\nu(q)}{kTV}\, n(\underline{q})\cdot n(-\underline{q})\right] \tag{5.20}$$

where $n(\underline{q})$ is the Fourier transform of the particle density [Eq. (7.6)]:

$$n(\underline{q}) = \sum_{j=1}^{N} \delta(\underline{r} - \underline{r}_j) \exp[-i\underline{q}\cdot\underline{r}] \tag{5.21}$$

and

$$v(\underline{q}) = \int v(r) \exp[-i\underline{q}\cdot\underline{r}] \, d\underline{r} \tag{5.22}$$

The calculations outlined briefly in this section are usually performed in the form of a perturbation of a reference system.[Sec. 3.2(c)]. The reference system is usually a hard-sphere solution and the perturbation a coulomb interaction. Thus the model used is still the "primitive model" introduced in Sec. 5.1(a). Comparisons with MC calculations using the same model are good up to concentrations of 2 M in some cases. Thus the approach used for the calculations is accurate, but the model used is still quite crude (see Introduction of Chap. 3).

(f) Integral Equation Calculations

The integral equations relating $g(r)$ to $v(r)$ can be solved for electrolyte solutions numerically. Both the PY and HNC [Sec. 3.2(b)] equations have been solved to obtain the radial distribution functions. Thermodynamic parameters can then be obtained from the $g(r)$ [Sec. 3.1 (b)]. The HNC approximation gives results for these solutions which are more consistent and in better agreement with MC simulations than the PY approximation, at least for fairly primitive models. Thus HNC calculations have been carried out for a number of models [17].

The calculations have been pursued for square-well or square mound models, as well as the primitive models. Figure 5.2 shows a square-mound potential. The distance d is taken as the diameter of a solvent molecule, while w can be either positive or negative. The energy w can be interpreted as the work necessary to replace a water of hydration by an ion. It can be used as an adjustable parameter, to obtain the best fit to experimental data. As expected from the discussion in Sec. 5.1(c), w is >0 for solutions having smaller ions, e.g., Li salts, indicating positive hydration, and <0 for larger ions, e.g., Cs salts.

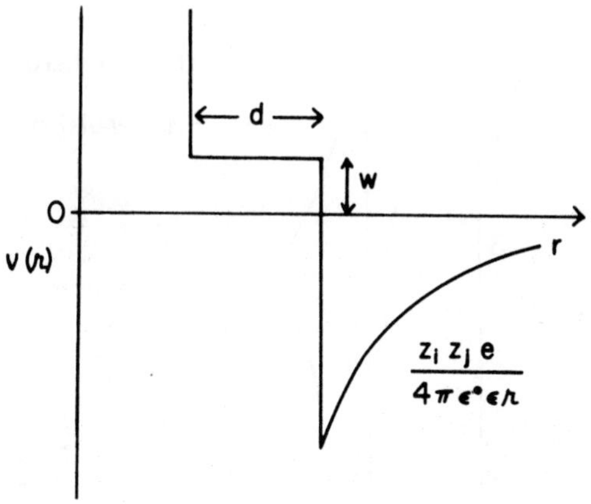

Fig. 5.2. Schematic diagram of $v(r)$ for a "square mound" potential.

Other HNC calculations [18] use a more sophisticated potential energy function. In addition to coulomb interaction, there is an r^{-9} repulsion term due to core repulsion, an r^{-4} term due to polarization, and a "Gurney" term. This last term represents the overlapping of the structure-modified regions (or "cospheres") about the ion. It is essentially given by a constant times the mutual volume occupied by the cospheres as calculated by geometrical considerations. The corresponding effect is described by the w term in the square-mound potential.

The softening of the repulsion has a considerable effect on the shape of $g_{ij}(r)$ as shown in Fig. 5.3 for a 1:1 electrolyte. The results also indicate that the hydration sphere of a strongly hydrated ion such as Li^+ is nevertheless quite easily penetrated by -1 anions. It is thus doubtful whether the large values of the DH distance parameter (4 Å as compared to 2.4 Å for crystallographic radii for LiCl) should be interpreted as being the distance of closest approach.

Thus these calculations include some allowance for ion-solvent effects, although the solvent is considered as a continuous medium. As with all these calculations it is assumed that the total potential energy is pairwise additive.

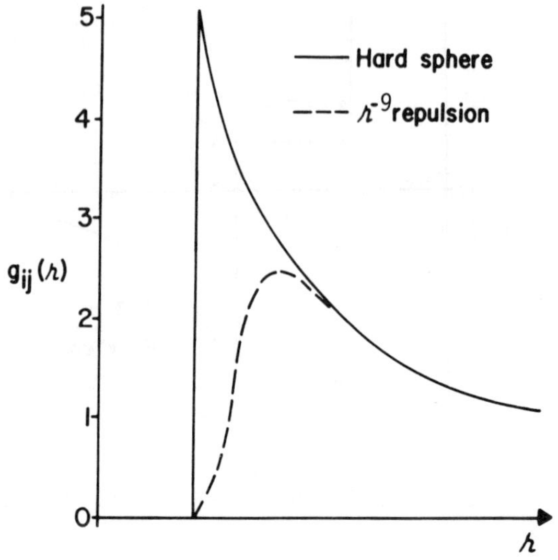

Fig. 5.3. Schematic diagrams of hard-sphere and r^{-9} repulsions.

5.3. SOLVENTS OTHER THAN PURE WATER

(a) Nonaqueous Solvents

Water is the most common solvent in electrolyte solutions, but is by no means a typical solvent. Although a more refined classification of solvents is available [19], it is usual to consider solvents in two classes: protic and dipolar aprotic.

Protic solvents form strong hydrogen bonds: methanol and ammonia are common examples. Dipolar aprotic solvents cannot form hydrogen bonds. Their dielectric constant must be reasonably high, e.g., above 15. Otherwise there would be so much ion pairing and other types of aggregation that freely solvated ions would hardly be present at all. Dimethylformamide, dimethylsulfoxide and acetone are common examples. A brief tabulation of the more common nonaqueous solvents and their properties is given in Table 5.1.

While water solvates both positive and negative ions fairly readily, other solvents solvate cations better than anions or vice versa. Cations seem to be strongly solvated in solvents containing an unshared

TABLE 5.1

Properties of Common Nonaqueous Solvents

	Structural formula	T_f (°C)	T_b (°C)	ε at 25°C
Methanol	CH_3-OH	-93.9	65.0	32.6
Ethanol	CH_3-CH_2-OH	-117.3	78.5	25.0
Acetone	$CH_3-CO-CH_3$	-95.4	56.2	20.7
Ammonia	NH_3	-77.8	-33.5	23.0 at T_b
Formamide	$CHO-NH_2$	-2.5	193	114
N,N-dimethylformamide	$CHO-N-(CH_3)_2$	-61.0	153.0	36.7
Acetonitrile	CH_3CN	-45.7	81.6	36.2
Dimethylsulfoxide	$(CH_3)_2-SO$	18.5	189	46.6
p-Dioxane	$O\genfrac{}{}{0pt}{}{CH_2-CH_2}{CH_2-CH_2}O$	11.8	101	2.2
Water	H_2O	0	100	79.0

electron pair. Thus dimethylsulfoxide solvates cations strongly, but anions weakly, as the positive end of the effective dipole representing the molecule is shielded by the methyl hydrogens.

The theories presented in Secs. 5.1 and 5.2 are, for the most part, also applicable to solvents other than water. Even concepts such as "structure-breaking" can be applied in some cases, e.g., for alcohols.

(b) Mixed Solvent Systems

A common use of mixed solvents is to observe the dependence of phenomena on the dielectric constant. Thus, for example, by studying the properties of a salt in solutions where the solvent is a mixture of water and dioxane in varying ratios, the dependence of the properties on ε can be followed. Although many mixed solvent systems involve water, studies have also been carried out in systems such as nitrobenzene-carbon tetrachloride [20].

Only in the primitive model, where the solvent is considered a continuum, is the effect of mixing solvents solely a change in ε. In many cases preferential solvation of ions by one of the solvent species occurs. In a water-dimethylsulfoxide mixture, anions would be expected to be solvated primarily by water molecules, as DMSO is a poor anion solvent.

It has thus been proposed that in some mixed solvent systems, it is the change in activity of one of the solvent components and not the change in ε that determines changes in the ion-pairing equilibrium constant [17]. In solutions of NaCl in water-dioxane mixtures, the hydration of ions does not seem to alter significantly with solvent composition. The ion pairing constant K (5.16) varies with solvent composition. However, a composition-independent K° can be written for

$$(Na^+ \cdot Cl^-)(H_2O)_j + k(H_2O) \rightleftarrows (Na^+)(H_2O)_m + (Cl^-)(H_2O)_n \qquad (5.23)$$

as

$$K^\circ = \frac{(a_{Na^+(H_2O)_m})(a_{Cl^-(H_2O)_n})}{(a_{Na^+Cl^-(H_2O)_j})(a_{H_2O})^k} = \frac{K}{(a_{H_2O})^k} \qquad (5.24)$$

In Eq. (5.24), K is the ion pairing association constant as written in (5.16).

If the hydration numbers m, n, and j for Na^+, Cl^-, and the ion pair $Na^+ \cdot Cl^-$, respectively, are assumed independent of the addition of dioxane, then the variation in K is due to variation a_{H_2O} and not to ε. The same type of model can be applied to nonaqueous solvent mixtures if one of the solvent components is quite inert.

Additional complications can arise in mixed solvent systems from interactions between the solvent components. Such effects can be treated through the theoretical approaches outlines in Chap. 4.

REFERENCES

The field of electrochemistry has a very well-developed literature. Thus there is choice of several books which give a thorough discussion of aspects from Secs. 5.1 and 5.2. These are Refs. 1 and 7 - 9. More recent advances can be found in the articles in GR6 and GR9.

1. J. O'M. Bockris and A. K. N. Reddy, Modern Electrochemistry, Vol. 1, Macdonald, London, 1970.
2. M. Arshadi, R. Yamdagni, and P. Kebarle, J. Phys. Chem., *74*, 1475 (1970), and previous papers.
3. J. S. Muirhead-Gould and K. J. Laidler, in Chemical Physics of Electrolyte Solutions (B. E. Conway and R. G. Barradas, eds.), Wiley, New York, 1966.
4. H. L. Friedman and C. V. Krishnan in GR9.
5. O. Y. Samoilov in GR6.
6. W-Y Wen in GR6.
7. R. A. Robinson and R. H. Stokes, Electrolyte Solutions, Butterworths, London, 1959.
8. H. S. Harned and B. B. Owen, The Physical Chemistry of Electrolytic Solutions, Reinhold, New York, 1958.
9. R. W. Gurney, Ionic Processes in Solution, Dover, New York, 1953.
10. G. Kortüm, Treatise on Electrochemistry, 2nd ed., Elsevier, Amsterdam, 1965.
11. F. Vaslow in GR6.
12. A. Bechtler, K. G. Breitschwerdt, and K. Tamm, J. Chem. Phys., *52*, 2975 (1970).
13. F. H. Stillinger and R. J. White, J. Chem. Phys., *54*, 3405 (1971) and preceding papers.
14. E. Rhodes in GR6.
15. H. L. Friedman, Ionic Solution Theory, Wiley-Interscience, New York, 1962.
16. H. C. Andersen and D. Chandler, J. Chem. Phys., *55*, 1497 (1971), and previous papers.
17. J. C. Rasaiah, J. Chem. Phys., *52*, 704 (1970).
18. P. S. Ramanathan and H. L. Friedman, J. Chem. Phys., *54*, 1086 (1971).

19. J. Padova in GR6.

20. A. S. Quist and W. L. Marshall, J. Phys. Chem., *72*, 1536 (1968).

Further Recent References

T. H. Lilley, "Electrolyte Solutions" in "Electrochemistry", Vol. 5, H. R. Thrisk, ed., The Chemical Soceety, London, 1975.

"Non-Aqueous Electrolytes Handbook", Vol. 2, G. J. Janz and R. P. T. Tomkins, eds., Academic Press, New York, 1973.

K. P. Mischenko and G. M. Poltoraskii, "Thermodynamics and Structure of Electrolyte Solutions", Plenum, London, 1972.

"Ionic Interactions", S. Petrucci, ed., Academic Press, New York, 1971.

H. Strehlow, W. Knoche, and H. Schneider, "Ionensolvation", Ber. Bunseng. physik. Chem., *77*, 760 (1973).

F. P. Buff, N. S. Goel, and J. R. Clay, "Short Range Electrostatic Interactions in Dielectric Media", J. Chem. Phys., *63*, 1367 (1975).

P. P. Schmidt and J. M. McKinley, "Continuous Charge Distribution Models of Ions in Polar Media. Part 1", J. C. S. Faraday II, *72*, 143 (1976).

D. M. Burley, V. C. L. Hutson, and C. W. Outhwaite, "A Treatment of the Volume and Fluctuation Term in Poisson's Equation in the Debye-Hückel Theory of Strong Electrolyte Solutions", Mol. Phys., *27*, 225, (1974).

R. A. Goldstein, P. F. Hay, and J. J. Kozak, "On the Relaxation of the Continuum Approximation in the Theory of Electrolytes II. Ion Distributions", J. Chem. Phys., *62*, 285 (1975).

L. Blum, "Solution of a Model for the Solvent-Electrolyte Interactions in the Mean Spherical Model", J. Chem. Phys., *61*, 2129 (1974).

G. Stell and S. F. Sun, "Generalized Mean Spherical Approximation for Charged Hard Spheres: The Electrolyte Regime", J. Chem. Phys., *63*, 5333 (1975).

C. L. Briant and J. J. Burton, "Molecular Dynamics Study of the Effect of Ions on Water Microclusters", J. Chem. Phys., *64*, 2888 (1976).

Chapter 6

DESCRIPTION OF TRANSPORT PROPERTIES OF LIQUIDS

In this chapter, the phenomenological equations describing transport processes are first derived from nonequilibrium thermodynamics. There are other ways of introducing the individual transport equations; however, the use of nonequilibrium thermodynamics unifies the various transport phenomena. Thus heat conductance, electrical conductance, diffusion, viscosity, and even general chemical reactions can all be viewed as special cases of the same general phenomenon.

Nonequilibrium thermodynamics also makes it possible to describe cross-effects such as the Soret effect, where diffusion occurs due to a thermal gradient. It does not contribute any knowledge about the actual values of the coefficients appearing in the transport equation, other than to predict the equality of some coefficients for cross-effects.

Section 6.2 considers some relatively simple models by which transport coefficients can be related to each other, and by which some aspects of their behavior can be described. In all these models, the detailed nature of the particles is not considered. At best they are assumed to be spheres of radius a. Thus several of the relationships obtained are strictly valid only in idealized situations. The motion of individual particles in liquids will be described in detail in Chap. 7.

Section 6.3 describes transport phenomena of particular interest in electrolyte solutions. In such systems electrical conductivity is a primary transport property, and it leads to some special effects. The longer range interactions present also require special consideration.

Much of the basic material presented in this chapter is further developed in Chaps. 7 and 9, in particular. Thus, in this chapter especially, the reader should be careful not to extrapolate the specific relationships given for simple models to more sophisticated cases. References giving more complete and detailed expositions should be consulted.

6.1. TRANSPORT EQUATIONS IN FLUIDS

(a) Navier-Stokes Equation

This equation is of great use in hydrodynamics, and will be used in several cases in discussions in this and following chapters. Thorough discussions can be found in Refs. 1 and 2. In the cases under discussion here the fluids can be assumed to be isotropic, and to contain only one component. In such a case, the equation of motion (conservation of momentum) [Eq. (19.9)] can be simplified to be

$$\rho \frac{d\underline{u}}{dt} = \rho \underline{F} + \underline{\nabla} \cdot \underline{\underline{\sigma}} \tag{6.1}$$

For the fluids under discussion, the stress tensor can be expressed assuming a linear relationship between stress and velocity gradient, as suggested by Eq. (19.19a). For such a (Newtonian) fluid, the components of $\underline{\underline{\sigma}}$ can be expressed as

$$\sigma_{ij} = -[p + (\frac{2}{3} \eta - \eta_v)\underline{\nabla} \cdot \underline{u}]\delta_{ij} + \eta \left(\frac{\partial u_i}{\partial r_j} + \frac{\partial u_j}{\partial r_i} \right) \tag{6.2}$$

The coefficients of shear viscosity η and volume or bulk viscosity η_v have been introduced here. δ_{ij} is a function such that $\delta_{ij} = 0$ for $i \neq j$, $\delta_{ij} = 1$ for $i = j$. The symbol $\partial u_i/\partial r_j$ indicates the partial derivative of the ith velocity component with respect to the jth coordinate.

The reason why such a complicated form results is that each element of the stress tensor σ_{ij} (a flux) is actually a linear combination of the nine derivatives of the velocity components with respect to distance coordinates. Only two coefficients, η and η_v, need to be introduced, however, in the case of an isotropic system.

Substitution of (6.2) into (6.1) gives the Navier-Stokes equation:

$$\rho \frac{d\underline{u}}{dt} = \rho \underline{F} - \underline{\nabla} p + \eta \nabla^2 \underline{u} + (\frac{1}{3} \eta + \eta_v)\ \underline{\nabla}(\underline{\nabla} \cdot \underline{u}) \tag{6.3}$$

For incompressible fluids, where $d\rho/dt = 0$, the equation of continuity states that $\underline{\nabla} \cdot \underline{u} = 0$. Thus the last term in (6.3) drops out in this common case.

(b) Stokes Formulas

The most commonly used "Stokes" formula gives an expression for the constant speed of a sphere moving through a fluid while under a constant force. It is often used in describing the motion of particles in liquids, and can also be used for the measurement of viscosity coefficients. The derivation of this relationship is only briefly outlined here, as a full solution is quite lengthy. The results for the rotation of a sphere are also given. Both cases are solutions of the Navier-Stokes equation (6.3).

The problem of a sphere moving in a liquid at rest is equivalent to the motion of liquid past a sphere at rest. A solution to the latter problem will be outlined here. A detailed solution can be found in Ref. 1.

The differential equations to be used are the Navier-Stokes equation (6.3) and the equation of continuity (19.7). For case of an incompressible fluid with no external forces, (6.3) becomes

$$\eta \nabla^2 \underline{u} - \underline{\nabla} p = 0 \tag{6.4}$$

and (19.7) becomes

$$\underline{\nabla} \cdot \underline{u} = 0 \tag{6.5}$$

As $\underline{\nabla} \times \underline{\nabla} p = 0$ for any scalar quantity such as p, then from (6.4) it follows that

$$\nabla^2 \, \underline{\nabla} \times \underline{u} = 0 \tag{6.6}$$

The velcoity $\underline{u}$ of the fluid can be considered as the sum of two velocities, $\underline{u} = \underline{u}' + \underline{u}''$. The velocity at infinity is $\underline{u}'$. The speed of the sphere moving through the liquid in the initial problem is thus given by $\underline{u}'$.

The boundary conditions that can be used are that $\underline{u} = 0$ on the surface of the sphere radius a, set in the center of the coordinate system. This is the "no-slip" approximation. Also, at $r \to \infty$, $\underline{u}'' = 0$.

With the aid of (6.5) and (6.6) it is possible to express $\underline{u}$ as

$$\underline{u} = \underline{\nabla} \times \underline{\nabla} \times (f\underline{u}') + \underline{u}' \tag{6.7}$$

where f is a scalar function

$$f = \frac{3}{4} r a + \frac{1}{4} \frac{a^3}{r} \tag{6.8}$$

When (6.7) and (6.8) are substituted back into (6.4), then it follows that

$$p = p_0 - \frac{3}{2}\eta \frac{\underline{u}' \cdot \underline{n}}{r^3} a \tag{6.9}$$

In (6.9), p_0 is the equilibrium pressure, at $r \to \infty$, and $\underline{n}$ a unit normal vector.

The total force $\underline{F}$ exerted on the sphere by the liquid in the direction $\underline{u}'$ can be expressed by integration over the surface of the sphere:

$$\int_A (-p \cos\theta + \left(\frac{3\eta}{2a}\right) |\underline{u}'| \sin^2\theta \quad d\underline{A} \tag{6.10}$$

The first term in the integral is due to the ordinary pressure of the fluid, while the second is due to frictional force at the surface from viscosity. The result is

$$\underline{F} = 6\pi a\eta\underline{u}' \tag{6.11}$$

In terms of the initial problem, F is the drag on the sphere as it moves through the fluid with a constant speed u'. Thus, the coefficient of drag, or the friction coefficient ζ is

$$\zeta = \frac{F}{u'} = 6\pi\eta a \tag{6.12}$$

Either (6.11) or (6.12) is referred to as Stokes formula.

A "Stokes formula" is also available for a sphere rotating with a constant rotational velocity $\underline{\omega}$ in a fluid. The solution for this model is

$$\zeta = 8\pi\eta a^3 \tag{6.13}$$

In this case ζ refers to the frictional torque per unit angular velocity.

(c) Isothermal Diffusion in Multicomponent Systems

For the case of isothermal diffusion ($\underline{\nabla} \ln T = 0$), the flux-force pairs [Eq. (19.19c)] lead to the general equation for a multicomponent system.

$$\underline{j}_i = \Sigma L_{ik} \underline{\nabla}_T \mu_k \tag{6.14}$$

If now the μ_i are considered as functions of T, p, and c_i, then

$$\underline{\nabla}_T \mu_i = \Sigma \frac{\partial \mu_i}{\partial c_k} \underline{\nabla} c_k \tag{6.15}$$

The summation in (6.15) is over one less component than in (6.14), as the Gibbs-Duhem equation (17.14) can be used to relate one of the μ_i to the others.

Combination of (6.14) and (6.15) then gives

$$-\underline{j}_i = \Sigma D_{ik} \underline{\nabla} c_k \tag{6.16}$$

where the diffusion coefficients D_{ik} are given by

$$D_{ik} = -\sum_{\ell} L_{i\ell} \frac{\partial \mu_\ell}{\partial c_k} \tag{6.17}$$

The coefficients D_{ik} do not necessarily follow the reciprocal relations even though the L_{ij} do so (Sec. 19.2). The form (6.16) (Fick's first law) is nevertheless preferred to (6.14) to describe diffusion, as concentration gradients are easier to measure.

Diffusion measurements are usually made relative to a solvent, rather than relative to the local center of mass. This alters the form of the coefficients D_{ik} somewhat from (6.17). Nevertheless, the diffusion equations in the specific example of two solute components are of the form

$$-\underline{j}_1 = D_{11} \underline{\nabla} c_1 + D_{12} \underline{\nabla} c_2 \qquad -j_2 = D_{21} \underline{\nabla} c_1 + D_{22} \underline{\nabla} c_2 \tag{6.18}$$

Density gradients (i.e., $\underline{\nabla}\rho_1$, $\underline{\nabla}\rho_2$) are at times used instead of the concentration gradients shown.

Thus a concentration gradient in component 1 can cause diffusion of component 2. Other such cross-effects are present, although few of them have been found to be significant for liquids. Thus, a concentration gradient can be set up due to a thermal gradient (Soret effect), and, conversely, a thermal gradient due to a concentration gradient (Dufour effect). Calculations regarding the Dufour effect in mixtures of organic liquids have been carried out in some detail [3], and predict a temperature difference due to the effect of the order of 0.2 K.

Such cross-effects are better known for the solid state: the absorption or evolution of heat due to flow of electrical current at metal junctions (Peltier effect), and the opposite (Seebeck) effect which is the basis for thermocouples. The setting up of a current in one direction due to a potential gradient in another direction (Hall effect) is another example.

(d) Fick's Second Law of Diffusion

In the case of a single diffusing component, (6.16) can be written as

$$\underline{j} = -D\,\underline{\nabla}c \qquad \text{or in 1-dimension} \qquad j = -D\,\frac{\partial c}{\partial x} \tag{6.19}$$

Equation (6.19) us used to define the diffusion constant D in practice.

For many experimental purposes, the variation of c with both time and position is observed. Equation (6.19) (Fick's first law) can be converted into another form (Fick's second law) in order to do this conveniently. The conversion can be done on the basis of the following one-dimensional model.

The amount of matter entering through some surface in the yz plane at a position x is given by

$$(j)_x = -\,D\left(\frac{\partial c}{\partial x}\right)_x \tag{6.20}$$

The amount leaving through a plane at x + dx is

$$(j)_{x+dx} = -\left(D\,\frac{\partial c}{\partial x}\right)_{x+dx} = -\left(D\,\frac{\partial c}{\partial x}\right)_x - \frac{\partial}{\partial x}\left(D\,\frac{\partial c}{\partial x}\right)_x dx \tag{6.21}$$

Thus the amount accumulating in the space dx is

$$(j)_x - (j)_{x+dx} = \frac{\partial c}{\partial t}\,dx = \frac{\partial}{\partial x}\left(D\,\frac{\partial c}{\partial x}\right)_x dx \tag{6.22}$$

Equation (6.22) can be generalized to three dimensions to give

$$\frac{\partial c}{\partial t} = \underline{\nabla}\cdot(D\underline{\nabla}c) \qquad \text{or} \qquad \frac{\partial c}{\partial t} = D\nabla^2 c \tag{6.23}$$

The latter form of (6.23) assumes D to be independent of position and concentration.

A particularly informative solution of the 1-D case (6.22) is when at $t = 0$ there is some initial amount of material A in a narrow zone at $x = 0$ in the yz plane. Diffusion then proceeds in the x-direction only. When D is taken as a constant, the solution to this problem is [e.g., see Eq. (19.24) and Fig. 19.1]:

$$c(x, t) = \frac{A}{(4\pi Dt)^{1/2}} \exp\left[-\frac{x^2}{4Dt}\right] \tag{6.24}$$

Equation (6.24) is in the form of a Gaussian function. Thus the mean square distance diffused in the time t is given by

$$\langle x^2 \rangle = 2Dt \tag{6.25}$$

In three-dimensions, the equivalent to (6.24) is

$$c(r, t) = \frac{A}{(4\pi Dt)^{3/2}} \exp\left[-\frac{r^2}{4Dt}\right] \tag{6.26}$$

Relation (6.25) is often referred to as the Einstein-Smoluchowski equation. Usually it is connected with "self-diffusion." The random motion of particles in a fluid [Sec. 6.2(a)] can be described by the diffusion equation. The concentration is then represented by the probability distribution of finding the particle. Thus the probability $w(r, t)\,dr$ of finding the particle in a shell thickness dr at r at t, given that it initially was at the origin is obtained by setting $A = 1$ and $w(r, t)\,dr = c(r, t)\cdot 4\pi r^2\,dr$.

$$w(r, t)\,dr = \frac{1}{2(\pi D^3 t^3)^{1/2}} \exp\left[-\frac{r^2}{4Dt}\right] r^2\,dr \tag{6.27}$$

The mean square distance from the origin is

$$\langle r^2 \rangle = \int r^2 w(r, t)\,dr = 6Dt \tag{6.28}$$

(e) Rotational Diffusion

Equation (6.23) can also be used for the problem of "rotational diffusion." The probability $w(\theta, \phi, t)$ of finding the axis of a molecule at some angle θ, ϕ at time t can be found, given the initial distribution $w(\theta, \phi, 0)$. This assumes that orientational motion of molecules can be described as a "rotational diffusion" [4].

The problem is equivalent to having a unit amount of "material" initially at (θ, ϕ, 0), and letting the "material" diffuse over the surface of a unit sphere. The equation describing this is

$$\frac{\partial w}{\partial t} = D_r \nabla^2 w = D_r \left\{ \frac{1}{\sin\theta} \frac{\partial}{\partial\theta} \left(\sin\theta \frac{\partial w}{\partial\theta} \right) + \frac{1}{\sin^2\theta} \frac{\partial^2 w}{\partial\phi^2} \right\} \qquad (6.29)$$

A general solution can be obtained for this equation, but the most interesting case is that when at t = 0, the material is all at the "north pole" of the sphere, i.e., $w(\theta, \phi, 0)$ is a δ function in the $\theta = 0$ direction. In this case, the solution of (6.29) is

$$w(\theta, \phi, t) = \sum_{\ell} \left(\frac{2\ell + 1}{4\pi} \right) P_\ell(\cos\theta(t)) \exp[-\ell(\ell + 1)D_r t] \qquad (6.30)$$

where the polynomials $P_\ell(x)$ are the Legendre polynomials. The average values of $P_1(\cos\theta(t))$ and P_2 are then

$$\langle P_1(\cos(\theta(t)))\rangle = \langle\cos(\theta(t))\rangle = \int P_1 w(\theta, \phi, t) \sin\theta\, d\theta\, d\phi$$

$$= \exp[-2D_r t] \qquad (6.31a)$$

$$\langle P_2(\cos(\theta(t)))\rangle = \frac{1}{2}\langle 3\cos^2(\theta(t)) - 1\rangle = \int P_2 w \sin\theta\, d\theta\, d\phi$$

$$= \exp[-6D_r t] \qquad (6.31b)$$

The final forms of (6.31a) and 6.31b) are so simple because of the orthogonality relations $\int P_\ell \cdot P_m \sin\theta\, d\theta\, d\phi = 0$ for $\ell \neq m$. Both $\langle P_1\rangle$ and $\langle P_2\rangle$ are of importance; as some experimental techniques yield information about P_1 (e.g., Chaps. 11 and 12) wile others give information about P_2 (e.g., Chaps. 12 and 13).

(f) Heat Conduction

A more practical form of the heat conduction equation can be derived starting with the relationship suggested in Eq. (19.19d)

$$\underline{q} = L\, \underline{\nabla} \ln T \qquad (6.32)$$

The coefficient of heat conduction λ is usually defined by

$$\underline{q} = -\lambda \, \underline{\nabla} \, T \tag{6.33}$$

Thus for the case where the only nonequilibrium effect present is a temperature gradient, $\lambda = -L/T$.

Another form of the heat conduction equation can be obtained by considering the amount of heat flowing into some arbitrary volume. This can be expressed [Sec. 19.1(a)] as

$$-\int_A \underline{q} \cdot d\underline{A} = -\int_V \underline{\nabla} \cdot \underline{q} \, dV = \int_V \lambda \, \nabla^2 T \, dV \tag{6.34}$$

Gauss' theorem is used in the first step, while (6.33) is used in the second.

The amount of heat entering the volume can also be written as

$$\int_V \rho T \, \frac{dS'}{dt} \, dV \tag{6.35}$$

Here S' is the entropy per unit volume. When (6.34) and (6.35) are equated,

$$\rho T \, \frac{dS'}{dt} = \lambda \, \nabla^2 T \tag{6.36}$$

The integral sign can be removed, as the volume chosen is an arbitrary one.

6.2. PRIMITIVE MODELS DESCRIBING TRANSPORT COEFFICIENTS

(a) Random-Walk Model of Diffusion

The thermal agitation in a fluid is present for all particles, with an average kinetic energy of $(3/2)kT$ per particle when classical statistical mechanics is applicable. In the case of larger particles, such as dust, this motion can be observed directly. The phenomenon is then usually referred to as Brownian motion.

For many purposes, the motion of a particular particle can be treated essentially as a random motion. A simple model describing such motion assumes that the particles make jumps of a mean distance ℓ at a mean frequency ν. The experimental diffusion coefficient D can then by expressed in terms of ℓ and ν.

A one-dimensional model will be considered in which a particle makes ν' (= $\nu/3$) jumps per unit time, each of length ℓ, in either the positive or the negative x direction at random. After a time t, there will have taken place $\nu' t = N$ jumps. Of these, m are assumed to be in the positive direction. The net distance traveled in this case would be

$$x = m\ell + (N - m)(-\ell) \tag{6.37}$$

The probability $w(N, m)$ that m of the N jumps will be in the positive sense is given by the appropriate coefficient of the binomial expansion. For equal probabilities of a positive or a negative jump,

$$w(N, m) = \frac{N!}{m!(N - m)!} \tag{6.38}$$

In the limit of large N, (6.38) can be converted using Stirling's formula to

$$w(N, m) = \left(\frac{2}{\pi N}\right)^{1/2} \exp\left[-\frac{2(m - \langle m \rangle)^2}{N}\right] \tag{6.39}$$

Here $\langle m \rangle$ is the most probable value for m, i.e., $\langle m \rangle = N/2$.

An interval dm in the number of jumps in the positive sense corresponds to an interval $dx = 2\ell\ dm$ in the distance traveled (6.37). Thus the probability $w(x, t)\ dx$ is given by

$$w(x, t)\ dx = \frac{1}{(2\ell^2 \pi \nu' t)^{1/2}} \exp\left[-\frac{x^2}{(2\ell^2 \nu' t)}\right] dx \tag{6.40}$$

In order to make it correspond to the $w(x, t)\ dx$ equation derived from (6.24), $w(x, t)\ dx = \frac{1}{A} c(x, t)\ dx$, it is necessary to postulate

$$D = \frac{1}{4} \cdot 2\ell^2 \nu' = \frac{\ell^2 \nu}{6} \tag{6.41}$$

Such a model of diffusion due to Brownian motion is not exact, and is unrealistic at very small values of t. Some of the shortcomings of the model are pointed out in Ref. 5. More sophisticated models are discussed in Chap. 7.

(b) Temperature Dependence of Transport Coefficients

The form of the temperature dependence of the transport coefficients D and η can be derived on the model of the jumping motion introduced in Sec. (a) above. The jump frequency ν and the distance ℓ do not have a clear meaning for the case of real liquids. However, if a type of lattice model is assumed (Chap. 2), then ℓ can be viewed as the distance between sites, and ν as the frequency of jumping from one site to a neighboring site.

The model for the derivation thus includes two layers of molecules. The distance between molecules is assumed to be ℓ, and the area per molecule is assumed to be ℓ^2. It is assumed also that a molecule must overcome an energy barrier ε_0 to jump to a neighboring lattice site.

First, viscosity will be considered. The coefficient η is given in such a model by

$$\eta = \frac{f\ell}{\Delta u} \tag{6.42}$$

Here f is the force per unit area of one layer of molecules with respect to another, ℓ is the distance between layers, and Δu the difference in velocity between layers. The force per molecule is thus $f\ell^2$.

The energy a molecule acquires in moving to a position at the top of a barrier due to the force is thus $f\ell^2 \cdot \frac{1}{2}\ell$. Thus the energy barrier height is either increased or decreased by an amount $\frac{1}{2}f\ell^3$ as shown in Fig. 6.1. The parameter ε_0 indicates the barrier height at 0 K.

The frequency of jumping can then be expressed using transition state theory (Sec. 19.5).

$$\nu = \frac{kT}{h}\exp\left[-\frac{\Delta G^{\#}}{kT}\right] = \frac{kT}{h}\cdot K^{\#} = \frac{kT}{h}\frac{(q^{\#})'}{q'}\exp\left[-\frac{\varepsilon}{kT}\right] \tag{6.43}$$

Here $K^{\#}$ is the "equilibrium constant" for the initial state $\rightleftarrows$ transition state equilibrium; $(q^{\#})'$ the partition function for a molecule in the transition state, excluding the electronic factor and the reac-

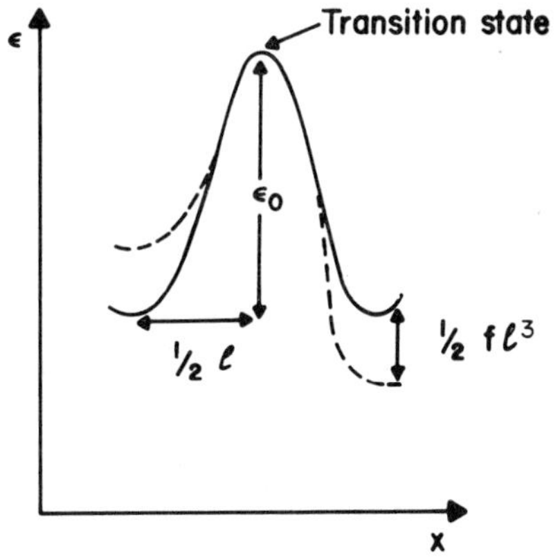

Fig. 6.1. Schematic diagram of the energy barrier for the basic motion involved in a model of diffusion and viscous processes. (After Ref. 6.)

tion coordinate; and q' the partition function for a molecule at a lattice site, excluding the electronic factor.

When the force f is present, then the rate in the forward direction, ν_+ will be different from the rate in the backward direction, ν_-. In one case $\varepsilon = \varepsilon_0 - \frac{1}{2} f\ell^3$, in the other $\varepsilon = \varepsilon_0 + \frac{1}{2} f\ell^3$. Thus the net rate of motion is

$$\nu = \nu_+ + \nu_- = \nu_0 \exp\left[\frac{\frac{1}{2} f\ell^3}{kT}\right] - \exp\left[-\frac{\frac{1}{2} f\ell^3}{kT}\right] \tag{6.44}$$

Here ν_0 is the rate when f = 0.

The difference Δu is thus given by

$$\Delta u = \ell\nu_0(\exp[+] - \exp[-]) \tag{6.45}$$

When (6.45) is substituted into the definition (6.42),

$$\eta = \frac{\ell f}{2\ell\nu_0 \sinh\ (f\ell^3/2kT)} = \frac{kT}{\ell^3\nu_0} + \cdots \tag{6.46}$$

The expansion of the sinh function can be cut off after the first term when $2kT >> f\ell^3$.

When now the form of ν is substituted from (6.43), and ℓ^3 is set equal to V/N, then

$$\eta = \frac{hN}{V} \exp\left[\frac{\Delta G_\eta^\#}{kT}\right] \simeq A_\eta \left[\frac{E_\eta}{kT}\right] \tag{6.47}$$

A standard Arrhenius type form has been used in (6.47) to introduce the activation energy for viscosity, E_η. The free energy of activation for viscosity, $\Delta G_\eta^\#$ is found empirically to be related to the energy of vaporization, ΔU_{vap} as [6]

$$\frac{\Delta U_{vap}}{\Delta G_\eta^\#} \simeq 2.45 \tag{6.48}$$

An expression for the diffusion constant can be easily obtained from the above model. The net flow through a plane can be expressed as

$$\nu\ell\left[c - \left(c + \frac{dc}{dx}\cdot\ell\right)\right] = -\ell^2\nu\,\frac{dc}{dx} = -D\,\frac{dc}{dx} \tag{6.49}$$

Here c is the number of molecules in some plane, and $(c + dc/dx\cdot\ell)$ is the number in a neighboring plane, while ν is the same as ν_0 in (6.44). Thus, for this one-dimensional model,

$$D = \ell^2\nu \tag{6.50}$$

The diffusion constant can then be expected to be of the form

$$D = A_D \exp\left[-\frac{E_D}{kT}\right] \tag{6.51}$$

E_D, the activation energy of diffusion, should also be the same as E_η on this crude model. Usually they are of the order of 16 kJ mol^{-1} for normal liquids. From (6.50) and (6.46), a relationship between η and D can also be obtained

$$\eta = \frac{1}{D}\frac{kT}{\ell} \tag{6.52}$$

Actual values of η and D cannot be obtained from this treatment unless the values of ε_0 and ℓ are given.

(c) Models for Thermal Conduction

There is no well-developed theory for thermal conduction in liquids. However, many liquids obey approximately the relationship

$$\frac{\lambda}{\eta} \simeq \frac{5}{2}\frac{k}{m} \tag{6.53}$$

where m is the molecular mass and k Boltzmann's constant. Equation (6.53) is a result derived for the case of dense hard-sphere gases [8].

A brief outline will be given of thermal conduction in gases to show the essential background behind the relationship (6.53). The model used is simple and somewhat unrealistic. It can also be used for consideration of thermal conduction in solids, however, when the solid is considered as a "phonon gas." Thermal conduction in solids occurs basically through the transmission of vibrational energy through acoustic waves (phonons).

The molecules in a gas are assumed to have an average speed u and a mean free path ℓ. Three planes intersecting the z axis are considered as shown in Fig. 6.2. The energy of a particle is taken to be $\frac{3}{2}kT$; thus u will be somewhat different for particles in the three planes.

The energy transferred from plane $+\ell$ to plane $-\ell$ is given (per unit area per unit time) as

$$E_- = \frac{1}{6}(cu)_{z+\ell}\cdot\frac{3}{2}k\left(T_1 + \frac{\partial T}{\partial z}(z+\ell)\right) \tag{6.54}$$

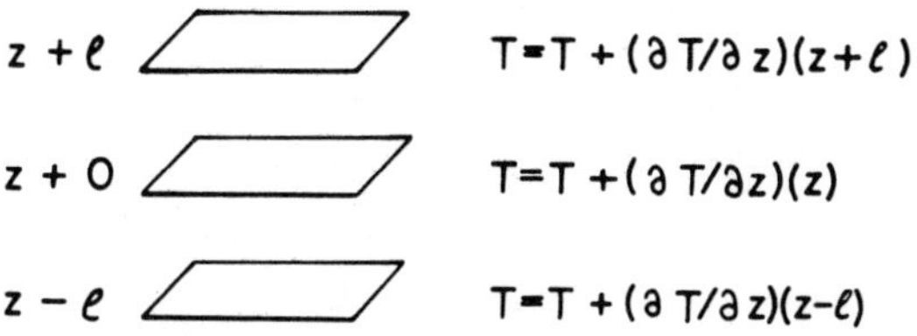

Fig. 6.2. Schematic diagram illustrating the model for heat conduction in a gas.

The factor 1/6 is included, as only that fraction of particles travel on the average in the negative z direction. The product of concentration and mean speed (cu) is calculated at $(z + \ell)$. An analogous expression can be obtained for E_+, the upward flow of energy. The net flow of energy (i.e., the net heat flow q) across z = 0 is then given by

$$q = -\lambda\left(\frac{\partial T}{\partial z}\right) = E_+ - E_- = -\frac{1}{2}\, cuk\ell\left(\frac{\partial T}{\partial z}\right) \tag{6.55}$$

It can usually be assumed that the product (cu) has the same value at $z + \ell$ and $z - \ell$.

From (6.33) and (6.55) the thermal conductivity λ is given by

$$\lambda = \frac{1}{2}\, cuk\ell = \frac{1}{2}\, cku^2\tau \tag{6.56}$$

where $\tau = \ell/u$ is the mean time between collisions. There are many other forms possible for λ. Equation (6.56) is only a rough approximation due to the simple model used.

The coefficient of viscosity can be calculated on this same model. Here a velocity component $\partial u_x/\partial z$ can be assumed present, and the net transfer of momentum (mu_x) to the z = 0 plane calculated in analogy to q [see also Sec. 6.2(b)]. The result is $\eta = \frac{1}{3}\, cmu\ell$. Thus on the basis of this model, the ratio λ/η is $\frac{3}{2}(k/m)$ [see Eq. (6.53)]. In more sophisticated models, the distribution of velocities must be considered as well as the heat capacity of internal modes, the finite size of the particles etc. This primitive discussion indicates the basis for expecting a relationship of the form (6.53).

(d) Mobilities of Particles

The concept of mobility is often used for discussing transport in liquids. The mobility u of a particle is defined as the mean drift velocity it attains under the influence of unit force. Thus u is simply the reciprocal of the friction coefficient ζ introduced earlier (6.12).

For diffusion, the driving force in the z direction per particle is $-\partial\mu/\partial z(1/L)$. Thus for component i, the diffusion equation can be written on a particle basis as the velocity of diffusion, u_i, where

$$u_i = \frac{u_i}{L}\left(-\frac{\partial\mu}{\partial z}\right) \tag{6.57}$$

In the case of an ideal solution [Eq. (4.1)],

$$\mu_i = \mu_i^\theta + RT \ln X_i \tag{6.58}$$

Here X_i is the mole fraction of i. The derivative of μ with respect to z is thus

$$-\frac{\partial\mu}{\partial z} = -\frac{RT}{X_i}\frac{\partial X_i}{\partial z} \simeq -\frac{RT}{c_i}\frac{\partial c_i}{\partial z} \tag{6.59}$$

A dilute solution has also been assumed. The velocity u_i is then equal to

$$u_i = -\frac{u_i kT}{c_i}\frac{\partial c_i}{\partial z} \tag{6.60}$$

Thus the diffusion current j_i in the z direction as defined by (6.19) is given as

$$j_i = -D_i\frac{\partial c_i}{\partial z} = c_i u_i = -u_i kT\frac{\partial c_i}{\partial z} \tag{6.61}$$

It follows that the diffusion coefficient D_i is given as

$$D_i = u_i kT = \frac{kT}{\zeta} \tag{6.62}$$

Equation (6.62) is often called the Einstein relation. It is noteworthy as it relates a steady drifting motion to the basically random motion associated with diffusion [see also Sec. 19.4(b)].

Some further relations can be derived with the introduction of Stokes formula (6.12). Combination of (6.12) with (6.62) leads to the Stokes-Einstein relation [see also Eq. (6.52)],

$$D_i = \frac{kT}{6\pi\eta a_i} \tag{6.63}$$

Here η refers to the overall viscosity, whereas D_i, a_i refer to the species i in solution. The factor 6 is at times varied in (6.63) to account for some "slip" of the fluid at the surface of the sphere [7].

A spherical particle in a continuous medium is assumed here, in addition to the approximations leading to (6.62). Despite the many approximations involved, (6.63) is meaningful enough that the "Walden product," $D_i\eta_j$ [also defined as $\Lambda_i^\infty \eta_j$ (6.66)] is observed to be fairly constant for numerous species i in various solvents with viscosity η_j as predicted by (6.63).

6.3. ELECTROLYTE SOLUTIONS

(a) Conductance

The mobility of ionic species is closely related to the conductivity. In this case the symbol u_i' will be used for the "electrochemical mobility," as the unit force is in this case not taken to be 1 newton, but tha due to a unit electric field (volt m^{-1}). Thus

$$u_i' = u_i z_i e \qquad \text{or} \qquad u_i' = \frac{u_i z_i e}{300} \tag{6.64}$$

if the charge $z_i e$ on the particle is expressed in esu and the field in V cm^{-1}.

The equivalent conductance Λ of an electrolyte can thus be related to the u_i'. For a symmetrical (z:z) electrolyte, neglecting activities

$$\Lambda = \Lambda(t_+ + t_-) = \Lambda_+ + \Lambda_- = F(u_+' + u_-') \tag{6.65}$$

The transport numbers t_+, t_- and the single-ion equivalent conductances Λ_+, Λ_- are introduced here. With the use of (6.62) and (6.64),

$$\Lambda^\infty = \frac{ze}{kT}(D_+ + D_-) = \frac{zF^2}{RT}((D_+ + D_-) \tag{6.66}$$

Equation (6.66) is often referred to as the Nernst-Einstein relation.

As written, (6.66) is valid only for a Z:Z electrolyte. Electrochemistry references, e.g., Ref. 9, can be consulted for more general relationships. The assumptions behind the Einstein relation are also inherent in (6.66) and effects described in Sec. 5.2, e.g., ion pairing, have been neglected. Therefore the Λ in (6.66) is written as Λ^∞ the limiting conductivity at infinite dilution, where (6.66) approaches exact validity for z:z electrolytes.

(b) Relaxation of the Ionic Atmosphere

The long-range forces present in electrolyte solutions make construction of models for transport in electrolytes more complex. One effect which must be considered for solutions of finite concentrations is the relaxation of the ionic atmosphere [Sec. 5.2(a)].

When the central ion being considered is at rest, then its ion cloud (ionic atmosphere) can be assumed to be spherically symmetric. When an ion moves, its ion cloud can not instantaneously adjust to its new position. The center of charge of the ion cloud does not coincide with the center of charge of the central ion, and the ion cloud is no longer spherical but "egg-shaped."

Consider a system which has been disturbed from equilibrium so that it has undergone a change in its charge density ρ. On removal of the disturbance, the system reverts to its original condition through a relaxation expression (19.34)

$$\frac{d\rho}{dt} = -\frac{1}{\tau}\rho \tag{6.67}$$

where $1/\tau$ is written for the coefficient λ in (19.34).

Another expression for $d\rho/dt$ can be written in terms of Ohm's law. For the general case, it can be written with the help of (19.7), (20.11), and (20.6) as

$$\frac{d\rho}{dt} = -\underline{\nabla}\cdot\underline{j} = \sigma\,\nabla^2\phi \tag{6.68}$$

Here ϕ is the electrical potential and σ the conductivity [see (6.71)].

Combination of (6.68) and (6.67) together with the Poisson equation (20.6) gives

$$-\frac{d\rho}{dt} = \sigma\,\nabla^2\phi = -\sigma\,\frac{\rho}{\varepsilon\varepsilon^\bullet} = \frac{\rho}{\tau} \tag{6.69}$$

Thus the relaxation time for the ionic atmosphere, τ is given as

$$\tau = \frac{\varepsilon\varepsilon^\bullet}{\sigma} \tag{6.70}$$

The conductivity σ can be expressed in terms of the mobilities u_i (or $u_i' = z_i e u_i$) by using (6.64) and (6.65).

$$\sigma = \Sigma c_i u_i z_i^2 e^2 = 2Ie^2\langle u\rangle = \kappa^2\varepsilon\varepsilon^\bullet kT\langle u\rangle \tag{6.71}$$

The last step is due to substitution of $\kappa^2\varepsilon\varepsilon^\bullet kT$ for $2Ie^2$ following the definition of the ionic atmosphere parameter κ in Eq. (5.8). The mean mobility $\langle u\rangle$ is defined as:

$$\langle u\rangle = \frac{\Sigma c_i z_i^2 u_i}{\Sigma c_i z_i^2} = \frac{\Sigma c_i z_i^2 u_i}{2I} \tag{6.72}$$

Thus another form can be obtained for (6.70)

$$\tau = \frac{1}{\kappa^2 kT\langle u\rangle} \tag{6.73}$$

which shows the dependence of τ on the parameter κ.

A force $\underline{F}_i$ is now considered applied to a "central" ion of species i. In the case of electrical conduction, $\underline{F}_i = z_i e\underline{E} = -z_i e\underline{\nabla\phi}$. This ion will then move with a velocity $\underline{u}_i = \underline{F}_i u_i$. However, because of the finite relaxation time τ of the ion atmosphere, the ion will be ahead of its atmosphere by a distance $u_i\tau$.

When there is no distortion of the ionic atmosphere, the total force between the ion and its atmosphere is $-e^2z_i^2\kappa^2/4\pi\varepsilon^\bullet\varepsilon$. This is equivalent to an attraction between two charges z_ie and $-z_ie$ a distance $1/\kappa$ apart. The relaxation effect separates the centers of positive and negative charge by an amount $u_i\tau$. The difference in the force on the ion due to the relaxation effect will then be taken as this force times the ratio $u_i\tau/(1/\kappa)$.

$$\delta\underline{F}_i = -\frac{e^2z_i^2\kappa\underline{F}_i u_i}{4\pi\varepsilon^\bullet\varepsilon kT\langle u\rangle} \tag{6.74}$$

This result is obtained on the basis of a model which is quite unrealistic at finite concentrations, i.e., of an ion, with a smeared-out "atmosphere" equivalent to a spherical distribution of charge at $1/\kappa$. It serves to illustrate an effect of the long-range forces present in electrolyte solutions, however, and will be useful in Chap. 9. More advanced treatments of this phenomenon are available. A recent theoretical extension, now verified experimentally [10] predicts the relaxation effect to be speeded up significantly through inclusion of diffusion-controlled ion association [Sec. 6.3(d)].

(c) Electrophoretic Effect

When an ion moves through the solution, it drags along with it the solution in its vicinity. Neighboring ions do not move in a stationary medium, but either with or against the stream of the first ion. This interdependence of the motions of ions is called the electrophoretic effect.

It can be illustrated quantitatively in the case of electrical conductance. In the presence of an electric field $\underline{E} = -\underline{\nabla}\phi$, an ion of charge $z_i e$ will be subjected to a force $z_i e\underline{E}$. The total ionic atmosphere associated with that ion will be subjected to a force $-z_i e\underline{E}$.

The central ion will then be carried in a direction given by $z_i\underline{E}$ due to the force $z_i e\underline{E}$. It will, however, also be carried in the opposite direction due to the motion of its immediate surroundings, i.e., its ionic atmosphere and the associated solvent molecules.

The velocity of this latter motion can be calculated assuming a simple model. Consider the entire charge $-z_i e$ of the ionic atmosphere to be on the surface of a sphere radius $1/\kappa$ [Eq. (5.8)]. Stokes formula (6.12) then predicts the velocity of this sphere to be

$$\underline{u}_{sp} = -\frac{z_i e\underline{E}\,\kappa}{6\pi\eta} \tag{6.75}$$

The velocity of the ion, $\underline{u}_i$, will then be diminished by this effect, in addition to the relaxation effect described in Sec. 6.3(b). The net velocity including both effects is then,

$$\underline{u}_i = z_i e\underline{E}u_i - \frac{z_i e\underline{E}\kappa}{6\pi\eta} - \frac{z_i^3 e^3\underline{E}\kappa u_i^2}{4\pi\varepsilon\varepsilon^{\bullet}kT\langle u\rangle} \tag{6.76}$$

(d) Diffusion-Controlled Processes

Reactions involving "chemical" interactions will not be discussed here. A description of this aspect can be found in Ref 11. The formation of various structures involving "physical" interactions such as those discussed in Chap. 1 often involves the diffusion together of the particles involved. Since the formation of ion pairs [Sec. 5.2(c)] is a common example, this topic is treated in Sec. 6.3.

A theory for such processes has been developed by Debye. A reaction between species A and B is assumed, which is considered to be completed if A and B diffuse to within a distance d_{ab} of each other.

The flux density $\underline{j}_a$ of A in an external potential ϕ is given by

$$\underline{j}_a = -D_a \underline{\nabla} c_a + \frac{c_a z_a e}{kT} \underline{\nabla}\phi \tag{6.77}$$

Here the definition of mobility, Fick's first law and the Einstein relation are all utilized, i.e., Eqs. (6.61), (6.19), and (6.62). An electrostatic potential is assumed here, with a potential energy ν per unit concentration.

Now a steady state is assumed, where A particles are diffusing into stationary B particles. When spherical symmetry is assumed, then the total flux of A through a surface a distance r from a B particle, J_a, can be written as

$$\begin{aligned} J_a &= \iint -D_a\left(\frac{\partial c_a}{\partial r} + \frac{c_a}{kT}\cdot\frac{\partial \nu}{\partial r}\right) r^2 \sin\theta \, d\theta \, d\phi \\ &= -4\pi r^2 D_a \exp\left[-\frac{\nu}{kT}\right] \frac{\partial}{\partial r}\left(c_a \exp\left[\frac{\nu}{kT}\right]\right) \end{aligned} \tag{6.78}$$

In the stationary state, the equation of continuity (19.7) also gives

$$\frac{\partial c_a}{\partial t} = -\underline{\nabla}\cdot J_a = -\frac{1}{r^2}\frac{\partial}{\partial r}(r^2 J_a) = 0 \tag{6.79}$$

Thus J_a is independent of r for $d_{ab} < r < \infty$. The boundary conditions for the problem are: $\nu \to 0$ as $r \to \infty$; $c_a = 0$ at $r = d_{ab}$; $c_a = \langle c_a \rangle$, the bulk concentration, as $r \to \infty$. Under these conditions, a solution can be found for J_a from (6.78)

$$J_a = -4\pi D_a \langle c_a \rangle / \int_{d_{ab}}^{\infty} \exp[\nu/kT] \frac{dr}{r_2} \tag{6.80}$$

This distance d_{ab} is sometimes equated to the ion size parameter a_i [Sec. 5.2(a)].

When the motion of B particles is included, then the factor D_a must be replaced by $(D_a + D_b)$. The total rate is then $k_{assoc}\langle c_a\rangle\langle c_b\rangle = -J_a\langle c_b\rangle$ where k_{assoc} is the rate constant for association (e.g., formation of ion pairs). The negative sign is needed as J_a refers to flow in the positive r direction (away from B). When conventional units are used, and the potential energy is taken as coulombic, then

$$k_{assoc} = \frac{Lz_a z_b e^2 (D_a + D_b) \times 10^{-3}}{\varepsilon^\bullet \varepsilon kT(\exp[Z_a Z_b e^2/(4\pi\varepsilon^\bullet \varepsilon d_{ab} kT] - 1)} \tag{6.81}$$

Here D_a, D_b are in units $cm^2\ s^{-1}$, $\langle c_a\rangle$, $\langle c_b\rangle$ in mol liter^{-1}, d_{ab} in m, and e, $\varepsilon^\bullet$, k in SI units. The expressions for k_{assoc} for functions $v(r)$ other than coulombic can be obtained starting from Eq. (6.80).

An analogous expression for the rate k_{diss} of dissociation reaction of a complex (A•B) has also been developed [12]. Here Eq. (6.78) is applicable, but the boundary conditions are different. The result in this case is

$$k_{diss} = \frac{4\pi(D_a + D_b)}{\int_{d_{ab}}^{\infty} \exp[v/kT]\ dr/r^2} \frac{\exp[v(d_{ab})/kT]}{\delta V} \tag{6.82}$$

Here δV is the volume containing one complex (A•B), i.e., $\delta V \simeq \frac{4\pi}{3} d_{ab}^3$. The ratio k_{diss}/k_{assoc} for the case when $v(r)$ is a coulombic potential energy gives the Fuoss equation for the ion pair dissociation constant K [Eq. 5.17)],

$$K = \frac{k_{diss}}{k_{assoc}} = \frac{3000}{4\pi L d_{ab}^3} \exp[v(d_{ab})/kT] \tag{6.83}$$

Several effects, such as those discussed in Secs. (b) and (c) above, have been neglected in this discussion. An example of a recent, more sophisticated version of diffusion controlled processes is available in Ref. 13. There hydrodynamic effects are shown to cause a substantial reduction in the recombination rate.

REFERENCES

Some additional references to nonequilibrium thermodynamics are given in Chap. 19. For a discussion of various transport equations, Refs. 1, 2, and 7 are quite complete. Discussions regarding transport in electrolyte solutions can be found in Ref. 9, and other references given in Chap. 5. Reference 5 gives a review of recent developments for electrolyte solutions.

1. L. D. Landau and L. M. Lifshitz, Fluid Mechanics, Pergamon, London, 1966.
2. V. G. Levich, Physicochemical Hydrodynamics, 2nd ed., Prentice-Hall, Englewood-Cliffs, N. J., 1962.
3. S. E. Ingle and F. H. Horne, J. Chem. Phys., *59*, 5882 (1973).
4. P. Debye, Polar Molecules, Dover, New York, 1929.
5. H. L. Friedman in GR6.
6. S. Glasstone, K. J. Laidler, and H. Eyring, Theory of Rate Processes, McGraw-Hill, New York, 1941.
7. H. J. V. Tyrrell, Diffusion and Heat Flow in Liquids, Butterworths, London, 1961.
8. S. Chapman and T. G. Cowling, The Mathematical Theory of Non-uniform Gases, Cambridge Univ. Press, London, 1953.
9. R. A. Robinson and R. H. Stokes, Electrolyte Solutions, 2nd ed., Butterworths, London, 1959.
10. L. Onsager and S. W. Provencher, J. Am. Chem. Soc., *90*, 3134 (1968) S. Highsmith and E. Grunwald, J. Phys. Chem., *78*, 1431 (1974).
11. I. Amdur and G. G. Hammes, Chemical Kinetics, McGraw-Hill, New York, 1966.
12. M. Eigen, Z. Physik. Chem., *1*, 176 (1954).
13. J. M. Deutch and B. U. Felderhof, J. Chem. Phys., *59*, 1669 (1973).

Further Recent References

S. I. Smedley and L. V. Woodcock, "Kirkwood-Rice-Allnatt Kinetic Theory of Transport in Liquids", J. C. S. Farad. II, *69*, 955 (1973).

W. E. Alley and B. J. Alder, "Studies in Molecular Dynamics XV. High Temperature Description of the Transport Coefficients", J. Chem. Phys., *63*, 3764 (1975).

K. D. Scarfe and I. L. McLaughlin, "Transport Coefficients for a Dense Fluid of Square-Well, Rough Spheres", J. Chem. Phys., *62*, 4639 (1975).

M. Papoular, "Critical Behavior of Cross-Transport Coefficients", J. Chem. Phys., *60*, 86 (1974).

J. L. Anderson and C. C. Reed, "Diffusion of Spherical Macromolecules at Finite Concentration", J. Chem. Phys., *64*, 3240 (1976).

P. L. Ermak, "A Computer Simulation of Charged Particles in Solution II. Polyion Diffusion Coefficient", J. Chem. Phys., *62*, 4197 (1975).

R. M. Fuoss, "Conductance-Concentration Function for Associated Symmetrical Electrolytes", J. Phys. Chem., *79*, 525 (1975).

P. G. Wolynes and J. M. Deutch, "Slip Boundary Conditions and the Hydrodynamic Effect of Diffusion Controlled Reactions", J. Chem. Phys., *65*, 450 (1976).

Chapter 7

MOLECULAR MOTIONS

In Chapter 6 dynamics in liquids was considered from a macroscopic view. In Secs. 6.2, 3 the macroscopic (phenomenological) transport coefficients related to some primitive microscopic models.

This chapter contains a discussion of dynamics in liquids from a microscopic point of view. In Sec. 7.1 van Hove functions are discussed as a means of describing the time dependence of local density fluctuations. These can be thought of as being density time correlation functions. Sections 7.2 and 7.3 discuss velocity and orientational time correlation functions, respectively. A description of the general properties of time correlation functions is included in Sec. 7.2, using velocity time correlation functions as a specific example.

The motion of the molecule as a whole is considered in this chapter. Intramolecular motions such as internal vibrations are introduced only in Sec. 7.4. The discussion is here also from a classical point of view using ensemble averages. Such a description is adequate for many purposes, but in some cases quantum-mechanical descriptions using Heisenberg matrices are very useful. Consideration of time correlation functions in terms of Heisenberg's observables is also outlined in Sec. 7.4. Such considerations are necessary groundwork for topics discussed in Chaps. 12 and 14.

As in the case with many statistical considerations, it is frustrating and seldom fruitful to try to imagine experimentally obtaining the functions introduced in the way suggested by the definitions and derivations in this chapter. In some of the later chapters, however, time correlation functions will be shown to be simply related to various experimental observables. Thus they give a concise description of basic molecular motions present in liquids, and can at the same time be obtained through experiment.

7.1. VAN HOVE FUNCTIONS

(a) Definitions

Chapter 3 contains an extensive discussion of density correlation functions which are time-independent. The direct correlation function $c(r)$, the total correlation function $h(r)$ and the pair distribution function $g(r)$ were introduced. It was pointed out that the function $g(r)$ could be expressed as

$$ng(\underline{r}) = \frac{1}{N} < \sum_{i \neq j} \delta(\underline{r} + \underline{r}_i - \underline{r}_j)> \tag{3.5}$$

The van Hove function can be considered to be the generalized, time dependent form of $g(r)$. It can be defined as [1]

$$G(\underline{r}, t) = \frac{1}{N} < \sum_{i,j} \delta(\underline{r} + \underline{r}_i(0) - \underline{r}_j(t))> \tag{7.1}$$

Here $\underline{r}_j(t)$ is the position of particle j at time t, while $\underline{r}_i(0)$ is the position of particle i at time 0. The summation in (7.1) includes the case of i = j, unlike (3.5).

For t = 0, (7.1) is essentially the same as (3.5) except the inclusion of i = j terms in the sum. Thus $G(\underline{r}, 0)$ can be expressed as

$$G(\underline{r}, 0) = \delta(r) + ng(\underline{r}) = G_s(\underline{r}, 0) + G_d(\underline{r}, 0) \tag{7.2}$$

This splitting is generalized for all values of t, i.e.,

$$G(\underline{r}, t) = G_s(\underline{r}, t) + G_d(\underline{r}, t) \tag{7.3}$$

As $t \to \infty$, $G_s(\underline{r}, t) \to 0$ and $G_d(\underline{r}, t) \to n$.

$G_s(\underline{r}, t)$ is the "self-correlation" function. Thus $G_s(\underline{r}, t)\cdot N$ gives the probability of finding a particle at a position $\underline{r}$ at time t if at t = 0 it was at the origin. In terms of (7.1), $G_s(\underline{r}, t)$ is given as

$$G_s(\underline{r}, t) = \frac{1}{N} <\sum_{i} \delta(\underline{r} + \underline{r}_i(0) - \underline{r}_j(t))> \tag{7.4}$$

The time development of this function will be discussed in Sec. 7.1(b).

$G_d(\underline{r}, t)$ is the "distinct" correlation function. $G_d(\underline{r}, t)\cdot N$ expresses the probability that if at t = 0 there is a particle at the origin, then there is another particle in position $\underline{r}$ at time t. In terms of Eq. (7.1) it is

$$G_d(\underline{r}, t) = \frac{1}{N} < \sum_{i \neq j} \delta(\underline{r} + \underline{r}_i(0) - \underline{r}_j(t))> \tag{7.5}$$

The time development of $G_d(\underline{r}, t)$ is discussed in Sec. 7.1(c).

The van Hove function can be thought of as a density time correlation function. A time dependent particle density $(\underline{r}, t)$ can be defined as

$$n(\underline{r}, t) = \sum_i \delta(\underline{r} - \underline{r}_i(t)) \tag{7.6}$$

$G(\underline{r}, t)$ can then be expressed in the form of a correlation function as

$$G(\underline{r}, t) = \frac{1}{n} \langle (n(0, 0)\ n(\underline{r}, t)) \rangle \tag{7.7}$$

A continuum interpretation of $G(\underline{r}, t)$ is easier to picture in terms of (7.7).

It should be noted that the ordinary van Hove functions introduced above contain no information regarding the correlation of orientations of the particles involved.

(b) Self-Correlation Function

When a random-walk model is assumed for the motion of molecules, then $G_s(\underline{r}, t)$ is essentially the same function as $w(\underline{r}, t)$ in (6.40), i.e., in three dimensions

$$G_s(\underline{r}, t) = \frac{1}{(4\pi Dt)^{3/2}} \exp\left[-\frac{r^2}{4Dt}\right] \tag{7.8}$$

This same result can be obtained, of course, by assuming $G_s(\underline{r}, t)$ to follow the laws derived for macroscopic continua. With the application of (6.23),

$$\frac{\partial G_s(\underline{r}, t)}{\partial t} = D\cdot\nabla^2 G_s(\underline{r}, t) \tag{7.9}$$

Such a simple description of $G_s(\underline{r}, t)$ is quite satisfactory in liquids for large values of $\underline{r}$. At smaller values, a more detailed model is needed. One such model is that incorporating "jump diffusion" [2]. Models of diffusion in liquids will be elaborated on in a later section.

Figure 7.1 shows the typical behavior of $G_s(\underline{r}, t)$ together with $1/n\cdot G_d(\underline{r}, t)$. It illustrates the relationships given for t = 0 and

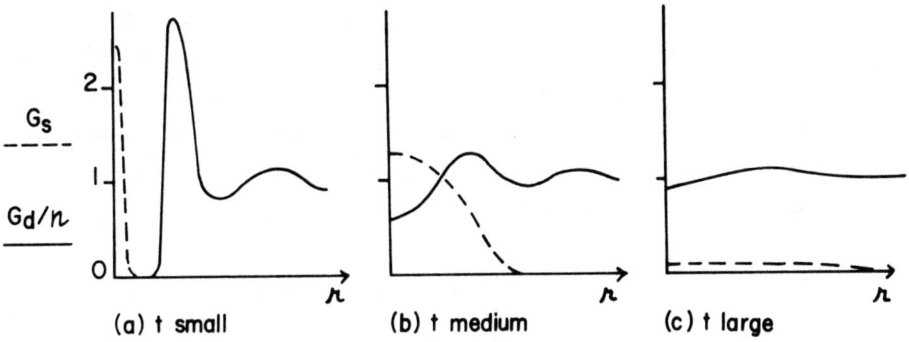

Fig. 7.1. Schematic diagrams of G_s and G_d/n at three different times to illustrate their time development.

$t \to \infty$ (7.2). As liquids can for most purposes be considered as isotropic, then it is satisfactory to take $G(\underline{r}, t) = G(r, t)$.

(c) Distinct Correlation Function

$G_d(\underline{r}, t)$ approaches a value n for either $r \to \infty$ or $t \to \infty$. Near the critical point, long-range correlations of macroscopic size can exist [Sec. 3.4(c)], and the approach of $G_d(\underline{r}, t)$ to an asymptotic value can take a long time.

The long-range part of $G_d(\underline{r}, t)$ in a liquid at equilibrium with no external forces can be thought of as being due to spontaneous density fluctuations (Secs. 18.5 and 19.3). The time development of such spontaneous fluctuations are often treated as though the initial nonequilibrium values had been produced by a suddenly released artificial constraint. The above statement can be thought of as a consequence of the fluctuation-dissipation theorem [Sec. 19.4(b)].

In treating the time development of $G_d(\underline{r}, t)$, it is easier to treat the time development of the Fourier components. This expresses the positional dependence of the density variation in terms of components with wave vectors $\underline{q}$ [Sec. 3.1(c)]. In the hydrodynamic region [Secs. 7.1(e), (f)], each fluctuation of wave vector $\underline{q}$ can then be assumed to be governed by the equation of continuity (19.7), the Navier-

Stokes equation (6.3) and the equation for heat transport (6.36). The Fourier transform of these equations must be used in the analysis [3].

The result is that for each value q, there are three plane wave fluctuations. Two correspond to damped ultrasonic waves propagating with a velocity in direction $\underline{q}$ and $-\underline{q}$, while the third is a nonpropagating fluctuation dependent on heat conductivity.

(d) Interpretation of Fourier Transforms

An "intermediate scattering function" $I(\underline{q}, t)$ is usually defined as the spatial Fourier transform

$$I(\underline{q}, t) = \int_V (G(\underline{r}, t) - n) \exp[i\underline{q}\cdot\underline{r}]\, d\underline{r} \tag{7.10}$$

The double Fourier transform of $(G(\underline{r}, t) - n)$ is usually called the "scattering law,"

$$S(\underline{q}, \omega) = \frac{1}{2\pi} \int_{-\infty}^{\infty} (G(\underline{r}, t) - n) \exp[i(\underline{q}\cdot\underline{r} - \omega t)]\, dt\, d\underline{r} \tag{7.11}$$

$S(\underline{q}, \omega)$ is related to the intermediate scattering function and the structure factor $S(q)$ as defined in Eq. (3.14) as

$$I(\underline{q}, t) = \int_{-\infty}^{\infty} S(q, \omega) \exp[i\omega t]\, d\omega$$

$$S(\underline{q}) = \int_{-\infty}^{\infty} S(\underline{q}, \omega)\, d\omega \tag{7.12}$$

In analogy to the interpretation of $S(\mathbf{q})$, [Sec. 3.1(c)], $S(\underline{q}, \omega)$ describes the distribution of density fluctuations present in the liquid in terms of the wave vectors $\underline{q}$ and frequencies ω.

The physical meaning of $S(\underline{q}, \omega)$ becomes easier to understand if a scattering process is considered. The relationship will simply be stated here. An outline of the derivation is given in Sec. 16.1(c).

For a scattering process, $S(\underline{q}, \omega)$ is proportional to the probability that the scattering particles impart to the liquid an amount of momentum $\hbar\, \underline{q}$ and an amount of energy $\hbar\omega$. Thus $\hbar\omega$ is simply the incident energy less the scattered energy of the particle (photon, neutron). The momentum transfer is given by $q^2 = k^2 + k_0^2 - 2kk_0 \cos\theta$.

The angle of scatter is given by θ, and k_0, k are the wave numbers of the incident and scattered particles, i.e., $k = 2\pi/\lambda$. As ordinary liquids are isotropic, the direction of the momentum transfer is not of importance.

(e) Solutions for S(q, ω) in the Hydrodynamic Region

In the case of some scattering processes (e.g., light scattering) from density fluctuations, the wavelength of the radiation is considerably larger than nearest-neighbor distances. Thus the liquid can be described as a continuous fluid and the continuity equation (19.7), the Navier-Stokes equation (6.3), and the heat flow equation (6.36) are applicable. T and ρ are chosen as the independent variables (note $\langle \delta T \cdot \delta\rho \rangle = 0$ (19.3)]. Thus δp and δS are expressed as

$$\delta p = \left(\frac{\partial p}{\partial \rho}\right)_T \cdot \delta\rho + \left(\frac{\partial p}{\partial T}\right)_\rho \cdot \delta T \qquad (7.13)$$

$$\delta S = \left(\frac{\partial S}{\partial \rho}\right)_T \cdot \delta\rho + \left(\frac{\partial S}{\partial T}\right)_\rho \cdot \delta T \qquad (7.13)$$

The three hydrodynamic equations and (7.13) can now be used to obtain S(q, ω) or I(q, t) by using their Fourier transforms [3] [see (7.16) for an example]. If thus the space transforms of these five equations are taken, then I(q, t) can be obtained by solving the initial value problem. This will not be done here for this rather complicated problem. The approach is illustrated in Sec. 7.1(f). For our purposes, a sufficiently accurate form for the results are:

$$I(q, t) = \left(1 - \frac{1}{\gamma}\right) \exp\left[-\frac{\lambda q^2 t}{\rho C_p}\right] + \frac{1}{\gamma} \exp[-\Gamma q^2 t] \cos (vqt) \qquad (7.14)$$

$$S(q\ \ \omega) = \left(1 - \frac{1}{\gamma}\right) \frac{(\lambda q^2/\rho C_p)}{((\lambda q^2/\rho C_p)^2 + \omega^2)} + \frac{1}{\gamma}\left(\frac{\Gamma q^2}{(\Gamma q^2)^2 + (\omega + vq)^2}\right)$$

$$+ \frac{1}{\gamma}\left(\frac{\Gamma q^2}{(\Gamma q^2)^2 + (\omega - vq)^2}\right) \qquad (7.15)$$

The symbol γ here is the ratio of specific heats, C_p/C_v. λ is the thermal conductivity and Γ is a decay rate, $\Gamma = v^3\alpha/\omega^2$ where v is the speed and α the pressure absorption coefficient for density waves propagating in the liquid [Eq. (10.2)].

From (7.14) it can be seen that the density Fourier components relax through two modes. A nonpropagating (constant pressure) mode at a rate related to the thermal conductivity, and a propagating (constant entropy) mode at a rate related to the absorption coefficient α of such propagating waves. These waves are referred to as Mandelshtam, Brillouin, Debye, thermal, or hypersonic waves and can be considered as the liquid equivalent to the phonons or Debye waves in solids (Sec. 18.2). They are discussed further in Chaps. 10, 14, and 16.

From Eq. (7.15) it can be seen that $S(q, \omega)$ as a function of ω (q = constant) is of the form of three Lorentzian functions (Fig. 20.1, E. (20.52)]. The central component has a half-width $2\lambda q^2/\rho C_p$. The other two components are centered $\pm vq$ from the central component and have half-widths $2\Gamma q^2$. They are shown in Fig. 14.2 in relation to light scattering experiments.

(f) Time Development of Concentration Fluctuations

Concentration fluctuations can be described by methods analogous to the description of density fluctuations in Sec. 7.1(e). The magnitude of concentration fluctuations $\langle\delta c^2\rangle$ is, according to (18.44), $\langle\delta c^2\rangle = kT/(N(\partial\mu/\partial c)_{p,T})$. In the hydrodynamic range, the time dependence of a concentration fluctuation is governed by (6.23), i.e.,

$$\frac{\partial}{\partial t}\,\delta c(\underline{r}, t) = D\,\nabla^2\,\delta c(\underline{r}, t)$$
$$\frac{\partial}{\partial t}\,\delta c(\underline{q}, t) = -Dq^2\,\delta c(\underline{q}, t) \qquad (7.16)$$

The spatial Fourier transform of Fick's law has been written here to illustrate transformation of transport equations from $\underline{r}$ to $\underline{q}$ space. Equation (7.16) predicts a simple exponential decay for $\langle\delta c^2\rangle$. With the assumptions outlined in Sec. 7.1(c),

$$\langle\delta c^2(q, t)\rangle = \langle\delta c^2(q, 0)\rangle \exp\left[-\frac{t}{2Dq^2}\right] \qquad (7.17)$$

A scattering law $S_c(q, \omega)$ can be constructed for concentration fluctuations by use of Fourier transform from t to ω space. Thus

$$S_c(q, \omega) \propto \frac{kT}{(\partial\mu/\partial c)_{p,T}} \cdot \frac{2Dq^2}{(Dq^2)^2 + \omega^2} \tag{7.18}$$

This is a Lorentzian function of half-width $2Dq^2$.

Relation (7.18) is interesting especially when systems are close to a critical point. There $(\partial\mu/\partial c)_{p,T}$ becomes very small [Sec. 4.1(b)]. Thus $\langle\delta c^2\rangle$ becomes very large. Also, as seen in Sec. 9.1(b), D becomes very small. The overall effect is that $S(q, \omega)$ becomes larger and its half-width smaller as a critical point is approached.

In the case of a one-component critical phenomenon, density corresponds to concentration. In that case the narrowing of the half-width is due to an increase in C_p near the critical point. The dynamics of fluids near the critical point has been considered in detail for both 1 and 2 component systems in Ref. 4.

7.2. VELOCITY TIME CORRELATION FUNCTIONS

(a) General Properties of Time Correlation Functions

The velocity time correlation function $G_v(t)$ is defined as

$$G_v(t) = \langle \underline{u}(0) \cdot \underline{u}(t) \rangle \tag{7.19}$$

Here $\underline{u}(0)$ is the velocity of a molecule at time 0, and $\underline{u}(t)$ the velocity of the same molecule at time t. The angle brackets indicate an ensemble average as usual.

In an infinitely dilute gas in an infinitely large container, a particle would continue to have its initial velocity at all times. In a liquid, however, it takes part in numerous collisions and would change both its direction and speed with time. It is possible to predict its velocity $\underline{u}(t)$, but only through solving the equations of motion for the particles in the liquid, e.g., by molecular dynamics simulation [Sec. 3.3(b)]. Probability statements can be made for the relationship of $\underline{u}(t)$ to $\underline{u}(0)$ through time correlation functions, however, without the laborious task of solving realistic equations of motion.

As the average kinetic energy per molecule is $3kT/m$, then for $t = 0$,

$$G_v(0) = |\underline{u}(0)|^2 = \frac{3kT}{m} \tag{7.20}$$

As $t \to \infty$, then $G_v(t) \to 0$, and all correlation disappears. This assumes the liquid to be at equilibrium and stationary. The behavior to be expected at intermediate times will be discussed later.

A time average expression can be given for $G_v(t)$ instead of the ensemble average given in (7.19). The zero of time for (7.19) was chosen arbitrarily. Thus $G_v(t)$ could equally well be chosen as

$$G_v(t) = \langle\underline{u}(t')\cdot\underline{u}(t' + t)\rangle \tag{7.21}$$

As the ensemble average can be equated to the time average through the ergodic theorem, then also

$$G_v(t) = \frac{1}{t''}\int_0^{t''} \underline{u}(t')\cdot\underline{u}(t' + t)\, dt' \tag{7.22}$$

Here t'' must take on large values for a reliable value of $G_v(t)$.

It should be noted that classical systems are also symmetrical with respect to time. Thus, $G_v(t) = G_v(-t)$.

The above considerations apply also to other time correlation functions. Some of the other more important ones will be discussed in this chapter. Yet others will be introduced in later chapters. They need not always refer to single particles as the $G_v(t)$ defined above.

(b) Spectral Density Functions

The Fourier transform $G(\omega)$ of $G(t)$ is often called the "spectral density" function for the quantity considered. The two functions $G(t)$ and $G(\omega)$ can be considered to be related to each other either by the Fourier cosine transform or the exponential form. For classical systems, $G(t) = G(-t)$ and both $G(t)$ and $G(\omega)$ are real. Here the exponential form is used.

$$G(\omega) = \frac{1}{2\pi} \int_{-\infty}^{\infty} G(t) \exp[-i\omega t]\, dt \qquad (7.23)$$

$$G(t) = \int_{-\infty}^{\infty} G(\omega) \exp[i\omega t]\, d\omega \qquad (7.23)$$

The function $G(\omega)$ is seen to express the weighting of the frequency components present in $G(t)$. This is as $\int_{-\infty}^{\infty} \exp[-i(\omega - \omega')t]\, dt$ is non-zero only if $\omega = \omega'$. The formal definition of a Dirac δ function is in fact:

$$\delta(\omega) = \frac{1}{2\pi} \int_{-\infty}^{\infty} \exp[i\omega t]\, dt \;; \qquad \int_{-\infty}^{\infty} \exp[-i\omega t] \cdot \delta(\omega)\, d\omega = 1 \qquad (7.24)$$

A familiar example of such a spectral density function appears in the Debye theory of solids. There the spectral density of vibrational modes is assumed to be proportional to ω^2 [Eq. (18.17)]. Similar behavior was seen to be the case in liquids for collective translational modes.

(c) Relationships to Diffusion and van Hove Functions

The function $G_v(t)$ can be shown to be simply related to the macroscopic diffusion coefficient D [5, 6]. A one-dimensional model will be used to outline this relationship.

The change in position of a particle along the x axis in a time interval τ is denoted by Δx. This distance can also be expressed as

$$\Delta x = x(\tau) - x(0) = \int_0^{\tau} u_x(t')\, dt' \qquad (7.25)$$

The mean square distance is then given by

$$\langle \Delta x^2 \rangle = \int_0^{\tau} dt' \int_0^{\tau} \langle u_x(t')\, u_x(t'') \rangle\, dt'' = 2D\tau \qquad (7.26)$$

The Einstein relation (6.25) has been used here.

A change of variables can be made, from t', t" to t', t = t" - t', and $\langle u_x(t') \cdot u_x(t'') \rangle$ can be expressed as $\langle u_x(0) \cdot u_x(t) \rangle$. Appropriate integration and change of integration limits then leads to

$$\langle \Delta x^2 \rangle = 2\tau \int_0^{\tau} \langle u_x(0) \cdot u_x(t) \rangle \left(1 - \frac{1}{\tau}\right) dt \tag{7.27}$$

For $\tau \to \infty$, i.e., $t/\tau \ll 1$, D can be expressed as

$$D = \int_0^{\infty} \langle u_x(0) \cdot u_x(t) \rangle \, dt = \frac{1}{3} \int_0^{\infty} G_v(t) \, dt \tag{7.28}$$

A thorough discussion of the relation between the diffusion coefficient and time correlation functions is given in Ref. 7.

Other transport coefficients can be related to time correlation functions by relationships similar to Eq. (7.21). The coefficient of shear viscosity, for example, is given by

$$\eta = \frac{1}{kTV} \int_0^{\infty} \langle \sigma_{xy}(0) \cdot \sigma_{xy}(t) \rangle \, dt \tag{7.29}$$

The time correlation function $G_\eta(t)$ for fluctuations in the shear stress σ_{xy} behaves quite similarly to $G_v(t)$. Relations such as (7.28) and (7.29) make it possible to obtain transport coefficients such as η and D from molecular dynamics simulations. Examples of such computations are given in Refs. 8 and 9.

$G_v(t)$ and $G_s(r, t)$ both describe the same general phenomenon of motion of a particle in a liquid, but in different ways. The exact relationship between these functions will be explored in Sec. 16.1(g).

(d) Oscillatory Motion

The translational motion of a particle in a solid would be oscillatory in nature. In liquids, as implied by the models in Chap. 2, the translational motion would also be expected in part to be of a vibrational nature. Thus the form of $G_v(t)$ and $G_v(\omega)$ for vibrational motion are discussed here. Models of overall-particle motion in liquids, involving such oscillatory motion, are discussed in Sec. (f) below.

A particle undergoing periodic motion along a coordinate x with a frequency ω_0 will have the same velocity at $t + (n/\omega_0)$, n = 0, 1,

2, ... At $t' = t + (n/2\omega_0)$ it will have an equal but oppocite velocity. Thus $G_v(t)$ for this type of motion is also of a periodic nature.

The form of $G_v(t)$ can be obtained using relationship (7.22). In the case of a repetitive motion such as here, the integration in (7.22) can be carried out over one full period. If $x \propto \sin \omega_0 t'$, then $u_x(t) \propto \cos \omega_0 t$, and

$$G_v(t) \propto \int_0^{t'=1/\omega_0} \cos \omega_0 t' \cdot \cos (\omega_0 (t' + t))\, dt' \propto \cos \omega_0 t \qquad (7.30)$$

The proportionality can be removed by referring back to (7.20) and setting

$$G_v(t) = \frac{kT}{m'} \cos \omega_0 t \qquad (7.31)$$

where m' is the "effective mass" for the motion considered.

The Fourier transform of a monochromatic periodic motion is simply a δ function. Thus

$$G_v(\omega) \propto \delta(\omega_0) \qquad (7.32)$$

and the motion contributes only one frequency in the spectral density function. If the oscillation is damped, then a distribution of frequencies about ω_0 is contributed.

This oscillatory motion does not contribute to diffusion. This can be seen from expression (7.28).

Such oscillatory motion would also be expected for the time correlation function describing free rotation [Sec. 7.3(a)]. However, there is generally a distribution of rotational velocities ω present. For the case of one plane, assuming classical motion, this distribution of velocities is [Eq. (18.5)]

$$W(\omega)\, d\omega = \frac{1}{2} \tau^2\omega^2 \exp\left[- \frac{\tau^2\omega^2}{2}\right] d\omega \qquad (7.33)$$

Here $\tau = I/kT$ is the time characteristic of free rotation. Since the time dependence of all the rotational states must be included in the ensemble average, the simple oscillatory nature is lost in the rotational correlation function. [See also Sec. 7.3(b)].

(e) Brownian Motion

Brownian motion was considered previously [Sec. 6.2(a)] as a random or stochastic process. A more rigorous treatment of random processes is possible by consideration of the Langevin equation, the equation of motion for a particle with a damping term and a stochastic driving force. The resultant spectral density function is valid for other random processes, e.g., electrical noise. The equation to be solved is thus

$$m\frac{d\underline{u}}{dt} = -\zeta\underline{u} + \underline{F}(t) \tag{7.34}$$

where ζ is the friction coefficient, and $\underline{F}(t)$ is a random force, such that $\langle\underline{F}(t)\rangle = 0$, and $\langle\underline{F}(0)\cdot\underline{F}(t)\rangle = 2\zeta kT\ \delta(t)$. This outlines the special case where the force has no "memory" as $\langle\underline{F}(0)\cdot\underline{F}(t)\rangle = 0$ for $t \neq 0$.

The solution for (7.34) involves use of Fourier-Laplace transforms and will not be given here. A detailed version of the solution can be found in Ref. 6. The solution for $G_v(t)$ for the special simple case described above is simply

$$G_v(t) = \frac{kT}{m} \exp\left[-\frac{t}{\tau}\right] \tag{7.35}$$

where $\tau = m/\zeta$.

Through (7.28), the diffusion coefficient D can be found as

$$D = \frac{1}{3}\int_0^\infty G_v(t)\ dt = \frac{kT}{m}\tau \tag{7.36}$$

Thus the Einstein relation (6.62), $D = kT/\zeta$, can also be obtained through considerations of velocity time correlation functions.

The spectral density of (7.35) is

$$G_v(\omega) = \frac{kT}{m}\cdot\frac{4\tau}{1 + \omega^2\tau^2} \tag{7.37}$$

by simple Fourier inversion. $G_v(\omega)$ is in this case essentially constant in the low-frequency ("white noise") region as shown in Fig. 7.2.

Such a model is quite adequate for the description of the total motion of a very large particle among smaller particles. It is not

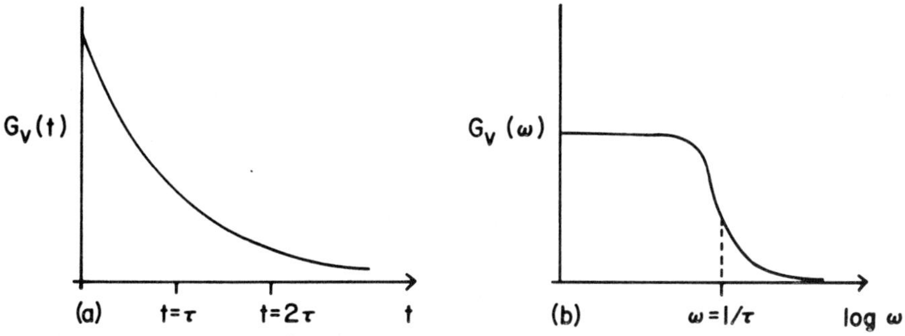

Fig. 7.2. Schematic diagrams showing $G_V(t)$ and $G_V(\omega)$ for the case of Brownian motion.

completely adequate if the particle considered is of the same size as the particles colliding with it, producing the force F(t). More complex models are then necessary which take account of the nonrandom aspects of F(t) by, for example, introducing an oscillatory motion.

(f) Models of Translational Motion in Liquids

The shape of $G_V(t)$ and $G_V(\omega)$ for liquids is typically of the form shown in Fig. 7.3 [10]. The region A can be considered to be due to diffusive (e.g., Brownian) type of motion, while B is due to damped oscillatory motion.

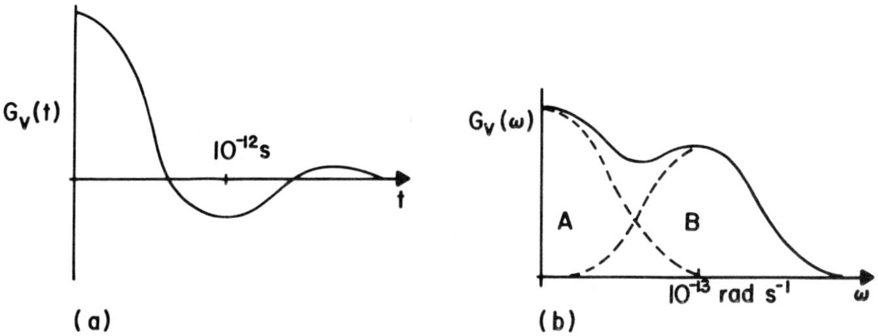

Fig. 7.3. Schematic diagrams showing the typical shapes of $G_V(t)$ and $G_V(\omega)$ for a liquid. (After Ref. 10.)

The oscillatory motion can be introduced into the model by assuming a molecule to undergo vibration in its cell on the average for a time τ_0. It then is displaced into another cell through some distance ℓ, where it again oscillates for a time τ_0, etc. After each step, it is assumed that there is a complete loss of memory. Such a model reduces to the Brownian motion, random-walk model for large values of $\underline{r}$, t. Thus in the limit of large $\underline{r}$, t, the relation in (7.8) is also valid. The model gives different results at small $\underline{r}$, t, however.

Instead of describing the displacement motion through a distance parameter ℓ, a parameter τ_d can be used. τ_d gives the time of the intervals during which displacement of a molecule occurs. Thus for a time τ_0 motion characterized by region B in Fig. 7.3 takes place, and for τ_d, that characterized by region A. Complete loss of memory again is assumed after every time τ_0 or τ_d. As $\tau_0 \to 0$ (without τ_d necessarily increasing), the random walk model is obtained.

The displacement motion of a molecule can be pictured to occur through a pairwise rolling motion. Thus during τ_d, a molecule can then be represented as a rigid rotator made up of two molecules.

In the discussion of $G_v(t)$ and the above models, the collective motion of molecules is not dealt with directly. Such aspects can be described through the distinct correlation function $G_d(\underline{r}, t)$. It is, however, also possible to introduce such collective motion by describing the motion during τ_0 through a phonon picture [10]. Other models for translational motion are reviewed in Ref 1.

7.3. ORIENTATIONAL CORRELATION FUNCTIONS

(a) Types of Orientational Time Correlation Functions

Orientational motion has been neglected in the discussion up to now. Such motion can, however, be detected in liquids by several experimental methods. In liquids, the free quantized rotational motion of molecules in the gas phase is restricted to varying degrees depending upon the molecule and the conditions.

The simplest orientational time correlation function describing such motion is $G_1(t)$

$$G_1(t) = \langle \underline{n}(0) \cdot \underline{n}(t) \rangle = \langle \cos\theta(0) \cdot \cos\theta(t) \rangle = \langle P_1(\underline{n}(0) \cdot \underline{n}(t)) \rangle \tag{7.38}$$

Here $\underline{n}$ is the unit vector in the direction of the dipole moment of the molecule. The symbol $G_1(t)$ is used as this function is one of a hierarchy or orientational time correlation functions of the Legendre polynomials. When rotation is assumed to be independent of translational and vibrational motions, then the dipole moment correlation $G_p(t)$ is

$$G_p(t) = \langle \underline{p}(0) \cdot \underline{p}(t) \rangle = p^2 G_1(t) \tag{7.39}$$

Thus $G_1(t)$ is at times referred to as the "dipole" correlation function.

Correlations of other Legendre polynomials are also important

$$G_2(t) = \langle P_2(\underline{n}(0) \cdot \underline{n}(t)) \rangle = \frac{1}{2} \langle 3(\underline{n}(0) \cdot \underline{n}(t))^2 - 1 \rangle \tag{7.40}$$

$G_2(t)$ is at times referred to as the "Raman" correlation function [Sec. 12.1(h)]. In general,

$$G_\ell(t) = \langle P_\ell(\underline{n}(0) \cdot \underline{n}(t)) \rangle = \langle P_\ell(\cos\theta(0) \cdot \cos\theta(t)) \rangle \tag{7.41}$$

Equations (7.38), (7.40), and (7.41) can be further simplified if θ is chosen so that at $t = 0$, $\theta = 0$. For the case of rotational diffusion, $G_1(t)$ and $G_2(t)$ are then given by Eq. (6.31). These functions are normalized, i.e., $G_1(0) = G_2(0) = \cdots = 1$.

More complicated time correlation functions involving orientational aspects are introduced in future chapters. Many of these will be written in a normalized form, e.g., Sec. 12.1(g),

$$G_\beta(t) = \frac{\langle \mathrm{Tr}\underline{\underline{\beta}}_v(0) \cdot \underline{\underline{\beta}}_v(t) \rangle}{\langle \mathrm{Tr}\underline{\underline{\beta}}_v(0) \cdot \underline{\underline{\beta}}_v(0) \rangle} \tag{7.42}$$

Where $\underline{\underline{\beta}}_v$ is the traceless part of the polarizability tensor. The angular momentum correlation function $G_J(t)$ is also of interest [Sec. 13.3(a)]. It is defined as

$$G_J(t) = \frac{\langle \underline{J}(0) \cdot \underline{J}(t) \rangle}{\langle \underline{J}(0) \cdot \underline{J}(0) \rangle} \tag{7.43}$$

where $\underline{J}$ is the angular momentum $\underline{J}_i = I\underline{n}_i \times \dot{\underline{n}}_i$.

Time correlation functions need not be restricted to single particles. An example of a correlation function defined for a bulk property, polarization, is given in Eq. (11.19).

(b) Models for Orientational Motion

Numerous models for the orientational motion of molecules in liquids have been suggested. Developments and reviews of these models can be found in Refs. 10 - 14.

Orientational motion can, to a large extent, be considered in analogy with translation. Instead of vibration (oscillation) about a lattice point, there is libration about an orientational axis. Instead of translational displacement, there is rotational motion. In analogy to the longitudinal ultrasonic waves due to oscillation, it should be expected that there could be collective motion due to libration, i.e., some form of orientational waves.

Two models of rotational motion have already been introduced. One is the rotational diffusion model [Sec. 6.1(e)], which corresponds to translational Brownian motion. Equation (6.31) gives the forms of $G_1(t)$ and $G_2(t)$ for this model. Another model is that of free rotation, corresponding to free translation. The $G_1(t)$ and $G_2(t)$ for that model are quite complex, however, as indicated in Sec. 7.2(d).

Yet another model is the orientational analog to the translational model in Sec. 7.2(f). Orientational motion is here described as follows [10]. The molecule undergoes libration for a time τ_0, then damped rotational motion for a time τ_1, etc. The rotational diffusion model is reached for $\tau_0 \rightarrow 0$ with τ_1 small as compared to the overall time scale.

A model referred to often as the "Gordon J-diffusion" model [15] is often used. In it the molecule is assumed to rotate freely between collisions. The collisions occur instantaneously, they are uncorrelated, and they completely randomize the angular momentum of a molecule. The results obtained from this model can also be achieved from other models [11,12]. It can be thought to be the limiting case of a more general theory [12].

All of these theories must give the same result in the limit of small t. For a normalized G(t), a Taylor expansion about t = 0 must have a form

$$G(t) = 1 - ct^2 + \qquad (t \to 0) \tag{7.44}$$

In the case of $G_1(t)$, the constant c is given by $c = kT/I$. The linear term must disappear as G(t) must be an even function of time.

Expansion of G(t) assuming Brownian motion (7.35) does not give a zero coefficient for the linear t term. This again illustrates the shortcomings of describing the $t \to 0$ limiting behavior in terms of stochastic processes [16].

7.4. QUANTUM MECHANICAL ASPECTS

(a) Description in Terms of Heisenberg Matrices

In the previous sections, the time correlation functions have been introduced in a classical manner. However, the position vectors $\underline{r}_j(t)$ in Eq. (7.1), and other classical quantities can also be considered as being Heisenberg observables (Sec 21.6).

When a quantum mechanical description is used, then the G(t) can become complex. The imaginary part of such complex correlation function can be interpreted as being due to disturbance of the system from equilibrium on observation. In the case of $G(\underline{r}, t)$, it can, however, be shown [1] that, although $G(\underline{r}, t)$ is complex, the function $G(\underline{r}, (t - i\hbar/2kT))$ is a real, even function.

In the Heisenberg approach to quantum mechanics, an operator $\hat{Q}$ corresponding to some classical quantity Q is time-dependent. Its equation of motion is given by Eq. (21.48):

$$\frac{d}{dt}\hat{Q}_H = \frac{i}{\hbar}[\hat{H}, \hat{Q}_H] \tag{7.45}$$

This equation is satisfied by

$$\hat{Q}_H(t) = \exp\left[\frac{i\hat{H}t}{\hbar}\right]\hat{Q}(0)\ \exp\left[-\frac{i\hat{H}t}{\hbar}\right] \tag{7.46}$$

The operators satisfy the same laws as the corresponding classical quantities.

The statistical equilibrium average is given as

$$\langle Q_H(t)\rangle = \Sigma w_j \langle j|\hat{Q}(t)|j\rangle \tag{7.47}$$

Here w_j is the initial probability of finding the system in the state $|j\rangle$. The description of such a state is the same in the Heisenberg description as in the Schrödinger picture at t = 0. For a system at thermal equilibrium, w_j is simply given as (18.4)

$$w_j = \frac{\exp[-E_j/kT]}{\Sigma\exp[-E_j/kT]} \tag{7.48}$$

where E_j is the energy of the state, i.e., $\hat{H}|j\rangle = E_j|j\rangle$.

A more general form of (7.38) is given as

$$\langle Q(t)\rangle = \mathrm{Tr}\ \hat{\rho}\underline{\underline{Q}}_H(t) \tag{7.49}$$

Here $\hat{\rho}$ is the initial density matrix (an operator) for the states $|j\rangle$. It has elements $\hat{\rho}_{jj} = |j\rangle w_j\langle j|$, $\hat{\rho}_{jk} = 0$, or in another bases set, n, m, $\hat{\rho}_{nm} = \Sigma\langle n|j\rangle w_j\langle j|m\rangle$. The elements of the Heisenberg matrix $\underline{\underline{Q}}(t)$ are $Q_{jk}(t) = \langle j|\hat{Q}(t)|k\rangle$.

Consideration of G(t) in terms of Heisenberg observables makes it possible to relate time correlation functions to experimental quantities in a simple manner [17,18]. As an example of the equivalence of the "classical" and the Heisenberg descriptions, the time correlation functions $G_m(t)$ for the transition dipole moment $\underline{m}_v$ for a vibrational band v will be given. It is discussed in more detail in Sec. 7.4(b), where vibrational relaxation is introduced, and is needed for discussions in Sec. 12.1.

The word "classical" is set in quotations above, as the transition dipole moment usually encountered is $m_{v,x} = \sum_{j,f}\langle j|\Sigma e_i x_i|f\rangle$, where j and f are the initial and final states involved, respectively. In this case, as in general throughout this volume, electronic transitions are not involved. Thus $\langle j|$ and $\langle f|$ differ only in the description of the nuclear states (i.e., vibration, rotation etc.) if the adiabatic approximation is assumed (Chap. 21). $\Sigma q_i\underline{r}_i$ is the dipole moment [Eq. (1.6)] operator $\hat{m}$, the summation being over the charges present in the molecule considered.

The expressions for $G_m(t)$ are thus

$$G_m(t) = \langle \underline{m}_v(0)\cdot \underline{m}_v(t)\rangle$$

$$= \Sigma\omega_j \langle j|\hat{m}(0)\cdot \hat{m}(t)|j\rangle$$

$$= \Sigma\omega_j \langle j|\hat{m}(0)\ \exp\left[\frac{i\hat{H}t}{\hbar}\right]\hat{m}(0)\ \exp\left[-\frac{i\hat{H}t}{\hbar}\right]|j\rangle$$

$$= \sum_{j,f} \omega_j \langle j|\hat{m}|t\rangle\langle t|\ \exp\left[\frac{i\hat{H}t}{\hbar}\right]\hat{m}\ \exp\left[-\frac{i\hat{H}t}{\hbar}\right]|j\rangle \qquad (7.50)$$

The Schrödinger (time-independent) and Heisenberg (time-dependent) operators $\hat{m}_v$ are identical at time t = 0, as are the Schrödinger (time-dependent) and Heisenberg (time-independent) states, $|j\rangle$, $|f\rangle$.

(b) Vibrational Relaxation

The function $G_m(t)$ can be assumed to be separable into two factors as $G_m(t) = G_{rot}(t)\cdot G_{vib}(t)$. The function $G_{rot}(t)$ describes the time dependence of $G_m(t)$ due to rotational motion. It is simply the function $G_1(t)$ introduced earlier (7.38) with the unit vector in the direction of $\underline{m}_v$.

The function $G_{vib}(t)$ is often referred to as the vibrational relaxation function. It describes the time correlation of the absolute value of $\underline{m}_v$, i.e.,

$$G_{vib}(t) = \langle|\underline{m}_v(0)|\,|\underline{m}_v(t)|\rangle$$

$$= \mathrm{Tr}\ (\hat{\rho}|\underline{\underline{m}}_v(0)|\,|\underline{\underline{m}}_v(t)|) \qquad (7.51)$$

In the second form, the relationship (7.47) has been used to give a general expression. The definitions of the matrices $\underline{\underline{m}}_v(0)$, etc. can be obtained from the discussion following Eqs. (7.47) and (7.50).

$G_{vib}(t)$ is usually assumed to have a considerably slower time variation than $G_1(t)$ in most liquids. Its form is usually taken as $G_{vib}(t) \propto \exp[-t/\tau_v]$ where τ_v is the vibrational relaxation time, but it is often considered to be a constant when the shape of $G_1(t)$ is being explored.

The size of τ_v can be thought to be governed by two factors. The finite lifetimes of the vibrational states involved will make $|\underline{m}_v(t)|$ different from $|\underline{m}_v(0)|$. In the case of absorption, the vibrationally excited $|f>$ states would (in the Schrödinger approach) most likely have shorter lifetimes than the initial ($|j>$) states, and would predominate in determining the size of τ_v. In addition, $|\underline{m}_v|$ would also be sensitive to perturbations of the molecule due to changes in its environment in the liquid. The latter effect is believed to dominate the vibrational relaxation mechanism in some cases [19].

REFERENCES

Thorough accounts of van Hove functions with special emphases on liquids can be found in Refs. 1 and 2. General descriptions of time correlation functions are given in Refs. 5 and 6, while their use for interpreting liquid dynamics is well covered in Ref. 17. There seems to be no single recent reference giving a reasonably detailed account of various models of translational and rotational motion in liquids. The references mentioned in the text describe various models.

1. A. Sjölander, Thermal Neutron Scattering (P. A. Egelstaff, ed.), Academic Press, New York, 1965.
2. GR2.
3. L. D. Landau and E. M. Lifshitz, Fluid Mechanics, Pergamon, London, 1959.
4. H. L. Swinney and D. L. Henry, Phys. Rev., *A8*, 2586 (1973).
5. R. Zwanzig, Ann. Rev. Phys. Chem., *16*, 67 (1965).
6. R. Kubo, Statistical Mechanics, North-Holland, Amsterdam, 1971.
7. M-K. Ahn, S. J. Knak Jensen, and D. Kivelson, J. Chem. Phys., *57*, 2940 (1972).
8. E. M. Gosling, I. R. McDonald, and K. Singer, Mol. Phys., *26*, 1475 (1973).
9. F. H. Stillinger and A. Rahman, J. Chem. Phys., *60*, 1545 (1974).
10. K-E. Larsson, Faraday Symp. Chem. Soc., No. 6, 122 (1972).

11. D. Chandler, J. Chem. Phys., *60*, 3508 (1974).

12. D. Kivelson and T. Keyes, J. Chem. Phys., *57*, 4599 (1972).

13. R. I. Cukier, J. Chem. Phys., *60*, 734 (1974).

14. D. E. O'Reilly, J. Chem. Phys., *57*, 885 (1972); *60*, 1607 (1974).

15. R. G. Gordon, J. Chem. Phys., *44*, 1830 (1966); R. E. D. McClung, ibid., *55*, 3459 (1971).

16. H. L. Friedman in GR6.

17. W. A. Steele, Transport Phenomena in Fluids (H. J. M. Hanley, ed.), Marcel Dekker, New York, 1969.

18. R. G. Gordon, J. Chem. Phys., *42*, 3658 (1965); *43*, 1307 (1965); *44*, 1830, 3083 (1966).

19. S. Bratoz, J. Rios, and Y. Guissani, J. Chem. Phys., *52*, 439 (1970).

Further Recent References

U. Buontempo, S. Cunsolo, and P. Dore, "Intercollisional Memory Effects and Short-Time Behavior of the Velocity-Autocorrelation Function from Translational Spectra of Liquid Mixtures", Phys. Rev., *A10*, 913 (1974).

D. Chandler, "Rough Hard Sphere Theory of the Self-Diffusion Constant for Molecular Liquids", J. Chem. Phys., *62*, 1358 (1975).

K-W. Li and J. S. Dahler, "Kinetic Theory of Density Fluctuations in a Classical Fluid", Mol. Phys., *31*, 295 (1976).

J. J. Weis and D. Levesque, "Molecular Dynamics Study of the Dynamical Structure Factor of Liquid Nitrogen", Phys. Rev., *A13*, 450 (1976).

D. Frenkel and G. H. Wegdam, "Rotational Diffusion Model with a Variable Collision Distribution II. The Effect of Energy Transfer", J. Chem. Phys., *61*, 4671 (1974).

B. J. Berne, "A Self-Consistent Theory of Rotational Diffusion", J. Chem. Phys., *62*, 1154 (1975).

D. Kivelson, "Comments on High Frequency Molecular Reorientation in Liquids", J. Chem. Phys., *63*, 5034 (1975).

M. Evans, "Rotational Velocity Correlation Function for Assessing Molecular Models for Gas and Liquid Phase Studies", J. C. S. Farad. II, *70*, 1620 (1974).

C. Brot and B. Lassier-Govers, "Rotational Diffusion and Reorientations in Molecular Crystals", Ber. Bunseng. physik. Chem., *80*, 31 (1976).

Part B

EXPERIMENTAL METHODS

Part B describes ways of experimentally elucidating structure and dynamics in liquids. Because it is not possible to give an exhaustive listing of all the methods available, only those which seem to be more commonly used were organized into the nine chapters in this part. Each chapter is organized in the same manner.

In the first section of each chapter, the theoretical background of the method is discussed. In most cases this section relates back to the discussion in part A, so that all the experimental methods relate back to the same basis. Only aspects of the theoretical background of a method applicable to liquids are discussed.

In the second section of each chapter, the experimental techniques involved are covered. Common experimental aspects which are not unique to a particular method are not discussed. Commercially available instruments are also not covered in any detail.

The third section of each chapter contains discussion of experimental results for specific systems. The results for nine specific systems are discussed in each chapter whenever good experimental data are available: These are (i) a monatomic liquid (usually argon), (ii) an organic liquid (usually benzene), (iii) water, (iv) a mixture of normal liquids, (v) a water-alcohol mixture, (vi) an aqueous electrolyte solution ($MgSO_4$ where possible), (vii) a nonaqueous electrolyte solution, (viii) a system with a critical solution, and (ix) a system of biological interest. Other systems are also discussed if interesting experimental work is available. An attempt has also been made to include examples in each chapter from papers published by the various groups which seem to be contributing regularly to the literature in that speciality. This may make it easier for readers interested in a particular speciality to follow the literature.

Chapter 8

INTERPRETATION OF THERMODYNAMIC DATA

This chapter outlines how conventional thermodynamic properties of liquids can be measured and used to elucidate the microscopic structure present in the liquids. No information regarding dynamic properties can be obtained from such measurements. As throughout this book, "abnormal" aspects, such as formation of glasses, liquid crystals, and quantum liquids, are not discussed.

There has been some discussion of the thermodynamic parameters for liquids in previous chapters, e.g., Secs 2.1 and 4.1. Section 1 in this chapter adds to this discussion, introducing aspects referred to in later sections, which were not needed for the introduction of theoretical models. Chapter 17 is often referred to here.

Section 2 outlines some of the more important methods for measurement of thermodynamic parameters. Here only methods making use of classical, macroscopic phenomena are discussed generally. In the following chapters, it will be seen that thermodynamic parameters can also be obtained through spectroscopy, ultrasonics, etc. The use of ultrasonic velocity to obtain κ_S is such an example, but it is included here as it has become quite a standard method for compressibility measurements.

The last section contains a selection of specific examples to show the range of phenomena which can be elucidated through thermodynamic measurements. Such a selection does not cover the types of phenomena exhaustively by any means. There is, for example, a vast amount of data on aqueous electrolyte solutions not dealt with here. Discussions are readily available of this in electrochemistry texts.

8.1. THEORETICAL RELATIONSHIPS

(a) Pure Liquids: Mechanical Properties

In principle, all the thermodynamic properties of a liquid can be obtained by appropriate mathematical expressions from G(N, p, T) (Chap. 17). The usual experimental system with N, p, T the independent variables is assumed. The complete knowledge of G necessary for this is in practice usually not available. The discussion of thermodynamic properties is thus usually divided into a discussion of the thermal properties and of the mechanical properties (i.e., the equation of state).

A phase diagram such as Fig. 2.2 shows only the regions of p, T at which phases can exist in equilibrium. No information is given

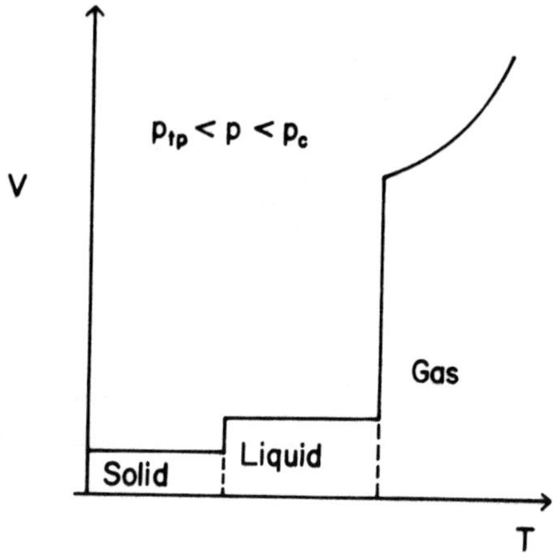

Fig. 8.1. Schematic diagram of volume vs temperature for a normal substance with $p_{tp} < p < p_c$.

regarding V(p, T). Curves of V vs T for a compound at a pressure $p < p_c$ and $p > p_{tp}$, where a liquid phase can exist, are typically of the form shown schematically in Fig. 8.1.

Except near the critical point, the volume change in vaporization, ΔV_{vap} is much greater than that in fusion, i.e., $\Delta V_{vap} >> \Delta V_f$. When $\Delta V_{vap} \simeq V_g$ (i.e., $V_g >> V_l$), and the gas is assumed to be ideal, then the Clausius-Clapeyron equation (2.1) can be obtained using the relationships in Chap. 17. ΔV_{vap} is always >0, and ΔV_f usually >0. Water is an exception, where $\Delta V_f < 0$. The compressibility κ and the thermal expansion α are generally much smaller for the liquid than for the gas. In the latter case κ and α can be reasonably estimated from the ideal gas law for pressures up to one atmosphere.

(b) Pure Liquids: Thermal Properties

The thermal properties can be displayed well through a curve of C_p (or C_v) vs T. By appropriate integrations, relative values of S, H (or U) can be obtained from such a curve. Figure 8.2 shows schematically C_p vs T for a substance at a pressure where all three phases can exist. Typically C_p (and C_v) in the liquid phase is higher. In

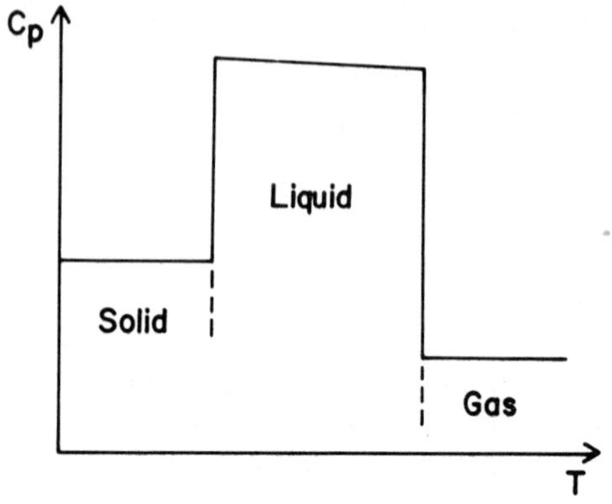

Fig. 8.2. Schematic diagram of C_p vs temperature for a normal substance.

Fig. 8.2 it is shown as decreasing with T; it can also have a minimum as a function of T [see Sec. 8.3(a)].

The heat capacity can be considered as a sum of two parts. The first arises from the excitation of mechanical degrees of freedom and is often (somewhat misleadingly) referred to as the "vibrational" part. When a degree of freedom can be considered classically, then it contributes $n\mathcal{R}/2$ to C_v ($\mathcal{R}$ for vibration or libration). If, as in the case of many internal vibrational degrees of freedom, the characteristic energy $\ll kT$, then the T dependence of the contribution to C_v is quite complex (Chap. 18).

There can also be a "configurational" contribution to C_v (or C_p) due to structural (configurational) changes occurring with changes in temperature. This is present essentially only in liquids. Gases have to a first approximation no "structure," and solids have essentially no change in structure with temperature. C_v of a gas is generally smaller than that for the corresponding solid. In the latter, translational and possible some rotational degrees of freedom are restricted to be vibrations and librations.

As at solid-liquid phase equilibrium, $\mu_s = \mu_l$, then $G_f = (\mu_l - \mu_s)\, n = 0$. Hence $\Delta H_f = T\,\Delta S_f$, where ΔH_f is the enthalpy (or latent heat) of fusion. Similarly, $\Delta H_{vap} = T\,\Delta S_{vap}$. Both ΔH_f and $\Delta H_{vap} > 0$

in all cases. The value of ΔS_{vap} is similar for most liquids, being approximated by Trouton's rule, $\Delta S_{vap} \simeq 11nR$, i.e., $\simeq 92$ J mol^{-1} K^{-1}. This represents an increase in the "effective" volume per molecule of 2×10^4 [i.e., $\Delta S = nR \ln (V_g/V_l)$] if volume expansion is assumed the primary cause of ΔS_{vap}.

(c) Activities of Components

The changes in the freezing points and the boiling points due to changes in composition as shown in Fig. 4.3 can be used to measure activities. For a pure solid in equilibrium with a liquid mixture at $T_{f'}$,

$$\mu^{\bullet}_{i,s} = \mu^{\bullet}_{i,l} + RT_{f'} \ln a_i \tag{8.1}$$

Thus the activity can be expressed as

$$\ln a_i = -\frac{\Delta G^{\bullet}_{i,f}}{nRT_{f'}} \tag{8.2}$$

where $T_{f'}$ is the freezing point of the solution. The derivative $da_i/dT_{f'}$ can be obtained from Eq. (8.2). With use of (17.34) the equation [see also (4.12)]

$$nR \int_1^{a_i} \frac{da_i}{a_i} = \int_{T_f}^{T_{f'}} \frac{\Delta H^{\bullet}_{i,f}}{T^2} \, dT \tag{8.3}$$

can be formulated, where the integration is from pure component i ($a_i = 1$, $T_{f'} = T_f$) to the solution with $T_{f'}$. Thus a relationship is obtained between a_i and $T_{f'}$ as [see also (4.13)]

$$\ln a_i = \frac{\Delta H^{\bullet}_{i,f}}{nR}\left(\frac{1}{T_f} - \frac{1}{T_{f'}}\right) \tag{8.4}$$

When a_i for component i is known, then the activity of the other component can be obtained through the Gibbs-Duhem equation (17.14). In terms of activities this gives

$$n_i d \ln a_i = -n_j d \ln a_j \tag{8.5}$$

Such an equilibrium can be also viewed from the point of view of solubility of component i in j at that temperature. Thus relationships between activity and solubility can be developed in an analogous manner.

A relationship analogous to (8.4) can be obtained for the boiling point elevation of i with addition of another component (solute). For Eq. (8.6) to be valid, the solute must have a negligible vapor pressure. When this is not the case, it is possible for $T_{B'} < T_B$

$$\ln a_i = \frac{\Delta H^\bullet_{i,vap}}{nR}\left(\frac{1}{T_{B'}} - \frac{1}{T_B}\right) \tag{8.6}$$

Yet another relationship can be obtained between the activity and a thermodynamic parameter. The osmotic pressure π is the vapor pressure difference between the pure solvent (i) and a solution. Thus

$$\mu^\bullet_i(T, p + \pi) + RT \ln a_i = \mu^\bullet_i(T, p) \tag{8.7}$$

Thus as $d\mu^\bullet = (V^\bullet/n)\ dp$

$$nRT \ln a_i = -\int_p^{p+\pi} V^\bullet_i\ dp = -V^\bullet_i \cdot \pi \tag{8.8}$$

if $V^\bullet_i$ is assumed independent of pressure, i.e., $\kappa_T = 0$.

Deviation from ideality of a solvent is often not expressed in terms of activity, but in terms of "osmotic coefficients." The molal osmotic coefficient ϕ is thus defined as

$$\ln a_i = -\frac{\nu m M_i}{1000}\phi \tag{8.9}$$

Here M_i is the molecular weight of the solvent, m the molality of the solution and ν the moles of particles per mole of solute. Non-idealities are more easily seen through ϕ than through a_i. From (8.8), the relation of ϕ to π can be obtained.

In the case of electrolyte solutions, activities can also be obtained from measurements of cell potentials. The standard potential (emf) of a cell, E^θ, is related to ΔG^θ for the cell reaction as

$$-nFE^\theta = \Delta G^\theta \tag{8.10}$$

where n is the number of moles of electrons transferred per unit cell reaction. Equation (8.9) follows from the definition of ΔG in terms of the reversible nonpressure work in a change [Eq. (17.6)]. With the use of Eq. (17.32), (8.10) can be expressed for the general reaction $\Sigma\nu_i I = 0$ (17.27) as

$$E^\theta = \frac{RT}{nF} \ln K \qquad\qquad E = \frac{RT}{nF} \ln \Pi_i (a_i)^{\nu_i} \qquad (8.11)$$

The second case generalizes the expression for nonstandard state potentials. Thus measurement of E under various conditions leads to information about a_i, [actually $a_\pm$ (17.25)].

8.2. EXPERIMENTAL TECHNIQUES

(a) Measurement of Density and Volume

A direct measurement of the density can be made with a pyknometer, or specific gravity bottle. In this case the mass of the liquid is obtained by weighing a known volume which has been well thermostated. A precision of 10 parts per million (ppm) is typical of such measurements [1]. Sources of error are uncertainties in the weight, volume, and impurities in the system.(e.g., dissolved gases). The volume is often fixed by filling the pyknometer until the meniscus is at the top of a capillary tube. An error due to evaporation during the weighing can be present in the case of highly volatile systems.

A precision of ±1 ppm in the measurement of density is possible by use of a magnetic float density cell (Fig. 8.3). In this case a float with appropriate mass and containing a bar magnet is immersed in the liquid. An electric current sent through a solenoid about the cell is then used to produce a magnetic field. A float is chosen which has a slightly higher specific gravity than the liquid. Then some current I_0 is needed to maintain the float in a stationary position. This current I_0 can be obtained by direct observation, or more accurately by extrapolating a curve of the rate of rising of the float vs current to zero rate of rise. Examples of such apparatus are given in Refs 2 and 3.

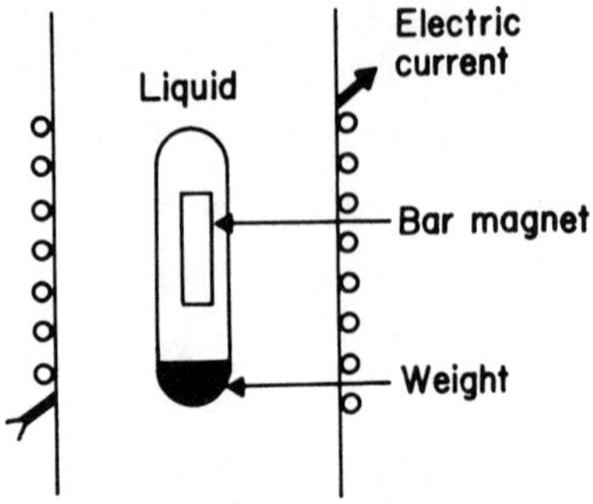

Fig. 8.3. Schematic diagram of a magnetic float densitometer. After Ref. 2.

High-precision densities can also be measured on the oscillating-tube principle. Here the frequency of the resonant vibration of a tube filled with the liquid is detected. This resonance frequency of the tube can be shown to be related to the density of a liquid as ρ = constant + constant/ν^2. An example of such an apparatus is shown in Ref. 4.

The above methods measure the absolute density of a liquid, although generally the apparatus is calibrated with standard liquids with known density. Often it is the change in density (volume) of a process that is of interest rather than the absolute value. In such cases dilatometers can be used to obtain ρ as a function of T or composition.

A dilatometer can be used to measure ΔV_m. Two liquids in a cell can be mixed by withdrawing a partition, e.g., some mercury which kept them separate. Then ΔV_m can be read directly by the change of height of mercury in a capillary connected with the mixing chamber [5]. This difference in height gives rise to a small uncertainty in ΔV_m due to a difference in pressure before and after mixing. A precision in ΔV_m of ±0.5% can be obtained by such a simple apparatus, when the volume change is of the order of 0.5 cm^3 mol^{-1}. A more sophisticated apparatus is described in Ref. 6.

The control of temperature is of vital importance in these and other experimental techniques. A temperature can be held constant to within ±0.001 K in most cases. Platinum resistance thermometers or thermocouples are often used for temperature measurements. In such cases, a cell with water at its triple point is often used as a reference. With such devices, temperature differences of ±0.0002 K can be measured quite easily. Beckman thermometers are also used to measure such temperature differences.

(b) Calorimetry

Measurement and control of temperature are even more essential when calorimetric measurements are undertaken. In such measurements, e.g., for ΔH_m, the experiments can be performed two basic ways. When the system is isolated from the surroundings, then a process where $\Delta H_m \neq 0$ will cause a change in temperature (the adiabatic case). If this change in temperature is counteracted by simultaneous supply (or withdrawal) of heat, then isothermal conditions prevail.

An example of an adiabatic calorimeter is given in Ref. 7, while an isothermal one is described in Ref. 8. Both of these are designed in particular for measuring ΔH_m for liquid mixtures. Reference 9 describes a system designed to measure heats of solution, ΔH_{sol}.

The heat quantities are in all cases measured by comparison with heat produced by a measured amount of electrical energy. This measurement itself contains little or no error. Major sources of error come from (i) heat exchange with surroundings; (ii) heat effects caused by stirring or other mechanical motion designed to ensure mixing or solution; (iii) incomplete mixing; (iv) evaporation or condensation processes; (v) impurities in the reagents; (vi) heats in breaking foils, bulbs, etc. to initiate the process. The importance of the effect varies with system and apparatus, and is not necessarily in the order listed.

The accuracy estimated for the measurements is typically of the order of 1% [10]. In Ref. 7, for example, the estimated error in the measurements is less than 0.5% when ΔH_m is greatest ($\simeq$113 J mol^{-1}).

There are discrepancies between these measurements and those of other authors by 1 to 2 J mol^{-1}. In Ref. 9, ΔH^{θ}_{sol} is reproducible to or within 0.2%, but differs by nearly 1% from other values.

Many variations of calorimeters have been developed. A microcalorimeter for samples <1g has been developed capable of a precision of 0.01% for measuring heat capacities [11]. Heat capacity and other ΔH measurements can also be made with a differential flow microcalorimeter [12]. The difference in C_p of a solution over the solvent, ΔC_p, can be accurately measured down to 10^{-6} J K^{-1} cm^{-3}.

(c) Measurement of Chemical Potential through Pressure

There are numerous methods of measuring the activities of components in liquids, and thus chemical potentials and free energy [Sec. 1(c)]. A common method is through the measurement of the partial pressures of the components present.

As can be seen from Fig. 4.4, the composition of the vapor is usually not the same as the composition of the liquid with which it is in equilibrium. Thus to obtain ΔG_m for a two-component system, the vapor composition as well as the total pressure is needed. It is, however, possible to obtain ΔG_m without direct measurement of the vapor composition by making use of the Gibbs-Duhem differential equation [10]. Usually a numerical method is used with recycling of data until self-consistency is obtained [13,14]. When one of the components is nonvolatile (i.e., has a negligible vapor pressure) then determination of vapor composition is not needed.

A number of such vapor pressure apparatuses are discussed in Ref. 14. As these are designed specifically for electrolyte solutions, only the total pressure is measured as the solutes are nonvolatile. Pressure measurements are often made using a differential manometer [13], although "dead weight" [15] or spiral quartz [16] gauges are also used. For differential measurements, one of the pure components is often used as a reference. The experimental precision in pressure measurements (~0.03 torr) is <1% [13], but uncertainties in ΔG_m obtained are of the order of 1%. When the composition of the vapor is measured, then density, refractive index or radioactivity can be used.

The determination of boiling and condensation temperatures is also used to get activities. Such measurements are usually referred to as "ebulliometry." The theory underlying such measurements is intimately related to pressure measurements. A detailed discussion of ebulliometry is given in [17].

(d) Other Methods of Measurement

There are various other methods of obtaining activities as discussed in Sec. 1(c). Freezing points are usually determined from cooling curves, with apparatuses that can become quite sophisticated, e.g., Ref. 18. T_f is obtained from changes in the cooling rate with temperature. In other cases optical criteria are used to observe temperatures of phase change, in particular when miscibility and critical phenomena are investigated [19]. Often freezing points, etc. are measured simply to obtain phase diagrams for the systems, and not primarily to determine activity.

When activity is measured from ΔT_f, then the temperature is predetermined, as T_f cannot be changed to any significant amount through pressure change. Thus ΔT_B measurements are in principle more useful, as T_B is quite sensitive to the pressure of the system, which can be varied. However, ΔT_B is usually smaller than the corresponding ΔT_f, and is more difficult to measure.

Solubility measurements can also be used to determine activities. The theoretical background for this is essentially the same as for ΔT_f, but the procedure is somewhat different.

The determination of activity from osmotic pressure measurements is also possible [Eq. (8.8)]. In principle such measurements should give precise results, as π can be considerable for even quite dilute solutions (e.g., 27 atm for a 1 m solution of sucrose at 25°C). A semipermeable membrane is necessary to make such measurements. The construction of such a membrane useful for a variety of solutes is difficult. Thus measurements are not extensive for solutions where the solute is not a rather large molecule.

In electrolyte solutions, cell potentials are widely used to determine activity. The experimental technique and associated problems are extensively discussed in most electrochemistry books, e.g., Refs. in Chap. 5.

Compressibility can be calculated from volume data. However, κ_S can also easily be obtained from measurement of the speed of ultrasound. The theoretical and experimental basis for this is described in Sec. 10.1(a) (see also Ref. 20). There is a dispersion present in many liquids (i.e., an increase in speed with frequency of ultrasound.) This is usually due to the relaxation of translational-vibrational equilibria [Sec. 10.1(c)]. The static κ_S is obtained at lower frequencies, below this relaxation frequency.

Surface effects are outside the scope of this book, but surface tension data is at times used in conjunction with other thermodynamic data. One method of measurement is to observe the difference in height of the liquid in two capillary tubes with different bores [21].

8.3. RESULTS FOR SPECIFIC SYSTEMS

(a) Properties of Argon and Benzene

Some thermodynamic properties of argon and benzene will be outlined here. The former is commonly chosen to test fundamental aspects of liquid theories, as it can be reasonably realistically described by simple models. The latter is an example of a complex nonpolar species. Water will be discussed by itself in the next part. These three liquids belong in classes 1, 3, and 5 of Rowlinson's classification [10]. Detailed data on thermodynamic properties of pure liquids is available in Refs. 10 and 22.

A common test of liquid theories is to compare the value of p, V, and T at the critical point, in particular the value of p_cV_c/nRT_c [Sec. 2.2(e)]. This should be the same for all liquids which obey the law of corresponding states [Sec. 18.4(c)]. For Ar, the value is 0.291, while for most organic molecules it is 0.27 to 0.28. Molecules with even larger noncentral forces have yet lower values. This is to be expected, as the form of the intermolecular pair potential $\nu(r)$ is for such molecules considerably different from that of Ar.

From the variation of V with (p, T), i.e., from the equation of state, it is possible to obtain values for the compressibility κ_T and the thermal expansion α. For Ar, $\kappa_T \simeq 2.0 \times 10^{-4}$ bar^{-1} and $\alpha \simeq 44 \times 10^{-4}$ K^{-1}, while for benzene, $\kappa_T \simeq 1.0 \times 10^{-4}$ bar^{-1} and $\alpha \simeq 12 \times 10^{-4}$ K^{-1}. Both α and κ increase with temperature for most liquids. Such results are often expressed in terms of the thermal pressure coefficient, $\beta_V = (\partial p/\partial T)_V = \alpha/\kappa_T$. When given as measured along the saturation curve, it is denoted by β_σ.

The vapor pressure of a pure liquid can experimentally be reasonably well represented by the Clausius-Clapeyron equation (2.1),

$$\ln p = A - \frac{B}{T} \tag{8.12}$$

where B is related to ΔH_{vap}. The accuracy of (2.1) can be illustrated by comparing for benzene the value of ΔH_{vap} from (8.12) (31, 960 J mol^{-1}) and the directly measured value (30, 780 J mol^{-1}). The difference seems to be due almost entirely to nonidealities in the vapor.

The entropy of vaporization ΔS_{vap} (= $\Delta H_{vap}/T_B$) for Ar is 9.0 n$\mathcal{R}$ and for benzene 10.5n$\mathcal{R}$. Such values fall reasonably close to the Trouton's rule value ($\simeq$ 11n$\mathcal{R}$). The larger value of ΔS_{vap} for benzene can be interpreted as being due to a greater degree of order for benzene in the liquid. Such an interpretation assumes that both substances are equally disordered in the vapor state. ΔS_{vap} and ΔH_{vap} are of course positive for all substances.

ΔH_f and ΔS_f are also >0 for all substances, and $\Delta V_f > 0$ for nearly all [Sec. 8.1(b)]. There is no rule for ΔS_f as there is for ΔS_{vap}. However, argon and the other "inert gases" all have a ΔS_f of 1.7n$\mathcal{R}$. Agreement in such comparisons is invariably better if carried out at a given reduced T* or p*, rather than at a given T or p.

The configurational heat capacity $C_{p,con}$ for Ar (i.e., that due to change in liquid structure) is of the order of 20 J K^{-1} mol^{-1} at 80 K, and increases monotonely with temperature until it $\to \infty$ at the critical point (T_c = 424 K). Benzene has at 293 K a $C_{p,con} \simeq 58$ J K^{-1} mol^{-1}, which decreases slowly with T at first. This is generally the case for more complex liquids, i.e., a greater $C_{p,con}$ and a minimum in $C_{p,con}$ vs T.

(b) Pure Water

Water is discussed in a section by itself, as it is an anomalous liquid from the point of view of thermodynamic properties. References 23 and 24 discuss these in detail and give further references.

The coefficients α and κ are both anomalous. α is negative until 4°C, and then becomes positive with a value $2.0 \times 10^{-4}\ K^{-1}$ at 20°C. κ_T decreases with temperature until 46°C, and then increases. Its value is of the order of 0.5×10^{-4} bar^{-1}. In addition, ΔV_f is <0 for water, as in the process ice → water at p = 1 atm, the volume decreases by 8.3%. The subsequent decrease in volume from 0 to 4°C is rather small, only of the order of 0.013%. These anomalous properties are of vital importance in natural processes.

There has been considerable discussion regarding other forms of liquid water ("superwater," "polywater," etc.) [25] but there seems now to be no acceptable evidence of its existance as a form of pure water [26]. The existance of "kinks" or abrupt changes in slope in the temperature dependence of the volume properties has been suggested, e.g., Ref. 27, but their sizes seem comparable to the precision of the measurements involved [28].

The ΔH_{vap} for water is anomalously high as compared to similar substances, e.g., H_2S, H_2Se. ΔS_{vap} is 13nR, but the high value of T_B makes ΔH_{vap} for water about twice that the H_2S. This can be considered as being due to the breaking of H bonds remaining in liquid water at T_B. The fraction of H bonds remaining can be estimated from the value of ΔH_f and $C_{p,con}$.

If a value 10.4 kJ mol^{-1} is assumed for the strength of an H bond, then about 52% of the H-bonds remain intact in liquid water at 0°C. An increase of the value of the H bond energy would increase this percentage, e.g., with 19 kJ mol^{-1} it would be about 90% [Sec. 1.3(b)]. At the boiling point the fraction of "unbroken H bonds" may still be considerable (up to 80% according to some authors), although others estimate it to → 0. Such discrepancies may in part be due to the interpretation of the vague term "unbroken H bonds."

The configurational $C_{p,con}$ for water is about 42 J mol^{-1} K^{-1}, i.e., over half the total C_p of 75 J mol^{-1} K^{-1}. In ice, C_V ($\simeq C_p$) $\simeq$ 36 and in steam, $C_V \simeq$ 27 J mol^{-1} K^{-1}. ($C_p \simeq C_V + nR \simeq$ 35 J mol^{-1} K^{-1} for steam).

The value of C_V for steam is to a large degree accounted for by the 6 $nR/2 = 3nR$ arising from translational and rotational modes. Intramolecular vibrations contribute a little. In ice, the motion can be assumed to be 3N intramolecular vibrations (hindered translations) and 3N librations (hindered rotations). If the Debye theory (Sec. 18.2) is used to calculate C_V on this model, then a value of 36 J mol^{-1} K^{-1} is obtained for ice in agreement with experiment.

The volume properties and thermal properties of liquid water can be explained on the basis of both the two state (H bond breaking) models and the H bond distortion model (Sec. 2.4). The high $C_{p,con}$ is due to breaking of H bonds with increase in T according to the former models. According to the latter, it is due to the increased distortion of the H bond with an increase in T.

The volume properties can be explained according to the former theories by an initial decrease in V_1 due to interstitial monomers fitting into the lattice structure. As T is increased, this effect is more than balanced out due to increased vibrational amplitudes due to increased T (increased "thermal expansion"). The distorted H bond model explains the decrease in V_1 as due to a collapse of the H bond structure, bringing nearest neighbors closer. No definitive proof for the correctness of one or the other model can be given.

(c) Mixtures of Simple Liquids

Experimental thermodynamic data and their relationship to models of molecular level structures will be discussed for two systems: in krypton-xenon and in aniline-toluene.

The first system is discussed to indicate how well the models discussed in Chap. 4 fit the experimental data when ab initio calculations (from pair potentials) are performed. The second system is discussed to indicate that useful information can be obtained for more complex systems even if the models described in Chap. 4 cannot be used in practice.

ΔV_m and ΔG_m^e have been calculated for the system krypton-xenon from density and total vapor pressure measurements [16]. For an equimolar mixture $\Delta G_m^e = 114.5 \pm 1.3$ J mol^{-1} and $\Delta V_m = -0.695 \pm 0.017$ cm^3 mol^{-1}. The ΔV_m vs X curve is asymmetrical, with the minimum at about mole fraction krypton $\simeq .45$.

Values of ΔV_m and ΔG_m^e for an equimolar mixture have been calculated for the system using a number of the theories outlined in Chap. 4. A Lennard-Jones potential is assumed, with the parameters for Kr-Xe interaction estimated from the Berthelot rules [Sec. 1.1(e)]. Values of σ and ε for Kr and Xe can be obtained from various sources (e.g., gas viscosities). The closest calculated ΔG_m^e value is 44 J mol^{-1} under such conditions (as compared to the experimental 114 J mol^{-1}). Values of ΔV_m can be obtained close to the experimental value. Monte-Carlo calculations using 6-12 potentials give $\Delta G_m^e \simeq 20$ J mol^{-1} and $\Delta V_m \simeq -0.40$ cm^3 mol^{-1} for this system. Thus agreement is quite poor.

The experimental ΔG_m^e values can be obtained from the calculations if the Berthelot rule is modified to have

$$\varepsilon_{ab} = (1 - k_{ab})(\varepsilon_{aa}\varepsilon_{bb})^{1/2} \tag{8.13}$$

With values of k_{ab} less than 0.1, several of the theories tested give the experimental ΔG_m^e. However, in most cases the ΔV_m value calculated deviates more from the experimental when $k_{ab} \neq 0$. An independent quantitative determination of k_{ab} should be possible for such systems as molecular beam experiments develop, and sufficiently precise values of ε_{ab} can be obtained [29]. There are also errors involved in the use of the 6-12 form for $v(r)$ and neglect of triple, etc. interactions [Sec. 1.1(g)].

(d) H-Bonding in Aniline-Toluene Mixtures

Experimental values of ΔH_m and ΔG_m^e have been obtained for the system aniline-toluene at several temperatures [30,31]. With ΔH_m available at several temperatures, the heat capacity of mixing $\Delta C_{p,m}$ is also available. Thermodynamic data for many liquid mixtures can be obtained from Refs. 32 and 22.

By some adjustment of the intermolecular potential parameters [Eq. (4.29)], it is possible to fit "the average potential model" theory to the experimental ΔH_m and ΔG_m^e data. This means again adjustment of the Berthelot rules. However, the calculated ΔV_m does not even agree in sign with the experimental. The AP model assuming dipole interactions does thus not fit the experimental data well.

The experimental data can also be explained on the basis of an association model (31). If a "Mecke-Kempter" model is assumed, with stepwise association of aniline with equal association constants, then the ΔG_m^e, ΔH_m and $\Delta C_{p,m}$ experimental data can all be fitted reasonably. The ΔH^θ for the association reaction, i.e., the energy of the N-H...N bond is used as an adjustable constant. The value for ΔH^θ obtained is -8500 ± 200 J mol^{-1}. Other association models (e.g., monomer-dimer-tetramer) do not give such good agreement with the experimental data available.

Evidence that the ΔH_m is due to H bond interactions can be obtained by comparison of the systems toluene-aniline, toluene-N-methylaniline and toluene-N,N-dimethylaniline.(Fig. 8.4). The dipole moment of the three anilines is about the same, but they differ with regard to the number of N-H bonds present. Mixtures of toluene-(ii) have a ΔH_m about twice that of toluene-(iii) (e.g., 1000 vs 500 J mol^{-1} at $X = 0.5$), while ΔH_m for toluene-(iv) mixtures is 90 J mol^{-1} [33].

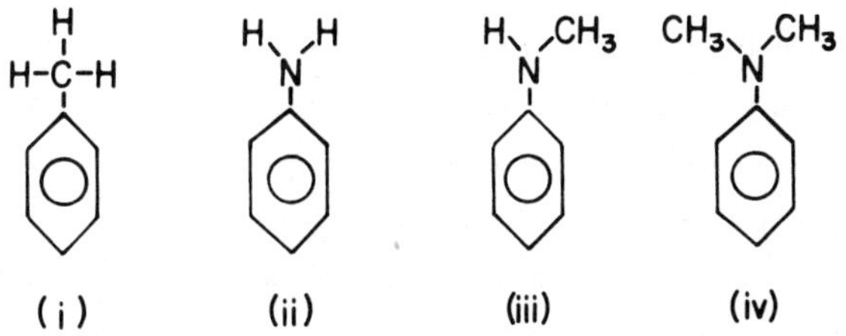

Fig. 8.4. Molecular structures of (i) toluene; (ii) aniline (p = 1.51D); (iii) N-methyl aniline (p = 1.64D); (iv) N,N-dimethyl-aniline (p = 1.58D).

Hydrogen-bonding by anilines in liquid mixtures has also recently been studied by means of "distribution coefficients" [34]. In this case the ratio of the concentration of aniline in two phases (an organic phase, e.g., cyclohexane, and an aqueous phase) at equilibrium is measured. The distribution coefficients extrapolated to zero concentration can then be related to various thermodynamic parameters. Anilines with N-H groups present are found to be favored (relative to other anilines) in the aqueous phase due to N-H•••O H bonding. However, Cl---H-O H bonding does not significantly aid in favoring the presence of cloroanilines in the aqueous phase.

(e) Volume Properties of Aqueous Mixtures with Alcohols

A number of interesting effects occur in water-nonelectrolyte solutions, especially at high mole fractions of water. Many of these phenomena can be illustrated by considering the volume properties of dilute aqueous solutions of alcohols. A discussion of water-alcohol systems is given in Ref. 35 and Sec. 4.3.

Some of the discussion of volume properties of dilute solutions is in terms of the "apparent molal volume" of the solute,

$$\phi_V = \frac{V - n_a V_a^\bullet}{n_b} = \frac{1000(\rho^\bullet - \rho)}{m\rho\rho^\bullet} - \frac{M_b}{\rho}; \quad V_b = \phi_V + m\left(\frac{\partial \phi_V}{\partial m}\right) \qquad (8.14)$$

Here a refers to water, b to the solute, and $^\bullet$ to pure water. m is the molality, n the number of moles, M the molecular weight, and ρ the density. Apparent molal expansibilities, etc. can also then be defined. The symbol V_b^∞ indicates the partial molal volume of the alcohol as $m \to 0$ (infinite dilution), and ΔV_b^∞ the volume of transfer of alcohol from pure alcohol to an infinitely dilute solution.

The temperature dependence of ΔV_b^∞ or of ϕ_V^∞ is at times used as a criterion for "structure promotion" of water by nonelectrolytes. ΔV_b^∞ is negative for the alcohols, presumably because on a transfer to water, the hydrocarbon parts of the alcohol molecule efficiently occupy the holes (or cages) in the structured (or icelike) forms present in liquid water.

A "structure promoter" favors the formation of structure in water at the expense of "unstructured" water. Since structured water has a lower thermal expansion, structure promoters would have abnormally low values of $d\phi_V/dT$ or $d(\Delta V_b^\infty)/dT$. ΔV_b^∞ vs T data for t-butanol ($(CH_3)_3$-COH) shows it to be a structure promoter at a temperature as high as 40°C, even though n-butanol acts as a reasonably normal solute at that temperature [36]. The large structure-promoting ability of t-butanol is also noted in [37] where $d\phi_V/dT$ is investigated for a number of aqueous nonelectrolyte systems.

A phenomenon related to the temperature dependence of the apparent molal expansibility $\phi_{exp} = d\phi_V/dT$ is the shift in the temperature of maximum density T_ρ. The "Depretz" rule states that the depression of T_ρ is directly proportional to the concentration of solute. This agrees reasonably well with experiments for many solutes [38]. The magnitude of ΔT_ρ should ideally be proportional to the molar volume of the solute, with structure-making or breaking also influencing ΔT_ρ. This latter effect does not seem to be predominant in electrolyte solutions [38], but in alcohol-water systems an increase in T_ρ can be obtained [35].

Figure 8.5 shows schematically the concentration dependence of the volume properties. It has been chosen to display $(V_b - V_b^\infty)$ vs X_b in order to set curves for 2 alcohols on the same figure. The experimental accuracy of such curves is discussed to some extent in Refs. 2 and 36, where experimental points for low X_b values ($X_b < 2 \times 10^{-3}$) are shown.

Such concentration curves should provide information regarding solute-solute interactions. Hence the limiting slope should $\rightarrow 0$. This is readily seen for the case of species with several hydroxyl groups such as sugars, but difficult for alcohols at lower temperatures.

Alcohol-alcohol interactions must "stabilize" water structure most in some intermediate concentration range (i.e., $X_b \simeq 0.02$ for t-butanol, $X_b \simeq 0.08$ for ethanol). Such stabilization, reflected in large negative V_b, is more pronounced at low temperatures. At higher concentrations, the alkyl parts of the alcohol have filled all the

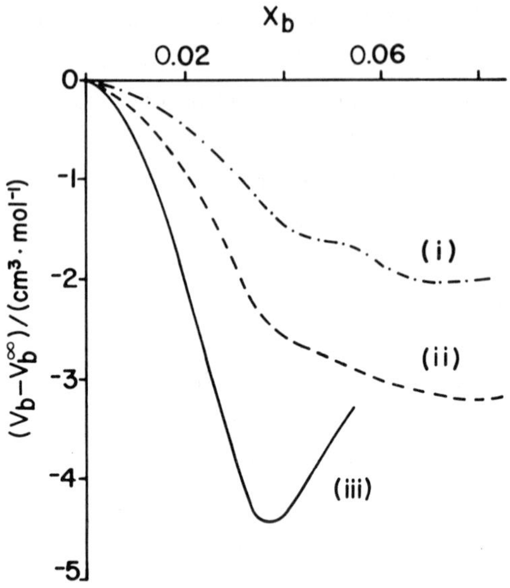

Fig. 8.5. The difference between partial molar volumes ($V_b - V_b^\infty$) vs alcohol mol fraction X_b in water for (i) Ethanol at 30°C; (ii) Ethanol at 10°C (V_b^∞ = 51.5 cm^3 mol^{-1}); (iii) t-butanol at 15°C (V_b^∞ = 86.5 cm^3 mol^{-1}). After Ref. 35.

available cavities in the water, and additional alcohol results in a breakdown of water structure. The nature of the structural stabilization is difficult to imagine, as a type of "autocatalysis" is indicated, i.e., a molecule of alcohol added to a solution $X_b \simeq 0.01$ produces more structure stabilization than one added at $X_b \simeq 0$.

An explanation for such a phenomenon could be that when alcohol is added to a solution already containing alcohol, there is a greater amount of structured water present due to the presence of the initial alcohol. Thus there are more "cavities" in the solution for the subsequent alcohol to fit into. A mutual stabilization of the structured form of water associated with the hydrocarbon parts of the alcohol can also be considered from the point of view of increased lifetimes of the structured (cage, clathrate) systems [2]. The alcohol-alcohol interactions must be of a very long-range, indirect type, as at $X_b \simeq 0.01$, the alcohol-alcohol distance is on the average ≃ 30 Å.

(f) Enthalpies of Hydration of Biologically Interesting Systems

The enthalpies of solution (usually hydration) of various organic molecules have often been studied as a function of the number of CH_2 groups present. Such molecules must contain at least one functional group such as, e.g., alcohol, amine, carboxylic acid etc., in order to be soluble in water to any extent

In most cases, e.g., Ref. 39, the experimental data (up to $c \simeq 0.05$ M in Ref. 39) is extrapolated to $c \to 0$ to obtain ΔH^{∞}_{sol}. Solvation enthalpies can then be calculated from $\Delta H^{\infty}_{solv} = \Delta H^{\infty}_{sol} - \Delta H_{vap}$ where ΔH_{vap} is the enthalpy of vaporization to form an ideal gas. Such calorimetric data can also be used to obtain $C^{\infty}_{p,b}$, the partial molar heat capacity of the solute b as $c_b \to 0$.

The solution enthalpy of a series of diethers R-CO-CH_2-CH_2-CO-R' plotted against the total number of carbon atoms n shows a minimum at $n = 4$. However both the solvation enthalpy and $C^{\infty}_{p,b}$ show a reasonably linear relationship (Fig. 8.6). In the case of $C^{\infty}_{p,b}$ the relationship has a slope of 92 ± 2 J K^{-1} mol^{-1} (C atom)$^{-1}$. The slope varies little with the basic functional group present, ranging from 84 ± 2 for carboxylic acids to 96 ± 4 for alcohols. Thus the "hydrophobic effect" [Sec. 3.1(d)] expressed by $C^{\infty}_{p,b}$ is strongly correlated to the total number of alkyl carbons, but is not very sensitive to the structure of the carbon chain or to the functional group present.

Studies at higher concentrations of aqueous solutions or organic compounds leads to consideration of "hydrophobic interactions" [40,41]. The term "hydrophobic" (more generally "solvophobic") interaction refers in these cases to the process of bringing two solute particles together from infinite separation in the solvent. The change in Gibbs free energy due to this process is then $\Delta G = \Delta G(HI) + \Delta U$. Here ΔU is the direct work of bringing the two solute molecules together. $\Delta G(HI)$ is the indirect part of the ΔG. In the case of two methane molecules, $\Delta G(HI) = \mu^{\theta}(\text{ethane}) - 2\mu^{\theta}(\text{methane})$ [41]. The $\Delta H(HI)$ and $\Delta S(HI)$ can be obtained from the $\Delta G(HI)$ as a function of temperature.

The $\Delta G(HI)$ for methane in water-ethanol mixtures is <0 and $\Delta S(HI)$ is >0 for the whole range water ethanol. $\Delta H(HI)$ is >0 for $X(\text{eth}) \leqslant 0.13$, but <0 for $X(\text{eth}) > 0.13$. The maximum effect occurs at $X(\text{eth}) \simeq$

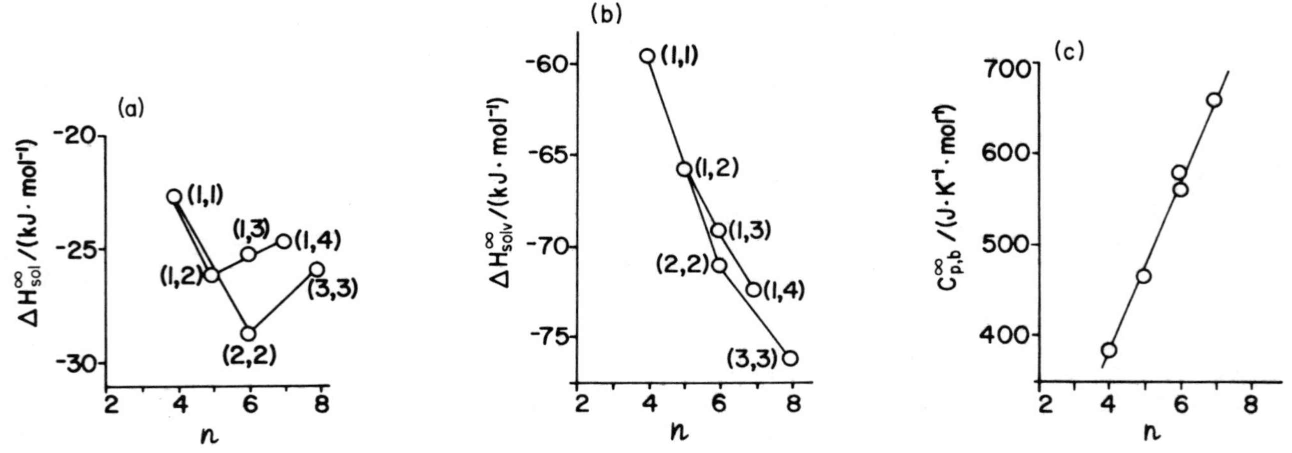

Fig. 8.6. (a) The limiting enthalpy of solution, H^{∞}_{sol}; (b) the limiting enthalpy of solvation, H^{∞}_{solv}; and (c) the limiting partial molar heat capacity $C^{\infty}_{p,b}$ of diethers $ROCCH_2CH_2OR'$ as a function of total number of carbon atoms, (1,2) indicates R = methyl, R' = ethyl; (1,3) methyl, propyl; (1,4) methyl, butyl, etc. After Ref. 39.

0.02 where $\Delta G(HI) \simeq -18$ kJ mol^{-1}, $\Delta S(HI) \simeq 55$ J K^{-1} mol^{-1}, $\Delta H(HI) \simeq$ 7 kJ mol^{-1}. A quantitative explanation of these effects is usually attempted through use of the Gurney cosphere-solvation concept [Sec. 5.2(f)].

(g) Critical Phenomena

At the critical point of a one-component system, and at the critical solution point of a two-component system, several thermodynamic properties $\to \infty$ or $\to 0$ [Secs. 3.4 and 4.1(b)]. The temperature range near T_c in which such anomalous behavior occurs can, however, be very small. In liquid mixtures it typically has ranges of $(T - T_c)/T_c \simeq$ 0.01, but in one-component systems it can have a range $(T - T_c)/T_c \simeq$ 0.0003. Thus there are experimental difficulties present in approaching and maintaining temperatures sufficiently close to T_c.

In one-component systems the p vs V isotherm (e.g., Fig. 2.3) is horizontal for $T = T_c$ at V_c. It also is horizontal in the two-phase region for $T < T_c$. Similarly, the curve of p_a vs X_a or μ_a vs X_a isotherm for a two component system (e.g., Fig. 4.4) should have a horizontal portion at $T = T_c$, $X_a = (X_a)_c$ and in the two phase region below (or above) T_c. Vapor pressure measurements for a binary liquid system have been carried out in the region of T_c [21]. The total vapor pressure vs composition is constant, as expected at temperatures in the two-phase region, and immediately above T_c in the one-phase region. More complete discussions of the thermodynamics of the critical region are available in Refs. 42 and 43.

Such vapor pressure data cannot be used to calculate any of the critical indices [Sec. 2.1(a) and Ref. 10]. The critical index β can, however, be calculated from the coexistence curve of liquid mixtures. A plot of the congruent concentration (i.e., that on the coexistence curve) vs $(T_c - T)^{1/3}$ gives for liquid mixtures a reasonably good linear relationship [10]; thus $\beta \simeq 0.33$. In one-component systems, β refers to the variation of $(V_c - V_1)$ (or $(V_g - V_c)$) vs $(T - T_c)$. The experimental data is best described by a value 0.35. A value of 0.35 is also found in the liquid mixture CH_4 plus CF_4, which has a critical solution point at 94.30 K at mole fraction CF_4 = 0.43 [44]. Thus, as anticipated, the critical indices seem to have the same value for both types of critical phenomena.

It has not been possible to calculate values of other critical constants for liquid mixtures. Heat capacity data is available [45, 46], and shows a large increase in C_p, e.g., 160 J mol^{-1} K^{-1} [45]. However, the index α referring to C_p has not been calculated for mixtures as yet. In one-component systems, α refers to variation of C_V and has a value of ~0.2.

The velocity of ultrasound should show a minimum at the critical point, as $\kappa_s \to \infty$, and as the speed is $\propto (\kappa_s)^{-1/2}$. Thus such measurements are used to examine the critical region [47]. Strong absorption and dispersion occur for ultrasound about a critical region, however, making a simple relationship between speed and thermodynamic properties impossible.

(h) Volume Effects in Aqueous Solutions of Electrolytes

The effect of alkyl(hydrocarbon) groups on water structure can also be observed in aqueous solutions of large organic ions (e.g., the tetraalkylammonium ions). Properties of such solutions are discussed in detail in Refs. 48 and 49. Their volume properties will be outlined here. Thermal properties of electrolyte solutions will be discussed in (i), i.e., for nonaqueous systems, as such discussions for aqueous systems are readily available (see Refs. in Chap. 5 and 50,51).

Figure 8.7 gives curves of ϕ_V vs $\sqrt{m}$ at 5°C for a number of electrolyte solutions: $MgSO_4$, KCl, Me_4NBr (tetramethylammonium bromide $(CH_3)_4NBr$), and Bu_4NBr ($(C_4H_9)_4NBr$). The precision in obtaining ϕ_V is estimated to be ± 0.1 cm^3 mol^{-1} [2]. As m → 0, calculation of ϕ_V involves subtraction of two large similar quantities (8.14). Thus even if ρ is known to 1 ppm, and m can be determined to ± 0.1%, the error in ϕ_V is considerable. The accuracy attainable in obtaining ϕ_V^∞ with recent apparatus is discussed in Ref. 52, where an accuracy of better than 0.01 cm^3 mol^{-1} is attained for ϕ_V^∞ of NaCl.

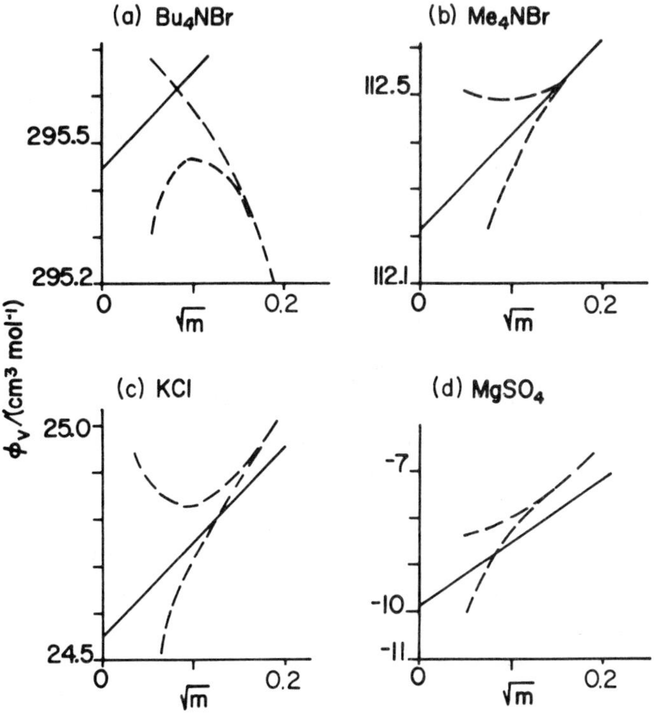

Fig. 8.7. Curves of apparent molar volume ϕ_V vs $\sqrt{m}$ for aqueous solutions of (a) Bu_4NBr, (b) Me_4NBr, (c) KCl, (d) $MgSO_4$. After Ref. 2.

The curves are shown drawn with a Debye-Hückel limiting law [Sec. 5.2(b)] slope dashed in. The volume changes are thought to be due to electrostriction of the solvent, and described according to the DH theory, allowing for a compressible solvent. With the same solvent, the limiting law slopes are proportional to ionic strength, i.e., the same for all the 1:1 electrolytes.

The limiting law is obeyed reasonably for KCl, but some positive deviations occur at higher concentrations. Positive deviations are expected when ionic hydration spheres begin to overlap. Electrostriction, i.e., ordering of the hydration molecules by ion-dipole interactions, makes the values of ϕ_V low.

In the case of small and highly charged ions, electrostriction effects are even greater, and the ϕ_V become negative, as for $MgSO_4$. Ion pairing occurs even at low concentrations in $MgSO_4$ solutions [Sec. 10.3(g)], and causes deviations from the limiting law. Such ion pair deviations are positive.

Me_4NBr obeys the limiting law quite reasonably, but higher alkylammonium halides show large negative deviations. In Me_4NBr, electrostrictive effects are of the same order of magnitude as water structuring effects due to the presence of nonpolar groups. In the higher alkylammonium ions, the latter effect predominates. The effect is thus the same as that for alcohol-water systems and shows the same type type of "cooperative stabilization" of water structure and a negative deviation in ϕ_V. Investigation of Me_4NBr has also been carried out in several different solvents [53].

There seems to be some difference in the behavior of alkyl organic ions and aryl organic ions, (e.g., tetraphenyl ions) as indicated by comparative studies of ϕ_V [54]. Aromatic groups do not seem to be as effective in filling voids in the network water.

When any alkyl groups present become very large, then micelle formation can occur. This results in a ϕ_V vs $\sqrt{m}$ curve as shown in Fig. 8.8 for sodium dodecyl sulfate [55]. The initial decrease in ϕ_V is for the same reasons as for Bu_4NBr, etc.

There are many topics in thermodynamics of aqueous electrolyte solutions which will not be discussed here. Some of these topics will be covered for the case of the less familiar nonaqueous solutions. Many of the phenomena are also well illustrated through transport properties, especially electric conduction, and will be discussed in Sec. 9.3.

(i) Enthalpy Effects in Nonaqueous Electrolyte Solutions

Several solvents can be used for electrolytes besides water. These are listed in Table 5.1. Other organic liquids can also be used, but if the dielectric constant ε is too low, then the solubility of nonorganic electrolytes becomes very small. Inorganic solvents such as H_2SO_4, HNO_3, and NH_3 are also used.

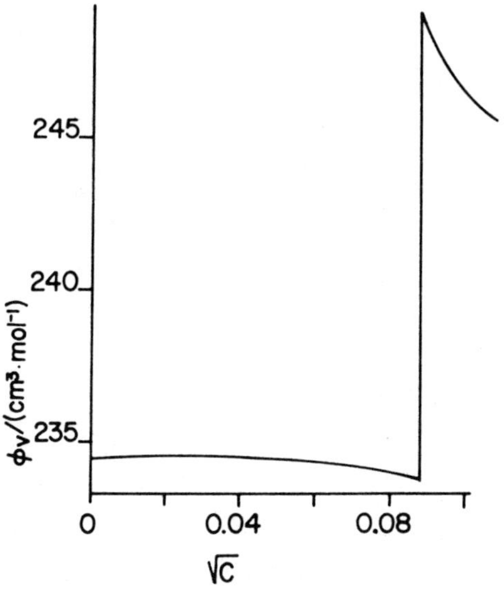

Fig. 8.8. Apparent molar volume ϕ_V vs c for sodium dodecyl sulfate illustrating micelle formation. After Ref. 55.

Nonaqueous and mixed solvents, besides their intrinsic interest are useful for checking the general validity of theories for electrolytes. When mixed solvents are used, alcohols of *p*-dioxane (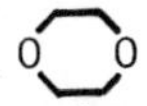) are often used together with water. A discussion of solubility data in the formamides illustrates some of the usefulness of nonaqueous solvent work. Mixed solvent systems will not be described as they are often used for the same purpose, i.e., to vary dielectric constants. An interesting example of the use of mixed solvents is described in Ref. 56, where the discussions in Secs. (e) and (h) above are combined and solutions of Bu_4NBr in water-t-butanol are investigated.

The heats of solution and dilution of a series of alkali earth chlorates and bromates (e.g., $Ca(ClO_3)_2$ in formamide (F), methylformamide (MF), and DMF) have been determined calorimetrically [57]. The precision of the calorimeter was determined as better than 1% through comparison to the heat of solution ΔH_{sol} of (KCl) in water.

However, the accuracy of the values of ΔH^{∞}_{sol} is of the order of ±3%. Difficulties in dissolution were present in several cases.

The Debye-Hückel limiting law predicts the heat of solution to be given by $\Delta H_{sol}(m) = \Delta H^{\infty}_{sol} + a\sqrt{m}$. The constant a can be calculated for 1:1 electrolytes in the solvents F, MF, and DMF. For F, the slope is so small that the variation in ΔH_{sol} cannot by detected. However, for MF, $a_{calc} = 4.1$ vs $a_{meas} = 4.4 \pm 1.2$ and for DMF, $a_{calc} = 10.4$ vs $a_{meas} = 10.1 \pm 2$. Thus the limiting law is obeyed surprisingly well in this range ($m < 0.05$).

If the crystal lattice energy of the salts is known, then the solvation energy $\Delta H^{\theta}_{i,solv}$ for the combined ions can be calculated from the heat of solution of the salt. This can then be compared to solvation model calculations, e.g., the Born theory (Sec. 5.2). Instead of expressing the results in terms of values of $\Delta H^{\theta}_{i,solv}$, enthalpies of transfer $\Delta H^{\theta}_{trans} = \Delta H^{\theta}_{i,solv}(\text{water}) - \Delta H^{\theta}_{i,solv}(\text{another solvent})$ can be calculated. This eliminates uncertainties caused by inaccurate knowledge of the lattice energies.

The agreement between the experimental and calculated values of $\Delta H^{\theta}_{trans}$ is poor. Solvation energies decrease with increasing size of cations, as expected, but those of anions increase. There is in addition no obvious correlation between the dielectric constant ε and $\Delta H^{\theta}_{i,solv}$ as expected according to the Born theory.

These results, and data on entropies of solvation of ions in nonaqueous solvents [58] suggest that the solvation energy (entropy) decreases (increases) with increased structure of the solvent. In [58], the "structure" of the solvent is quantitatively estimated through the deviation of the solvent boiling point from the value in an extrapolation of model compounds. Thus water has a value 174, F 162, MF 128, DMF 98, etc.

In a structured solvent, intermolecular (solvent) interactions compete more readily with ion-solvent interactions, and ion-solvent influences are not as great (i.e., solvation energy is smaller). The amount of disordering of the structure should increase with the amount of structure in the solvent before introduction of the ion. If this is the major effect determining the size of $\Delta S^{\theta}_{trans}$ then solvation entropy should increase with structure, as observed. Hence the Born model is quite inadequate to represent ion-solvent interactions in such cases, as it assumes the solvent to be a continuum.

REFERENCES

Most of the references listed refer to specific systems or to specific apparata. The best general reference for data on nonelectrolytes (both one- and two-component systems) is Ref. 10. Electrolyte systems are well covered in GR9, while water and aqueous systems are reviewed in Refs. 23, 24, and 48.

1. M. E. Friedman and H. A. Scheraga, J. Phys. Chem., *69*,3795 (1965).
2. F. Franks and H. T. Smith, Trans. Farad. Soc., *63*, 2586 (1967).
3. F. J. Millero, Rev. Sci. Instr., *38*, 1441 (1967).
4. P. Picker, E. Tremblay, and C. Jolicoeur, J. Sol. Chem., *3*, 377 (1974).
5. W. A. Duncan, J. P. Sheridan, and F. L. Swinton, Trans. Farad. Soc., *62*, 1090 (1966).
6. H. D. Pflug and G. C. Benson, Can. J. Chem., *46*, 287 (1968).
7. J. E. Bennett and G. C. Benson, Can. J. Chem., *43*, 1913 (1965).
8. A. E. Pope, H. D. Pflug, B. Dacre, and G. C. Benson, Can. J. Chem., *45*, 2665 (1967).
9. H. L. Friedman and Y-C. Wu, Rev. Sci. Inst., *36*, 1236 (1965).
10. GR3.
11. J. Suurkuusk and I. Wadsö, J. Chem. Thermodyn., *6*, 667 (1974).
12. P. Picker, P. A. Leduc, P. R. Phillips, and J. E. Desnoyers, J. Chem. Thermodyn., *3*, 631 (1971).
13. W. J. Gaw and F. L. Swinton, Trans. Farad. Soc., *64*, 637 (1968).
14. S. D. Christian, J. Chem. Phys., *64*, 764 (1960).
15. R. H. Davies, A. G. Duncan, G. Saville, and L. A. K. Stavely, Trans. Farad. Soc., *63*, 855 (1967).
16. J. C. D. Calado and L. A. K. Stavely, Trans. Farad. Soc., *67*, 289 (1971).
17. W. Swietoslawski, Ebulliometric Measurements, Reinhold, New York, 1945.
18. R. Battino and G. W. Allison, J. Phys. Chem., *70*, 3417 (1966).

19. E. H. W. Schmidt, in Critical Phenomena (M. S. Green and J. V. Sengers, eds.), NBS Misc. Pub., 273 (1960).

20. V. F. Nozdrev, Application of Ultrasound in Molecular Physics, Gordon and Breach, New York, 1963.

21. A. N. Campbell, E. M. Kartzmark, S. C. Anand, Y. Cheng, H. P. Dzikowski, and S. M. Skrynyk, Can. J. Chem., *46*, 2399 (1968).

22. J. Timmermans, Physico-Chemical Constants of Pure Organic Compounds, Elsevier, New York, 1950 - 1965.

23. GR5.

24. G. S. Kell, in GR7.

25. B. V. Derjaguin, Scientific American, *223*, 52 (1970).

26. B. V. Derjaguin, in Recent Advances in Adhesion (L. H. Lee, ed.), Gordon and Breach, New York, 1973.

27. G. Antonoff and R. J. Conan, Science, *109*, 255 (1949).

28. M. Falk and G. S. Kell, Science, *154*, 1013 (1966).

29. J. M. Parsons, T. P. Schafer, P. E. Siska, F. P. Tulley, Y. C. Wong, and Y. T. Lee, J. Chem. Phys., *53*, 3755 (1970).

30. D. D. Deshpandee and M. V. Pandya, Trans. Farad. Soc., *64*, 1456 (1968).

31. H. Kehiaian and K. S-Kehiaian, Trans. Farad. Soc., *62*, 838 (1968).

32. Selected Data on Mixtures, International Data Series, Thermodynamics Research Center, Texas A & M University.

33. K. S-Kehiaian and H. Kehiaian, Bull. L'Acad. Polon. Sci.(Chemie), *13*, 659 (1965).

34. A. Gomez, J. Mullens, and P. Huyskens, J. Phys. Chem., *76*, 4011 (1972).

35. F. Franks and D. I. G. Ives, Quart. Rev., *20*, 1 (1966).

36. F. Franks and H. T. Smith, Trans. Farad. Soc., *65*, 2962 (1969).

37. J. L. Neal and D. A. I. Goring, J. Phys. Chem., *74*, 658 (1970).

38. A. J. Darnell and J. Greyson, J. Phys. Chem., *72*, 3021 (1968).

39. K. Kusano, J. Suurkuusk, and I. Wadsö, J. Chem. Thermodyn., *5*, 757 (1973).

40. H. L. Friedman and C. V. Krishnan, J. Sol. Chem., *2*, 119 (1973).

41. M. Yaacobi and A. Ben-Naim, J. Sol. Chem., *2*, 425 (1973).

42. R. L. Scott, Ber. Bunsenges. Physik. Chem., *76*, 296 (1972).

43. G. A. Chapela and J. S. Rowlinson, J. C. S. Farad. I, *70*, 584 (1974).

44. M. Simon, A. A. Fannin, Jr., and C. M. Knobler, Ber. Bunseng. Phys. Chem., *76*, 321 (1972).

45. H. Schmidt, G. Jura, and J. H. Hildebrand, J. Phys. Chem., *63*, 297 (1959).

46. M. A. Anisimov, A. V. Voronel, and T. M. Ovodova., Sov. Phys. JETP, *34*, 583 (1972).

47. A. G. Chynoweth and W. G. Schneider, J. Chem. Phys., *20*, 1777 (1952).

48. F. J. Millero, in GR6.

49. P. S. Ramanathan, C. V, Krishnan, and H. L. Friedman, J. Sol. Chem., *1*, 237 (1972).

50. H. L. Friedman and C. V. Krishnan, in GR9.

51. H. L. Anderson and R. H. Wood, in GR9.

52. H. E. Wirth and F. K. Bangert, J. Phys. Chem., *76*, 3488, 3491 (1972).

53. C. de Visser and G. Somsen, J. C. S. Faraday I, *69*, 1440 (1973).

54. G. Jolicoeur, P. R. Philip, G. Perron, P. A. Leduc, and J. E. Desnoyers, Can. J. Chem., *50*, 3167 (1972).

55. F. Franks, M. J. Quickenden, J. R. Ravenhill, and H. T. Smith, J. Phys. Chem., *72*, 2668 (1968).

56. R. K. Mohanty, T. S. Sarma, S. Subramanian, and J. C. Ahluwalia, Trans. Farad. Soc., *67*, 305 (1971).

57. A. Finch, P. J. Gardner, and C. J. Steadman, J. Phys. Chem., *71*, 2996 (1967).

58. C. M. Criss, R. P. Held, and E. Luksha, J. Phys. Chem., *72*, 2970 (1968).

Further Recent References

J. A. Larkin, "Thermodynamic Properties of Aqueous Non-Electrolyte Mixtures I. Excess Enthalpy for Water + Ethanol at 298.15 to 383.15 K", J. Chem. Thermodyn., *7*, 137 (1975).

J. W. Lorimer, B. C. Smith, and G. H. Smith, "Total Vapor Pressures, Thermodynamic Excess Functions and Complex Formation in Binary Liquid Mixtures of Some Organic Solvents and Sulphur Dioxide", J. C. S. Faraday I, *71*, 2232 (1975).

S. Goldman, "The Calculation of Effective Pair Potentials in Solution from Activity Coefficient Data: Nitrobenzene in Benzene", Can. J. Chem., *53*, 2608 (1975).

A. Péneloux, R. Deyrieux and E. Neau, "Réduction des Données sur les Equilibres Liquide-Vapeur Binaires Isothermes. Critères de Précision et de Cohérence. Analyse de l'Information", J. Chim. Phys., *72*, 1107 (1975).

R. H. Stokes and M. Adamson, "Thermodynamics of Dilute Solutions of Ethanol (1) in *p*-Xylene (2) from Freezing-Point and Enthalpy of Dilution Measurements", J. C. S. Faraday I, *71*, 1707 (1975).

H. Klein and D. Woerman, "Specific Heat of Binary Liquid Mixtures Near the Critical Mixing Point", Ber. Bunseng. physik. Chem., *79*, 1180 (1975).

B. B. Benson and D. Krause, Jr., "Empirical Laws for Dilute Aqueous Solutions of Nonpolar Gases", J. Chem. Phys., *64*, 689 (1976).

F. Franks, M. Pedley, and D. S. Reid, "Solute Interactions in Dilute Aqueous Solutions. Part 1 - Microcalorimetric Study of the Hydrophobic Interaction", J. C. S. Faraday I, *72*, 359 (1976).

C. Jolicoeur and G. Lacroix, "Thermodynamic Properties of Aqueous Organic Solutes in Relation to their Structure. Part III. Apparent Molal Volumes and Heat Capacities of Low Molecular Weight Alcohols and Polyols", Can. J. Chem., *54*, 624 (1976).

G. L. Amidon, S. H. Yalkowsky, S. T. Anik, and S. C. Valvani, "Solubility of Nonelectrolytes in Polar Solvents V. Estimation of the Solubility of Aliphatic Monofunctional Compounds in Water Using a Molecular Surface Area Approach", J. Phys. Chem., *79*, 3442 (1975).

S. Terasawa, H. Itsuki, and S. Arakawa, "Contribution of Hydrogen Bonds to the Partial Molar Volumes of Nonionic Solutes in Water", J. Phys. Chem., *79*, 2345 (1975).

J-L. Fortier and J. E. Desnoyers, "Thermodynamic Properties of Alkali Halides. V. Temperature and Pressure Dependence of Excess Free Energies in Water", J. Sol. Chem., *5*, 297 (1976).

D. Feakins and C. T. Allan, "Studies in Ion Solvation in Non-Aqueous Solvents and their Aqueous Mixtures. Part 18", J. C. S. Faraday I, *72*, 314 (1976).

W. H. Leung and F. J. Millero, "The Enthalpy of Formation of Magnesium Sulfate Ion Pairs", J. Sol. Chem., *4*, 145 (1975).

D. Rosenzweig, J. Padova, and Y. Marcus, "Thermodynamics of Mixed Electrolyte Solutions. V. An Isopiestic Study of the Aqueous Systems Tetra-n-propylammonium Bromide - Sodium Bromide and Tetramethylammonium Bromide - Sodium Bromide at 25°C", J. Phys. Chem., *80*, 601 (1976).

Chapter 9

INTERPRETATION OF TRANSPORT COEFFICIENTS

Chapter 9 can be viewed as a continuation of Chapter 6. In Sec. 9.1 the discussion of the relationship of transport coefficients to models is continued from Secs. 6.2 and 6.3. The coefficients for electrical conductivity, diffusion, and viscosity are discussed separately with a view to developing the relationships used in practice for experimental determination and interpretation of them.

Section 9.2 describes methods of measuring such coefficients. Only "classical" phenomenological methods of measurement are included. It will be seen in later chapters that the coefficient of self-diffusion D* can be measured by other methods, e.g., nuclear magnetic resonance [Sec. 13.3(f)]. The discussion of the results for specific systems in Sec. 9.3 is from the point of view of only that information obtained through such "classical" measurements.

Again the examples in Sec. 9.3 are chosen to illustrate the range of phenomena which can be elucidated through measurement of transport coefficients

9.1. THEORETICAL BACKGROUND

(a) Variation of Conductance with Concentration

In Chap. 4.3 the relaxation and electrophoretic effects were introduced, and expressions derived for them [(6.74) and (6.75)]. These relationships were derived on the basis of a simplified analysis of a primitive model. More sophisticated considerations show them to be only first-order approximations. Derivation of more accurate forms is, however, quite complicated and beyond the scope of this book.

When only these two effects are considered, then the conductivity can be expressed as

$$\Lambda = (\Lambda^{\infty} - \delta\Lambda)\left(1 + \frac{\delta F}{F}\right) \tag{9.1}$$

Here $\delta\Lambda$ expresses the electrophoretic effect and $\delta F/F$ the relaxation effect. A limiting law for concentration $c \to 0$ named after Onsager can from (9.1), (6.76) and (5.8) be shown to be of the form

$$\Lambda = \Lambda^{\infty} - A\sqrt{c} \tag{9.2}$$

Here A is a constant with respect to concentration, but dependent on η, ε, T, and the limiting conductances Λ_{+}^{∞} and Λ_{-}^{∞}.

Although the relaxation and electrophoretic effects are predominant, other effects are nonnegligible in some cases. There may not be complete dissociation so that ion-pairing may have to be taken into account (5.16). The viscosity of the medium can be changed noticeably by the presence of ions [Sec. 9.1(c)], expecially in the case of large ionic species. Another effect usually included with the relaxation effect is the production of a virtual osmotic force $\delta\pi$ which increases Λ. Thus the form of Λ then becomes [1]

$$\Lambda = \alpha(\Lambda^{\infty} - \delta\Lambda)\,\frac{1 + \frac{\delta F}{F} + \frac{\delta\pi}{F}}{1 + \mathfrak{f}c} \qquad (9.3)$$

Here α is the degree of dissociation, and $(1 + \mathfrak{f}c)$ a factor arising from the increase in viscosity (9.16). α, $\delta\Lambda$, δF, and $\delta\pi$ are all functions of the concentration c. A symmetrical electrolyte ($|z_+| = |z_-|$) is assumed here.

The concentration dependence of the quantities in (9.3) have been calculated for the case of a symmetrical electrolyte. A primitive model is assumed (i.e., charged spheres of radius a in a continuous medium). A more precise form of $\delta\Lambda$ is obtained by solving the Navier-Stokes equation (6.3) for the velocity field created in a solution with ions in motion. The analysis of δF is quite complex, and even when linearization is used to simplify the analysis, terms in $c^{1/2}$, c log c and c appear. $\delta\pi$ can be estimated by integrating the virtual force field about the ion. The viscosity effect can be corrected for experimentally, or by estimating $\mathfrak{f}c = \frac{5}{2}$ times the volume fraction of the solvent [Sec. 9.1(c)]. α can be expressed through an association equilibrium constant K_a. This is the inverse of the ion-pair dissociation constants in (5.16) and (5.17).

For practical purposes the equation used is

$$\begin{aligned}\Lambda_\eta &= \Lambda(1 + \mathfrak{f}c) \\ &= \Lambda^{\infty} - S(c\alpha)^{1/2} + E(c\alpha)\log(c\alpha) - J(c\alpha) - K_a(c\alpha)y_{\pm}^2\Lambda_\eta \qquad (9.4)\end{aligned}$$

The form is appropriate for c < 0.01 M, due to the linearization estimates made. Equation (9.4) expresses Λ_η in terms of three parameters, Λ^{∞}, a, and K_a. The molar activity coefficient $y_{\pm}$ and the degree of dissociation α are usually related through (5.16) and (5.10). The exact forms of S, E, J will not be given here for the sake of brevity. They are available in Refs. 1 and 2 and other more recent electrochemistry texts.

When association is believed negligible (i.e., $K_a \simeq 0$), then in the analysis of results, a preliminary value of Λ^∞ is usually estimated through extrapolation. When Λ^∞ is known, S and E can be calculated. For example, at 25°C for 1:1 electrolytes, for the commonly used units of Λ ($cm^2\ equiv^{-1}\ ohm^{-1}$)

$$S = \frac{159.35\Lambda^\infty}{\varepsilon^{3/2}} + \frac{4.7779}{\eta\varepsilon^{1/2}} \qquad E = \frac{2.559 \times 10^5\Lambda^\infty}{\varepsilon^3} - \frac{1122.3}{\eta\varepsilon^3} \tag{9.5}$$

Next the expression

$$\Lambda'_\eta = \Lambda_\eta + Sc^{1/2} - Ec \log c = \Lambda^\infty - Jc \tag{9.6}$$

is plotted vs c. From this plot, values of Λ^∞ and J can be obtained from the intercept and slope. If the value of Λ^∞ differs much from the initial estimate, then the procedure can be repeated until self-consistency is obtained. The value of the ion size parameter a can be read off a curve of J vs a, since J is a complicated function of a.

For an aqueous 1:1 solution at 25°C when a = 5 Å, the J term contributes typically about 1.5% of the value of Λ_η at 0.01 M. In such a case, K_a is of the order of 0.3, so that an association term would contribute 0.3% to Λ_η. When the K_a term cannot be neglected, then analysis becomes more complex (e.g., Ref. 3). A separation of the J and K_a terms is difficult at $c \to 0$ as $y_\pm^2$ does not differ much from unity.

To increase the range of the Fuoss-Onsager equation (9.4), a term in $c^{3/2}$ has been introduced [3]. It has also been extended to the case of asymmetric electrolytes [4]. Other equations have also been suggested for analysis of conductivity data [5]. However, (9.4) is probably the most commonly used form. These equations are discussed in detail and compared in Ref. 6.

(b) Diffusion in Two-Component Systems

(1) Self-Diffusion

In Sec. 6.2 the discussion regarding diffusion assumed that the coefficients were those of "self-" or "tracer-" diffusion. The term tracer arises from the measurement of such values by radioactive tracers [Sec. 9.2(b)]. In a one-component liquid, the self-diffusion coefficient will be denoted by D*; and in a two-component by D^*_a and D^*_b. The symbol $D^{*\infty}_b$ denotes D^*_b as $c_b \to 0$ (or $X_b \to 0$ if mole fractions are used).

D^*_b is a function of the concentration in nonideal cases. If the effect of viscosity on mobility is neglected, then the dependence can be seen from Sec. 6.3(e) to be

$$D^*_b = D^{*\infty}_b \frac{\partial \ln a_b}{\partial \ln X_b} = D^{*\infty}_b \frac{1 + d \ln y_b}{d \ln c_b} \tag{9.7}$$

Two forms are shown in (9.7) to indicate that various composition scales can be chosen. Stokes law (6.12) indicates that the mobility u is proportional to $1/\eta$. Assuming this relationship to hold, then (9.7) can be expressed taking account of changes in η as

$$D^*_b = D^{*\infty}_b \frac{\eta}{\eta^\bullet_a} \frac{1 + d \ln y_b}{d \ln c_b} \tag{9.8}$$

Here $\eta^\bullet_a$ is the viscosity of pure component A.

(2) Electrolyte Solutions

In electrolyte solutions, there is, as indicated in Eq. (6.66) a close relation between the limiting equivalent conductivities Λ^∞_+, Λ^∞_- and the diffusion coefficients D^*_+, D^*_-. At $c \to 0$, the relationship is simply

$$D^{*\infty}_i = \frac{RT\Lambda^\infty_i}{|z_i|F^2} = \frac{2.661 \times 10^{-7}\Lambda^\infty_i}{|z_i|} \tag{9.9}$$

There is a relaxation effect present for ionic self-diffusion, but it is of a different form from (6.74). Investigation of D_i^* for electrolytes is not developed well enough to indicate whether the forms suggested are valid [7].

In electrolyte solutions, electrical neutrality requires that both positive and negative ions move at the same speed. Hence a diffusion coefficient D_b exists for the electrolyte as a whole. The velocity of an ion, u_i, in the x direction is obtained by extending (6.57):

$$u_i = \mathcal{u}_i\left(-\frac{1}{L}\frac{\partial\mu_i}{\partial x} + z_i e E\right) \qquad (9.10)$$

This velocity must be the same for both positive and negative species. Eliminating E from the expression $u_+ = u_-$ and applying the relationship $\nu_+ z_+ + \nu_- z_- = 0$ results in

$$j = c_b u = -\frac{c_b}{L}\cdot\frac{\mathcal{u}_+\mathcal{u}_-}{\nu_+\mathcal{u}_- + \nu_-\mathcal{u}_+}\cdot\frac{\partial\mu_b}{\partial x}\cdot\frac{\partial c_b}{\partial x} \qquad (9.11)$$

Here μ_b is the chemical potential of the solute, i.e., $\mu_b = \mu_+ + \mu_-$. D_b can then be obtained by comparing (9.11) to Fick's law (6.20):

$$D_b = \frac{(\nu_+ + \nu_-)\Lambda_+^\infty\Lambda_-^\infty RT}{\nu_+ z_+(\Lambda_+^\infty + \Lambda_-^\infty)F^2}\cdot\left(1 + \frac{d\ \ln\ y_\pm}{d\ \ln\ c_b}\right)$$

$$= D_b^\infty\left(1 + \frac{d\ \ln\ y_\pm}{d\ \ln\ c_b}\right) \qquad (9.12)$$

Equation (9.12) is known as the Nernst-Hartley expression.

Most of the variation in D_b with c_b is due to the activity expression. A relaxation effect is not present for diffusion of the total electrolyte, but a small electrophoretic effect exists. This is different than that for electric conductivity, since here the positive and negative ions are moving in the same direction, while in conductivity they are moving in opposite directions. Corrections in D_b due to these effects are only of the order of 1/10 the magnitude of the corresponding corrections for electrical conductivity.

(3) Mutual Diffusion

Expression (9.12) neglects changes in viscosity, but it also neglects the counterdiffusion of solvent necessary to prevent volume discrepancies in the system. When in a two-component system B is diffusing to the right, then there must be some flow of material to the left in order to keep the volume from building up on the right of the system. Thus the net effect can be described as "pure diffusion" of B combined with a "bulk flow" in the opposing direction. In such cases it is sufficient to describe concentration changes of either components through diffusion by a single diffusion coefficient D_{ab}. This is referred to as the "mutual" or "inter"-diffusion coefficient.

When V_a and V_b are assumed independent of composition, then an expression for D_{ab} can be readily derived [7,8]. With the use of the Gibbs-Duhem relation (17.14),

$$D_{ab} = (D_b^* \ln X_a + D_a^* \ln X_b)\left(1 + \frac{\partial \ln f_b}{\partial \ln X_b}\right) \tag{9.13}$$

Equation (9.13) is known as the Hartley-Crank law. It can be expressed in various other forms. A common one is

$$D_{ab} = (X_b D_a^{*\infty} + X_a D_b^{*\infty}) \frac{\eta_b^{\bullet}}{\eta} \frac{d \ln X_a f_a}{d \ln X_a} \tag{9.14}$$

In (9.14) the inverse relation between u and η has been assumed. The Hartley-Crank law takes on even more complex forms if correction terms are set in for electrolyte solutions.

(c) Viscosity in Multicomponent Systems

In analysis of experimental viscosity data, it is at times useful to consider the "relative" viscosity of a solute, $\eta_r = \eta/\eta_a^{\bullet}$. At other times the "specific" viscosity, $\eta_b^* = (\eta_r - 1)/c_b$, is considered, or the "intrinsic" viscosity $[\eta]_b$,

$$[\eta]_b = \lim_{c_b \to 0} \eta_b^* = \lim_{c_b \to 0} \frac{\eta - \eta_a^{\bullet}}{\eta_a^{\bullet} c_b} \tag{9.15}$$

Yet other authors use the "excess" viscosity, $\eta^e = \eta - \eta_a^{\bullet} X_a - \eta_b^{\bullet} X_b$.

In electrolyte solutions, η_r can be shown to have a form (the Jones-Dole equation) [8]

$$\eta_r = 1 + A\sqrt{c} + Bc \tag{9.16}$$

The $\sqrt{c}$ term appears when electrostatic contributions to the stress dyadic are considered [9]. The linear term is interpreted as being due to a variety of effects.

The coefficient A arises essentially from a relaxation effect. When a stationary velocity gradient du_x/dy is present in an electrolyte solution, then there will be a stationary deformation $\tau \cdot du_x/dy$ present in the ionic atmosphere due to the relaxation effect. The coefficient η expresses the stress transferred (force exerted) per unit velocity gradient per unit area. The total transfer of force between an ion and its atmosphere at a distance $1/\kappa$ due to the deformation is [see, e.g., (6.74)]

$$\frac{e^2 z_i^2 \kappa^2}{4\pi\varepsilon^\bullet\varepsilon} \; \frac{(du_x/dy)\tau}{1/\kappa} \tag{9.17}$$

When the expression for τ is substituted into (9.17), then the contribution to η from this effect can be seen to be proportional to κ, i.e., to $\sqrt{c}$ [see Eqs. (6.72) and (5.8)]. Detailed accounts of this derivation can be found in Refs. 8 and 9.

The B coefficient can be considered to be a sum of three separate contributions: η^E, the increment due to the size and shape of ions; η^A, an increase in η due to the ordering of the solvent molecules in the vicinity of the ion; and η^D, a decrease due to the disruptive presence of the ions. The latter two terms are manifestations of the structure-making, structure breaking phenomenon discussed previously (Sec. 5.1), and cannot be treated rigorously yet.

The effect of ionic volumes (named η^E after Einstein) is also called the "obstruction" effect. In the case of nonelectrolytes, $\eta_r = 1 + 2.5\phi$ for this effect, where ϕ is the volume fraction of the obstructing particles present. This result comes from a solution of the hydrodynamic equations with the particles considered as rigid spheres in a continuous viscous medium with a "no-slip" assumption (6.1

9.2. EXPERIMENTAL TECHNIQUES

(a) Electrical Conductivity

(1) Conductivity

Measurement of electrical conductivity can be made with a precision better than 0.02% if proper precautions are taken. Reference 7 discusses such measurements in some detail and gives examples of apparatus, both electrical bridge networks and conductivity cells.

Most measurements are made with alternating current in the audio frequency range. The use of higher frequencies results in greater polarization errors and in greater effects due to stray capacitances. To avoid some of the latter problems, water should not be used as the thermostat fluid. A bridge (e.g., Wheatstone bridge) can be used to measure the resistance in the conductivity cell. A null measurement for AC needs to have both a variable capacitance and resistance to match the complex impedance of the cell.

The design of conductivity cells requires some ingenuity to achieve optimum effects, especially if measurements are to be made at different frequencies. The electodes, for example, are often coated with platinum-black to minimize electrode effects, and have two independent leads to eliminate effect of lead resistance. The specific conductivity is calculated from the measured resistance through a "cell constant," which depends on the geometry of the cell. KCl solutions are usually used as the standards for determining this constant. The cell constant varies with temperature, configuration of leads, etc.

Direct current measurements eliminate the effects of capacity in the cell circuit. However, polarization effects and contact potentials cause some complications. In such cases, the potential difference due to the current in the cell is measured by two "probe" electrodes, while two other electrodes introduce the current.

(2) Transport Numbers

In the case of thermodynamic measurements in electrolyte solutions, it is not possible to separate out experimentally the contribution of the positive and negative ion. In the case of conductivity, it is possible to measure the transport numbers of the species (i.e., fraction of charge carried by the species) (6.65). The earliest measurement of transport numbers was done by the "Hittorf" method, which is still used in refined form.

In the Hittorf method, dc is passed through the cell, and the concentration of species in the solution at the two electrodes then analyzed. Side-reactions at the electrodes and the accuracy of the concentration analysis are the factors limiting the precision of this method.

Transport numbers can also be measured through a "moving boundary" method. Here two solutions with a common ion are placed in a tube so that they form a boundary. A passage of dc will then cause this boundary to move. If the common ion is an anion, then the transport number t_+ of the cation to be measured is $t_+ = A \cdot d \cdot c_+ F/Q$ where A is the cross section of the tube, d the distance the boundary has moved during passage of an amount of charge Q, c_+ the concentration and F the Faraday constant. The accuracy of the method depends on proper design of apparatus and "reference" electrolyte to produce a sharp boundary. Several variations are given in [7].

In addition, transport numbers can be measured through cell potentials of concentration cells, and centrifugal cells.

(b) Measurement of Diffusion by Classical Methods

Diffusion coefficients can be measured by a variety of means. In this chapter only "classical" methods will be considered. Other methods are discussed in subsequent chapters. Apparatus for "classical" measurements are described in Refs. 10 and 7.

(1) Steady-State Methods

In steady-state methods of measuring D, conditions are arranged so that the gradient dc/dx is held constant. This is most often done by introducing a porous diaphragm between two volumes which have different values of c. The diaphragm must be calibrated with some standard liquid, and the solutions above and below the diaphragm must be stirred to keep the diffusion process confined only to the pores in the diaphragm. Adsorption effects and hydrodynamic streaming through the diaphragm can occur if a proper diaphragm is not chosen.

After a steady state is achieved in the diaphragm, the concentrations on the two sides are determined. When diffusion has proceeded for a time (often days), the concentrations are again measured. Fick's first law can then be solved with the proper boundary conditions and the coefficient D obtained. Difficulties arise in the interpretation due to the concentration dependence (here equivalent to the time dependence) of D.

Absolute measurements of D can be obtained if two diaphragms are used [11]. Here the value of the gradient and the rate of diffusion can both be obtained in the space between the diaphragms without the use of a calibrating standard. Accuracies of the order of 1% can be obtained for values of D at concentrations less than 5×10^{-4} mol l^{-1} of electrolyte. In this case, as in many other measurements, the "integral" diffusion coefficient $\langle D \rangle$ is measured, where

$$\langle D \rangle = \frac{1}{(c' - c'')} \int_{c''}^{c'} D(c)\, dc \qquad (9.18)$$

(2) Free-Diffusion Methods

Instead of a steady-state method, free diffusion can be utilized to measure D. Thus initially a sharp boundary is formed, e.g., between the solution and the pure solvent. The boundary is usually horizontal with the denser medium below. Diffusion is then allowed to take place, and the development of the concentration as a function of distance and time observed. From the results, D can be calculated by the appropriate solution of Fick's second law.

When electrolyte solutions are involved, then c(x, t) can be followed by measuring the conductivity in the solutions, in a direction perpendicular to the diffusion direction x. This can be done by sets of electrodes at appropriate positions in the diffusion cell.

When c(x, t) results in the variation n(x, t) of the refractive index, then optical methods can also be used to follow c(x, t). A common way of observing this is through "Gouy" interference patterns. When the initial diffusion boundary is at x = 0 (i.e., c = 0 for x > 0, $c = c_1$ for x < 0 at t = 0), then a solution of Fick's second law (6.24) gives

$$\frac{dc}{dx} \propto \exp\left[-\frac{x^2}{4Dt}\right] \tag{9.19}$$

Thus both the concentration and refractive index gradients are as shown schematically in Fig. 9.1.

Thus light sent through the cell as shown in Fig. 9.2 will form an interference pattern, as the diffusion cell acts as a type of prism. At point A(x = 0), the gradient dn/dx is greatest, and light is deflected down to point *a* on the screen. At B and B', the gradients are equal, and the deflection is down to *b*. Since the path from B to *b* differs from that from B' to *b*, then interference occurs and bands are produced. Thus an interference pattern is produced. At short times, dn/dx is greater at A, and the pattern is distributed over a large distance on the screen. As time proceeds, the point *a* moves upward until at large t (dn/dx → 0), light is only observed at c. A quantitative description of this phenomenon cannot adequately be given by geometrical optics. A detailed explanation can be found in Ref. 10.

There are many optical and cell designs available exploiting the Gouy effect. Determination of diffusion coefficients accurate to better than 0.1% are possible using this method. Limiting aspects are the number of interference fringes which can be utilized in the analysis and the precision in forming the initial boundary. This can be formed by withdrawal of a diaphragm, bringing solutions into contact by sliding one solution over the other (sheared boundary cell), or by allowing them to flow together.

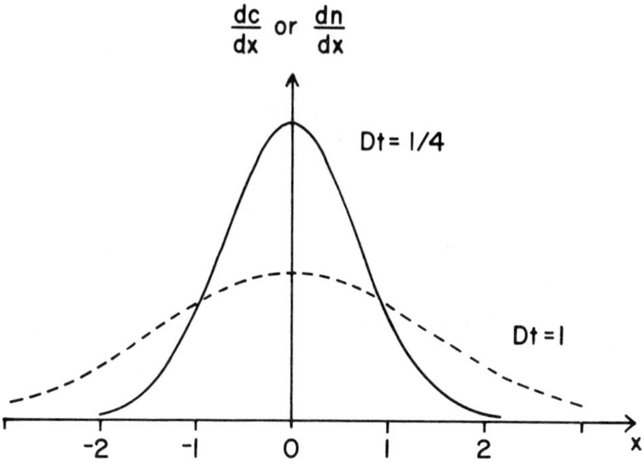

Fig. 9.1. Schematic diagram of the variation of dc/dx or dn/dx with distance and time.

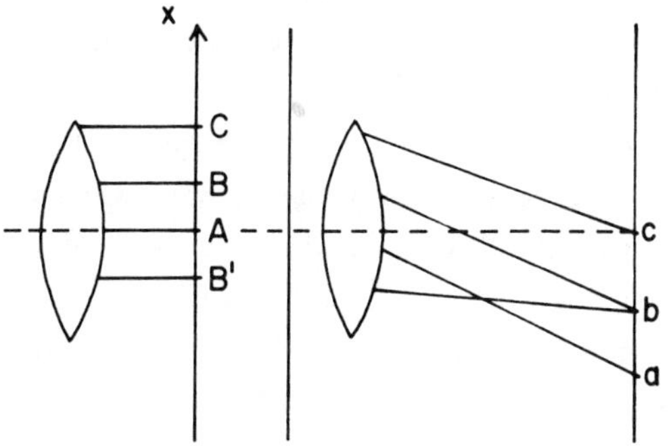

Fig. 9.2. Schematic diagram to illustrate the Gouy effect.

(3) Tracers

The use of radioactive tracers to measure D* is included in this chapter under "classical" methods. Two methods are commonly employed. In one, a diaphragm is used to separate the solution containing the radioactive isotope from the isotopically normal solution [as in Sec. 9.2(b)(1)]. The increase in radioactivity in the latter solution with time is then observed.

In the "capillary" method, a capillary tube with a solution containing radioactive isotopes is immersed in a large vessel containing isotopically normal solution. By stirring the solution, the boundary condition $c = 0$ can be maintained for the radioactive material. Fick's second law can then be solved for the given configuration and boundary conditions. The concentration of tracer material in the capillary can be determined through radioactive counting. One critical aspect in such determinations is the rate of stirring of the bulk solution, to maintain a condition $c = 0$, yet prevent turbulence. Due to this and other problems, the accuracy of such tracer measurements is not much better than 10% in some cases.

(c) Viscometers

The measurement of viscosity is in most cases made through timing the flow of liquid through a capillary of some length under the force of gravity. On solution of the Navier-Stokes equation for such a situation, Poiseuille's law can be arrived at, i.e., the volume discharged $= \pi a^4 \Delta p / 8\eta\ell$. Here a is the radius of the capillary, Δp the pressure difference between the ends of a capillary of length ℓ.

In practice, viscometers are calibrated with standards, so that quantitative use of Poiseuille's law is not necessary. Reproducibilities of better than ±0.02% are possible in such viscometers. (e.g., Cannon-Fenske). In order to obtain absolute values to a good accuracy, corrections to the inverse relationship between volume and viscosity may have to be made for drainage and kinetic energy effects.

Viscometers are also available which utilize Stokes law. Thus the rate of fall of spheres in the liquid to be tested is measured. Each sphere must be calibrated with some standard liquids.

In addition to the most common viscosity coefficient η ("dynamic" viscosity), there exist two other coefficients. A "kinematic" viscosity $\nu = \eta/\rho$ is used in some cases, but usually for gases rather than liquids. A coefficient of "bulk" viscosity η_v is also defined through $\sigma_{xx} = \eta_v (du_x/dx)$ (19.8).

(d) Other Transport Coefficients

(1) Thermal Conductivity

In the measurement of the thermal conductivity λ in liquids, the major difficulty is to eliminate convection effects from the systems. Reference 10 discusses this problem in detail. One recent method has a self-descriptive name, the "transient hot wire method" [12], but most measurements are made with a steady-state apparatus, i.e., heat flow is measured under conditions of constant thermal gradient.

Convection currents can be eliminated in such apparatus if a thin horizontal layer of liquid is used (1 to 5 mm), heated from the top. Values of λ accurate to $\pm 1\%$ can be achieved by such a method. The temperature gradient is obtained by measuring the temperatures of the top and bottom metal plates in contact with the liquid. Heat flow can be measured through the electrical energy required to maintain the temperature of the hot plate.

Other geometrical arrangements of heat sources and sinks have been used. One consists of vertical concentric metal cylinders with a thin layer of liquid in between; another of a heated metal plate inside a cooled metal shell with liquid in between.

(2) Cross-Effects

Of the many coefficients possible to describe cross-effects (19.2) the only one measured extensively in liquids is the Soret coefficient S_T, or the coefficient of thermal diffusion. There is no theory available to explain the values obtained for S_T in liquids, however. Reference 10 and, more briefly, Ref. 13 discuss experimental apparatus and results for this effect.

The Soret effect relates the formation of a concentration gradient due to the presence of a thermal gradient. The thermal gradient is produced by setting the liquid between two horizontal plates about 10 mm apart, with the upper about 10 K warmer. Since the effect is small, it may take a long time for a steady state to be set up (of the order of 10 hr). The concentration gradient produced can then be observed either optically, or through electric conductance in the case of electrolytes [Sec. 9.2(b)].

9.3. RESULTS FOR SPECIFIC SYSTEMS

(a) Viscosity in Pure Liquids

In Chap. 6, equations were derived for η and D* on the basis of a relatively primitive model [(6.47) and (6.50)]. A more refined version of this theory based on the Lennard-Jones-Devonshire model of liquids [Sec. 2.2(c)] is available [14]. In the latter treatment, the activation energy is considered as arising from two contributions. One is the potential barrier to be overcome for transport to occur as in the primitive (Eyring) theory. The second is a contribution expressing the effect of the number density of unoccupied sites next to a molecule. An estimate for this can be obtained through consideration of the excess volume of the liquid (Sec. 2.3).

The more refined theory predicts the absolute values of η and D* to within 12% of the experimental values [14,15]. The Eyring theory, as given in the simplified form (6.47), gives agreement only to within 75%. In the latter calculations, the value of E_η was estimated as being $\Delta U_{vap}/2.45$ (6.48). Other theoretical approaches for the calculation of η and D* are given in Ref. 15.

The relationship between E_η and ΔU_{vap} has been investigated experimentally in detail [16]. For nonassociated liquids, the ratio $E_\eta/\Delta U_{vap}$ is different from 0.22 only for molecules of irregular geometrical shape. Molecules which are approximately spherical (e.g., carbon tetrachloride, cyclohexane) have a higher ratio (≃0.33) while flatter, more elongated molecules (e.g., benzene) have an intermediate value (≃0.27).

An explanation for this can be that spherically shaped molecules form a liquid which is microscopically more homogeneous than that formed by irregularly shaped ones. Thus there are fewer cases where an exceptionally large amount of free space is available for flow to occur. With irregular molecules, there is more heterogeneity as local close-packed regions are interspersed with regions containing a considerable amount of free volume. Hence viscous flow is relatively easier in such locally more heterogeneous liquids.

In the case of associated compounds (e.g., alcohols, amines), the ratio has a value greater than 0.22 for asymmetric molecules only when there are strong specific interactions. This can be due to the maintenance of these interactions in flow processes. Thus the compounds can be thought of as being in the form of polymers from the point of view of their flow properties.

Generally, liquids made up of nonspherical molecules do not show an Arrhenius-type temperature dependence of the viscosity. In such liquids, molecular rotation is hindered sufficiently that the molecule cannot rotate several times between translational jumps. Such freedom of rotation between translational jumps is thought necessary for the model leading to the Arrhenius form to be applicable [17]. The temperature dependence of η of four isomeric hexanes have been studied in order to investigate the effect of molecular structure [18]. The effects can be explained in a satisfactory manner by a significant structure theory [Sec. 2.3(c)] extended to explain dynamic as well as thermodynamic properties.

It should be noted that the viscosity discussed above is the low frequency limit of a frequency dependent viscosity [Sec. 10.1(b)]. The relaxation time for viscoelastic behavior is however so small in normal liquids that it is not possible to detect it. If the liquids can be sufficiently supercooled, then the longer relaxation time can be detected by a decrease in η in the MHz range. The results of such experiments on a series of aromatic liquids [19] show a viscous behavior which can be fitted with a "Cole-Davidson" plot [Eq. (11.17); Fig. 11.5).

(b) Anomalies in Transport Properties of Pure Water

The absolute values of η and D^* for water in its normal liquid range are not anomalously different from those of other liquids as shown in Table 9.1. Its thermal conductivity is somewhat higher than "normal," however. Several anomalous aspects of the transport coefficients arise when T and p dependence is considered. They are given in terms of the cgs units commonly found in the literature.

TABLE 9.1

Transport Data for Three Liquids

	T/K	$D^*/(cm^2\ s^{-1})$	$\eta/(poise)$	$\lambda/(J\ s^{-1}\ cm^{-1}\ K^{-1})$
Benzene	279	1.7×10^{-5}	8.0×10^{-3}	1.6×10^{-3}
Argon	85	1.6×10^{-5}	2.8×10^{-3}	1.2×10^{-3}
Water	298	2.2×10^{-5}	8.9×10^{-3}	5.8×10^{-3}

(1) Self-Diffusion

The self-diffusion coefficient of water has been measured by various means. The results of such measurements [20] are presented to indicate the degree of accuracy of such measurements. Tracer methods have been used with ^2H, ^3H, and ^{18}O the tracers. Results for 298 K vary from 2.22 to 2.26 x 10^{-5} $cm^2\ sec^{-1}$, with precision estimates of the order of ±0.06. D* has also been measured from the mixing of H_2O and D_2O using optical detection [Sec. 9.2(b)] giving a result 2.272 ± 0.003 x 10^{-5} $cm^2\ sec^{-1}$. Temperature dependent studies give an activation energy $E_D \simeq 19$ kJ mol^{-1}.

(2) Viscosity

The viscosity of most liquids increases rapidly as pressure is increased. However, at lower temperatures liquid water has $\partial\eta/\partial p < 0$ as p is initially increased from 1 atm [21]. On the basis of transition state theory, this means a negative volume of activation. This can be interpreted as being due to a shift of the "structured-monomer" equilibrium to the less space-filling monomer form on increase in p. The destruction of structure makes it easier for flow processes to occur.

(3) Thermal Conductivity

The thermal conductivity for water is anomalous as at p = 1 atm only water has $d\lambda/dT > 0$ [22]. Other liquids can have $d\lambda/dT > 0$ at higher pressures, e.g., toluene at p > 2000 atm [23]. To explain this, λ

can be divided up into $\lambda' + \lambda''$. The former is the contribution to λ due to conduction in the structured (framework) water, and the latter in the monomer (cavity) water. Just as in ice, $d\lambda'/dT < 0$; in addition, the ratio of framework water decreases as T increases.

A positive $d\lambda''/dT$ is postulated due to both an increase in the amount of monomer present and due to an increase in the specific conductance of the monomer. The latter effect can occur if there is an increase in the relaxation time τ_p for the momentum of the cavity molecules. As T increases, the framework water breaks down, and the channels in which cavity molecules can move increase in size due to greater thermal fluctuations leading to $d\tau_p/dT > 0$. Other explanations of this anomalous behavior can be found in Ref. 10.

(4) Electrical Conductivity

There exists also a small electrical conductivity in water due to its self-ionization to form hydrogen and hydroxyl ions. Those species have very high mobilities, $u_+ = 3.62 \times 10^{-3}$, $u_- = 1.98 \times 10^{-3}$ $cm^2\ V^{-1}\ sec^{-1}$. This gives pure water at 25°C an electrical conductivity (dc) of $5.7 \times 10^{-8}\ \Omega^{-1}\ cm^{-1}$. To explain these considerably higher mobilities (e.g., that of H_3O^+ is 7 times that of Na^+), it has been postulated that part of the motion occurs not due to the motion of the actual proton (hydrodynamic mechanism) but to the shifting of H bonds as shown in Fig. 9.3 (proton-transfer mechanism). An analogous figure can be drawn for the OH^- diffusion.

The rate of proton transfer in $H_2O + H_3O^+ \rightarrow H_3O^+ + H_2O$ is very rapid [Sec. 11.3(d)]. Calculations indicate that essentially no hydrodynamic motion of H^+ is necessary to explain the high value of u_+ [24] [see also Sec. 9.3(g)].

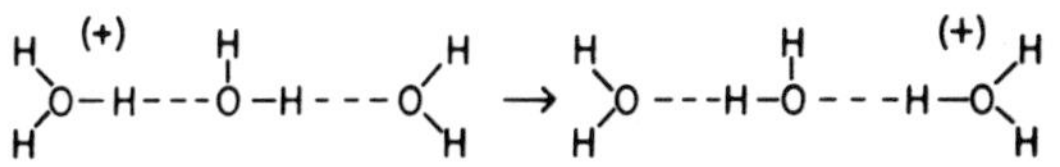

Fig. 9.3. Schematic diagram illustrating proton transfer conductance.

(c) Viscosity in Aqueous Liquid Mixtures

A large number of liquid mixtures containing associated compounds show a maximum in η at some intermediate concentration [25]. This is usually a sign of a strong specific interaction causing complex formation. Thus the compositions where the excess viscosity $\eta^e = \eta - \eta_b X_b - \eta_a X_a$ show maxima correlate to a limited extent with the maxima of the ΔH_m. Effects due to ΔV_m, ΔS_m^e can also be included [26].

Temperature-dependent data can also be interpreted in terms of an entropy of activation for the viscous process (6.47):

$$\eta = \frac{Lh}{V} \exp\left[-\frac{\Delta S_\eta^\#}{R}\right] \exp\left[\frac{\Delta H_\eta^\#}{RT}\right] \tag{9.20}$$

Thus, for example, the system dimethylsulfoxide-water shows a dramatic increase in $\Delta S_\eta^\#$ in the region of 0.3 mole fraction DMSO [27]. This can be interpreted as an extensive disordering process caused by viscous flow. The disordering can be due to disturbance of the DMSO $(H_2O)_2$ complexes believed present.

In nonelectrolyte mixtures, the relative viscosity η_r is usually fitted by an equation $\eta_r = 1 + Bc$ instead of with (9.16). The $\sqrt{c}$ term is due to ion atmosphere effects which are not present in nonelectrolytes. A term in c^3 must be added if investigations are to be extended to the 1 M range in concentration. A study of aqueous solutions of alcohols, ureas, and amides [28] gave straight-line plots of B vs V_b, the partial molal volume, for each of the three series of compounds with slopes identical to ±2%. This slope is, however, a factor of 1.8 higher than that predicted by the Einstein volume effect [Sec. 6.1(c)] where $\eta_r = 1 + 2.5\phi$. More sophisticated theories assuming nonspherical particles do not produce a coefficient more than ±0.2 from 2.5.

The value of B is determined by factors other than size, however, in particular the effect of the solute in structuring the solvent around it. The B values for all three series of compounds can be described with reasonable success (Fig. 9.4) as

$$B = 2.5 \times 10^{-3} V_b + 0.055n - 0.087k \tag{9.21}$$

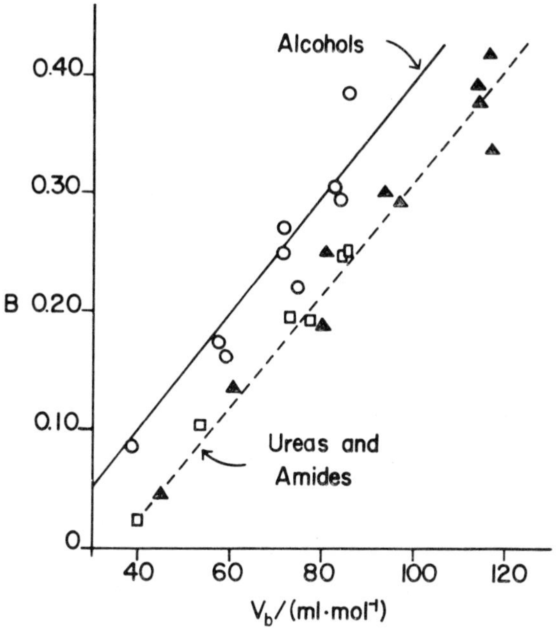

Fig. 9.4. The viscosity coefficient B vs partial molar volume V_b for 9 alcohols o, 10 ureas ▲, and 6 amides □, After Ref. 28.

Here V_b is in milliliters per mole, n is the number of carbons in the amide and urea or the number of CH_3 and CH_2 groups in the alcohols. k = 1 for alcohols and k = 2 for ureas and amides. The $0.055n$ term can then be considered to be a contribution towards higher viscosity due to "structure-making" in the solvent by the alkyl groups. The k causes a decrease in viscosity due to "structure-breaking" in the solvent due to polar functional groups [see Secs. 1.1(c); 5.1(c); 8.3 (f), (h)].

(d) Relationships Between Viscosity and Diffusion

The Stokes-Einstein relationship (6.63) for one-component liquids predicts $kT/\pi\eta D^*a$ to be a constant. The value should be 6 if Stokes law is obeyed and if no "slip" at the surface of the sphere is assumed. If full slip is assumed then the value is 4. For nine quite different liquids, this ratio was found to be on the average 4.07 [14]. The range of values was from 3.18 (mercury) to 5.24 (methyl alcohol). The value of a used was the Lennard-Jones σ as obtained from gas-phase measurements. The temperature dependence of this ratio has also been tested [15] and has been found for benzene to be 3.61 ± 0.75% and for carbon tetrachloride 3.79 ± 0.6% in a 30° interval.

The assumptions on which Stokes law is based [Sec. 6.2(b)] are not really valid for the molecular-level processes occurring. Nevertheless, it seems to describe phenomena on such a scale surprisingly well. A low value of the ratio could be interpreted as indicating that a "full-slip" situation is more realistic. This is reasonable, as a "no-slip" situation implies that a molecule could not move relative to its nearest neighbors.

In two-component systems, diffusion and viscosity are related by the Hartley-Crank law in its form in (9.14). Systems such as those in Sec. 9.3(c), which have association present, do not follow this law well. This can be due to the formation of complexes which change the nature of the diffusing species. Form (9.13) gives reasonable values of the mutual diffusion coefficient in such systems when D_a^* and D_b^* are known [26].

In nonassociated systems, form (9.14) should apply. It is found, however, that it does not correct properly for solution nonideality [29]. Thus although the product ηD^* is essentially composition independent in the system chloroform ($CHCl_3$)-(CCl_4), the mutual diffusion coefficient predicted by (9.14) is not in quantitative agreement. The factor $d \ln a_b / d \ln X_b$ seems to correct for thermodynamic nonidealities only in a semiquantitative manner.

The model of diffusion of larger molecules in a solvent composed of smaller molecules (e.g., aqueous solutions of biological molecules with molecular weights > 500) cannot be of the Eyring type [Sec. 6.2(b)]. Instead diffusion must proceed by a flow mechanism resulting from movement of the solvent molecules about the macromolecule.

Equation (6.63) should then apply, and D should be $\propto 1/a$, or $\propto M$, the molecular weight, if the density of the macromolecules is assumed constant. A plot of log D vs log M is linear for M varying from 500 to 8000 (17 points) [30]. From the slope and the average density the ratio $kT/\pi\eta D_a$ is found to be 5.3, i.e., closer to the "no-slip" than to the "full-slip" Stokes law value. The activation energy for the diffusion of macromolecules is then E_η for the solvent. i.e., about the same as E_D for the solvent.

Molecular dynamics simulation has been carried out on such a system of one large particle in a solvent of small particles [31]. The diffusion coefficient can be obtained from the velocity autocorrelation function from (7.28). For an initial time period ($\simeq 10^{-13}$ sec), $G_v(t)$ does not follow the hydrodynamic model well. However, the hydrodynamic model is approached in an asymptotic manner. With solute particles ≃3 times the size of solvent particles, the hydrodynamic region is reached in the order of the time for eight collisions.

(e) Viscosity and Diffusion Near the Critical Temperature

The mutual diffusion coefficient D_{ab} should approach 0 at the critical solution point of a binary mixture, as $d\mu_b/dX_b \rightarrow 0$ (4.10). This effect has been observed experimentally in systems with both upper and lower critical solution temperatures, and as a function of both T and X_b [32].

At the same time, the viscosity increases as the critical solution point is approached. This is explained as being due to the long-range concentration fluctuations which arise in that region [Sec. 4.2(e)]. The theories available [33,34] explain the temperature dependence of this extra viscosity reasonably [35-37] for both kinds of systems. However, it is not possible to decide on the basis of experimental results as to which theory gives the correct mathematical form of the function η^e vs $|T - T_c|/T_c$. The composition dependence of η^e is poorly described by theories. Experiments indicate that η^e is related to composition by a Gaussian distribution centered about the critical composition [37].

Even though $D_{ab} \rightarrow 0$, the self-diffusion coefficients D_a^*, D_b^* show no anomalous behavior [35]. A decrease in D_b^* would be expected due to the increase in η on the basis of the Einstein-Stokes relation (6.63). However, the mobility of the molecules does not seem to be affected by the extra viscosity present in the critical solution region [Sec. 13.3(d)].

Viscosity effects also show up in the critical region of a one-component system, as critical phenomena can be considered in more general terms [Secs. 4.2(e) and 3.4]. There is, however, no equivalent to a mutual diffusion coefficient in a one-component system.

(f) Electrical Conductivity in Aqueous Solutions of Strong Electrolytes

There is a very large volume of experimental data available regarding transport phenomena in aqueous electrolyte solutions. Some of the aspects studied will be illustrated in this section and the two following, but this does not exhaust the types of phenomena that can be elucidated through transport studies in electrolyte solutions.

For most practical purposes, aqueous solutions of alkali metal halides, hydroxides, and perchlorates can be assumed to be fully dissociated. However, accurate conductance data analyzed by recent more sophisticated equations suggest the presence of ion pairing with association constants at 25°C as shown in Table 9.2. For $NaClO_4$, the

TABLE 9.2

Association Constants for Simple Electrolytes

Electrolyte	K_a	a/Å	Ref.
CsI	0.93	5.49	3
CsBr	1.07	5.55	3
CsCl	0.41	4.59	38
RbCl	0.28	4.95	38
KCl	0.01, 0.12	5.22	38
$CsClO_4$	1.69	2.28	39
$RbClO_4$	1.35	2.69	39
$KClO_4$	0.98	3.32	39

data gave a K_a of essentially 0 (as for KCl above), and for $LiClO_4$, small negative values were obtained.[39].

The association sequence K < Rb < Cs found for the chlorides and the chlorates, and the sequence of a with K > Rb > Cs can be explained through solvation considerations. The smaller cations have a higher charge density at their surface and thus orient the solvent molecules more. This makes ion pairing less likely to occur and increases the effective size of the ions. The models of ion pairing in Sec. 5.2(c) are not detailed enough to account for such effects.

An increase in K_a can be obtained at very high temperatures or very low solution densities (i.e., low pressures) [40]. The dielectric constant of water decreases as T increases and p decreases. An explanation for the pressure (density) effect can also be obtained if the ion-pairing equilibrium is considered as

$$Na^+(H_2O)_m + Cl^-(H_2O)_n \rightleftarrows Na \cdot Cl(H_2O)_p + qH_2O \qquad (9.22)$$

Here m, n, p, and q represent hydration numbers.

When density is changed, then the concentration (and activity) of free water will be changed. The association constant can be written as

$$K_a = \frac{a_{NaCl}}{a_{Na^+}\, a_{Cl^-}} = \frac{a_{NaCl}\,(a_{H_2O})^q}{a_{Na^+}\, a_{Cl^-}} \; \frac{1}{(a_{H_2O})^q} = K_{a,0} \frac{1}{(a_{H_2O})^q} \qquad (9.23)$$

where $K_{a,0}$ is a "true" equilibrium constant. Plots of log K_a vs log c_{H_2O} (essentially vs log a_{H_2O}) are linear. From the slope a value of 10.2 was found for q, independent of temperature. This is the excess of the number of water molecules solvating the sodium and chloride ions as compared to the NaCl ion pair (molecule).

Measurements of Λ at high T and p have also been carried out for alkali metal hydroxides [41]. At lower concentrations (below 4 M for KOH), Λ increases with pressure, but at higher concentrations it decreases. Finally it approaches a limit set by Walden's rule [Sec. 6.2(e)] due to increase in η with p.

This can be explained when Λ_{OH^-} is considered to be made up of a hydrodynamic and a proton transfer component. At low concentrations, the proton transfer mechanism accounts for most of the conductivity (60% as $c \to 0$ for OH^-). As pressure is increased, this conductance is increased as the pressure assists in the proton exchanges by providing some of the energy needed to bring the O atoms close enough to allow for an H-bond switch. At high concentrations, an increasing fraction of water molecules are bound to ions and are unable to partake in proton transfer chains. Thus hydrodynamic mechanisms become predominant.

(g) Diffusion in Aqueous Electrolyte Solutions

Although there are a number of diffusion studies in electrolyte solutions, the theoretical aspects are not well developed when concentrations are more than limiting. An extension of the Hartley-Crank equation is needed, taking into account the extra effects present in ionic solutions. From the available theories, hydration numbers can be extracted from an analysis of the diffusion coefficient as a function of concentration. For this it is necessary to know the activities and the viscosities.

Such an analysis on diffusion data for the strong electrolytes lithium and sodium perchlorates [42] gave reasonable hydration numbers (6.0 for $LiClO_4$, 2.8 for $NaClO_4$). Other quite different numbers can be obtained from other theories, however.

Diffusion studies on tetrabutylammonium halide solutions show a decrease in diffusion coefficient with increasing anion size [43]. The ratio $D_b/(1 + d \ln y_\pm / d \ln c_b)$ is referred to as the "mobility term" M [Eqs. (9.10 - (9.12)]. This mobility term is found to increase with increasing anion size, suggesting that ion pairs are being formed, and that the degree of ion pairing increases with anion size. Ion-pair formation is also suggested by the fact that $M(\eta/\eta^\bullet)$ increases with concentration. The $\eta/\eta^\bullet$ factor is included as an inverse relationship is expected between u and η. the mobility of one ion pair should be greater than that of two separate oppositely charged ions.

(h) Viscosity and Conductivity in Nonaqueous Electrolytes

In studies of viscosity, the parameters in the Jones-Dole equation (9.16) can be obtained from a plot of $(\eta_r - 1)/\sqrt{c}$ vs $\sqrt{c}$. The intercept gives the A coefficient and slope B. Such an analysis has been carried out for sodium, potassium and cesium iodide in 11 different solvents [44]. The A coefficients were all in a range 0 to 0.1, while B ranged from -0.13 to +1.14.

As in the case of aqueous solutions, the largest cation (i.e., that with least surface charge density) gives the lowest B values. This is due to the small value of η^A and a large negative value of η^D [Sec. 9.1(c)]. The large ion breaks the solvent structure, but the electric field is not strong enough to orient the solvent molecules to any extent.

The B values were also found generally to increase with length of the solvent alkyl chains if the polar (solvating) group remained the same (e.g., butanol, pentanol, hexanol). As the size of the solvent molecule increases, so also does the hydrodynamic entity consisting of the ion and oriented solvent molecules.

Conductance measurements in nonaqueous electrolyte solutions indicate the presence of ion pairs in such solutions due to the lower dielectric constants. Analysis is complicated, as unlike water, several solvents solvate only one of the two kinds of ions readily. Thus dimethylsulfoxide and acetonitrile (Table 5.1) do not solvate anions readily. It is often useful to consider the Walden product $(\Lambda_i \eta_a)$ of ions in searching for information about their solvation.

Thus the limiting Walden product $\Lambda_+^\infty \eta_a^\bullet$ for large cations (e.g., tetraalkyl ammonium) is about the same in methanol, ethanol, and acetonitrile. $\Lambda_+^\infty \eta_a^\bullet$ is also found to increase linearly with $1/a_+$, where a_+ is the crystallographic radius of the cation. This is predicted by (6.63). For smaller cations ion-solvent interactions are of predominant importance, and $\Lambda_+^\infty \eta_a^\bullet$ decreases with $1/a_+$ due to the stronger ion-solvent interactions with smaller ions. Anions are progressively more solvated as their size decreases (i.e., $\Lambda_-^\infty \eta_a^\bullet$ decreases with $1/a_-$), but the effect for the series (ClO_4^-, I^-, Br^-, Cl^-) is considerably less for acetonitrile than for the alcohols.

Consideration of Walden products has also been carried out for mixed solvent systems [45]. It is predicted that $\Lambda_i^{\infty}\eta$ can be a complicated function of the solvent composition if the ion in question interacts so strongly with one or both of the solvent components that a chemical equilibrium can effectively be thought to exist. Such effects are not found in studies of the tetrabutylammonium salts in various mixed solvents [46]. The Walden product is, however, found to be dependent on the dielectric constant of the solvent as $1/\varepsilon$. The "Stokes" radius of the ion (6.63) can then be thought of as being $a_i = a_i^{\infty} + \text{constant}/\varepsilon$. This effect cannot solely be due to "dielectric friction," as the slopes of a_i vs $1/\varepsilon$ curves are different for the ion in different solvent pairs as shown in Fig. 9.5. All the curves of a_i vs $1/\varepsilon$ in Fig. 9.5 converge to the same value of a_i at the point where the solvent is pure solvent (butyronitrile). There must be a specific dependence of the mobility on the size and shape of the solvent molecules surrounding the ion.

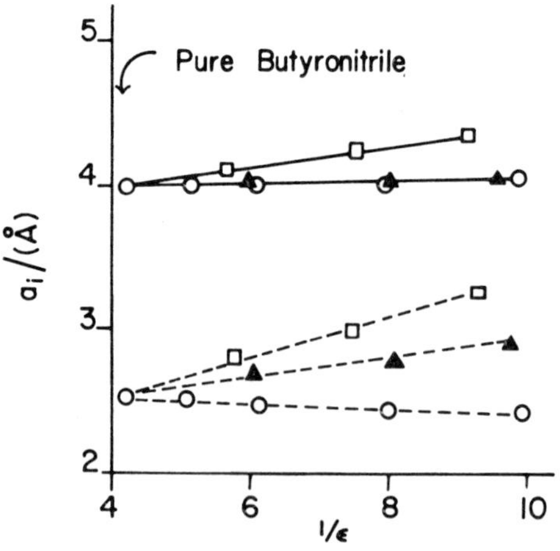

Fig. 9.5. Plots of the Stokes radius vs $1/a_i$ for (i) tetrabutylammonium —— and (ii) bromide --- ions in mixed solvents of butyronitrile (C_3H_7-CN) and Dioxane o, Carbon tetrachloride ▲, and Benzene □. After Ref. 46.

REFERENCES

Both theoretical and experimental approaches to transport in electrolyte solution are covered well in [7]. A more thorough discussion of viscosity for such solutions is in [8]. Diffusion and thermal conductivity are thoroughly discussed in [10].

1. R. M. Fuoss, J. Am. Chem. Soc., *81*, 2659 (1969).
2. H. Falkenhagen, W. Ebeling, and W. D. Kraeft, in Ionic Interactions (S. Petrucci, ed.), Academic Press, New York, 1971.
3. K-L. Hsia and R. M. Fuoss, J. Am. Chem. Soc., *90*, 3055 (1968).
4. T. J. Murphy and E. G. D. Cohen, J. Chem. Phys., *53*, 2173 (1970).
5. E. Pitts, B. E. Tabor, and J. Daly, Trans. Farad. Soc., *65*, 849 (1969).
6. D. P. Sidebottom and M. Spiro, J. C. S. Faraday I, *69*, 1287 (1973).
7. R. A. Robinson and R. H. Stokes, Electrolyte Solutions, 2nd ed., Butterworths, London, 1959.
8. H. S. Harned and B. B. Owen, The Physical Chemistry of Electrolytic Solutions, 3rd ed., Rienhold, New York, 1958.
9. R. H. Stokes and R. Mills, Viscosities of Electrolytes and Related Properties, Pergamon, London, 1965.
10. H. J. V. Tyrrell, Diffusion and Heat Flow in Liquids, Butterworths, London, 1961.
11. D. E. Elrick, D. E. Smiles, and R. A. Wooding, J. Chem. Soc. Farad. Trans. I, *68*, 691 (1972).
12. E. McLaughlin and J. F. T. Pittman, Phil. Trans. Roy. Soc., *270*, 557 (1971).
13. K. E. Grew, in Transport Phenomena in Fluids (J. M. Hanley, ed.), Marcel Dekker, New York, 1969.
14. E. McLaughlin, Trans. Farad. Soc., *55*, 28 (1959).
15. A. F. Collings and R. Mills, Trans. Farad. Soc., *66*, 2761 (1970).
16. L. H. Thomas, Trans. Farad. Soc., *62*, 1 (1966).
17. D. B. Davies and A. J. Matheson, Trans. Farad. Soc., *63*, 596 (1967).
18. L. D. Eicher and B. J. Zwolinski, J. Phys. Chem., *76*, 3295 (1972).
19. D. B. Davies, A. J. Matheson, and G. M. Glover, J. C. S. Faraday II, *69*, 305 (1973).

20. GR5.

21. G. S. Kell, in GR7.

22. I. S. Andrianova, O. Ya. Samoilov, and I. Z. Fisher, Zh. Strukt. Khimii, *8*, 813 (1967).

23. R. Kandiyoti, E. McLaughlin, and J. F. T. Pittman, J. C. S. Faraday I, *69*, 1953 (1973).

24. I. Ruff and V. J. Friedrich, J. Phys. Chem., *76*, 2954 (1972).

25. R. J. Fort and W. R. Moore, Trans. Farad. Soc,, *62*, 1112 (1966).

26. Y. Oishi, Y. Kamei, and A. Nishi, J. Chem. Phys., *57*, 574 (1972).

27. S. A. Schichman and R. L. Amey, J. Phys. Chem., *75*, 98 (1971).

28. T. T. Herskovits and T. M. Kelly, J. Phys. Chem., *77*, 381 (1973).

29. C. M. Kelly, G. B. Wirth, and D. K. Anderson, J. Phys. Chem., *75*, 3293 (1971).

30. S. Nir and W. D. Stein, J. Chem. Phys., *55*, 1598 (1971).

31. G. Subramanian, D. Levitt, and H. T. Davis, J. Chem. Phys., *60*, 591 (1974).

32. R. Haase, Ber. Bunsenges, Physik. Chem., *76*, 256 (1972).

33. M. Fixman, Advan. Chem. Phys., *6*, 175 (1963).

34. K. Kawaski, Ann. Phys., *61*, (1970).

35. A. Stein, S. J. Davidson, J. C. Allegra, and G. F. Allen, J. Chem. Phys., *56*, 6164 (1972).

36. J. Brunet and K. E. Gubbins, Trans. Farad. Soc., *64*, 1255 (1968).

37. B. C. Tsai and D. McIntyre, J. Chem. Phys., *60*, 937 (1974).

38. H. S. Dunsmore, S. K. Jalota, and R. Paterson, J. C. S. Farad. Trans. I, *68*, 1583 (1972).

39. A. D'Aprano, J. Phys. Chem., *75*, 3290 (1971).

40. A. S. Quist and W. L. Marshall, J. Phys. Chem., *72*, 684 (1968).

41. D. A. Lown and H. R. Thrisk, Trans. Farad. Soc., *67*, 132 (1971).

42. A. N. Campbell and B. G. Oliver, Can. J. Chem., *47*, 2681 (1969).

43. H. Kim, A. Revzin, and L. J. Gosting, J. Phys. Chem., *77*, 2567 (1973).

44. J. P. Bare and J. F. Skinner, J. Phys. Chem., *76*, 434 (1972).

45. P. Hemmes, J. Phys. Chem., *78*, 907 (1974).

46. A. D'Aprano and R. M. Fuoss, J. Sol. Chem., *3*, 45 (1974); *4*, 175 (1975),

Further Recent References

G. Delmas, P. Purves, and P. de Saint-Romain, "Viscosities of Mixtures of Branched and Normal Alkanes with Tetrabutyltin. Effect of Orientational Order of Long-Chain Alkanes on the Entropy of Mixing", J. Phys. Chem., *79*, 1970 (1975).

E. Grushka, E. J. Kitka Jr., and H. T. Cullinan Jr., "Binary Liquid Diffusion Prediction in Infinitely Diluted Systems using the Ultimate Volume Approach", J. Phys. Chem., *80*, 757 (1976).

C. J. Skipp and H. J. V. Tyrrell, "Diffusion in Viscous Solvents. Part 2 - Planar and Spherical Molecules in Propane-1,2-diol at 15, 25 and 35°C", J. C. S. Faraday I, *71*, 1744 (1975).

C. F. Mattina and R. M. Fuoss, "Conductance of the Alkali Halides XIII. Cesium Bromide, Lithium-7 Chloride, and Lithium-7 Iodide in Dioxane-Water Mixtures at 25°C", J. Phys. Chem., *79*, 1604 (1975).

C. McCallum and A. D. Pethybridge, "Conductance of Acids in Dimethylsulfoxide. II. Conductance of Some Strong Acids in DMSO at 25°C", Electrochim. Acta, *20*, 815 (1975).

R. C. Paul, J. S. Banait, and S. P. Narula, "Physico-Chemical Studies in Non-Aqueous Solvents VII. Conductance and Solvation Studies of 1:1 Electrolytes in Hexamethylphosphotriamide", Z. physik. Chem. Neue Folge, *94*, 200 (1975).

T. L. Broadwater, T. J. Murphy, and D. F. Evans, "Conductance of Binary Asymmetric Electrolytes in Methanol", J. Phys. Chem., *80*, 753 (1976).

N. Matsuura, K. Umemoto, and Y. Takeda, "Formulation of Stokes Radii in DMF, DMSO and Propylene Carbonate with Solvent Structure Cavity Size as Parameter", Bull. Chem. Soc. Japan, *48*, 2253 (1975).

B. S. Krumgal'z, "Temperature Variation of the Ionic Components of the Coefficient B in the Jones-Dole Equation for Viscosity", Russ. J. Phys. Chem., *48*, 1163 (1974).

J. M. McDowall, N. Martinus, and C. A. Vincent, "Study of Ion-Solvent Interactions in Formamide + Water Mixtures by the Measurement of Viscosity of Sodium Chloride Solutions", J. C. S. Faraday I, *72*, 654 (1976).

P. Turq, D. Ilzycer, M. Chemla, and Y. Roumegous, "Etude de la Relation Autodiffusion-Conductibilité dans des Solutions d'Electrolytes Associés", J. Chim. Phys., *71*, 233 (1974).

R. D. Singh and M. M. Husain, "Studies on Solutions of High Dielectri-Constant. Walden Product in Formamide, N-Methylformamide, N-Methylacetamide and N-Methylpropioamide at Different Temperatures", Z. physik. Chem. Neue Folge, *94*, 193 (1975).

V. P. Pogodin, T. P. Koryagina, and M. Kh. Karapent'yants, "Thermal Conductivity of Electrolyte Solutions in Formamide III. Partial Molar Thermal Conductivities of Alkali Metal Halides", Russ. J. Phys. Chem., *49*, 358 (1975).

Chapter 10

ULTRASONIC ABSORPTION

As in Chap. 8 to 16, this chapter begins with a section describing the theoretical basis for the use of ultrasonic absorption to elucidate structure and dynamics in liquids. The derivation of the basic results useful for interpretation of ultrasonic absorption phenomena makes use of the Navier-Stokes equation (6.3), the continuity equation (19.7), thermodynamic relationships (see Chap. 17 for a summary), and several basic assumptions.

A major assumption used throughout is that the absorption is very much smaller than the velocity, when expressed as the imaginary part of a complex velocity. Another is the assumption of linear variation in density, temperature, etc. with pressure. Yet another the additivity of absorption from various effects. All these assumptions seem to be justified on comparison of theory with results.

In the derivation, classical systems are first examined and the equations for velocity and absorption derived for them. The absorption can be considered as arising from the imaginary part of a complex velocity. As the velocity is dependent on the compressibility κ_s, the contribution to the complex compressibility from the presence of an equilibrium, $\delta\kappa$ is then discussed.

Next the frequency dependence of the $\delta\kappa$ is examined, and the standard form of the single-relaxation equation derived. Then $\delta\kappa$ is expressed in terms of thermodynamic properties of the system. Finally problems arising from the presence of multiple relaxations are discussed.

Extensions of parts of this basic theory can be found in several parts of Sec. 3. Nevertheless, many sophistications are not included in these notes. The reader should refer to books specializing in ultrasonics for these (Refs. 1-3).

Section 2 on experimental techniques includes also a short section on temperature and pressure jump methods, as these can be thought of as being special simple cases of the theory described in Sec. 10.1. Brillouin scattering techniques for high (GHz) frequencies is not included in Chap. 10, but is discussed in Chap. 14 (light scattering).

There is a wide variety of systems discussed in Sec. 3. As shown in Sec. 10.1, ultrasonic absorption can be caused by any equilibrium with a nonzero ΔH^θ or ΔV^θ. This general applicability makes it possible to study a wide variety of phenomena. It can also be a disadvantage, as assignment of the equilibria responsible for absorption effects can be quite difficult in cases. The phenomena in Secs. 10.3 (a), (b) are therefore included even though they are not directly related to the aims of this book. It is important to be aware of these effects when using ultrasonics to study liquid structure and dynamics.

10.1. THEORETICAL BASIS

(a) Sound in Classical Systems

This discussion assumes the sound (or ultrasound) wave to be a plane longitudinal wave propagating in the x direction. This corresponds to the case for most experimental methods. As a sound wave is essentially a pressure wave propagating adiabatically, then p, ρ, T and the local (medium) velocity u all vary as the wave passes.

For a sinusoidal wave, the variation in pressure can be written as

$$p = p_0 + p' = p_0 + p_0' \exp[-\alpha x + i\omega(t - \frac{x}{v})] \qquad (10.1)$$

Here p is divided up into an equilibrium pressure p_0 and an "acoustic pressure" p'. The acoustic pressure varies in a manner typical of a plane wave in the x direction with a radial frequency ω, velocity v, and absorption coefficient α.

This variation can also be expressed as

$$\exp[-\alpha x + i\omega(t - \frac{x}{v})] = \exp[-\alpha x + i(\omega t - kx)] \qquad (10.2)$$

Where k is the wave vector or propagation constant $k = \omega/v$. It can also be expressed as

$$\exp[-\alpha x + i\omega(t - \frac{x}{v})] = \exp[i(\omega t - k^*x)] \qquad (10.3)$$

where k* is a complex quantity,

$$k^* = \frac{\omega}{v^*} = \frac{\omega}{v} + i(-\alpha) \qquad (10.4)$$

The acoustic variables ρ', T', and u'(= u as $u_0 = 0$) are also introduced, all with a variation such as Eqs. (10.1)-(10.3). Such acoustic variables are assumed so small that second-order terms in them are negligible.

A longitudinal wave has (medium) velocity gradients in the propagation direction only. When the volume viscosity is assumed zero, then the Navier-Stokes equation (6.3) reduces to

$$\rho_0 \frac{\partial u}{\partial t} = - \frac{\partial p'}{\partial x} + \frac{4}{3}\eta \frac{\partial^2 u}{\partial x^2} \tag{10.5}$$

The assumption $\eta_V = 0$ is not justified, as the presence of η_V has been detected in liquid Argon, in agreement with theoretical predictions [4]. The η_V term is however left out, as values of η_V cannot be measured by other means, while values of the shear viscosity η are available (Chap. 9).

The continuity equation (19.7) for this case becomes

$$\frac{\partial p'}{\partial t} = -\rho_0 \frac{\partial u}{\partial x} \simeq -\rho \frac{\partial u}{\partial x} \tag{10.6}$$

When now a non-absorbing fluid is considered ($\eta = \alpha = 0$), then substitution of u, p', ρ' in the form (10.2) into (10.5) and (10.6) gives:

$$v^2 = \frac{p'}{\rho'} = \frac{1}{\rho\kappa_S} \tag{10.7}$$

The symbol κ_S expresses the adiabatic compressibility,

$$\kappa_S = - \frac{1}{V}\left(\frac{\partial V}{\partial p}\right)_{ad} = \frac{1}{\rho}\left(\frac{\partial \rho}{\partial p}\right) \quad \frac{1}{\rho}\frac{\rho'}{p'} \tag{10.8}$$

Equation (10.7) is often referred to as the Laplace equation for the speed of sound.

Now (10.7) can be used together with the previous equations to obtain an expression for α. Such a derivation gives a useful result as in essentially all cases of interest $\alpha \ll \omega/v$. Thus the existence of an absorption does not disturb the propagation velocity to any great extent. The resultant equation for α is frequently called Stokes equation for viscous absorption,

$$\alpha_\eta = \frac{2\eta\omega^2}{3\rho v^3} \tag{10.9}$$

The classical absorption α_c is for the case of nonmetallic liquids adequately described by (10.9). In the case of liquids with high thermal conductivity, an additional absorption occurs due to this effect. A derivation of the Kirchoff equation for heat conduction can be found in standard ultrasonics texts [1-3].

(b) Complex Adiabatic Compressibility

Experimentally it is found that the absorption α is greater -- often much greater -- than the classical absorption (10.9). This can be explained in terms of the presence of equilibria in the liquid which contribute a complex component to the compressibility κ when a sonic wave passes through. This in turn causes v and k to become complex, leading to the absorption of energy (10.4).

An expression will be derived for the extra absorption α' present due to an equilibrium. Such an absorption is then assumed to be additive to α_η and any absorption effects due to other processes.

In the derivation, the adiabatic compressibility will be assumed equal to the isentropic compressibility. This is equivalent to the assumption $\alpha' \ll \omega/v$, and is valid in essentially all cases.

The degree of advancement, or the progress variable, of the equilibrium will be designated by ξ (Sec. 17.4). Then κ_S can be written as a complex quantity

$$\kappa^* = -\frac{1}{V}\left(\frac{\partial V}{\partial p}\right)_S = -\frac{1}{V}\left(\frac{\partial V}{\partial p}\right)_{S,\xi} - \frac{1}{V}\left(\frac{\partial V}{\partial \xi}\right)_{S,p}\left(\frac{\partial \xi}{\partial p}\right)_S = \kappa_\infty + \delta\kappa^* \tag{10.10}$$

The contribution to κ^* from the equilibrium is $\delta\kappa^*$. The symbol κ_∞ is used for the remaining part of the compressibility as it is κ_S in the case of changes occurring at very high frequencies where the contribution $\delta\kappa^*$ is "frozen out."

This frequency dependence of $\delta\kappa^*$ is next considered. When a sinusoidally varying disturbance of the equilibrium occurs, then the equilibrium value, ξ_{eq}, for the degree of advancement varies as

$$\xi_{eq} = \xi_{eq,0} + \delta\xi_{eq} \exp[i\omega t] \tag{10.11}$$

However the actual degree of advancement, ξ_{ac}, may have a value different from ξ_{eq} as it takes the system a finite time to react to a change in ξ_{eq} caused by a p or a T change. This is described by a relaxation equation (19.34):

$$\frac{d\xi_{ac}}{dt} = -\frac{1}{\tau}(\xi_{ac} - \xi_{eq}) \qquad (10.12)$$

The effect is demonstrated for the case of square wave (Fig. 10.1) and sinusoidal (Fig. 10.2) changes in ξ_{eq}.

Note that for $\Delta t \ll \tau$ the equilibrium is "frozen out." This can also occur if the frequency ω in (10.11) becomes very great.

In the sinusoidal case, ξ_{ac} can be assumed to vary as

$$\xi_{ac} = \xi_{ac,0} + \delta\xi_{ac} \exp[i\omega t] \qquad (10.13)$$

When $\xi_{ac,0}$ is set equal to $\xi_{eq,0}$ then substitution of (10.11) and (10.13) into (10.12) gives

$$\delta\xi_{ac} = \frac{\delta\xi_{eq}}{1 + i\omega\tau} \qquad (10.14)$$

Thus $\delta\kappa^*$ can be written as

$$\delta\kappa^* = -\frac{1}{V}\left(\frac{\partial V}{\partial \xi}\right)_{S,p}\left(\frac{\partial \xi_{ac}}{\partial p}\right)_S = -\frac{1}{V}\left(\frac{\partial V}{\partial \xi}\right)_{S,p}\left(\frac{\partial \xi_{eq}}{\partial p}\right)_S \cdot \frac{1}{1 + i\omega\tau} \qquad (10.15)$$

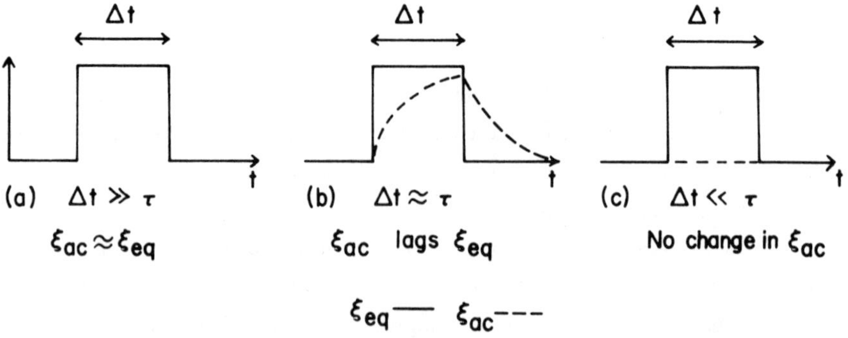

Fig. 10.1. Schematic illustration of ξ_{ac} for the case of square-wave changes in ξ_{eq} at three different time scales.

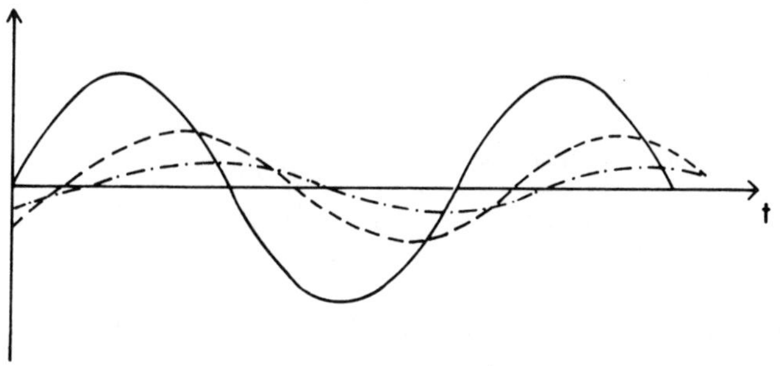

Fig. 10.2. Schematic illustration of ξ_{ac} for the case of sinusoidal changes in ξ_{eq} for different values of $\omega\tau$.

Note that in (10.10), ξ really referred to ξ_{ac}. No subscript is necessary in the factor $(\partial V/\partial\xi)$. Then

$$\kappa^* = \kappa_\infty + \frac{\delta\kappa}{1 + i\omega\tau} \tag{10.16}$$

where

$$\delta\kappa = -\frac{1}{V}\left(\frac{\partial V}{\partial\xi}\right)_{s,p}\left(\frac{\partial\xi_{eq}}{\partial p}\right)_s \tag{10.17}$$

In the discussion that follows, no subscript will be used for ξ. It will refer to the equilibrium value ξ_{eq} in all cases.

(c) Forms of the Single Relaxation Equation

Expressions for v and α' can be readily obtained if the Laplace equation (10.7) is assumed to hold for complex quantities. This is equivalent to the previously used assumption $\alpha' \ll \omega/v$. In this case,

$$(k^*)^2 = \frac{\omega}{v^*}^2 = \omega^2\rho\kappa^* \tag{10.18}$$

where $k^* = \omega/v - i\alpha'$.

When now (10.16) is substituted for κ^*, then (10.18) becomes:

$$(k^*)^2 = \frac{\omega^2}{v^2} + (\alpha')^2 + i(-\frac{2\alpha'\omega}{v})$$

$$= \frac{\omega^2\rho[\kappa_0 + \omega^2\tau^2\kappa_\infty]}{1 + \omega^2\tau^2} + \frac{i[-\omega^2\rho\omega\tau\delta\kappa]}{1 + \omega^2\tau^2} \qquad (10.19)$$

Here $\kappa_0 = \kappa_\infty + \delta\kappa$.

The imaginary part of (10.19) can be used to get an expression for the absorption per wavelength, μ

$$\mu = \alpha'\lambda = \alpha' \frac{v \cdot 2\pi}{\omega} = - \frac{v^2\pi}{\omega^2} Im\ (k^*)^2 = \frac{\pi v^2\rho\delta\kappa \cdot \omega\tau}{1 + \omega^2\tau^2} \qquad (10.20)$$

When the assumption $\kappa_0 \simeq \kappa_\infty \simeq \kappa_s \simeq 1/\rho v^2$ is used, then (10.20) becomes

$$\mu = \pi \frac{\delta\kappa}{\kappa} \cdot \frac{\omega\tau}{1 + \omega^2\tau^2} = 2\mu_m \frac{\omega\tau}{1 + \omega^2\tau^2} \qquad (10.21)$$

The quantity $\delta\kappa/\kappa$ is often referred to as the "relaxation strength" ε. μ_m is the maximum value of μ.

The real part of (10.19) can be used to check the assumption of small dispersion. For $\alpha' << \omega/v$, the real part of (10.19) gives

$$\frac{1}{v^2} = \frac{1}{\omega^2} Re(k^*)^2 = \frac{\rho\kappa_0 + \rho\kappa_\infty\omega^2\tau^2}{1 + \omega^2\tau^2} \qquad (10.22)$$

With the notation $v_0^2 = 1/\rho\kappa_0$ and $v_\infty^2 = 1/\rho\kappa_\infty$,

$$\frac{v_0^2}{v^2} = 1 - \frac{\delta\kappa}{\kappa_0} \frac{\omega^2\tau^2}{1 + \omega^2\tau^2} \qquad (10.23)$$

Ultrasonic dispersion in liquids is seldom looked for or exploited in the standard frequency ranges used. At high frequencies (Chap. 14) it is used to detect relaxation phenomena, however.

For experimental purposes, the absorption equation is often written in a form

$$\frac{\alpha}{\nu^2} = \frac{A}{1 + \nu^2/\nu_r^2} + B \qquad (10.24)$$

Here ν_r is the relaxation frequency of the equilibrium considered $\nu_r = 1/2\pi\tau$, and B is the absorption present due to other effects with higher relaxation times. A is related to the relaxation strength as

$$A = \frac{4\pi\mu_m\tau}{v} \tag{10.25}$$

Yet another, less common method is to express the results in a form used for dielectric relaxation (Chap. 11). In this case the dispersion (10.23) must be measured, and thus cannot be neglected. The acoustic analogue to the Debye equation (11.14) then becomes:

$$\left(\frac{v_0^2}{v^2} - \frac{v_0^2 + v_\infty^2}{2v_\infty^2}\right)^2 + \left(\frac{\alpha'\lambda}{\pi} \cdot \frac{v_0^2}{v^2}\right) = \left(\frac{v_\infty^2 - v_0^2}{2v_\infty^2}\right)^2 \tag{10.26}$$

A plot of $(\alpha'\lambda v_0^2/\pi v^2)$ vs (v_0^2/v^2) then should for a single relaxation process give a semi-circle centered on the horizontal axis. When more than one relaxation time is involved, the form becomes more complex (Sec. 11.1).

The relationships given above involve in cases approximations which can be removed in more sophisticated treatments. They are, however, adequate for the description of most phenomena studied.

(d) Forms of the Relaxation Strength

(1) General Form

The relaxation strength $\delta\kappa/\kappa$ must be written in terms of the thermodynamic parameter of the equilibrium concerned, From (10.17) $\delta\kappa$ can be written as:

$$\delta\kappa = -\frac{1}{V}\left(\frac{\partial V}{\partial \xi}\right)_{p,T}\left(\frac{\partial \xi}{\partial p}\right)_S = -\frac{1}{V}\left(\frac{\partial V}{\partial \xi}\right)_{S,p}\left[\left(\frac{\partial \xi}{\partial p}\right)_T + \left(\frac{\partial \xi}{\partial T}\right)_p\left(\frac{\partial T}{\partial p}\right)_S\right] \tag{10.27}$$

This can be further extended to give

$$\delta\kappa = -\frac{1}{V}\left[\left(\frac{\partial V}{\partial \xi}\right)_{p,T} - \left(\frac{\partial V}{\partial S}\right)_{p,\xi}\left(\frac{\partial S}{\partial \xi}\right)_{p,T}\right]\left[\left(\frac{\partial \xi}{\partial p}\right)_T + \left(\frac{\partial \xi}{\partial T}\right)_p\left(\frac{\partial T}{\partial p}\right)_S\right] \tag{10.28}$$

Other thermodynamic variables such as the heat capacity C_p and the expansivity α_e must now be extended as $C_p = C_{p,\infty} + \delta C_p$ etc. in analogy with (10.10). Thus

$$\delta C_p = \left(\frac{\partial H}{\partial \xi}\right)_{p,T}\left(\frac{\partial \xi}{\partial T}\right)_p = \Delta H \left(\frac{\partial \xi}{\partial T}\right)_p \tag{10.29}$$

ΔH is the enthalpy change per unit reaction.

$$\delta \alpha_e = \frac{1}{V}\left(\frac{\partial V}{\partial \xi}\right)_{p,T}\left(\frac{\partial \xi}{\partial T}\right)_p = \frac{\Delta V}{V}\left(\frac{\partial \xi}{\partial T}\right)_p \tag{10.30}$$

The use of Maxwell's relations (17.8), forms such as (10.29) and (10.30) and other thermodynamic relationships allow $\delta\kappa/\kappa$ to be put into a useful form. The actual derivation will not be carried out here, as it is lengthy but quite straightforward [1]. When $\delta C_p << C_p$, $\delta\kappa << \kappa$ etc., then the following form can be obtained:

$$\frac{\delta\kappa}{\kappa} = (\gamma - 1)\frac{\delta C_p}{C_{p,\infty}}\left[1 - \frac{\Delta V}{\Delta H}\frac{C_p}{\alpha_e V}\right]^2 \tag{10.31}$$

Here γ is the ratio of specific heats. Both volume and enthalpy effects are accounted for in (10.31).

(2) Thermal Relaxation

In the case of pure "thermal" relaxation, ΔV can be assumed equal to zero. Then (10.31) involves only the calculation of δC_p. From (10.29), δC_p can further be expressed as

$$\delta C_p = \Delta H \left(\frac{\partial \xi}{\partial \ln K}\right)_p \left(\frac{\partial \ln K}{\partial T}\right)_p \tag{10.32}$$

From standard thermodynamics (17.34):

$$\left(\frac{\partial \ln K}{\partial T}\right)_p = \frac{\Delta H^\theta}{RT^2} \tag{10.33}$$

Thermal relaxation often involves a unimolecular equilibrium of the type

$$\underset{\text{State I}}{A} \underset{k_{21}}{\overset{k_{12}}{\rightleftarrows}} \underset{\text{State II}}{B} \tag{10.34}$$

In such a case,

$$K = \exp\left[-\frac{\Delta G^\theta}{RT}\right] = \frac{\xi}{1 - \xi} \tag{10.35}$$

Appropriate differentiation and substitution gives the result

$$\delta C_p = \left(\frac{\Delta H^\theta}{RT}\right)^2 \frac{\exp[-\Delta G^\theta/RT]}{(1 + \exp[-\Delta G^\theta/RT])^2} \tag{10.36}$$

It has now also been assumed that $\Delta H \simeq \Delta H^\theta$. In many cases $\Delta H^\theta << T\Delta S^\theta$, so that $\Delta G^\theta = \Delta H^\theta$ is used as an approximation.

(3) Structural Relaxation

In some cases, such as for pure water at 4°C, both $(\gamma - 1)$ and α_e in (10.31) become zero, and the expression thus meaningless. For this reason $\delta\kappa/\kappa$ can be written in another form more useful for "structural" relaxation rather than thermal relaxation.

$$\frac{\delta\kappa}{\kappa} = \frac{\Delta V^\theta}{VRT}\left[\Delta V^\theta - \frac{\Delta H^\theta \alpha_e}{C_p}\right]\left(\frac{\partial \xi}{\partial \ln K}\right)_p \tag{10.37}$$

The ΔH^θ term can be neglected in the case of studies in most aqueous solutions, as α_e/C_p is very small (e.g., 0 at 4°C, 0.2 at 20°C).

The last factor $(\partial\xi/\partial \ln K)$ in (10.37) can be of the same form as in (10.36). Often a dissociation equilibrium is involved, i.e.,

$$\underset{\text{State I}}{A} \underset{k_{21}}{\overset{k_{12}}{\rightleftarrows}} \underset{\text{State II}}{B + C} \tag{10.38}$$

For the simplest case, where $c_c = c_b$, the factor can be shown to be

$$\frac{\partial \xi}{\partial \ln K} = c \cdot V \cdot \sigma \frac{(1 - \sigma)}{(2 - \sigma)} \tag{10.39}$$

where σ is the degree of dissociation and c the stoichiometric concentration.

The above relationships are again too simple for some systems. Most systems involving electrolytes must be considered in the light of more sophisticated formulas involving activity coefficients [1,3].

(e) Forms of the Relaxation Times

The relaxation time for a unimolecular equilibrium (10.34) can be expressed simply in terms of the rate constants. First the concentration variables Δc_I and Δc_{II} must be introduced. These are the deviations of c_I and c_{II} from their equilibrium values $c_{I,eq}$; $c_{II,eq}$. For an equilibrium of the form (10.34), $\Delta c_I = -\Delta c_{II}$.

As defined by (10.12), τ is then given by

$$\frac{1}{V}\frac{d\xi}{dt} = -\frac{1}{\tau}\Delta c_I = -k_{12}(c_{I,eq} + \Delta c_I) + k_{21}(c_{II,eq} + \Delta c_{II}) \quad (10.40)$$

Now as $k_{12}c_{I,eq} = -k_{21}c_{II,eq}$, and as $\Delta c_I = -\Delta c_{II}$, it can be seen from (10.40) that

$$\frac{1}{\tau} = k_{12} + k_{21} \quad (10.41)$$

For an equilibrium of the type (10.38) the equation is somewhat more complex. In that case, $\Delta c_a = -\Delta c_b = -\Delta c_c = \Delta c$. Thus

$$\frac{1}{V}\frac{d\xi}{dt} = -\frac{1}{\tau}\Delta c = -k_{12}(c_{a,eq} + \Delta c) + k_{21}(c_{b,eq} - \Delta c)(c_{c,eq} - \Delta c) \quad (10.42)$$

When the $(\Delta c)^2$ term is neglected and the equilibrium condition is used, the result becomes

$$\frac{1}{\tau} = k_{12} + k_{21}(c_{b,eq} + c_{c,eq}) \quad (10.43)$$

These examples of the most common equilibria encountered serve to show how relaxation times are connected to rate constants. Equations (10.41) and (10.43) are satisfactory for many cases, but in others, more sophisticated treatments are necessary.

(f) Multiple and Continuous Relaxation Times

The presence of a single relaxation time has been assumed in the previous discussions. If several relaxations are present, each with relaxation parameters A_i, τ_i, then (10.24) simply becomes

$$\frac{\alpha}{\nu^2} = \sum_i \frac{A_i}{1 + \nu^2/\nu_{i,r}^2} \tag{10.44}$$

All absorptive processes are included in (10.44), even classical absorption.

The form of (10.44) is straightforward, but the interpretation of the A_i and $\nu_{i,r}$ in terms of the thermodynamic and kinetic parameters of the equilibria involved can become complex. Such complexity occurs if the equilibria are interrelated. A full discussion of the general problem is available [1,9] and will not be covered here. Instead a common more simple case will be discussed.

A coupled system of the type

$$\underset{(I)}{A + B} \underset{k_{21}}{\overset{k_{12}}{\rightleftarrows}} \underset{(II)}{C} \underset{k_{32}}{\overset{k_{23}}{\rightleftarrows}} \underset{(III)}{D} \tag{10.45}$$

is often found with k_{12}, $k_{21} >> k_{23}$, k_{32}. In such a case τ_1 (for step I, II) is as before,

$$\frac{1}{\tau} = k_{21} + k_{12}(c_a + c_b) = k_{21} + k'_{12} \tag{10.46}$$

Step II, III is more complicated.

The rate of change of c_d can be written as

$$\frac{dc_d}{dt} = \frac{d\,\Delta c_d}{dt} = k_{23}c_c - k_{32}c_d = -\frac{1}{\tau}\Delta c_d \tag{10.47}$$

In this case, however, $\Delta c_c \neq -\Delta c_d$ necessarily, as c_c is also involved in step I, II.

Mass conservation requires that $\Delta c_a + \Delta c_c + \Delta c_d = 0$ and $\Delta c_a = \Delta c_b$ The step I, II is essentially also at equilibrium, so that $c_c/c_a c_b = K_{12}$.

Using these expressions, Δc_c and Δc_d can be related as

$$\Delta c_c = -\frac{\Delta c_d k'_{12}}{(k'_{12} + k_{21})} \tag{10.48}$$

This gives the result on substitutioniinto (10.47):

$$\frac{1}{\tau_2} = k_{32} + k_{23}\frac{k'_{12}}{k'_{12} + k_{21}} \qquad (10.49)$$

Some liquid systems cannot even be treated on the basis of a large number of discrete relaxations. Instead, a continuum of relaxation times must be introduced. The summation in (10.44) in such cases cases must be replaced by an integral with some appropriate weighting function.

10.2. EXPERIMENTAL TECHNIQUES

(a) Standard Pulse Techniques

The most widely used method of making ultrasonic measurements is through a pulse technique. A typical pulse apparatus is schematically shown in Fig. 10.3.

A pulsed oscillator 1, sends out pulses containing a frequency ν. Such pulses are usually only 1 to 10 μsec. in duration and have a repetition rate of about 60 sec^{-1}. Problems of heating the system

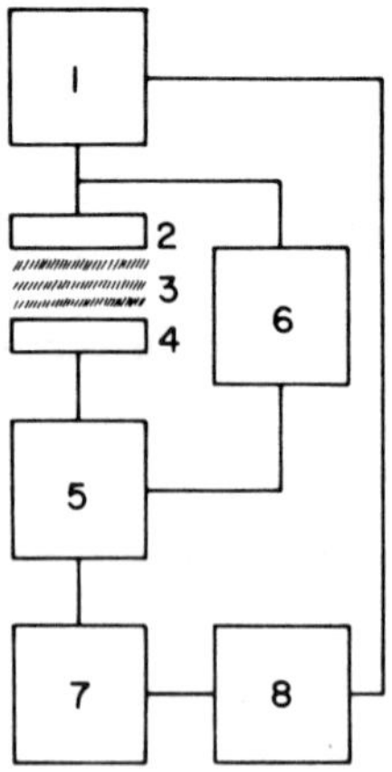

Fig. 10.3. Schematic block diagram of a pulse apparatus.

due to the absorption process are thus eliminated, as the signal is on for only an extremely small fraction of the total time. Interference problems from reflected pulses are also lessened.

The electric signal is sent to a transducer 2, where it is converted to an ultrasonic signal. Usually quartz is used as transducer material, although other piezoelectric materials can be used [5]. For frequencies up to about 300 MHz, excitation of the resonant and odd harmonic frequencies of quartz crystals is used. At higher frequencies, up into the GHz region, the ultrasonic pulses can be produced by surface excitation of crystal rods in the electric field of a resonant cavity [6].

Such ultrasonic pulses can be introduced directly into the liquid sample, or else be sent in through a delay rod. After traveling through the liquid 3, for some distance, the pulse is converted back to an electric pulse. This can be done through some matched transducer 4, or by the initial transducer 2, if the ultrasonic pulse has been reflected back.

After preamplification 5, and amplification 7, the pulse can be displayed on the oscilloscope 8, with a sweep triggered by the oscillator. The absorption coefficient α can then be obtained from the dependence of the intensity of the pulse on the distance traveled. Such an intensity can be measured by some attenuator 6, in parallel or in series with the ultrasonic pulses.

An accuracy of better than 2% can be obtained by the pulse technique at frequencies from about 1 to 250 MHz. At low ν the absorption can become so low that the attenuation of the pulse cannot be measured accurately. There is a limitation on the pathlength through which a plane wave can travel without being appreciably affected by diffraction. With a greater cross-sectional area of the wave, this length can be extended somewhat.

A high-frequency limit appears in normal apparata because of the difficulty of generating high frequency sound with resonant transducers. Because of the high absorptions, path lengths also become so small that interference effects from various reflected pulses is unavoidable. Usually 1GHz is the high-frequency limit. Measurements at even higher frequencies up to 10GHz can however be made through Brillouin scattering (Chap. 14).

Velocity measurements can be carried out simultaneously with absorption measurements. A simple method is to observe the distance of travel at which interference occurs between various reflected pulses. Thus λ can be measured and v calculated through a knowledge of ν. The precision of such results is about 1%. Specialized methods have been developed to make particularly accurate measurements of changes in velocity.

There is a limit of about 1% in the absolute accuracy of pulse method measurements because of the use of pulses of a finite length. A pulse of duration Δt has a spread of frequencies of the Fourier components of the frequencies present given by $\Delta\nu \simeq 1/\Delta t$.

(b) Debye-Sears Effect

Absorption measurements can also be carried out in the medium frequency region by exploiting the Debye-Sears effect. Although it is not as common as the pulse technique, it is outlined here as its basis is of some use in an introductory discussion of Brillouin scattering (Sec. 14.1).

A plane continuous ultrasonic beam travelling through a liquid causes a variation in p and T which is repeated at a distance λ. Thus a regular variation in the index of refraction is set up, and the system resembles a diffraction grating with a spacing λ. A collimated light beam with wavelength λ_ℓ passing through the tank will thus give rise to an interference pattern as predicted by the Bragg relation. This diffraction pattern will appear with maxima at angles (Fig. 14.1) such that

$$2\lambda \sin\frac{\theta}{2} = n\lambda_\ell; \quad (n = 1, 2, 3 \cdots) \qquad (10.50)$$

An analysis of the intensity distribution in the diffraction pattern is complex [3]. For low sound intensity, however, the total diffracted light intensity is proportional to the amplitude of the ultrasound. The absorption coefficient can thus easily be obtained from the light intensity as a function of the pathlength of the sound.

As this "diffraction grating" is actually moving at a velocity v, a Doppler effect shifts the light frequency ν_ℓ. In the first-order diffraction image, ν_ℓ is raised by an amount ν, the frequency of the ultrasound (Fig. 14.3). This effect is not of interest here, but is the basis for measurement of the velocity of hypersonic (>1 GHz) waves through Brillouin scattering.

(c) Low Frequency Measurements

The dimensions of pulse apparatus [Sec. 10.2(a)] can be increased to carry out measurements at low frequencies. If such scaling up is impractical, then two other methods can be used, "radiation pressure" and "reverberation sphere" techniques.

An ultrasonic beam has a radiation pressure proportional to the energy density in the beam. Such a radiation pressure can be mechanically measured by, for example, observing the force it exerts on a reflecting surface. As well, the pressure gradient can be measured reasonably precisely. Knowledge of the energy density, and thus the intensity, at two distances can be traslated into a value for α. Measurements with such apparatuses at frequencies as low as 130 kHz have been reported [7].

Measurements at even lower frequencies (4 kHz) have been carried out using a "reverberation sphere." Sonic energy is introduced into a sphere filled with the liquid by means of a small transducer attached to the exterior. When a steady-state level of sound energy is at tained, the electrical input to the transducer is cut off. The transducer is then used as a detector to follow the decay of the sound level in the sphere.

On the basis of the simplest model, the pressure at the wall will decay as $\exp[-\alpha v t]$. Here reflection losses are neglected and the sound is assumed to travel purely in a radial mode. In practise, numerous corrections must be made. Reference 8 gives an example of such an apparatus. A resonance method using parallel plates rather than a sphere is described in Ref. 9.

A total frequency range from about 50 kHz to 1GHz can thus be reached with reasonable accuracy if at least three different apparatuses are used. Thus phenomena with relaxation times from 2×10^{-5} to 10^{-9} sec can be studied by ultrasonic absorption. Few laboratories have such extended equipment, however. With the more standard pulse equipment, phenomena with relaxation times in the range 3×10^{-7} to 4×10^{-9} sec can be investigated directly.

(d) Temperature and Pressure Jump

These methods can be considered to be simple cases of the theory presented in Sec. 1. Instead of the sinusoidal variation of p and T in ultrasonics, a step-function change in p and T can be applied at some time t_0. As

$$\frac{\partial \ln K}{\partial T} = \frac{\Delta H^\theta}{RT^2} \qquad \text{and} \qquad \frac{\partial \ln K}{\partial p} = -\frac{\Delta V^\theta}{RT} \tag{10.51}$$

then changes in the equilibrium constant K can be caused.

The equilibrium value of the degree of advancement ξ_{eq} is thus of the form

$$\xi_{eq} = \xi_{eq,1} \quad \text{for} \quad t < t_0 \qquad \xi_{eq} = \xi_{eq,2} \quad \text{for} \quad t > t_0 \tag{10.52}$$

The actual value for ξ then becomes

$$\xi = \xi_{eq,1} \quad \text{for } t < t_c$$

$$\xi = \xi_{eq,1} + (\xi_{eq,2} - \xi_{eq,1})\left(1 - \exp\left[-\frac{t - t_0}{\tau}\right]\right) \tag{10.53}$$

By following ξ as a function of t, the value of τ can be measured.

A temperature jump is usually brought about by discharge of a capacitor through the liquid. This takes of the order of 1 μsec time. Thus reactions with $\tau < 10^{-6}$ sec cannot be studied by this method. Changes in ξ can be observed by techniques such as aborption spectrometry or polarimetry. Reference 10 describes the use of such a method.

A pressure jump can be brought about by rupture of a diaphragm. Thus the solution rupturing the diaphragm changes its pressure from some high pressure to atmospheric pressure. Even with changes in p as high as 100 atm, however, the change in ξ is generally so small that its detection is quite difficult.

10.3. RESULTS FOR SPECIFIC SYSTEMS

(a) Conformational Isomerism

In unassociated (i.e., nonpolar) liquids containing several atoms (e.g., benzene, carbon disulfide, carbon tetrachloride, etc.) ultrasonic absorption occurs at the usual experimental frequencies (~50 MHz) mainly due to the thermal relaxation. The effect of the variation of T in the ultrasonic wave predominates, and thus form (10.31) for $\delta\kappa/\kappa$ is useful. Two types of thermal relaxation will be considered. For both types, most cases can be considered to be unimolecular equilibria such as (10.34). Thus (10.36) and (10.41) are often applicable.

One such type of phenomenon is the case of equilibria between rotational and other conformational isomers. By studying the temperature dependence of δC_p and τ, values can be obtained for ΔH^{θ}, ΔS^{θ}, and the activation enthalpy $\Delta H^{\#}$ and entropy $\Delta S^{\#}$ for reactions such as shown in Fig. 10.4. Other examples can be found in Ref 1 and 11.

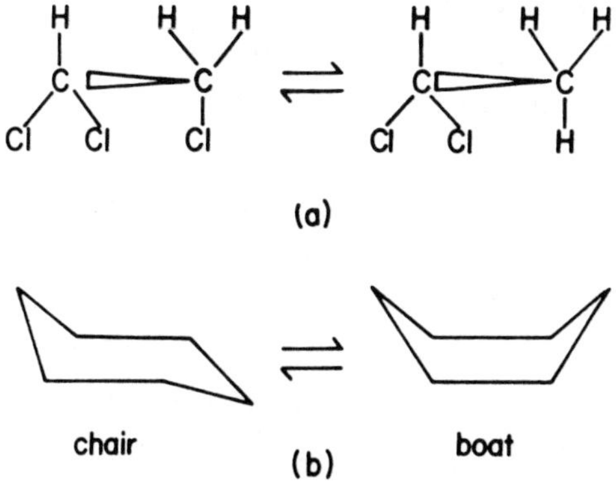

Fig. 10.4. Schematic illustration of the conformational isomers of (a) 1,1,2 trichloroethane and (b) cyclohexane.

(b) Vibrational Relaxation

Another type of thermal relaxation is usually referred to as "vibrational relaxation." The equilibrium responsible for absorption is $A \rightleftarrows A^{\dagger}$, where $A^{\dagger}$ indicates a vibrationally excited form of the species A [see also Sec. 12.3(a)]. Absorption due to vibrational relaxation is present at low megahertz frequencies in most unassociated liquids.

For many such "Kneser" liquids, the relaxation time lies close to 1 GHz (i.e., $\tau \simeq 10^{-9}$ sec), and can only be recently obtained with some difficulty [10.2(a)]. Carbon disulfide has a relaxation at ≃70 MHz, however, and has thus been widely studied. Experimental data is now available for higher frequencies, including some data from Brillouin scattering [12].

The data plotted in the form suggested by (10.26) form a half-circle with center on the abscissa (see Fig. 10.5). Thus a single relaxation time is present in the system. The value of ΔH^{θ} also shows that all the vibrational modes must be involved in this relaxation. Thus vibration-vibration transfer in this case must be considerably faster than vibrational-translational transfer. The analogous results for benzene show several relaxations to be present, as the plot of $(\mu v_0^2/\pi v^2)$ vs (v_0^2/v^2) does not take the shape of a semicircle (see, e.g., Fig. 11.3 and 11.4). A further discussion of the vibrational relaxation of benzene is in Sec. 14.3(b).

Methods of approaching vibrational relaxation from a theoretical point of view are discussed in Ref. 13. A further discussion is in Ref. 14 where the magnitude of the "relaxing acoustic specific heat" is compared to that calculated from spectroscopic data.

Monatomic liquids such as argon do not of course have absorption due to vibrational relaxation. Excess absorption in argon is due to a substantial bulk viscosity η_V (10.4), which is about 1.8 times the shear viscosity η. Theoretical calculations for η_V from the point of view of expressions analogous to (7.29) can be made, but there is no experimental method other than ultrasonic absorption which can give an experimental value of η_V.

(c) Water and Other Associated Liquids

In associated liquids such as water and alcohols, the absorption is thought to be due to the disturbance of various structural forms differing in volume. The form (10.37) is in these cases more suitable for $\delta\kappa/\kappa$.

Various models of liquid water have been proposed to explain its ultrasonic absorption properties. Evaluation of some of these can be found in Ref. 2. The simplest reasonably successful model was due to Hall in 1948. The essential features of the model are outlined below (see also Ref. 15).

Water is assumed to exist in two states, with the equilibrium distribution given by $c_I/c_{II} = \exp[-\Delta G^\theta/RT]$. These states have different partial molar volumes, and thus ΔV^θ is nonzero.

In going from one state of packing to another, the same basic process occurs as in shear viscosity. Thus the temperature dependence of τ is taken to be the same as the temperature dependence of τ_η, the average time between two successive jumps a molecule makes from one site to another [see Sec. 6.2(b)].

Values for ΔV^θ and ΔG^θ can then be chosen either by observing other properties of water, or by fitting the experimental ultrasonic absorption data using these as adjustable parameters. To fit the data with a two-state model, the open (ice-type) structure must be assumed to have a higher energy. This is contrary to other models of liquid water.

The existance of a characteristic jump time τ_η in liquids predicts the appearance of viscous relaxation. When viscosity is great, then the assumption of stress being proportional to the velocity gradient breaks down. If the time of application of a force is short as compared to the time τ_η, then the liquid exhibits rigidity and acts in effect as a solid.

Thus η is in effect frequency dependent [see also Secs. 9.3(d) and 7.2(c)]. The derivation of the form of $\eta(\omega)$ will not be given here. Instead, by analogy with the relaxation of the compressibility, the frequency dependence of η is written as

$$\eta(\omega) = \frac{\eta_0}{1 + \omega^2\tau_s^2} \tag{10.54}$$

Here η_0 is the ordinary shear viscosity and τ_s the shear relaxation time.

In highly-hydrogen-bonded liquids such as glycerol (CH_2OH-$CHOH$-CH_2OH) a broad distribution of relaxation times τ_s seem to be present. Only in liquids where viscosity varies according to the Arrhenius form (6.45) have single shear viscosity relaxations times been found [16]. The butyl alcohols show from the plot suggested by 10.26 (Fig. 10.5) that they have only a single relaxation [17]. The curves are represented by semicircles with the center on the abscissa, as expected for single relaxation processes. Relaxation of the shear as well as the volume viscosities take place, so that the presence of a single relaxation indicates identical relaxation times for the two viscosities.

Some associated liquids show thermal as well as a structural relaxation. Investigations in liquid ammonia [18] show the α/ν^2 to be

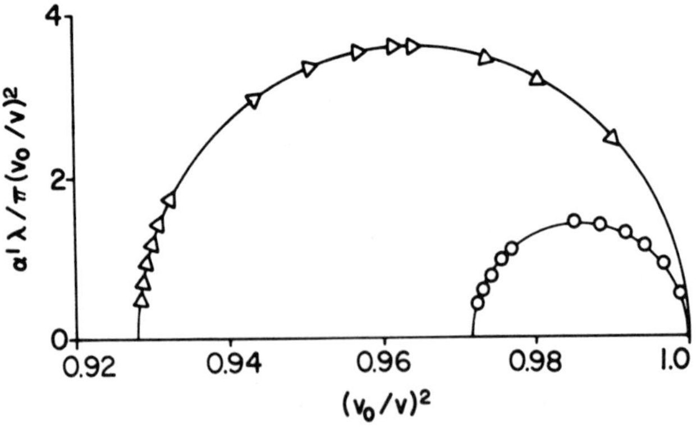

Fig. 10.5. $(\alpha'\lambda/\pi)(v_0^2/v^2)$ versus $(v_0/v)^2$ plotted for isobutyl alcohol, —△— -50°C, —o— -15°C. After Ref. 17.

frequency dependent at lower frequencies (<30 MHz). This is interpreted as being due to the thermal relaxation process, possibly an H-bond breaking rotation of the ammonia molecule.

(d) Liquid Mixtures-Unassociated Liquids

Binary mixtures of unassociated liquids show at lower frequency a characteristic curve for α/ν^2 versus composition. It is convex downward, i.e., α/ν^2 is less than that assuming a linear variation.

The reason for this type of shape is that collisions between different molecules seem often to be more effective in translational-vibrational energy transfer than collisions between like species. When like species collide, vibrational quanta are identical, and a

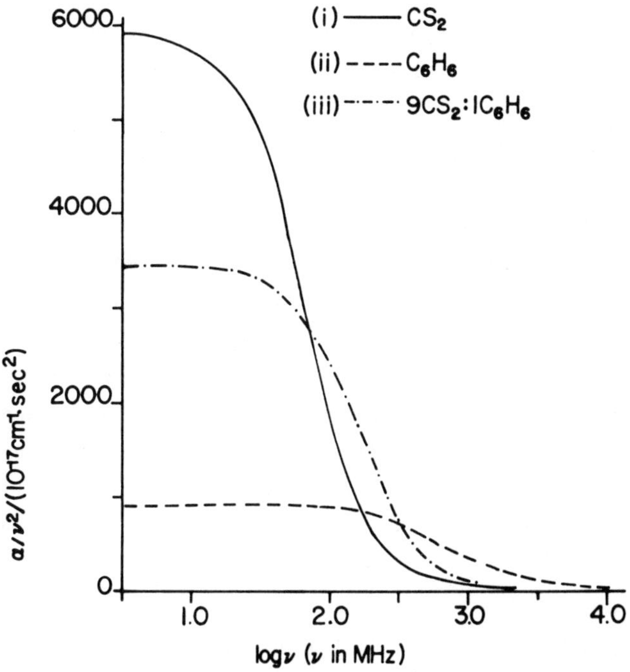

Fig. 10.6. α/ν^2 versus log ν for (i) —— liquid carbon disulfide, (ii) ---- liquid benzene, (iii) —·—·— a 9:1 mol ratio of CS_2 to benzene. After Ref. 19.

resonant transfer of vibrational energy can result instead of transfer from vibrational modes to other modes.

Thus the relaxation time τ is smaller than expected on a linear assumption and (10.25) predicts a curve convex downward at low frequencies. This need not be the case at higher frequencies, where ν approaches ν_r. This effect is shown in Fig. 10.6 for the system CS_2-C_6H_6. References 19 and 20 give more examples.

(e) Alcohol-Water Mixtures

Liquid mixtures involving two associated liquids usually show an absorption maximum at some intermediate concentration. Alcohol-water mixtures have been particularly widely studied, but the experimental results can be interpreted in several ways.

They show a distinct maximum in absorption at low mole fractions of alcohol. Such behavior can be interpreted as being due to equilibria between interstitial alcohol molecules and alcohol molecules in the lattice [Sec. 8.3(e)]. Such an equilibrium would be very sensitive to pressure and would give rise to ultrasonic absorption [21].

At low mole fractions of alcohol, all the alcohol can be accomodated interstitially and absorption is low. An optimum equilibrium for absorption is reached at higher mole fraction (about 0.1 for t-butanol-water). At yet higher mole fractions the water lattice is considerably disturbed.

The ethanol-water system has been investigated and the results interpreted assuming two relaxation processes to be present [22]. The relaxations present are postulated to be due to processes of the type $C_2H_5OH(H_2O)_n \rightleftarrows C_2H_5OH + n \cdot H_2O$, with the formation of water structures around nonpolar groups proceeding in several distinguishable steps.

An alternative explanation for the ultrasonic absorption has been proposed [23]. The excess absorption is here attributed to local concentration fluctuations. If the concentration dependence of the specific volume and enthalpy in the system is nonlinear, then there is a contribution to the specific volume and enthalpy from the fluctuations. They can thus be influenced by the ultrasonic wave [see also Sec. 4.2(e)].

The kinetics of the process of establishing a new distribution is described in terms of diffusion. When the concentration fluctuations are expressed in terms of a spatial Fourier series, then each Fourier component exhibits a single relaxation time [Sec. 7.1(f)]. A broad relaxation spectrum is predicted when a continuous distribution (e.g., Debye distribution) of wavenumbers is assumed. The agreement between the predictions of this theory and experiment are reasonably good [24].

(f) Critical Phenomena

Close to the critical point of a single component system or a binary mixture the absorption increases in most cases. Only in one system has this effect not been noted [25]. Such behavior can be explained by a theory similar to that outlined above.

Close to the critical point, $\partial\mu/\partial\rho$ (in a one-component system) or $\partial\mu/\partial c \simeq 0$ [Sec. 4.1(b)]. Thus density or composition fluctuations are large. The absorption can then be considered to be due to the disturbance of these fluctuations by the temperature variation in the ultrasonic wave. The frequency dependence is again described by a continuum of relaxation times, even though a single relaxation time has been noted by other methods [Sec. 11.3(g)]. A summary of this theory is given in Ref. 26, while Ref. 27 outlines another. A general review is available in Ref. 28.

From an analysis of the temperature dependence of the ultrasonic data, it is possible to calculate values of the Debye correlation length ℓ (3.60). Such values can then be compared to values obtained by other methods [see Sec. 15.3(d)].

It is not possible in such analysis to use the temperature range right up to the critical solution point. As in the case of X-ray [Sec. 15.3(d)] and dielectric [Sec. 11.3(g)] data, the absorption at temperatures very close to the critical solution temperature indicates that there is no change in the magnitude of the correlation length (see e.g., Fig. 15.8). This may be due to gravitational effects whereby the system is microscopically in two phases, but does not "sediment out" to form a clear meniscus [29].

There can be difficulties in the interpretation of ultrasonic data in some cases. In the exception noted [25], the excess absorption due to critical phenomena seem at some frequencies to be swamped out be contributions from effects present in all alcohol-water systems. When nonassociated liquids are involved, it is difficult to estimate the magnitude of the excess absorption due to critical phenomena, as the "background curve" is lowered by thermal relaxation from the linear [Sec. 10.3(d)].

A frequency analysis is also difficult to carry out if data in a limited range only is available. A single-relaxation equation can be fitted to any set of ultrasonic absorption data if the frequency range is small enough.

(g) Aqueous Solutions of 2:2 Electrolytes

The use of ultrasonics in the study of structure and dynamics in liquids was initiated by the explanation of the large absorption in seawater. This absorption arises from the disturbance of the ion-pairing equilibria

$$\underset{\text{I}}{(Mg^{+2})_{aq} + (SO_4^{-2})_{aq}} \underset{k_{21}}{\overset{k_{12}}{\rightleftarrows}} \underset{\text{II}}{Mg^{+2}\cdot H_2O\cdot H_2O\cdot SO_4^{-2}}$$

$$k_{32} \uparrow\downarrow k_{23}$$

$$\underset{\text{IV}}{(Mg^{+2}\cdot SO_4^{-2})_{aq}} \underset{k_{34}}{\overset{k_{43}}{\rightleftarrows}} \underset{\text{III}}{Mg^{+2}\cdot H_2O\cdot SO_4^{-2}} \qquad (10.55)$$

Each of the three equilibria would have a relaxation time τ_i. These would be quite complex functions of the rate constants as seen from the analysis of a simpler case in Sec. 10.1(f).

The form (10.37) can be used for the relaxation strength in this analysis. As activity coefficients must be considered in these cases, both the form of $\delta\kappa/\kappa$ and τ become considerably more complicated. Because of these complexities, there is still disagreement in the analysis of experimental data on $MnSO_4$ such as shown in Fig. 10.7 [30]. The uncertainty in the experimental data contribute to the difficulty in definitive assignment of steps.

The data for a 0.5 M $MnSO_4$ solution on the 3-step (4-stage) model in (10.55) give

$k_{12} = 4 \times 10^{10}$ mol 1^{-1} sec^{-1}	$k_{23} = 2.8 \times 10^{9}$ sec^{-1}	$k_{34} = 2.7 \times 10^{7}$ sec^{-1}
$k_{21} = 2.0 \times 10^{9}$ sec^{-1}	$k_{32} = 3.7 \times 10^{8}$ sec^{-1}	$k_{43} = 2.2 \times 10^{7}$ sec^{-1}
$K_{12} = 0.05$	$K_{23} = 0.77$	$K_{34} = 1.1$
$\Delta V_{12} = -18.3$ cm^3 mol^{-1}	$\Delta V_{23} = 13.3$ cm^3 mol^{-1}	$\Delta V_{34} = -3.5$ cm^3 mol^{-1}

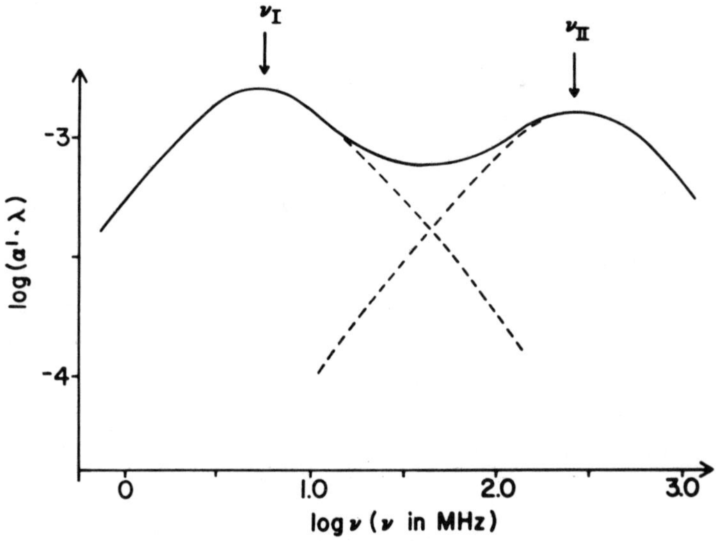

Fig. 10.7. Log($\alpha'\cdot\lambda$) versus log ν for the system 0.1 M manganese sulfate at 20 to 25°C. After Ref. 30.

A two step model, where stages II and III are not distinguished can also be used to interpret the data satisfactorally. For a 0.1 M $MnSO_4$ solution, the parameters are

$k_{1,23} = 8 \times 10^{10}$ mol^{-1} liter sec^{-1} $\quad$ $k_{23,4} = 2 \times 10^{7}$ sec^{-1}
$k_{23,1} = 10 \times 10^{8}$ sec^{-1} $\quad$ $k_{4,23} = 2 \times 10^{7}$ sec^{-1}
$K_{1,23} = 0.013$ $\quad$ $K_{23,4} = 1.0$
$\Delta V_{1,23} = -9$ cm^3 mol^{-1} $\quad$ $\Delta V_{23,4} = -2$ cm^3 mol^{-1}

Even later data can be found in Ref. 31.

The rate constant k_{12} can be taken to be essentially the same for all 2:2 sulfates. This is because it describes the formation of an ion pair from two free ions [Sec. 6.3(d)]. The process is diffusion-controlled, and not governed by chemical aspects.

(h) Solutions of Univalent Electrolytes

It is not possible to study such ion-pairing formation for simpler species (e.g., alkali-halides) in aqueous solutions because the dissociation is essentially complete. Ion pairing of alkali halides in nonaqueous solutions can be observed through ultrasonic absorption, but quantitative analysis is in cases difficult due to the lack of thermodynamic data and the sensitivity of the data to traces of water [32]. In cases of lithium perchlorate in tetrahydrofuran solution, the equilibrium between an ion pair and a triple ion is thought to be detected [33].

Studies of tetraalkylammonium salt solutions have been carried out both in aqueous [34] and nonaqueous [35] solvents. In the case of aqueous solutions, an ion association equilibrium is likely to be responsible for a part of the extra ultrasonic absorption observed. However, part of the excess absorption may also be due to some equilibrium involving the alkyl chains analogous to the equilibria giving rise to excess absorption in water-alcohol systems [Sec. 10.3(e)]. The Romanov-Solovyev theory [23] relating ultrasonic absorption to thermodynamic properties [see Sec. 10.3(e)] has been applied to tetraethyl- and tetra-n-butylammonium bromide solutions [34]. The predictions of the theory are in agreement with trends observed.

In non-aqueous solutions, the ion association phenomenon is believed to be responsible for the major part of the observed excess absorption [35]. It is however possible in cases to have other equilibria contribute, e.g., rotational equilibria involving the alkyl side chains. Such a rotational process does not seem to contribute significantly to absorption in tetraalkylammonium halide solutions in methanol and propanol.

Although effects due to ion association equilibria do not seem to be present in ultrasonic absorption in most aqueous alkali halide solutions [see, e.g., Sec. 9.3(f)], an increase or decrease in α/ν^2 is noted if the concentration is large enough (m in the range up to 16 mol kg solvent^{-1}) [36]. These effects are explained as being due to a structural relaxation process. The structural absorption is considered to be made up with contributions from bulk (undisturbed) water and various regions around cations and anions.

The structural absorption of the outer region around ions is relatively smaller than that of bulk water. Thus as initially the amount of bulk water decreases and the amount of "outer region" water increases, there is a decrease in total structural absorption at lower ($\simeq$3 m) concentrations. When ions such as Li^+ are present, then the absorption increases again at higher concentrations when the contribution of the inner region becomes dominant. At higher concentrations, the outer region effect decreases due to overlapping of these regions. Both the number of water molecules involved in the various regions and the relaxation times (10^{-12} sec) can be estimated through such an analysis.

(i) Proton Transfer Reactions

An important case of ion-pairing processes is that of proton transfer reactions. Usually the relaxation time is so high that the actual relaxation of the proton (hydroxyl) transfer reaction cannot be observed. At low frequencies, it contributes an excess absorption.

The magnitude of such an absorption can be calculated if the diffusion constants (6.77), the equilibrium constant K and ΔV^{θ} is known. It can be written as

$$\frac{\alpha'}{\nu^2} = \frac{2\pi^2\rho v(\Delta V^\theta)^2}{RT} \; \frac{\alpha(1 - \alpha)}{2 - \alpha} \cdot c \cdot \frac{1}{k_{12}} \cdot \frac{1}{K + 2\alpha c} \qquad (10.56)$$

with the help of (10.31), (10.39), and (10.43). An expression for k_{12} can be found in (6.81). A value of D can be obtained from α'/ν^2 vs c data even if ΔV^θ is not known, and absolute rates of proton transfer reactions can be measured in inorganic acids in the cases where ΔV^θ values are known [37].

In basic solutions, rates involving the hydroxyl ion can be investigated. Thus the rates involved in the equilibrium $-RNH_2 + H_2O \rightleftarrows -RNH_3 + OH^-$ have been investigated [38]. There is a decreasing trend in the association rate constant with increase in molecular weight as expected from diffusion-controlled rate theory (6.81). In basic purine solutions [39] there is an added complication in the analysis of experimental results, as the effect of dimerization must be included.

Proton-transfer reactions in solutions of proteins have also been detected [40]. In such complex solutions it is difficult to conclusively find the equilibrium responsible for the excess absorption. "Ultrasonic titration curves" are thus often determined for solutions, i.e., α is measured as a function of pH. Such curves show a maxima in α at some values of pH.

A contribution of the form 10.56 can be considered to be present from all possible proton (and hydroxyl) transfer processes present. The magnitude of such contributions can be estimated. They can then be simply added as the reactions are not of a series form such as in Sec. 10.1(f).

For bovine serum albumin solution, the excess absorption is thus the sum of the contributions of 215 separate equilibria per molecule [41]. Qualitative agreement of theory with experiment is obtained as seen in Fig. 10.8.

In other cases, the excess absorption is assumed due to conformational changes [42,43]. The absorption at pH 8 in poly-L-lysine solution has been interpreted as being due to the coil-helix equilibrium.

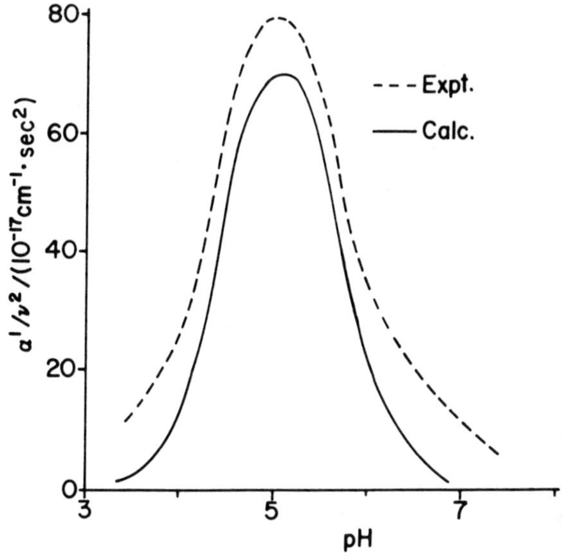

Fig. 10.8. α'/ν^2 versus pH for bovine serum albumin solution, ——— theory, ----- experiment. After Ref. 41.

Such conformational equilibria have also been studied by T-jump methods. In this case, solutions of lysozyme show a relaxation time in the 10^{-3} sec range [44]. At ultrasonic frequencies, these equilibria would be "frozen out."

REFERENCES

A review of most aspects of ultrasonic absorption in liquids can be found in the contributions in [1]. Both [2] and [3] give a description of ultrasonics in general.

1. W. P. Mason (ed.), Physical Acoustics, Vol. II, Part A. Academic Press, New York, 1965.
2. K. F. Herzfeld and T. A. Litovitz, Absorption and Dispersion of Ultrasonic Waves, Academic Press, New York, 1959.
3. R. T. Beyer and S. V. Letcher, Physical Ultrasonics, Academic Press, New York, 1969.
4. D. G. Naugle, J. H. Lemsford, and J. R. Singer, J. Chem. Phys., *45*, 4669 (1966); P. Gray and S. A. Rice, J. Chem. Phys., *41*, 3689 (1964).

5. T. F. Hunter and R. H. Bolt, Sonics, Wiley John and Sons, New York, 1955.

6. K. G. Plass, Acoustica, *19*, 236 (1967/1968).

7. D. N. Hall and J. Lamb, Proc. Phys. Soc., *73*, 354 (1959).

8. T. Yasunaga, N. Tatsumoto, and M. Miura, J. Chem. Phys., *43*, 2735 (1965).

9. F. Eggers and T. Funck, Rev. Sci. Instrum., *44*, 969 (1973).

10. M. C. Rose and J. Stuehr, J. Am. Chem. Soc., *93*, 4350 (1971).

11. G. Ecclestone, B. Walsh, E. Wyn-Jones, and H. Morris, Trans. Farad. Soc., *67*, 3223 (1971), and previous papers.

12. P. K. Habibullaev, M. G. Haliulin, S. S. Aliyev, M. I. Shakhparanov, and D. V. Lanshina, Paper P-0-37, 6th Int. Cong. Acoustics, Tokyo (1968).

13. P. K. Davis and I. Oppenheim, J. Chem. Phys., *57*, 505 (1972).

14. P. K. Habibullaev and M. I. Shakhparanov, Soviet Phys.-Acoustics, *18*, 251 (1972).

15. C. M. Davis and J. Jarzynski in GR6,7.

16. R. Kono, G. E. McDuffie, and T. A. Litovitz, J. Chem. Phys., *44*, 965 (1966).

17. T. Mamanov, K. Parpiev, and P. K. Habibullaev, Soviet Phys.-Acoustics, *15*, 537 (1970).

18. D. E. Bowen, J. Chem. Phys., *59*, 4686 (1973).

19. J. L. Hunter, J. M. Davenport, and D. Sette, J. Chem. Phys., *55*, 762 (1971).

20. P. K. Habibullaev and M. G. Haluilin, Soviet Phys.-Acoustics, *15*, 120 (1969).

21. F. Franks and D. I. G. Ives, Quart. Rev., *20*, 1 (1966).

22. S. G. Bruun, P. G. Sorensen, and A. Hvidt, Acta. Chem. Scand., Ser. A, *28*, 1047 (1974).

23. V. P. Romanov and V. A. Solov'ev, in Water in Biological Systems (M. F. Vuks and A. I. Sidorova, eds.), Vol. II, 1, Consultants Bureau, 1971.

24. W. D. T. Dale, P. A. Flavelle, and P. Kruus, Can. J. Chem., *54*, 355 (1976).

25. R. J. Fanning and P. Kruus, Can. J. Chem., *48*, 2052 (1970).

26. V. P. Gutschick and C. J. Pings, J. Chem. Phys., *55*, 3840 (1971).

27. K. Kawasaki, Phys. Rev. A., *3*, 1097 (1971).

28. C. W. Garland, in Physical Acoustics, Vol. VII (W. P. Mason and R. N. Thurston, eds.), Academic Press, New York, 1970.

29. P. Kruus, Can. J. Chem., *42*, 1712 (1964).

30. L. G. Jackopin and E. Yeager, J. Phys. Chem., *74*, 3766 (1970).

31. A. Bechtler, K. G. Breitschwerdt, and K. Tamm, J. Chem. Phys., *52*, 2975 (1970).

32. D. R. Dickson and P. Kruus, Can. J. Chem., *49*, 3107 (1971).

33. P. Jagodzinski and S. Petrucci, J. Phys. Chem., *78*, 917 (1974).

34. M. J. Blandamer and D. Waddington, J. Chem. Phys., *52*, 6247 (1970).

35. J. Stuehr, T. Noveske, and D. F. Evans, J. Phys. Chem., *77*, 912 (1973).

36. K. G. Breitschwerdt and H. Kistenmacher, J. Chem. Phys., *56*, 4800 (1972).

37. L. W. Green, P. Kruus, and M. J. McGuire, Can. J. Chem., *54*, 3152 (1976).

38. M. M. Emara, G. Atkinson, and E. Baumgartner, J. Phys. Chem., *76*, 334 (1972).

39. M. Brennan and K. Kustin, J. Phys. Chem., *76*, 2838 (1972).

40. J. Lang, C. Tondre, and R. Zana, J. Phys. Chem., *75*, 374 (1971).

41. M. Hussey and P. D. Edmonds, J. Phys. Chem., *75*, 4012 (1971).

42. R. C. Parker, L. J. Slutsky, and K. R. Applegate, J. Phys. Chem., *72*, 3177 (1968).

43. S. Kh. Sadykhova and I. E. El'piner, Soviet Phys.-Acoustics, *16*, 101 (1970); G. Schwarz, Molecular Relaxation Processes, Chemical Soc. S.P. 20, Academic Press, New York, 1966.

44. J. Owen, E. Eyring, and D. Cole, J. Phys. Chem., *73*, 3918 (1969).

Further Recent References

M. M. Farrow, S. L. Olsen, N. Purdie, and E. M. Eyring, "Automatic Ultrasonic Absorption Spectrometer", Rev. Sci. Instrum., *47*, 657 (1976).

M. S. Tunin, "The Fine Structure of the Rayleigh Light Scattering Line and the Mechanism of Acoustic Relaxation in Liquid Perfluoromethylcyclohexane", Russ. J. Phys. Chem., *48*, 500 (1974).

A. V. Narasimham and B. Manikiam, "Ultrasonic Studies of Liquids Using Hole Theory", J. Chem. Phys., *63*, 2350 (1975).

E. B. Petrunina, V. P. Romanov,aand V. A. Solov'ev, "Calculation of the Kneser Relaxation Times in a Liquid According to the Binary-Collision Model", Sov. Phys. Acoust., *21*, 481 (1976).

D. E. Bowen, M. A. Preisand, and S. R. Feighny, "Ultrasound Propagation in NH_3-H_2O Mixtures", J. Chem. Phys., *62*, 808 (1975).

R. Zana and J. Lang, "Ultrasonic Absorption in Relation to H Bonding in Solutions of Alcohols I. Isomeric Octyl Alcohols in Non-Polar Solvents", Adv. Mol. Relax. Proc., *7*, 21 (1975).

M. M. Emara and G. Atkinson, "The Kinetics of Self-Association of Ethanol in Ethyl Chloride", Adv. Mol. Relax. Proc., *6*, 233 (1974).

E. A. G. Aniansson, S. N. Wall, M. Almgren, H. Hoffmann, I. Killmann, W. Ulbricht, R. Zana, J. Lang, and C. Tondre, "Theory of the Kinetics of Micellar Equilibria and Quantitative Interpretation of Chemical Relaxation Studies of Micellar Solutions of Ionic Surfactants", J. Phys. Chem., *80*, 905 (1976).

P. W. Ward, J. A. Cowan, and R. K. Pathria, "Critical Attenuation of Ultrasound in Argon", Can. J. Phys., *53*, 29 (1975).

J. Thoen and C. W. Garland, "Sound Absorption and Dispersion as a Function of Density near the Critical Point of Xenon", Phys. Rev., *A10*, 1311 (1974).

S. I. Makhkamov, P. K. Habibullaev, and M. G. Halialin, "Acoustic Relaxation in Certain Carboxylic Acids", Sov. Phys.-Acoustics, *20*, 391 (1975).

F. H. Fisher, "Dissociation of Na_2SO_4 from Ultrasonic Absorption Reduction in $MgSO_4$-NaCl Solutions", J. Sol. Chem., *4*, 237 (1975).

S. Harada, T. Yasunaga, K. Tamura, and N. Tatsumoto, "Ultrasonic and Laser Temperature-Jump Studies of the Nickel Monocarboxylate Complex Formation Reactions in Solution", J. Phys. Chem., *80*, 313 (1976).

R. Carpio, F. Borsay, C. Petrovic, and E. Yeager, "Ultrasonic and Hypersonic Properties of Ionic Hydrate Melts", J. Chem. Phys., *65*, 29 (1976).

Chapter 11

DIELECTRIC RELAXATION

The topics covered in this chapter are related quite directly to numerous other chapters. Electrical conductivity (Chap. 9) is a related property which must be taken into account when dielectric studies of electrolyte solutions are undertaken. Dielectric relaxation is formally related to ultrasonic absorption (Chap. 10) as both involve relaxation phenomena and have thus analogous mathematical forms. The topics in this chapter are related to the resonance absorption discussed in Chap. 12 as the dielectric relaxation present in liquids corresponds in gases to resonance rotational absorption, and as vibrational absorption can also be considered in terms of a complex permittivity just as dielectric relaxation. The molecular phenomena that can be studied by dielectric relaxation can also be studied through nuclear magnetic resonance (Chap. 13) and light scattering (Chap. 14).

Besides dielectric relaxation, the chapter also covers other closely related phenomena. The Kerr effect and the field dissociation effect are discussed together with other phenomena involving essentially a static field. Changes in the permittivity due to resonance absorption are covered in more detail in Chap. 12.

The approach to developing the appropriate theoretical background is in this case quite straightforward. Thus the subsection headings should be sufficient to outline the developmnet. It can be considered to be an extension of the material in Secs. 20.1 and 1.1.

11.1. THEORETICAL BACKGROUND

(a) *The Static Dielectric Constant*

The static dielectric constant will be denoted by ε_0, as it is more properly the relative permittivity at the limit of frequency $\omega \to 0$. The operative definition of ε_0 is the relation $\varepsilon_0 = C/C^{\bullet}$, where $C^{\bullet}$ is the capacity of a condenser in vacuum, and C its capacity when the dielectric medium is placed between the plates.

Figure 11.1 illustrates how the insertion of a dielectric alters the capacitance of a condenser (per unit area) from $C^{\bullet} = \mathcal{Q}/V$ to $C = (\mathcal{Q} + P)/V$. To have the same net amount of charge $\mathcal{Q}$ at the positive plate with the dielectric medium inserted, and amount $\mathcal{Q} + P$ must be stored on the plate to cancel out the polarization charge P in the medium at the plate.

From the point of view of individual molecules, $\underline{P}$ can be written as $\underline{P}(t) = 1/V \cdot \Sigma \underline{p}_i(t)$. Here $\underline{p}_i(t)$ is the instantaneous electric dipole

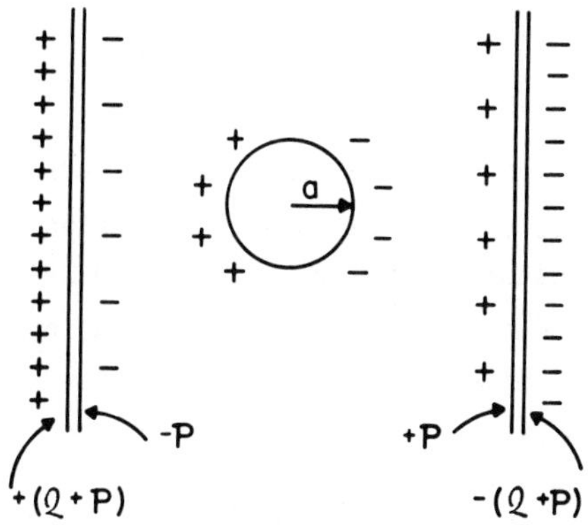

Fig. 11.1. Schematic diagram to illustrate the appearance of polarization charge on insertion of a dielectric between the plates of a condenser.

vector of the ith molecule. The summation is over all the molecules in the volume V. There may be correlation present between the $\underline{p}(t)$ of neighboring molecules. On a first approximation, however, the dipoles are considered independent of each other.

The behavior of a molecule in the dielectric can be investigated on a simple model assuming the molecule to be in a cavity radius a. The effective field $\underline{E}_{eff}$ in the cavity can be obtained from the solution of the equations of electrostatics, considering the medium to be continuous. It can also be considered to be arising from the three sources: (i) the charge on the condenser plates, (ii) the charge on the outer surface of the dielectric, and (iii) the charge on the surface of the cavity. Any molecule present in the cavity is assumed to give no net contribution to $\underline{E}_{eff}$. The contributions from (i) and (ii) are $\underline{E} + \underline{P}/\varepsilon^\bullet$ and $-\underline{P}/\varepsilon^\bullet$, while that from (iii) is

$$\frac{1}{4\pi\varepsilon^\bullet}\int\frac{\underline{P}\cdot 2\pi a^2}{a^2}\sin\theta\, d\theta\, d\phi = \frac{\underline{P}}{3\varepsilon^\bullet} \tag{11.1}$$

Thus the field $\underline{E}_{eff}$ is in this approximation

$$\underline{E}_{\text{eff}} = \left(\underline{E} + \frac{\underline{P}}{\varepsilon^\bullet}\right) - \frac{\underline{P}}{\varepsilon^\bullet} + \frac{\underline{P}}{3\varepsilon^\bullet} = \underline{E} + \frac{\underline{P}}{3\varepsilon^\bullet} \tag{11.2}$$

The polarization $\underline{P}$ can be considered to arise from three sources, $\underline{P} = \underline{P}_{\text{at}} + \underline{P}_{\text{el}} + \underline{P}_{\text{or}}$. The first two contributions together are often referred to as "distortion polarization," and are due to the polarizability of individual molecules as discussed in Sec. 1.1(c). The distortion of the geometry of the atoms is given by $\underline{P}_{\text{at}}$, while the distortion of the electronic distribution is $\underline{P}_{\text{el}}$. The contribution of these two terms is then

$$\underline{P}_{\text{at}} + \underline{P}_{\text{el}} = \frac{N}{V}\cdot\underline{p}_{\text{ind}} = \frac{N}{V}\cdot\alpha\varepsilon^\bullet\underline{E}_{\text{eff}} \tag{11.3}$$

Here $\underline{p}_{\text{ind}}$ is the induced dipole, assumed proportional to $\underline{E}_{\text{eff}}$ (1.16).

If the molecule has a permanent dipole $\underline{p}$, then it contributes an orientational term $\underline{P}_{\text{or}}$. In a field $\underline{E}_{\text{eff}}$, there is an instantaneous energy due to the presence of $\underline{p}$ given by Eq. (1.17):

$$\mathcal{V}_{\text{inst}} = -\underline{p}\cdot\underline{E}_{\text{eff}} = -pE_{\text{eff}}\cos\theta \tag{11.4}$$

The time (ensemble) average contribution from such preferential orientation of dipoles to $\underline{P}$ is then (1.20)

$$\underline{P}_{\text{or}} = \frac{N}{V}\,\frac{\int p\cos\theta\,\exp[-pE_{\text{eff}}\cos\theta/kT]\,d\tau}{\int\exp[-pE_{\text{eff}}\cos\theta/kT]\,d\tau} \tag{11.5}$$

The integration is over all orientations with $d\tau = \sin\theta\,d\theta\,d\phi$. When $pE_{\text{eff}} \ll kT$, then the exponentials can be expanded, and only the leading nonzero terms kept. In this case

$$P_{\text{or}} \simeq \frac{N}{V}\,\frac{p^2E_{\text{eff}}}{3kT} \tag{11.6}$$

When (11.6), (11.3), and (11.2) are combined, the "Clausius-Mossotti" relation is obtained in the form

$$\frac{3(\varepsilon_0 - 1)}{\varepsilon_0 + 2} = \frac{N}{V}\;\alpha + \frac{p^2}{3\varepsilon^\bullet kT} \tag{11.7}$$

Nonlinear effects and electric saturation are neglected in (11.7). In addition, local forces due to the discrete nature of the medium are neglected. Effects due to any field set up in the medium and in the cavity due to the presence of polarizable, polar molecules in the cavity itself are also left out. Thus (11.7) does not apply well to a polar liquid.

There are several more refined approaches to the problem of obtaining $\underline{E}_{eff}$ [1,2]. A commonly used form is one due to Onsager. Here the molecule is treated as a point dipole in a cavity. Thus there is included a reaction field set up by the polarization which the dipole induces in its surroundings. It can be written in the form

$$\frac{3(2\varepsilon_0 + \varepsilon_\infty)(\varepsilon_0 - \varepsilon_\infty)}{\varepsilon_0(\varepsilon_\infty + 2)^2} = \frac{N}{V}\,\frac{p^2}{3\varepsilon^{\bullet}kT} \tag{11.8}$$

Here the relative permittivity ε_∞ is introduced. It refers to the value of ε at higher frequencies, where orientational contributions to $\underline{P}$ have dropped out, and $\underline{P}$ is given by (11.3).

(b) Polarization

When the permittivity ε is measured for alternating electric fields, it is found to be frequency-dependent. At frequencies typically of the order of 10^{11} Hz, the contribution of $\underline{P}_{or}$ to $\underline{P}$ drops out (or is "frozen out") as the molecules are no longer able to reorient themselves to follow the field and maintain an equilibrium distribution (see Fig. 10.1). This decrease of ε from ε_0 to ε_∞ due to the "freezing out" of $\underline{P}_{or}$ is referred to as dielectric relaxation. In gases, the orientational motion of molecules is not hindered, and instead of a relaxation process, a resonant rotational absorption can occur. This may also occur to some extent in liquids [Sec. 11.3(a)].

At infrared frequencies, there can occur resonance conditions with regard to distortions of the atomic geometry, and resonant vibrational transitions can occur. At frequencies higher than these, the contribution of $\underline{P}_{at}$ to $\underline{P}$ is no longer present. In this optical frequency region, $\varepsilon = n^2$, where n is the index of refraction.

At yet higher frequencies (usually the ultraviolet) resonance can occur with regard to various electronic distortions. When this broad frequency region has been passed through, then contributions from $\underline{P}_{el}$ to $\underline{P}$ have disappeared, and $\varepsilon \to 1$ (see Fig. 11.2).

Removed from resonant absorption frequencies, the speed of electromagnetic waves is given as $c^{\bullet}\sqrt{\varepsilon\mu}$ (20.36). As μ varies negligibly in this whole frequency range, then $c \propto \sqrt{\varepsilon}$. Near resonance, the dispersion is typically as shown in Fig. 11.2. The exact form will be discussed in more detail in Chap. 12. In the optical range, n usually increases with ω due to the presence of absorption bands in the ultraviolet.

There is present a relative narrow absorption band at the frequencies where resonance occurs. The disappearance of $\underline{P}_{or}$ is due to a relaxation process, however, so that the absorption involved has a

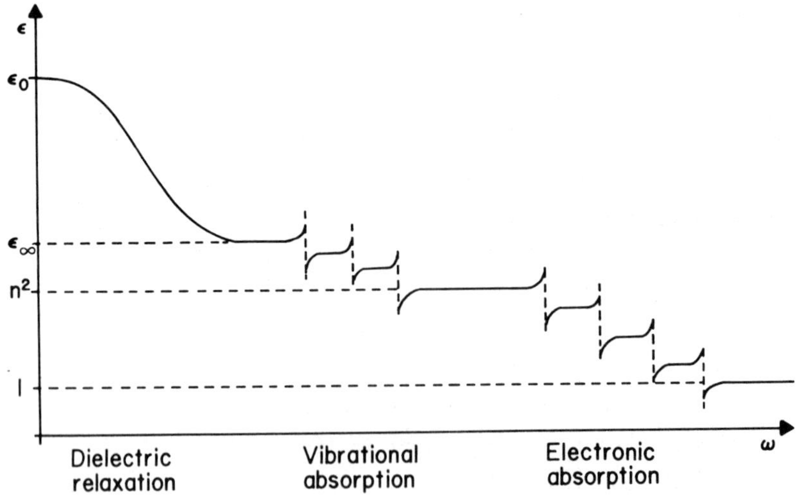

Fig. 11.2. Schematic diagram illustrating the change in ε with frequency over a wide frequency range.

broader frequency range. The mathematics for the relaxation of $\underline{P}_{or}$ is analogous to that for the relaxation of $\delta\kappa$ in ultrasonic absorption [Sec. 10.1(b)].

(c) The Complex Permittivity (Single Relaxation Time)

The relaxation of the orientational polarization $\underline{P}_{or}$ can be described in terms of a relaxation time τ in analogy to (10.12) as

$$\frac{d\underline{P}_{or}}{dt} = -\frac{1}{\tau}(\underline{P}_{or} - \underline{P}_{or,eq}) \qquad (11.9)$$

Here $\underline{P}_{or}$ is the instantaneous value of the polarization, while $\underline{P}_{or,eq}$ is the equilibrium value, given as

$$\underline{P}_{or,eq} = (\varepsilon_0 - \varepsilon_\infty)\varepsilon^{\bullet}\underline{E} \qquad (11.10)$$

The reasons for assuming such a linear rate are discussed in Sec. 19.4.

In direct analogy to the relaxation of the ordering parameter ξ [Eqs. (10.12)-(10.14)] with a periodic driving force, the time dependence of $\underline{P}_{or}$ can be expressed as

$$\underline{P}_{or}(t) = \frac{\varepsilon^{\bullet}(\varepsilon_0 - \varepsilon_\infty)\underline{E}_0 \exp[i\omega t]}{1 + i\omega t} \qquad (11.11)$$

Thus there is an out of phase component of $\underline{P}_{or}$. The total polarization can be expressed then as

$$\underline{P}^*(\omega) = \underline{P}' - i\underline{P}'' = \varepsilon^*\varepsilon^{\bullet}\underline{E} = (\varepsilon' - i\varepsilon'')\varepsilon^{\bullet}\underline{E} \qquad (11.12)$$

Here a complex permittivity ε^* has been introduced.

When (11.12) and (11.11) are combined, the solutions for ε' and ε'' are

$$\varepsilon' = \varepsilon_\infty + \frac{\varepsilon_0 - \varepsilon_\infty}{1 + \omega^2\tau^2} \qquad \varepsilon'' = \frac{\varepsilon_0 - \varepsilon_\infty}{1 + \omega^2\tau^2}\cdot\omega\tau \qquad (11.13)$$

The relationship can be written as the "Debye equation"

$$\left(\varepsilon' - \frac{\varepsilon_0 + \varepsilon_\infty}{2}\right)^2 + \varepsilon''^2 = \left(\frac{\varepsilon_0 - \varepsilon_\infty}{2}\right)^2 \qquad (11.14)$$

A plot of ε'' vs ε' then gives a circle with center at $(\varepsilon_0 + \varepsilon_\infty)/2$ and radius $(\varepsilon_0 - \varepsilon_\infty)/2$. The various points can be obtained at various frequencies. The maximum value of ε'' occurs at $\omega\tau = 1$.

The phase lag between $\underline{P}$ and $\underline{E}$ leads to an absorption of energy. The rate of heat absorption is given by potential times current. In this case the current density is $d\underline{P}/dt$. Thus the average rate of heating, on appropriate substitution is

$$\langle \underline{E} \cdot \frac{d\underline{P}}{dt} \rangle = \frac{E_0^2 \varepsilon^{\bullet} \varepsilon'' \omega}{2} \tag{11.15}$$

The real component $\underline{P}'$ is in phase with $\underline{E}$, i.e., the real component of $d\underline{P}/dt$ is out of phase with $\underline{E}$ and "stores" rather than dissipates energy. If there is an ohmic (direct current) conductivity, then this contribution must be subtracted from the total heating when ε'' is determined.

(d) Multiple Relaxation Times

In many cases, a plot of ε'' vs ε' (an "Argand diagram") does not produce the "Debye semicircle" predicted by (11.14). If three distinct relaxation times are present for example, then a plot of ε'' vs ε' may be of the type shown in Fig. 11.3(c). In this case there would be three distinct dipolar species present, each of which has a different relaxation time. The dotted curves give the relation for the three relaxations. However, the experimental data (i.e., ε'', ε' measured as a function of ω) usually do not give distinct maxima as the absorption bands for individual relaxations are quite broad (more than 1 decade half-width) and overlap is likely. This shown schematically in Fig. 11.3(a,b) (see also Fig. 11.11).

A fairly common type of experimental shape for the Argand diagram (i.e., ε'' vs ε') is a "Cole-Cole" arc. Here the experimental points form an arc of a circle, but with the center below the ε' axis [Fig. 11.4(a)]. Such an arc can be described by the equation

$$\frac{\varepsilon^* - \varepsilon_\infty}{\varepsilon_0 - \varepsilon_\infty} = \frac{1}{1 + (i\omega\tau)^{(1-h)}} \tag{11.16}$$

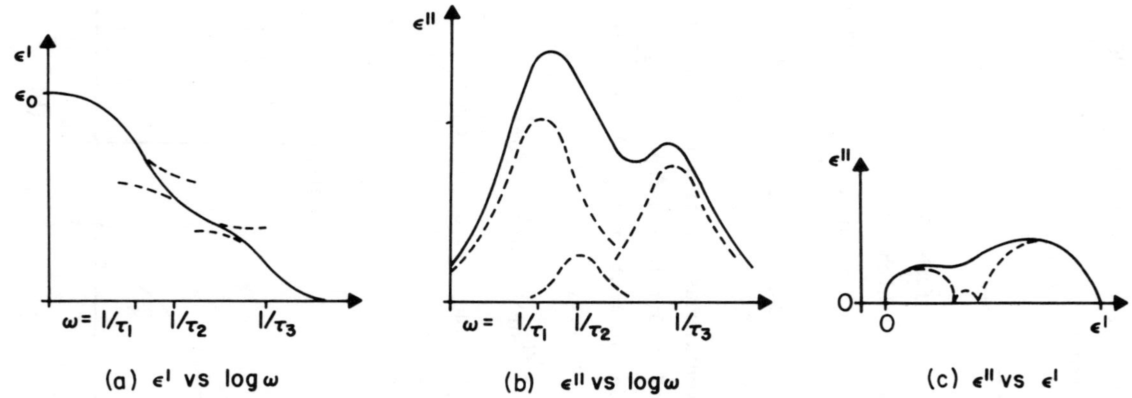

Fig. 11.3. Diagrams illustrating the effect on ε' and ε'' of the presence of 3 separate relaxation processes. (a) ε' vs log ω, (b) ε'' vs log ω, (c) ε'' vs ε'.

It can be explained as being due to a symmetric distribution of relaxation times as shown in Fig. 11.4(b) where the statistical weight of the relaxation time distribution $g(\tau)\ d(\log \tau)$ is shown.

Another common type of result is a skewed "Cole-Davidson" arc, which can be represented as

$$\frac{\varepsilon^* - \varepsilon_\infty}{\varepsilon_0 - \varepsilon_\infty} = \frac{1}{(1 + i\omega\tau)^d} \tag{11.17}$$

Figure 11.5 shows the form of the Argand diagram together with the distribution $g(\tau)\ d(\log \tau)$ which gives rise to it.

The distribution $g(\tau)$ is related to ε' and ε'' as

$$\frac{\varepsilon' - \varepsilon_\infty}{\varepsilon_0 - \varepsilon_\infty} = \int_0^\infty \frac{g(\tau)\ d(\ln \tau)}{1 + \omega^2\tau^2} \qquad \frac{\varepsilon''}{\varepsilon_0 - \varepsilon_\infty} = \int_0^\infty \frac{g(\tau)\omega\tau\ d(\ln \tau)}{1 + \omega^2\tau^2} \tag{11.18}$$

The appearance of a continuous spectrum of relaxation times can be considered in terms of a correlation function $G_{or}(t)$ [Sec. 7.3(a)] describing the time development of $\underline{P}_{or}$. When a field is maintained until t = 0 and then removed,

$$\langle \underline{P}_{or}(0)\cdot\underline{P}_{or}(t)\rangle = \langle \underline{P}_{or}(0)\cdot\underline{P}_{or}(0)\rangle\cdot G_{or}(t) \tag{11.19}$$

The same function $G_{or}(t)$ can also be written as

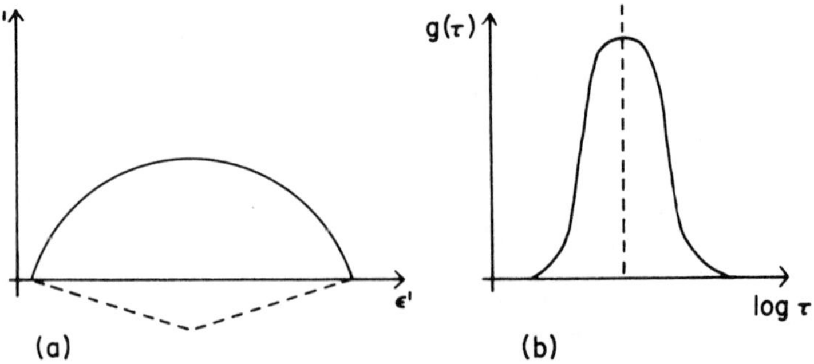

Fig. 11.4. Diagrams illustrating (a) a Cole-Cole arc and (b) the distribution of relaxation times giving rise to it.

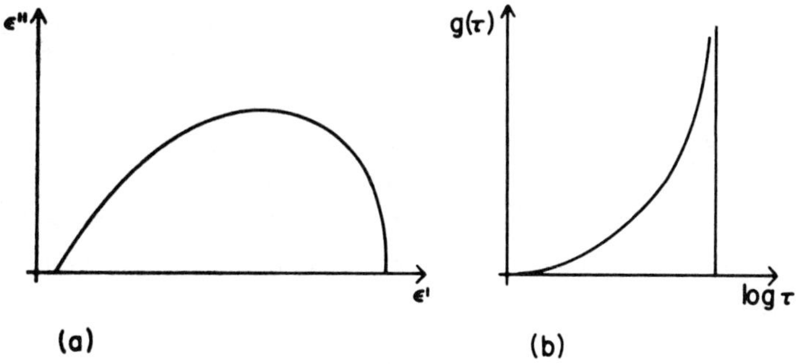

Fig. 11.5. Diagrams illustrating (a) a Cole-Davidson arc and (b) the distribution of relaxation times giving rise to it.

$$G_{or}(t) = \int_0^\infty \exp\left[-\frac{t}{\tau}\right] g(\tau)\, d(\ln \tau) \tag{11.20}$$

It is then possible, in analogy with (11.19) to (11.12) to consider the case where there is a periodic field.

This time correlation $G_{or}(t)$ is not the same as $G_1(t)$ (7.38) for the molecular electric dipole moment. There can be correlations between neighboring dipoles present, and the effective field is different from the applied field.

(e) Relaxation Times Interpreted in Molecular Terms

A single relaxation time implies that all the molecules or groups relaxing have the same average environment in the time scale suggested by τ. By referring back to the discussion in Chap. 6, it is possible to obtain a relation between τ and molecular rotational motion for simple cases.

When rotational diffusion is assumed, then a microscopic relaxation time τ_r can be defined as

$$\tau_r = \frac{1}{2D_r} = \frac{\zeta}{2kT} \tag{11.21}$$

Here relation (6.31a) has been used together with the rotational analogy of (6.62). ζ is the friction coefficient for rotational motion.

If furthermore the macroscopic viscosity η is assumed to apply at molecular levels, then through (6.13),

$$\tau_r = \frac{4\pi\eta a^3}{kT} \qquad (11.22)$$

(11.22)

The relaxation time τ_r is not identical to the macroscopic τ in the previous discussion. When the internal field $\underline{E}_{\text{eff}}$ is assumed described by (11.2), then

$$\tau = \frac{\varepsilon_0 + 2}{\varepsilon_\infty + 2} \cdot \tau_r \qquad (11.23)$$

A more refined treatment of the internal field gives a more realistic relation

$$\tau = \frac{3\varepsilon_0}{2\varepsilon_0 + \varepsilon_\infty} \cdot \tau_r \qquad (11.24)$$

Several assumptions are made in the above treatment. One of these is to neglect the effect of inertia in determining the rotational velocity of molecules. The inertia is negligible if $I/\zeta \ll 2\pi/\omega$, i.e., if the time taken for the friction to counteract the inertial motion is $\ll$ the period of the disturbance. This assumption is valid for most cases. Measurements at the very high frequencies which should show inertia effects are seldom available due to experimental difficulties (Sec. 11.2).

There are numerous treatments relating microscopic motion to experimental dielectric relaxation times [1,2]. Transition state theories similar to that described in Sec. 6.2(b) are available, introducing activation parameters for the dipole rotation motion. These will not be outlined here, as they are in essence analogous to that in Sec. 6.2(b).

Some models of orientational motion have been discussed previously (Secs. 6.1(e) and 7.3). Another model used primarily for dielectric relaxation is one in which the spontaneous appearance of "excess free volume" or "defects" is considered. When such a fluctuation occurs, then a dipole can change its orientation essentially instantaneously. In its absence, the orientation occurs with a relaxation time τ_r. In such a case, the dipole correlation function $G_1(t)$ (7.38) is given as

$$G_1(t) = \frac{\langle \underline{p}(0)\cdot\underline{p}(t)\rangle}{\langle \underline{p}(0)\cdot\underline{p}(0)\rangle} = \exp\left[-\frac{t}{\tau_r}\right](1 - w(t)) \tag{11.25}$$

Here $w(t)$ is the probability that arrival of a "Glarum defect" has caused a relaxation by a time t.

The function $G_1(t)$ is related according to a very simple model to the dielectric properties as

$$\frac{\varepsilon^* - \varepsilon_\infty}{\varepsilon_0 - \varepsilon_\infty} = 1 - i\omega \int_0^\infty G_1(t)\ \exp[-i\omega t]\ dt \tag{11.26}$$

The internal field has been assumed equal to the external in (11.26) [3]. As pointed out in (11.24), this is not the case in reality, and the actual case is much more complicated [4].

With the use of (11.25) and (11.26), values $\varepsilon^*(\omega)$ can then be computed. A Debye single-relaxation form of the relaxation is obtained if $w(t)$ is negligibly small. If the arrival of defects is described by a characteristic time τ_g, then a Cole-Cole arc with h = 0.5 is obtained for $\tau_g \gg \tau_r$. A Cole-Davidson arc with d = 0.5 is obtained for $\tau_g = \tau_r$. Such fluctuation treatments have been extended further [5].

Aspects of such interpretation of dielectric relaxation data in terms of molecular-level structure and dynamics will be continued in Sec. 11.3 for specific examples. The problems involved in the theoretical analysis are quite complicated, and several approaches to the problem can be found. These are compared and criticized in Refs. 6 and 7.

(f) Effects of Strong Static Fields

When a strong static electric field is applied to a liquid, it becomes birefringent. Thus the refractive index $\eta_\parallel$ for radiation with the electric vector parallel to the applied field differs from $\eta_\perp$. This is known as the Kerr effect and is quantitatively described through the Kerr constant, B_λ, which is a function of wavelength λ.

$$B_\lambda = \frac{n_\parallel - n_\perp}{\lambda E^2} \tag{11.27}$$

The effect is greatest for liquids where the molecules have permanent dipole moments, but it also occurs in nonpolar liquids if there is an anisotropy in the polarization [see Sec. 12.1(g)]. The molecules align themselves to minimize the electrostatic energy as given by (11.4) if they are polar. Nonpolar molecules align themselves so that the axis with the largest polarizability is parallel to the field. The value of B_λ can then be related to the principal polarizability components as defined by the diagonalized polarizability tensor $\underline{\underline{\alpha}}$ and the components of the dipole moment.

Kerr constants are of importance in obtaining the components of $\underline{\underline{\alpha}}$ and $\underline{p}$, and only of indirect aid in elucidating intermolecular structural aspects. They will thus not be pursued further.

If there is an equilibrium present in the liquid, then the equilibrium constant can depend on the electric field as [6] [see also Eq. (17.34)]:

$$\frac{\partial \ln K}{\partial E} = \frac{\Delta P^\theta}{RT} \tag{11.28}$$

Here ΔP^θ is the difference in partial molar polarizabilities between reagents and products. Strong fields are required to make the equilibrium constant K vary appreciably, but the degree of dissociation of weak electrolytes in dilute solution can be altered sufficiently to make use of the "dissociation field effect" to study ion recombination reactions (e.g., Ref. 9).

11.2. EXPERIMENTAL TECHNIQUES

(a) Low Frequency Methods (<200 MHz)

The apparatus used to determine ε' and ε" depends very much on the frequency at which they are to be determined. For frequencies up to about 200 MHz it is possible to apply standard circuit theory. At higher (microwave) frequencies, different approaches must be taken.

To measure ε^* at frequencies for which circuit theory can be applied, it is necessary to measure the total impedance of a condenser (cell) with the dielectric medium in it. There are numerous designs for such cells [1,2]. A cell composed of two concentric cylinders with the dielectric material between them is commonly used. From the total impedance Z of the cell,

$$Z = \frac{1}{i\omega C + 1/R} = \frac{1}{i\omega\varepsilon^* C^\bullet} \tag{11.29}$$

the "dielectric constant" ε' and the "dielectric loss" ε'' can be determined as $\varepsilon' = C/C^\bullet$; $\varepsilon'' = 1/\omega RC^\bullet$. If the liquid has an ohmic (direct current) conductance σ, then this must be corrected for to give (11.15):

$$\varepsilon'' = \varepsilon''_{meas} - \frac{\sigma}{\omega\varepsilon^\bullet} \tag{11.30}$$

At the very lowest frequencies, bridges can be used to measure R and C. In this case the impedance of the cell is matched with a precision impedance (condenser and resistor). Apparatus based on bridge methods have been designed to go up to 40 MHz. At higher frequencies, however, stray capacitances cause increasingly great error.

In most liquids at normal temperatures, ε'' is negligibly small at frequencies less than about 1 MHz. Thus measurements in the very lowest frequency range are in most cases useful for determining ε_0. From the variation of ε_0 with temperature (11.8) dipole moments of molecules can be obtained. Some liquids can, however, be cooled sufficiently to move the absorption to the low frequencies to exploit the accuracy of the available techniques.

From frequencies of kHz up to hundreds of MHz, apparatus making use of resonant circuits (e.g., "Q-meters") can be used to measure ε' and ε''. The precision of such measurements is not as good as with specially designed bridge methods, but a large frequency range can be covered with one instrument. In this case a circuit is tuned to a resonant frequency $\omega_{res} = 1/\sqrt{LC}$. The tuning can be carried out by varying the capacity of a precision condenser to compensate for the change $C^{\bullet} - C$ caused by the dielectric. The loss ε'' is obtained through the half-width of the resonance curve. This is described by the "Q" of the circuit, where $1/Q = \varepsilon''/\varepsilon' = \tan\delta$ the "loss tangent."

The change in the resonance frequency of the cell circuit can also be used to observe the changes in C on inserting the dielectric. Such frequency changes can be measured accurately when the signal is mixed with that from a fixed frequency (crystal) oscillator. The difference frequency between the frequencies of two oscillators can be arranged to have a large relative variation, even though the variation $\delta\omega/\omega$ in the cell frequency itself is very small.

(b) Coaxial Lines and Waveguides

At higher frequencies, where the wavelength becomes of the order of sample dimensions, circuit theory cannot be used. Instead, electromagnetic effects must be analyzed on the basis of Maxwell's equations (20.3). Unshielded wires would for such frequencies cause a considerable radiation loss in energy through their action as antennas. Thus transmission of electromagnetic energy is usually either through a coaxial line, or at higher frequencies, through a hollow metal pipe (waveguide), usually with a rectangular cross section $a \times b$.

The theory behind coaxial lines and waveguides will not be outlined here. It is based on solutions of Maxwell's equations with appropriate boundary conditions. In the case of waveguides, it is found that there are various possible modes of oscillation of the electric and magnetic field by which the energy can be transmitted. Thus in a rectangular waveguide, transmission in the x direction occurs as

$$\underline{E}_j = \underline{E}_{j,o} \exp[i\omega t - \gamma_j x] \tag{11.31}$$

Here γ_j is the propagation factor for the jth mode, and is given by

$$\gamma_j = i\left[\frac{\omega^2\varepsilon^*}{C^2} - \left(\frac{m\pi}{a}\right)^2 - \left(\frac{n\pi}{b}\right)^2\right] = \alpha_j + i\beta_j \tag{11.32}$$

The integers m and n define the particular mode j considered. The wavelength of the mode must be less than a critical value determined by m, n, a, and b. In coaxial transmission, there is no such critical wavelength value, and the last two terms in (11.32) drop out.

Coaxial lines are used in the lower frequency range, from about 100 MHz ($\lambda \simeq 3$ m) to 5 GHz ($\lambda \simeq 0.06$ m). One line can cover about a decade in frequency, i.e., about a factor of 10. At lower frequencies, resonance methods with circuit parameters are more convenient. At higher frequencies, there are difficulties in determing the geometry properly.

Individual apparatus using waveguides have a very narrow frequency range, about a quarter of that of a coaxial line. The lower and upper frequency limits are about 3 GHz ($\lambda \simeq 0.1$ m) and greater than 60 GHz ($\lambda \simeq 5 \times 10^{-3}$ m). Both limits are geometrical; at lower frequencies the physical size becomes too great, while at higher frequencies, components cannot be made precise enough with such small dimensions.

(c) High-Frequency Methods

Some of the more common high frequency methods are outlined below. A review of recent developments with specific references can be found in Ref. 10.

(1) Resonance Methods

In such methods, a microwave cavity is brought into a state of resonance just as in the case of a circuit. Energy is introduced into the cavity by a loop or probe protruding into it. A second probe well removed from the first can be used as a detector of the field strength in the cavity. The resonant frequency and the Q of the cavity can then be measured for the case of an empty and a (partially) filled cavity. If the frequency of the microwave oscillator cannot be altered, then a resonant condition can be brought about by altering the length of the cavity.

(2) Transmission Methods

In such methods, the "attenuation constant" α and the "phase constant" β (11.32) of a mode in a coaxial line or a waveguide are determined. A standing wave pattern can be set up, and the distances between minima (or maxima) determined by some probe. The dielectric constant ε' can be obtained from the wavelength so determined, and the dielectric loss ε'' from the width of the minima. Several refined versions of this method have been developed [1]. Accuracies of about 0.5% are possible for the permittivity and about 2% for tan δ.

(3) Bridge Methods

Bridge methods have been developed for microwaves using a circuit schematically shown in Fig. 11.6. The signal from the source (usually a klystron) is split into two. The attenuator and phase shifter in the comparison circuit are then adjusted to give a net zero signal at the detector. The experiment can be repeated with different amounts of dielectric liquid in the cell to obtain γ for the chosen mode in the dielectric.

In an apparatus such as that outlined briefly above, essentially only a single frequency can be employed. To make measurements at a reasonably different frequency (e.g., different by a factor of 1.5), another apparatus with a different geometry is necessary.

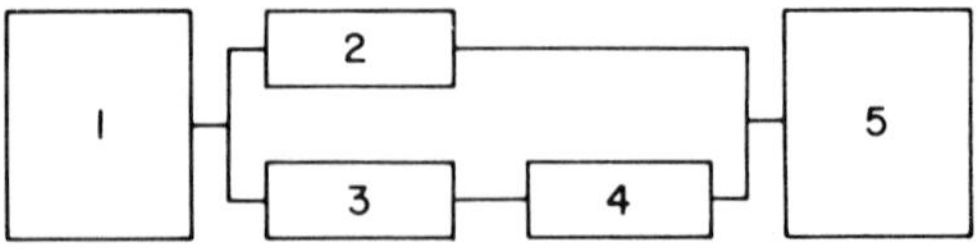

Fig. 11.6. Schematic diagram illustrating a bridge method for making dielectric measurements. (1) Source, (2) Cell, (3) Attenuator, (4) Phase shifter, (5) Detector. After Ref. 11.

(4) Free Wave (Interferometer) Methods

At extremely high frequencies (>50 GHz), waveguide measurements become difficult due to the small dimensions and the increase in metallic losses. Measurements are nevertheless possible at considerably higher frequencies if methods derived from optical spectroscopy are used [12]. Figure 11.7 shows schematically an apparatus analogous to the Michelson interferometer.

The source here is a harmonic generator doubling the frequency of a klystron. The signal is split into two equal parts. One goes to a reference arm with a variable attenuator and a reflector (an adjustable shorting plunger). The other half is transmitted into free space, collimated by a lens and sent to a variable length cell containing the dielectric. The reflected signals from the two arms are then mixed and detected.

A very similar system is used for absorption and dispersion measurements in the far-infrared and shorter wavelengths. "Fourier transform" spectroscopy can be carried out with such an apparatus if the mirrors (reflectors) are moved back and forth [Sec. 12.2(c)].

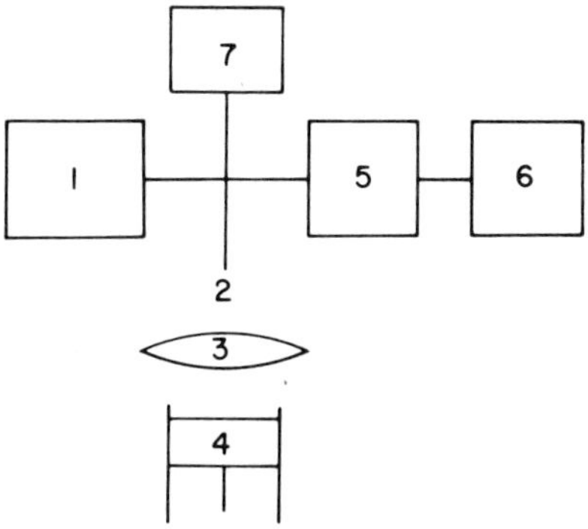

Fig. 11.7. Schematic diagram illustrating a free wave method for making dielectric measurements. (1) Source, (2) Free space, (3) Dielectric lens, (4) Cell with variable length, (5) Attenuator, (6) Reflector, (7) Detector. After Ref. 10.

Both the phase and the amplitude of the radiation from the two arms can be compared. As the length of the cell is varied, maxima and minima are detected in the superposed signal. This gives the wavelength and ε'. The loss is obtained by observing the decrease in the size of the maxima, and increase in the minima, as the path length in the liquid is varied. The precision possible for ε' is about 0.2% while for ε'' it is about 2%. It should be noted that $\lambda \simeq 0.21$ cm ($\nu \simeq 5$ cm^{-1}) can be considered to be nearly at the border of the "far-infrared" region [Sec. 11.3(a)].

(d) Transient Methods

Relaxation times can also be measured by sudden changes in the electric field instead of the periodic variation discussed in Secs. (a) to (c) above. The response of the dielectric to the voltage change is then observed as a function of time. Such methods are useful for studies of systems where the response is slow, and have been used for such studies for some time. They have recently been extended to also cover the higher frequency ranges [13,14].

The basic principle behind such time domain spectroscopy (TDS) is to send a step voltage through a coaxial line. A sample of the material in the line partially reflects this voltage. The time dependence of the reflected signal is then observed. The "response function" $\varepsilon'(t)$ [i.e., essentially $P_{or}(t)$, Sec. 11.1(c)] can then be obtained. Alternately, $\varepsilon(\omega)$ can be obtained through the appropriate Fourier transform [Sec. 7.2(b) and 13.2(e)]. The advantages of a TDS method are that a frequency range from kHz to 15 MHz can be covered with one apparatus, and that relatively little time is required for the actual measurements.

Apparatuses utilizing the dissociation field effect for measurements of recombination rates also employ sudden voltage changes [15]. High fields are required for a change in the equilibrium constant to be noticeable. Such a high field can also give rise to heating [Sec. 10.2(d)]. Thus single pulses are usually used, and the concentration of ionic species must be low.

The variation of concentration in ionic species can be followed through the conductivity. This can be done comparatively against a reference to eliminate conductivity changes due to distortion of the ionic atmosphere by the field (Wien effect). Spectrophotometric observation of the transient concentration behavior can also be used [16].

11.3. RESULTS FOR SPECIFIC SYSTEMS

(a) Dielectric Absorption in Benzene

In the case of nonpolar liquids such as benzene, no dielectric loss would be expected. Thus ε'' would be zero in the whole frequency range and there would be no dispersion (i.e., ε' would be constant). Thus benzene is often used as a solvent molecule when dipolar species are investigated in the form of dilute solutions [see Sec. 11.3(e)].

A small amount of dielectric loss has, however, been observed in benzene and other nonpolar liquids [17]. Detection of this with any precision is dificult as ε'' is very small ($\tan\delta \simeq 10^{-3}$). The presence of even very small amounts of dipolar impurities, e.g., water, can give rise to a dielectric loss. Furthermore, the loss achieves a maximum at the lowest wavelengths attainable with microwave apparatus ($\simeq 2 \times 10^{-3}$ m).

Figure 11.8 shows a plot of the dielectric loss data for benzene together with far infrared absorption results. Thus both a wavelength scale (in cm) and a wavenumber scale (in cm^{-1}) are given, as in the IR it is common to use wave numbers to describe the radiation. The range in which dielectric relaxation measurements were possible is given by $\overset{DR}{\longleftarrow}$ ($\lambda < 0.2$ cm), and low energy far infrared limit by $\overset{FIR}{\longrightarrow}$ ($\tilde{\nu} > 17$ cm^{-1}). Chapter 12 describes some of the techniques for obtaining IR spectra at low frequencies.

The absorption as shown in Fig. 11.8 can be interpreted as being due to a relaxation process with a relaxation time $\simeq 10^{-12}$ sec, and a broad resonance absorption centered between 10 and 100 cm^{-1} [Sec. 12.3(c)]. From the size of $\tan\delta$, the effective dipole moment responsible for the dielectric loss is 0.12 D. It is possible for such

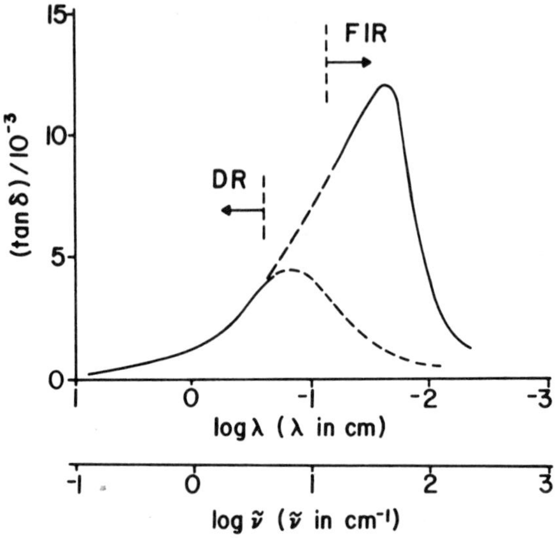

Fig. 11.8. Loss tangent (tan δ) for benzene as a function of $\tilde{\nu}$ and λ in the microwave to far infrared range. —— Experimental data, — — interpolation, --- single relaxation extrapolation. After Ref. 17.

a dipole to be induced in a nonpolar molecule through collisions with its neighbors. Such collision-induced absorption seems to be general in all liquids [17].

The magnitude of both the collision-induced dipole moment and its transition dipole (21.45) can be calculated. In this case a dipole moment is induced in a molecule in the presence of others through the fields produced by the quadrupole [or e.g., in CH_4 the octopole, Sec. 12.3(c)] of the molecules [see Secs. 1.1(a),(c)]. Sizes of the induced dipoles can be calculated from the knowledge of the Lennard-Jones parameters, the polarizability and the multipole magnitudes of the molecules. The calculated $\underline{p}_{ind}$ is 0.17 D for benzene.

The resonance absorption is more precisely interpreted as being due to lattice-type vibrations of the molecules in the cage formed by their neighbors. Such a "cage" would have an asymmetric configuration. The short lifetime of the configurations and coupling of the "lattice" vibrations with other motions produce a broadening of the resonance absorption. The value of $\partial p_{ind}/\partial r$ calculated on this model is 0.11

units as compared to 0.38 obtained from the integrated absorption. Considering the crudeness of the model used for calculation, the order of magnitude agreement is satisfactory.

There are other interpretations to this phenomenon both for nonpolar and polar systems [3,18]. Some interpretations approach the problem from the point of view of perturbation of rotational motion in gases [18]. Absorption in the far-infrared region is discussed further in Sec. 13.3(c) in terms of other interpretations. Light scattering arising from the same basic molecular motions is also discussed in Sec. 14.3(d).

(b) Static Dielectric Constant of Water

The static dielectric properties of liquid water are still under investigation. Thus recent studies have been made of the Kerr effect [19] and of the dielectric constant at high temperatures and pressures [20,21]. Discussions are also available in [22] and [10].

If the static dielectric constant for water is calculated from (11.7) using gas-phase results for α and p, then the result is 13. This is only 1/6 of the observed (20°C) value 80.5. The calculated value using a more realistic expression for the local field (11.8) is 27. Thus such approaches neglecting orientational correlation between polar molecules are not very successful in describing the dielectric properties of water.

When there is correlation between the orientation of neighboring molecules, then the average dipole moment of water molecule exceeds its gas-phase value. There is an extra contribution arising from the polarization of the molecule by the net nonzero field of its neighbors. An expression for ε in terms of the correlation between positions and orientations of molecules has been developed using this approach by Kirkwood. There is still some controversy regarding the relationship between the macroscopic ε and the microscopic parameters in the theory.

Values of ε for water can be calculated through the Kirkwood theory using the various models of water proposed. The continuum (bond-bending) model [Sec. 2.4(c)] gives reasonable results, as do the multistructure theories if only a small fraction of broken H bonds is assumed. However, the multistructure (bond-breaking) models do not give correct dielectric constant values if the relatively large fraction of monomers necessary to explain thermodynamic data is used for dielectric calculations.

(c) Dielectric Relaxation in Water

The frequency dependence of ε', ε" for water are shown schematically in Fig. 11.9. A log scale is used for ε', ε" to indicate the weakness of the high-frequency process. The ε' and ε" curves in the wavenumber region >10 cm^{-1} are shown even though this is poorly investigated (Sec. 12.2), and even though it is in the far-infrared region showing primarily resonance absorption. It has been proposed that besides the relaxation at about 0.5 cm^{-1} there is another relaxation process at 125 cm^{-1}. This has however not been confirmed due to the difficulty of obtaining ε' and ε" data in this region.

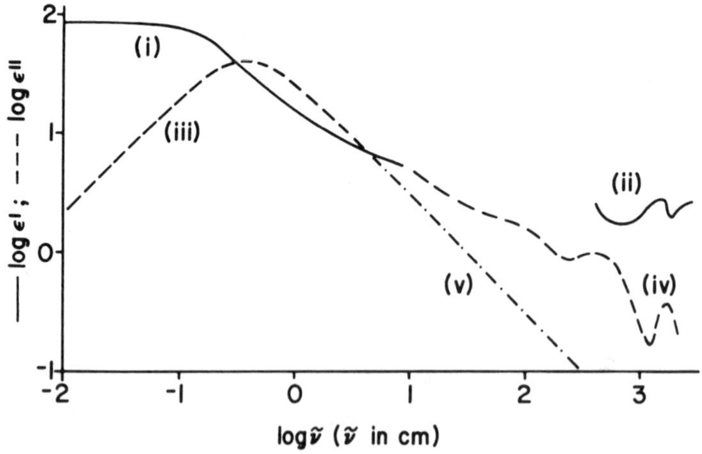

Fig. 11.9. Graph of log ε' —— and log ε" --- vs log ν̃ for water from 10^{-2} to 10^{3} cm^{-1}. Curves (i) and (iii) are from data listed in Ref. 10, curve (ii) from Ref. 25 and curve (iv) from Ref. 26. Curve (v) shows the ε" curve extrapolated assuming a single relaxation.

The principal relaxation process at about 0.5 cm^{-1} ($\tau \simeq 10.0 \times 10^{-12}$ sec at 20°C [22]) accounts for about 90% of the static dielectric constant. The values of experimental dielectric relaxation times are compared with those calculated from molecular dynamics computer simulation in Ref. 23 [see Sec. 2.3(b)]. Agreement is good. It is essentially a single relaxation process as the Cole-Cole parameter is very small, $h \simeq 0.01$ (11.16). At lower temperatures, h increases somewhat to have a value $h \simeq 0.04$ near 4°C [24]. It is also possible to fit the data with two single-relaxation processes with relaxation times a factor of about 2 different [24]. The temperature dependence indicates an activation energy of about 2 kJ mol^{-1}. Water in benzene solution has a much shorter relaxation time of $\sim 1.0 \times 10^{-12}$ sec [22].

This suggests that the relaxation is due to a dipole orientation, including H bond breaking [see also Sec. 11.3(f)]. More sophisticated models of the molecular process are available, some postulating two relaxations with essentially the same value of τ [10]. A "bond-breaking" model of water is favored, as "bond-bending" models would be expected to give a much wider distribution of relaxation times. The process is reasonably well described by (11.22) with a value of a = 1.4 Å.

A broad absorption region is present at higher frequencies in water. Otherwise the curve of ε'' would follow the characteristic form for a relaxation process as shown in (v) in Fig. 11.9. There is some difficulty in determining whether relaxation or resonance phenomena are responsible for such an absorption [see Sec. 12.3(e)].

The narrowness and the small temperature sensitivity of the absorption near 700 cm^{-1} indicate it to be a resonance effect. This conclusion is supported by isotope effects, as the D_2O absorption peak is at a frequency 1.4 ($\sim\sqrt{2}$) times lower as expected if the vibration involving H (or D) is involved.

The broad absorption near 200 cm^{-1} can be due to a relaxation phenomenon. It is sufficiently broad, and is associated with a decline in ε'. The ε'' data in the region can be fitted reasonably with a second relaxation for which $\varepsilon_0 = 4.1$ (i.e., ε_∞ for the first relaxation is 4.1) and $\varepsilon_\infty = 1.8$. Raman absorption has however been detected in this region, and has been interpreted in terms of resonance phenomena [Sec. 12.3(e)].

(d) Proton Transfer Kinetics in Water and Solutions

The rate constants for the equilibrium

$$H_3O^+ + OH^- \underset{k_d}{\overset{k_r}{\rightleftarrows}} H_2O + H_2O \tag{11.33}$$

have been measured through the field dissociation effect using square pulse electric fields. The change in the degree of dissociation was detected by electrical conductivity [27]. The rates obtained at 25°C are $k_r = 1.4 \times 10^{11}\ M^{-1}\ sec^{-1}$ and $k_d = 2.5 \times 10^{-5}\ sec^{-1}$.

The results when interpreted according to a diffusion-controlled model [Sec. 6.3(d)] indicate that the recombination reaction is "complete" when the species have diffused to within 7 Å, i.e., to within 2 or 3 H bonds. Rapid proton transfer along H bonds completes the reaction (see e.g., Fig. 9.4). The rate of such H-bond transfers is up to $10^{14}\ sec^{-1}$.

Dissociation field effects using strong pulsed fields have also been utilized to observe the kinetics of ion pairing equilibria for many species besides water. Solutions of both inorganic [28] and organic [16] weak electrolytes have been studied by this method. The solutions must be quite dilute to prevent conductance heating from becoming a major effect. Measured recombination rates for weak acids (e.g., indicators) are in good agreement with diffusion-controlled rate theory [Sec. 6.3(d)].

Contributions to dielectric absorption should also appear from ion pairing equilibria in a manner analogous to ultrasonics [Sec. 10.3 (g)]. In this case the equilibrium constant is dependent on field strength (11.28) rather than pressure or temperature. Such effects have not been found as yet due to the relatively low fields used in ac dielectric absorption studies.

(e) Solutions of Alcohols in Nonpolar Solvents

A large number of studies of solutions of polar liquids in nonpolar solvents (benzene, cyclohexane, carbontetrachloride, etc.) have been carried out. Many of these are for the determination of dipole moments. Such studies elucidate primarily intramolecular phenomena, although information on association equilibria can be obtained [29]. Other studies, covering a wide frequency range, give information re intermolecular structures and dynamics [30-32]. The particular case of solutions of alcohols will be discussed here, with some reference to solutions of monoalkyl benzenes.

(1) Solutions of Alcohols

On the basis of analysis of Argand diagrams for alcohol solutions such as those shown in Fig. 11.10 [31], it is possible to fit the data with two or three relaxations. The data covers a wavelength range from 0.2 to 60 cm.

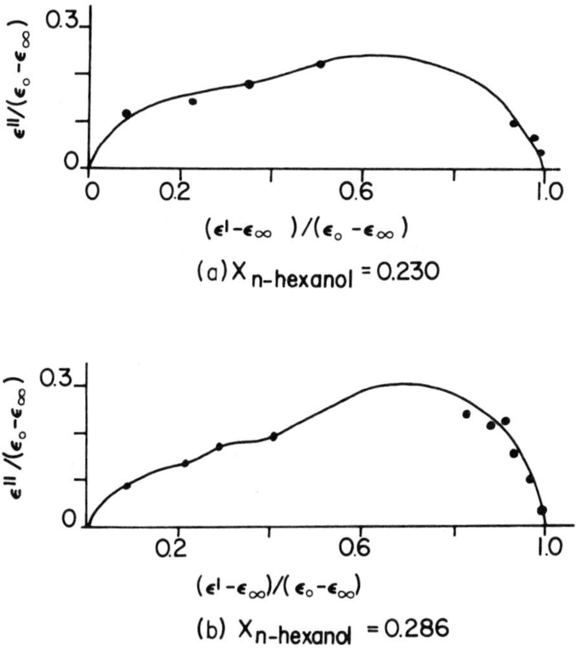

Fig. 11.10. Graphs of ε'' vs ε' for n-hexanol in n-heptane, (a) Mol fraction 0.230, (b) Mol fraction 0.286. After Ref. 31.

The lowest frequency relaxation appears only at higher concentration and has a relaxation time $\tau_1 \approx 300 \times 10^{-12}$ sec, increasing with concentration and the size of the alcohol molecule. The molecular origin of this relaxation seems to be the breaking of an H bond of an alcohol in a sheet of hydrogen-bonded hydroxyl groups and subsequent rotation. The activation energy of this relaxation is approximately that for the breaking of an H bond, and it does not vary widely from alcohol to alcohol.

The intermediate relaxation has a time $\tau_2 \approx 40 \times 10^{-12}$ sec. This time generally increases with increasing concentration except at the point where the first (τ_1) relaxation is postulated to appear. When the analysis is carried out in terms of three rather than two relaxations, then τ_2 decreases. The relaxation is most likely to be due essentially to rotation of the monomer, but the concentration dependence suggests that it may be a weighted average of monomer and polymer rotations.

The highest frequency relaxation ($\tau_3 \approx 3 \times 10^{-12}$ sec) is believed to be due to the OH group orientation through rotation about the C-O bond. It is the predominant process at the smallest concentrations.

A solvent dependence is present in the behavior of these relaxation times [32]. In aromatic solvents (e.g., benzene), solute-solvent interactions are better able to compete with solute-solute interactions. Thus there is not as great a tendency for multimers to form, and the intermediate relaxation time τ_2 is smaller in aromatic (benzene) solutions than in aliphatic (e.g., n-heptane) solutions.

Both association of alcohol molecules and interactions of alcohol with solvent molecules can be studied with static dielectric measurements [29,33]. The results for n-heptanol in carbon tetrachloride [29] are interpreted as giving evidence of a monomer-dimer-trimer or tetramer association equilibrium, with a heat of association for the dimer of 40 kJ mol^{-1}. There is a considerable deviation from an ideal association model in the results for alcohols in saturated hydrocarbons [33]. The deviation is explained as being due to solvation effects. Such a model leads to very large values for the number of solvent molecules solvating a molecular dipole, up to 100 when the temperature is close to the melting temperature of the solvent.

(2) Solutions of Monoalkyl Benzene

More than one relaxation time can also be obtained in solutions where there are no specific H-bond interactions. Thus methyl-, ethyl-, isopropyl-, and t-butyl benzene in cyclohexane solution all show two single relaxation times [30]. The data in this case were analyzed through a plot of ε' vs $\varepsilon''\omega$. When two relaxations are present, then this gives a curve with limiting slopes $-\tau_1$, and $-\tau_2$ [see e.g., Eq. (11.13)].

One of the relaxations can be associated with molecular reorientation. The second shorter relaxation time ($\tau_2 \approx 5 \times 10^{-12}$ sec) is believed to be due to some intramolecular process such as rotation about the aryl-alkyl bond. For such rotations to contribute to dielectric relaxation, there must be some π-bond character in the aryl-alkyl bond. For a pure single (σ) bond there is no dipole moment perpendicular to the bond.

(f) Aqueous Nonelectrolyte Solutions

In mixtures of water with other polar liquids, the single relaxation process (at 0.5 cm^{-1}, $\tau \approx 10 \times 10^{-12}$ sec) splits into two [34,35]. The results for methanol-water are shown in Fig. 11.11 [35], indicating how the Argand diagram can be interpreted in terms of two relaxation processes. The value of $\varepsilon_{\infty,2}$ is greater than n^2, so that a third relaxation is expected at higher frequencies.

Such data can be explained in terms of models resembling those presented in Sec. 8.3(d). The lower frequency relaxation ($\tau_1 \approx 30 \times 10^{-12}$ sec) is interpreted as reorientation possible on dissociation of water-water, water-methanol, or methanol-methanol H bonds. The second relaxation ($\tau_2 \approx 4 \times 10^{-12}$ sec) is believed associated with "linked jumps" between OH and OCH_3 groups in mixed alcohol-water structures [35].

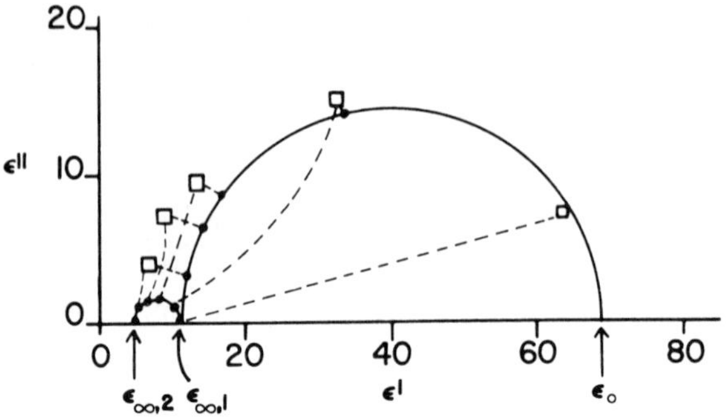

Fig. 11.11. Graph of ε" vs ε' for methanol in water at 20°C. (Mol fraction methanol = 0.16). The experimental points □ are split into contributions from two relaxation processes. After Ref. 35.

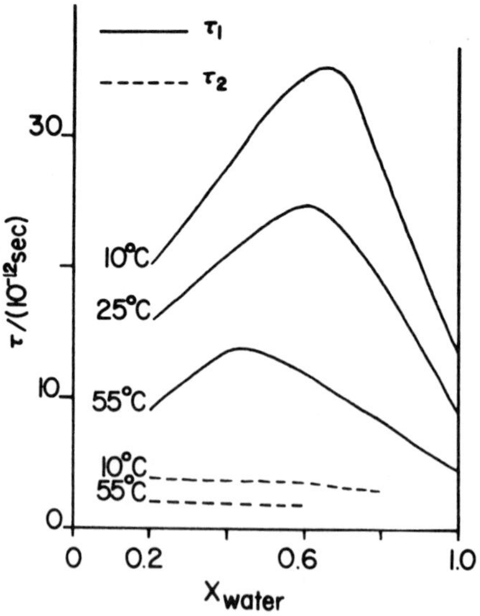

Fig. 11.12. Relaxation times τ_1 and τ_2 at various temperatures as functions of composition for water-dioxane mixtures. After Ref. 34.

The results in the case of dioxane-water mixtures are interpreted on a somewhat different model [34]. As shown in the data in Fig. 11.12, there are again two relaxation times in the mixture, the high frequency relaxation τ_2 not being present in pure water.

In pure water, the structure is fluctuating very rapidly, so that averaged over the time required for relaxation, the molecules and their environments are approximately the same. Thus only a single relaxation time is observed in pure water. When dioxane is added, the cooperative nature of the formation and breaking of H-bonded clusters is disturbed, and the relaxation time τ_1 is lengthened. The forces between dioxane and water molecules have a maximum effect when the ratio of water to dioxane is that present on the average in the intermolecular complexes formed.

The introduction of dioxane molecules also screen some water molecules from their neighbors. This gives them the possibility of relaxing with a shorter time τ_2. Water molecules attached to dioxane molecules should also be able to orient by rotation about the bond with a short time close to τ_2. In pure water, these processes become restricted to be libration. The magnitude of τ_2 in such systems is of the order of magnitude of the τ for water in benzene [Sec. 11.3(b)].

(g) Critical Phenomena

In the region of phase separation in binary mixtures an appreciable increase in ε'' is observed [36,37] (see also "Further Recent References). This extra absorption reaches a maximum some 1 to 2°C before the phase separation temperature is reached on the single phase side. This is the same effect as observed in ultrasonic absorption [10.3(f)] and density [36], suggesting a thermodynamic, "microscopic," critical point is reached before phase separation occurs due to sedimentation [see also Sec. 15.3(f) and Fig. 15.8]. As the critical temperature is approached, the frequency dependence indicates a broadening out to a distribution of relaxation times, with the most probable relaxation time tending towards a maximum.

An explanation of this phenomenon analogous to the explanation for the increase in viscosity [Sec. 9.3(d)] has been proposed [38]. The extra dielectric absorption can be viewed as arising from a coupling of molecular rotation and diffusion. Fluctuations near the critical point produce an overall dipole moment which responds to the applied periodic field. The net result is a diffusion process.

The relaxation times of the concentration fluctuations near the critical point can be observed through application of strong pulsed fields [39]. When one of the components is a polar liquid, then the critical solution temperature is shifted on application of an electric field due to a change in the free energy of mixing. The relaxation of the critical concentration fluctuations on application or removal of the field can be followed through the change in light-scattering intensity.

A single relaxation time τ was found satisfactory for explaining the transient behavior observed. The magnitude of τ is of the order of magnitude obtained from light-scattering studies [Sec. 14.3(g)]. and it has a temperature variation proportional to $|T - T_c|^{-0.9}$. The interpretation of this phenomenon is discussed in some detail in [40].

(h) Hydration of Ions

In studying electrolyte solutions, the dielectric loss ε'' can be obtained from the total loss of energy only after subtraction of the loss due to ohmic conductivity (11.30). Even in the case of a relatively poor conductor such as pure water ($\sigma = 1 \times 10^{-6}$ ohm^{-1} cm^{-1}) the conductivity loss is greater than the dielectric loss at frequencies less than 20 MHz. Studies involving electrolytes are thus most commonly carried out at lower frequencies only for dilute solutions of partially dissociating salts in nonaqueous solvents [1].

Ion-pair species formed by weak electrolytes in solution will have a high effective dipole moment and the relaxation of these species can be observed. In order to observe the relaxation at lower, measurable frequencies, the solution can in cases be supercooled [41].

The geometric size of such "ion-pair dipoles" can then be obtained with (11.22) from the magnitude of the τ of the relaxation process observed on introduction of the salt.

Both ionic and molecular relaxation must be considered in solutions of strong electrolytes. The interpretation of dielectric studies of lithium perchlorate in tetrahydrofuran (C_4H_8O)-benzene mixtures [42] thus leads to information on solvation and ionic motion both. The decrease of polarization on introduction of the ions can be accounted for by having the contribution from the polar solvent molecules decreased because these molecules would be solvating the cation (about five per ion). The low part of the spectrum is interpreted as due to linear motion of the ions between collisions. The value of a time between collisions estimated on this model is in reasonable agreement with that predicted assuming Brownian linear motion [Sec. 7.2(e)]. Orientational relaxation of ion pairs does not seem to contribute to any measured dielectric relaxation.

Studies of quite concentrated solutions of strong electrolytes in water can be carried out at higher frequencies [43-45]. In general there is a decrease in the static permittivity and a shift in the principal relaxation time with increasing concentration of salt in both aqueous and nonaqueous solutions.

In aqueous solutions, the water molecules can be considered to be divided into three "subliquids," "free" water, "anion" water, and "cation" water. The relaxation time of the solution is then a weighted average of the reorientation times for the molecules in the three types of liquids. A more sophisticated version of this model [44] takes account of the residence time of the hydrating molecules. When a small cation such as Li^+ is involved, then the reorientation of an individual hydrating molecule is also dependent on the rotation of the hydrated ion as a whole.

Ratios of several relaxation times can be found on analysis of the data. Thus the ratio of the reorientational time of molecules in bulk water to the mean residence time of hydrating molecules is calculated to be 0.3 for Li^+, about 1 for Na^+, K^+, and Rb^+, and 2 for Cs^+. In such calculations, nuclear magnetic resonance data [Sec. 13.3(g)] must be included in cases.

REFERENCES

References 1 and 2 give a fairly complete coverage of most aspects of dielectric relaxation. Some more recent developments are outlined in [10]. Aspects relating to dissociation field effects are covered in [15]. Reference 4, in spite of its early date, covers many of the underlying principles.

1. N. E. Hill, W. E. Vaughan, A. H. Price, and M. Davies, Dielectric Properties and Molecular Behavior, Van Nostrand-Reinhold, New York, 1969.
2. C. P. Smyth, Dielectric Behavior and Structure, McGraw-Hill, New York, 1955.
3. G. Birnbaum and E. R. Cohen, J. Chem. Phys., *53*, 2885 (1970).
4. P. Debye, Polar Molecules, Dover, New York, 1929.
5. J. E. Anderson and R. Ullman, J. Chem. Phys., *47*, 2178 (1967).
6. U. M. Titulaer and J. M. Deutch, J. Chem. Phys., *60*, 1502 (1974).
7. R. Lobo, J. E. Robinson, and S. Rodriguez, J. Chem. Phys., *59*, 5992 (1973).
8. L. DeMaeyer, M. Eigen, and J. Suarez, J. Am. Chem. Soc., *90*, 3157 (1968).
9. A. P. Persoons, J. Phys. Chem., *78*, 1210 (1974).
10. J. B. Hasted in GR7.
11. W. F. Hassell, M. D. McGee, S. W. Tucker, and S. Walker, Tetrahedron, *20*, 2137 (1964).
12. S. K. Garg, H. Kilp, and C. P. Smyth, J. Chem. Phys., *43*, 2341 (1965).
13. M. J. C. van Gemert, Philips Res. Repts., *28*, 530 (1973).
14. R. H. Cole, J. Phys. Chem., *78*, 1440 (1974).
15. M. Eigen and L. DeMaeyer, in Technique of Organic Chemistry, Vol. VIII, Part II (S. L. Friess, E. S. Lewis, and A. Weissberger, eds.), Interscience, New York, 1963.
16. J. J. Auborn, P. Warrick, Jr., and E. M. Eyring, J. Phys. Chem., *75*, 2488 (1971).
17. S. K. Garg, J. E. Bertie, H. Kilp, and C. P. Smyth, J. Chem. Phys., *49*, 2551 (1968).
18. S. H. Glarum, Molecular Phys., *27*, 1139 (1974).
19. Y. Chen and W. H. Orttung, J. Phys. Chem., *76*, 216 (1972).

20. V. M. Jansoone and E. U. Franck, Ber. Bunsenges. Phys. Chem., *76*, 943 (1972).

21. K. R. Srinivasan and R. L. Kay, J. Chem. Phys., *60*, 3645 (1974).

22. GR5.

23. F. H. Stillinger and A. Rahman, J. Chem. Phys., *57*, 1281 (1972).

24. E. H. Grant and R. J. Sheppard, J. Chem. Phys., *60*, 1792 (1974).

25. M. R. Querry, B. Curnutte, and D. Williams, J. Opt. Soc. Am., *59*, 1229 (1969).

26. D. A. Draegert, N. W. B. Stone, B. Curnutte, and D. Williams, J. Opt. Soc. Am., *56*, 64 (1966).

27. M. Eigen and L. DeMaeyer, Z. f. Elektroch., *59*, 986 (1955).

28. P. Hemmes, L. D. Rich, D. L. Cole, and E. M. Eyring, J. Phys. Chem., *75*, 929 (1971).

29. P. Bordewijk, M. Kunst, and A. Rip, J. Phys. Chem., *77*, 548 (1973).

30. W. F. Hassell and S. Walker, Trans. Farad. Soc., *62*, 861 (1966).

31. L. Glasser, J. Crossley, and C. P. Smyth, J. Chem. Phys., *57*, 3977 (1972).

32. J. Crossley, J. Phys. Chem., *75*, 1790 (1971).

33. J. Malecki and J. Jadzyn, J. Phys. Chem., *78*, 1203 (1974).

34. S. K. Garg and C. P. Smyth, J. Chem. Phys., *43*, 2959 (1965).

35. N. V. Chekalin and M. I. Shakhparanov, Russ. J. Phys. Chem., *45*, 250 (1971).

36. K. V. Arkhangelski and V. K. Semenchenko, Russ. J. Phys. Chem., *41*, 692 (1967).

37. I. Lubezky and R. McIntosh, Can. J. Chem., *51*, 545 (1973).

38. N. S. Sneider, J. Chem. Phys., *56*, 233 (1972).

39. P. Debye, C. C. Gravatt, and M. Ieda, J. Chem. Phys., *46*, 2352 (1967).

40. M. J. Cooper and R. D. Mountain, J. Chem. Phys., *48*, 1064 (1968).

41. M. Davies, P. J. Hams, and G. Williams, J. C. S. Farad. II, *69*, 1785 (1973).

42. J. P. Badiali, H. Cachet, A. Cyrot, and J. C. Lestrade, J. C. S. Farad. II, *69*, 1339 (1973).

43. J. Barthel, H. Behret, and F. Schmithals, Ber. Bunseng. Physik. Chemie., *75*, 305 (1971).

44. K. Giese, Ber. Bunseng. Physik. Chemie., *76*, 495 (1972).

45. U. Kaatze, Ber. Bunseng. Physik. Chemie., *77*, 447 (1973).

Further Recent References

J. B. Hasted, "Aqueous Dielectrics", Chapman and Hall, London, 1973.

D. Kivelson and P. Madden, "Theory of Dielectric Relaxation", Mol. Phys., *30*, 1749 (1975).

D. E. Sullivan and J. M. Deutch, "Molecular Theory of Dielectric Relaxation", J. Chem. Phys., *62*, 2130 (1975).

A. H. Clark, P. A. Quickenden, and A. Suggett, "Multiple Reflection Time Domain Spectroscopy", J. C. S. Farad. II, *70*, 1847 (1974).

R. H. Cole, "Evaluation of Dielectric Behavior by Time Domain Spectroscopy II. Complex Permittivity", J. Phys. Chem., *79*, 1469 (1975).

J. W. Kress and J. J. Kozak, "Estimate of the Intermolecular Polarization Contribution to the Static Dielectric Constant of Water", J. Chem. Phys., *64*, 1706 (1976).

U. Stumper, "Dielectric Absorption of Liquid Normal Alkanes in the Microwave and Far Infrared Regions", Adv. Mol. Relax. Proc., *7*, 189, (1975).

M. F. Shears, G. Williams, A. J. Barlow, and J. Lamb, "Comparison of Dielectric Relaxation and Viscoelastic Retardation in Three Viscous Liquids", J. C. S. Farad. II, *70*, 1783 (1974).

I. Danielewicz-Ferchmin, "Influence of a Strong Electric Field on the Dielectric Permittivity of Alcohols II. Temperature Effect", Chem. Phys., *8*, 208 (1975).

B. J. Cooke and S. Walker, "Influence of Dipole Inclination to Principal Axes on Molecular Relaxation Time", Adv. Mol. Relax. Proc., *7*, 221 (1975).

V. S. Ushakova, I. V. Zhilenkov, and G. M. Zhuravets, "Dielectric Properties of Nitrobenzene near the Crystallization Point", Russ. J. Phys. Chem., *48*, 1043 (1974).

R. Finsy and R. van Loon, "Dielectric Relaxation in 1,1,1-Trichloroethane/Cyclohexane Solutions", J. Chem. Phys., *63*, 4831 (1975).

C. Campbell, G. Brink, and L. Glasser, "Dielectric Studies of Molecular Association. Concentration Dependence of Dipole Moment of 1-Octanol in Solution", J. Phys. Chem., *79*, 660 (1975).

A. Suggett, "Molecular Motion and Interactions in Aqueous Carbohydrate Solutions. III. A Combined Nuclear Magnetic and Dielectric-Relaxation Strategy", J. Sol. Chem., *5*, 33 (1976).

B. L. Brown and G. P. Jones, "High and Low Field Permittivity and Conductivity Measurements for Mixtures of Alcohols and Proton Acceptors", J. C. S. Farad. II, *71*, 1877 (1975).

E. Jakusek, M. Pajdowska, and L. Sobczyk, "Dielectric Relaxation of Hydrogen-Bonded Complexes", Chem. Phys., *9*, 205 (1975).

R. Halliwell, D. A. Hutchinson, and R. McIntosh, "A Re-examination of the Nitrobenzene-2,2,4-Trimethyl Pentane System in the Consolute Region and of the Thermodynamical Considerations Concerning the Value of ε' at the Consolute Point", Can. J. Chem., *54*, 1139 (1976).

D. Ménard and M. Chabanel, "Dipole Moment and Dimerization Equilibria of Inorganic Salts Dissolved in Weakly Polar Solvents", J. Phys. Chem., *79*, 1081 (1975).

Chapter 12

INFRARED AND RAMAN SPECTROSCOPY

This chapter can in a way be considered as a continuation of Chap. 11, as it examines ε" at energies above the microwave region (i.e., $\tilde{\nu} \gtrsim 10\ cm^{-1}$). The absorption processes present here are however due to resonance rather than relaxation phenomena.

The discussion does not cover those many aspects of spectroscopy which are used to elucidate molecular structure, identify functional groups, etc. As previously, the basic geometry and force constants of the species involved is assumed known, but perturbation of these properties due to interactions present in liquids is dealt with in some detail.

Electronic energy levels of molecules are not altered appreciably through the relatively weak intermolecular interactions. Thus spectra involving electronic transitions (mostly visible and ultraviolet) are not discussed here [see Sec. 1.2(c)]. X-ray absorption and emission are not discussed at all, as here energies of "core" electrons are involved, and these are essentially left unperturbed by even intramolecular forces. Thus the resonant transitions discussed are essentially of a vibrational nature (intramolecular, intermolecular, or librational).

In inelastic light scattering there is an arbitrariness in defining the limit between "Raman" and "Brillouin" (Chap. 14) scattering. Here only those processes believed to involve transitions between discrete molecular energy states are included under Raman scattering.

12.2. THEORETICAL BACKGROUND

(a) Types of Spectroscopy

In the gas phase, molecular spectroscopy [1,2] can conveniently be divided into the following categories:

1. Microwave spectroscopy, involving transitions between rotational energy levels
2. Infrared spectroscopy, involving transition between vibrational energy levels, superposed by rotational transitions

3. Optical and ultraviolet spectroscopy, involving transitions between electronic energy levels, superposed by vibrational and rotational transitions (as indicated in the introduction, this type of spectroscopy is not of primary interest when intermolecular aspects are of interest).

In liquids, rotational motion is damped to such an extent that quantized rotational energies for molecules are often no longer meaningful. Thus microwave spectroscopy becomes instead for many cases dielectric relaxation (Chap. 11). In some cases transitions between broad rotational levels can be seen in the far-infrared. The underlying theory behind this will not be discussed, as it is analogous to the IR (vib-rot) theory, only with $\Delta v = 0$ instead of 1. Rotational motion of molecules can also in liquids become directionally restricted. Such an oscillation in the orientation is referred to as "libration."

Intramolecular vibrational motions are perturbed somewhat in liquids due to intermolecular forces. The superposed rotational structure is also no longer discrete but shows up instead in the shape of the vibrational band. Other motions of a vibrational kind come into being; libration (restricted rotation), and intermolecular vibration (restricted translation). These motions can be studied by Raman scattering as well as by infrared absorption.

In Raman spectroscopy, the difference $\Delta\nu = \nu_{inc} \pm \nu_{ram}$ in the frequency between the incident (ν_{inc}) and the Raman scattered (ν_{ram}) radiation is measured. Thus measurements can be made at relatively high frequencies ($\nu_{ram} \gg \Delta\nu$) where transmission problems for cell materials may not be as great, and where detection may be more effective [Sec. 12.2(b),(c)]. Problems due to extremely large infrared absorption can also be avoided in cases. As the selection rules for Raman and infrared spectroscopy are different, it is possible to observe some vibrational transitions with Raman spectroscopy which are not "infrared active" and vice versa.

The discussion of the theoretical background in this chapter is organized to deal first with an aspect common to IR and Raman spectroscopy. This involves the shift in energy for transitions between vibrational states due to changes in the environment. In Sec. 12.1 (c),(d) problems of particular interest to IR spectroscopy are discussed, while Secs. 12.1(e)-(h) refer to Raman spectroscopy. Much of the discussion is based on the material in Chaps. 20-21.

(b) *Frequency Shifts in Vibrational Transitions*

The central frequency for a transition <v'| to <v"| is determined by the values $E_{v'}$ and $E_{v''}$ (Sec. 21.2). The values of E_v for intramolecular vibrational modes can be perturbed sufficiently by intermolecular forces so that a frequency shift $\Delta\nu = \nu_{\text{liquid}} - \nu_{\text{gas}}$ can be observed. Several theories explaining this change in frequency with change in molecular environment are available [3].

Many of these theories are based on a model of a dipole in a cavity in a continuous dielectric medium. A shift $\Delta\nu$ then results from instantaneously induced polarization of the medium (solvent), producing a reaction field [e.g., Eq. (20.42)]. Such considerations lead to an expression

$$\frac{\Delta\nu}{\nu} \quad \frac{\varepsilon - 1}{2\varepsilon + 1} \qquad (12.1)$$

The constant of proportionality in (12.1) depends only on the properties of the solute molecule. The value n^2 is suggested as appropriate for use as ε in (12.1) as molecular polarization [Sec. 11.1(b)] has a relaxation time which is too long to contribute to the effect.

Equation (12.1) is of limited use, and gives quite poor agreement with experiment in the case of polar solvents, even when the approach is made more sophisticated. Specific interactions between solute and solvent molecules are not considered in any such "solvent continuum" approach. Such interactions are especially important for stretching vibrations of X-H bonds, where the solute proton can form an H bond with the solvent. On H-bonding, the vibrational mode corresponding essentially to the X-H stretching frequency is lowered [Sec. 12.3(g)]. The X-H deformation frequency seems to show an upward shift with H-bonding.

(c) IR Band Intensities

The intensity of vibrational transitions is given by Eq. (21.44). The instantaneous dipole moment $\underline{p}$ for a vibrating dipole can be expanded as

$$\underline{p} = (\underline{p})_{\xi=0} + \left(\frac{\partial \underline{p}}{\partial \xi}\right)_{\xi=0} \cdot \xi + \cdots \qquad (12.2)$$

Here $(\underline{p})_{\xi=0}$, $(\partial\underline{p}/\partial\xi)_{\xi=0}$ are values of $\underline{p}$, $\partial\underline{p}/\partial\xi$ calculated when the normal coordinate involved, ξ, has a value zero. As they are constants, they can be taken outside the integrals to be evaluated for obtaining the transition dipole moment $\underline{m}_{v',v''}$ for the vibrational band concerned [Sec. 21.4(b)]. As the vibrational wavefunctions form an orthogonal set (21.5), then the major term in $\underline{m}_{v',v''}$ is

$$\underline{m}_{v',v''} = \left(\frac{\partial \underline{p}}{\partial \xi}\right)_{\xi=0} \langle v''|\xi|v'\rangle \qquad (12.3)$$

Thus the intensity of absorption is $\propto |(\partial\underline{p}/\partial\xi)_{\xi=0}|^2$. As the dipole moment of the X-H stretching mode is more sensitive to bond length when there is H-bonding present (i.e., -X-H---Y), then there is an increase in intensity of the X-H absorption on H-bonding.

The selection rules discussed in Sec. 21.5 can also be obtained from (12.3). It is easier to consider the symmetry selection rules from the point of view of the symmetry properties of the total dipole moment, however. Although $(\partial\underline{p}/\partial\xi)_{\xi=0}$ is a constant (a scalar) when the normal coordinates are used as a basis set, it can be a vector with symmetry properties when expressed in terms of physical coordinates.

In polyatomic molecules where there are several infrared active normal modes (e.g., water, Sec. 21.5), the spectrum can be quite complicated. Transitions can take place, e.g., between the ground state of all normal modes to a state where more than one normal mode is excited, or to where a normal mode is excited by more than one quantum step ("combination" and " overtone" bands) [4].

(d) IR Band Shapes

The shape of a vibrational band can be described by a normalized intensity function $I(\omega)$. The appearance of such a continuous band in liquids can be considered to be due to the overlapping of very broad lines due to the superposed rotational transitions. In liquids each vibration-rotation component would be broadened due to the poorly defined rotational states. As shown in Eq. (20.52), if there is more "friction" present in a motion of a radiator or absorber, then the corresponding line is broadened.

The above view of the appearance of a band shape is from the Schrödinger description of quantum mechanics (Sec. 21.4). Such an interpretation is of use when it is neaningful to discuss quantized states for the motion involved. A state is meaningful if it exists for a time greater than the time of transition. A molecule can be in a number of states because of a number of different environments. If, however, the change in environments is very rapid compared to the transition time, then only one state due to the average environment is meaningful for that transition process.

The Heisenberg picture of spectroscopy (Sec. 21.6) is thus more instructive in many considerations when liquids are concerned [5]. Here the time development of the system is of prime interest rather than the energy states. The expressions useful for the Heisenberg picture can be obtained by use of (21.41), introducing the Heisenberg operators through the correspondence principle [6]. Other direct quantum-mechanical derivations are available in several places [5,7, 8].

Such derivations start with the expression corresponding to (21.43) and (21.44) for an absorption band,

$$I(\omega') \propto \sum_{jf} \rho_j |\langle f|\underline{\varepsilon}\cdot\underline{m}_{v'v''}|j\rangle|^2 \delta\left(\frac{E_j - E_f}{\hbar} - \omega'\right) \tag{12.4}$$

Here ω' is the displacement of frequency from the band center, $|j\rangle$ and $|f\rangle$ the quantum states for the initial and final rotation-translation quantum states, ρ_j the equilibrium probability of a molecule being in the states $|j\rangle$, $\underline{\varepsilon}$ a unit vector in the direction of the electric vector of the incident radiation, and $\underline{m}_{v',v''}$ the transition dipole moment vector for the vibrational band where $v' \to v''$. The δ function can be expressed as $\delta(\omega) = 1/2\pi \int_{-\infty}^{\infty} \exp[i\omega t]\, dt$ (7.24).

When the eigenvalues E_j and E_f are expressed in terms of the Hamiltonian operator for the rotation-translation motion, $\hat{H}_{r,t}$ [Eq. (2.44)] and the $\delta(\omega')$ is written as an integral, then

$$I(\omega') \propto \int_{-\infty}^{\infty} \Big(\sum_{jf} \rho_j \langle j|\underline{\varepsilon}\cdot\underline{m}_{v',v''}|f\rangle\langle f|\exp\left[\frac{i\hat{H}_{r,t}t}{\hbar}\right] \underline{\varepsilon}\cdot\underline{m}_{v',v''}$$

$$\cdot\exp\left[-\frac{i\hat{H}_{r,t}t}{\hbar}\right] |j\rangle \exp[-i\omega' t]\, dt$$

$$\propto \int_{-\infty}^{\infty} \sum_{j} \rho_j \langle j|(\underline{\varepsilon}\cdot\underline{m}_{v',v''}) \exp\left[\frac{i\hat{H}_{r,t}t}{\hbar}\right] (\underline{\varepsilon}\cdot\underline{m}_{v',v''})$$

$$\cdot\exp\left[-\frac{i\hat{H}_{r,t}t}{\hbar}\right] |j\rangle \exp[-i\omega' t]\, dt \qquad (12.5)$$

Here the sum over the complete set of final states $|f\rangle$ has been taken in the second step. If (21.49) is used to define a Heisenberg operator $\underline{\varepsilon}\cdot\underline{m}_{v',v''}(t)$, and if (21.17) is used to define the equilibrium statistical average, then

$$I(\omega') \propto \int_{-\infty}^{\infty} \langle(\underline{\varepsilon}\cdot\underline{m}_{v',v''}(0))\ (\underline{\varepsilon}\cdot\underline{m}_{v',v''}(t))\rangle \exp[-i\omega' t]\, dt \qquad (12.6)$$

When next an isotropic sample is assumed and results are averaged over the polarization directions $\underline{\varepsilon}$, then

$$I(\omega') = \frac{1}{2\pi} \int_{-\infty}^{\infty} \langle\underline{m}_{v',v''}(0)\cdot\underline{m}_{v',v''}(t))\rangle \exp[-i\omega' t]\, dt$$

$$= \frac{1}{2\pi} \int_{-\infty}^{\infty} \langle m_{v',v''}(0)\cdot m_{v',v''}(t)\rangle\langle\underline{n}(0)\cdot\underline{n}(t)\rangle \exp[-i\omega' t]\, dt$$

$$= \frac{1}{2\pi} \int_{-\infty}^{\infty} G_{vib}(t)\cdot G_1(t) \exp[-i\omega' t]\, dt \qquad (12.7)$$

Here $G_1(t)$ is the time correlation function $G_1(t)$ (7.38) for the unit vector $\underline{n}(t)$ in the direction of the transition dipole moment $\underline{m}_{v',v''}(t)$ and $G_{vib}(t)$ is the vibrational relaxation function (7.51).

It has been assumed above that there is no vibration-rotation interaction. As shown in Secs. 12.3(a),(b), the effect of vibrational relaxation can not be neglected, especially in larger molecules. It is neglected in earlier theoretical and experimental considerations, but is included in more recent studies [8,9].

(e) Basis of Raman Spectroscopy

The appearance of Raman lines due to vibrational transitions will be considered from a classical point of view initially. For many purposes it can be viewed in direct analogy with IR spectroscopy except that an induced dipole $\underline{p}_{in}$ is involved instead of a permanent dipole $\underline{p}$.

An incident electric field $\underline{E} = \underline{E}_0 \cos \omega t$ at a molecule induces in it an electric dipole moment $\underline{p}_{in} = \underline{\underline{\alpha}}\,\underline{E}$ [Eq. (1.16)]. The direction of $\underline{p}_{in}$ is generally not the same as that of $\underline{E}$ due to off-diagonal elements in $\underline{\underline{\alpha}}$. This will be discussed further in (1.f). In analogy with (12.4) the instantaneous polarizability $\underline{\underline{\alpha}}(t)$ can be expressed as

$$\underline{\underline{\alpha}} = (\underline{\underline{\alpha}})_{\xi=0} + \left(\frac{\partial \underline{\underline{\alpha}}}{\partial \xi}\right)_{\xi=0} \cdot \xi + \cdots \qquad (12.8)$$

Now ξ is assumed to vary as $\xi = \xi_0 \cos \omega_\xi t$, i.e., with a frequency ω_ξ characteristic of that normal mode. An expression for $\underline{p}_{in}$ can then be obtained on applying this assumption to (12.8). The product-sum rule for trigonometry functions must be applied. The result is

$$\underline{p}_{in} = (\underline{\underline{\alpha}})_{\xi=0}\, \underline{E}_0 \cos \omega t + \frac{1}{2} \underline{E}_0 \xi_0 \left(\frac{\partial \underline{\underline{\alpha}}}{\partial \xi}\right)_{\xi=0} \Big(\cos (\omega + \omega_\xi)t + \cos (\omega - \omega_\xi)t\Big) \qquad (12.9)$$

Referring back to the classical picture of an oscillating dipole (20.49), Eq. (12.9) then predicts that ratiation is scattered with the incident frequency ω(Rayleigh scattering), and with Raman frequencies $\omega \pm \omega_\xi$. The intensity of the scattered light is $\propto \omega^4$. Other factors of proportionality can also be found from (12.9) [10]. Such a classical model predicts the "Stokes" $(\omega - \omega_\xi)$ and "anti-Stokes" $(\omega + \omega_\xi)$ lines to be equally intense, except for the ω^4 effect. This is not in agreement with the more realistic quantum-mechanical model.

From the point of view of quantum mechanics, a transition from $|v'\rangle$ to $|v''\rangle$ can be considered to occur due to the presence of the induced dipole $\underline{p}_{in}$ instead of the permanent dipole $\underline{p}$. In analogy with (21.45), the probability of transition is then $\propto |P_{x,v',v''}|^2 \ldots$ etc., and $\propto \omega^4$, where $|P_{x,v',v''}|$ is of a more complex form than $m_{x,v',v''}$ due to the tensor nature of $\underline{\underline{\alpha}}$. Thus,

$$P_{x,v',v''} = \langle v''|E_{x,0}\alpha_{xx}|v'\rangle + \langle v''|E_{y,0}\alpha_{xy}|v'\rangle + \langle v''|E_{z,0}\alpha_{xz}|v'\rangle \tag{12.10}$$

A Raman transition is possible only if at least one of the components of the polarizability matrix $(\alpha_{jk})_{v',v''}$ is nonzero. Only six components need be considered, as $\alpha_{xy} = \alpha_{yx}$, etc. The selection rules described as outlined in Sec. (21.5) arise from symmetry considerations of these matrix elements.

(f) Depolarization of Raman Lines

The polarizability tensor $\underline{\underline{\alpha}}$ is often considered as being a combination of a symmetric, $\underline{\underline{\alpha}}^s$, and an asymmetric, $\underline{\underline{\beta}}$, tensor. The symmetrical part is described by the invariant α^s,

$$\alpha^s = \frac{1}{3}(\alpha_{xx} + \alpha_{yy} + \alpha_{zz}) \tag{12.11}$$

While the asymmetric part is described by the anisotropy β,

$$2\beta^2 = [(\alpha_{xx} - \alpha_{yy})^2 + (\alpha_{yy} - \alpha_{zz})^2 + (\alpha_{zz} - \alpha_{xx})^2 + 6(\alpha_{xy}^2 + \alpha_{yz}^2 + \alpha_{zx}^2)] \tag{12.12}$$

If axes x, y, z are chosen as the principal axes of the "polarizability ellipsoid," then only diagonal elements of $\underline{\underline{\alpha}}$ are nonzero and (12.12) is simplified.

Raman scattering is performed in nearly all cases through observing light scattered at right angles. If light is incident along the z axis (Fig. 12.1), then the light scattered in the direction of x axis would be observed. There are several different combinations of polarization of incident and scattered light. If the incident light is polarized with electric vector in the y-z plane (vertical V), then the scattered light can be with the polarization either in the vertical (xy) plane (VV) or the horizontal (xz) plane (VH). Similarily it is possible to have HV and HH scattering.

In all cases except VV scattering, the plane of polarization is changed. This "depolarization" is possible only through anisotropic ($\underline{\underline{\beta}}$) scattering. The polarized (VV) scattering is due to both isotropic ($\underline{\underline{\alpha}}^s$) and anisotropic ($\underline{\underline{\beta}}$) scattering. The intensities I for polarized and depolarized scattering can then be expressed as

$$I_{pol}(\omega) = I_{VV}(\omega) = I_{iso}(\omega) + \frac{4}{3} I_{an}(\omega) \qquad (12.13)$$

$$I_{depol}(\omega) = I_{VH}(\omega) = I_{HV}(\omega) = I_{HH}(\omega) = I_{an}(\omega) \qquad (12.13)$$

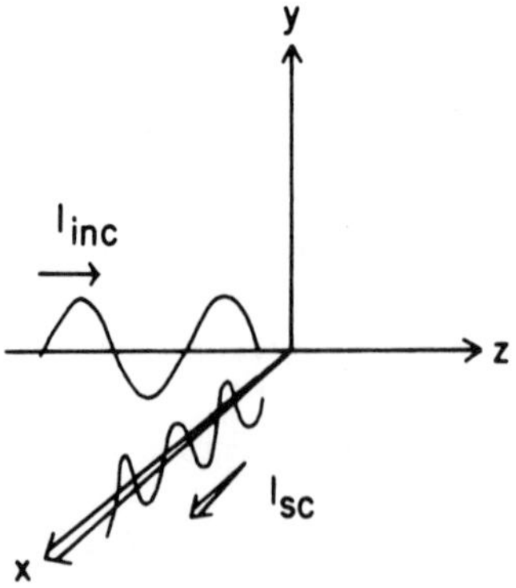

Fig. 12.1. Schematic diagram illustrating VV scattering. The plane of polarization of I_{inc} is in the yz plane and of I_{sc} in the xy plane.

Here $_{iso}$ and $_{an}$ indicate contributions from isotropic and anisotropic scattering. The intensities can also be expressed in terms of differential cross sections $d^2\sigma/d\Omega\, d\omega$ into a frequency range $d\omega$ and a solid angle element $d\Omega$.

(g) Raman Band Shapes

The complete treatment of the Raman effect by quantum mechanics leads to the expression [11]

$$\frac{d^2\sigma}{d\omega d\Omega} = \omega^4 \sum_j \rho_j \sum_f |\langle f|\underline{\varepsilon}_{inc}\underline{\alpha}_{v'v''}\cdot\underline{\varepsilon}_{ram}|j\rangle|^2$$

$$\cdot\, \delta(\omega_{ram} - \omega_{inc} + \omega_\xi + \omega_f - \omega_j) \tag{12.14}$$

The symbols in (12.14) are the same as in (12.4), with $_{inc}$ indicating incident light, $_{ram}$ Raman (scattered) light, and ω_ξ the radial frequency of the vibrational transition $v' \to v''$ involved. The δ function assures conservation of energy.

The steps as shown in (12.4)-(12.7) can be applied to (12.14). In this case the isotropic and the anisotropic parts must be considered separately. When use is made of the expansion (12.8), then the resulting expressions are [12]

$$I_{iso}(\omega') = \left|\frac{\partial\alpha^S}{\partial\xi}\right|^2 \int_{-\infty}^{\infty} G_v(t)\, \exp[i\omega't]\, dt$$

$$I_{an}(\omega') = \int_{-\infty}^{\infty} G_v(t) \left\langle \frac{\partial\underline{\underline{\beta}}_{v'v''}}{\partial\xi}(0)\cdot\frac{\partial\underline{\underline{\beta}}_{v'v''}}{\partial\xi}(t)\right\rangle \exp[i\omega't]\, dt \tag{12.15}$$

Thus the isotropically scattered radiation is not broadened by orientational relaxation, as $\underline{\underline{\alpha}}^S$ is by definition orientation-independent. The anisotropically scattered radiation (depolarized) is broadened by both orientational and vibrational relaxation.

Further analysis of the depolarized scattering [11] indicates that in the special case where the normal vibration involved is totally symmetric in a linear or symmetric top molecule, and where vibrational relaxation can be neglected [see also 14.1(f)],

$$I_{an}(\omega') = I_{depol}(\omega') \propto \langle \mathrm{Tr}\, \underline{\underline{\beta}}_{v'v''}(0)\cdot\underline{\underline{\beta}}_{v'v''}(t)\rangle$$

$$= \frac{1}{2\pi} \int_{-\infty}^{\infty} G_2(t) \exp[-i\omega' t]\, dt \qquad (12.16)$$

The definition of the average in the first form is given in (7.42), while $G_2(t)$ is defined by (7.40). Relationships for transitions involving vibrations with other types of symmetries are discussed in Ref. 9.

(h) Stimulated Raman Effect

In addition to the normal, "spontaneous", Raman spectroscopy described above, two other types of Raman spectra can now be obtained [13]. High-intensity light sources are necessary to achieve these effects. The theory underlying these effects is discussed in Refs. 14 and 15.

A "hyper-Raman" spectrum can be obtained due to the presence of a hyperpolarizability. The proportionality between $\underline{p}_{in}$ and $\underline{E}$ given by $\underline{\underline{\alpha}}$ is correct only as a first approximation. At higher fields, a term in E^2 can no longer be neglected. The selection rules for this effect are different from those of the normal Raman effect [13].

A stimulated Raman effect can also be seen with high intensity incident light. In this case the intensity of radiation of frequency ν_{ram} is so intense that it can stimulate radiation of this same frequency. This is the Raman equivalent to the stimulated emission (21.46) which leads to laser action. Selection rules for this effect are the same as for the normal Raman spectra. Transitions are preferentially enhanced by this effect, however, and the band widths are narrowed [16].

12.2. EXPERIMENTAL TECHNIQUES

Much of the experimental work in Raman and IR spectroscopy is done with standard spectrometers available commercially. Some of the fundamental aspects of such spectrometers are nevertheless outlined here as they are also of importance in noncommercial, specially designed apparatus.

(a) Sources of Radiation

(1) Infrared

To obtain the complete infrared band shape as given by $I(\omega)$, a source of radiation giving a continuum is necessary. Such a continuum in the IR range can be obtained by a appropriate "blackbody." Heated filaments or "globars" (carborundum at about 1200°C) are commonly used, as are mercury lamps [17]. At the lowest frequencies, single frequency radiation from masers or high harmonics of klystrons are also used [Sec. 11.2(c)].

Radiation from a continuum is often filtered before being sent into a monochrometer. A scattering filter can be used to eliminate higher frequencies. In this case the radiation is reflected from a mirror with surface irregularities. Only radiation with a wavelength long as compared to these irregularities will be properly reflected. Polyethylene blackened with carbon black can also be used to eliminate radiation with a wavenumber >400 cm^{-1}. Gratings and prisms can be used to obtain dispersion of the radiation. The prism material must be such as to be transparent in the frequency range of interest. The radiation must also in cases be introduced to the sample in vacuum or in dry air due to nontransparency of species present in normal air.

(2) Raman

Only a single frequency light source is necessary for Raman studies. This frequency should not be in the vicinity of any resonant absorptions in the system. A common light source has been a mercury arc designed to give a high output in a sharp 4358 Å line with little background radiation [10].

Lately it is more common to use lasers as sources of the intense monochromatic light necessary. A listing of lasers of use in Raman spectroscopy is given in [18]. Most often an argon or helium-neon gas laser is used. These lasers can be adjusted to give one of several lines, unually 4880 Å for the former and 6328 Å for the latter. For stimulated Raman spectroscopy, more intensity is required. This requirement is met through solid state pulsed lasers, e.g., ruby at 6943 Å.

Filters can be used to eliminate radiation in unwanted regions, especially when mercury arcs are used for sources. Various solutions can be used to filter out radiation above and below 4358 Å, for example.

(b) Cells

(1) Infrared

There can be problems in finding suitable cell window materials for the IR region, especially when aqueous solutions are to be studied. Insoluble, IR transparent materials are required. Calcium fluoride is useful in the 2.5 to 8 μm (i.e., to 1250 cm^{-1}) range, silver chloride for 2.5 to 25 μm, polyethylene for 15-330 μm and quartz for 50-330 μm (i.e., to 30 cm^{-1}) [19].

Water absorbs intensely in much of the IR region, so that very small pathlengths are necessary when studying aqueous solutions, e.g., 0.075 mm [18]. The use of D_2O allows investigations of some frequency regions not available with H_2O because of excessive absorption. Special techniques can be used to obtain the optical constants in this high-frequency region [20]. Reflection rather than transmission method can be used, and absorption (i.e., ε'') can be obtained from a knowledge of index of refraction (i.e., ε') as a function of frequency and vice versa through the Kramer-Kronig relations. Relations between ε'' and ε' are discussed in Sec. 11.1(c).

In most cases, IR spectra are taken using a double-beam spectrometer. Absorption due to cell window materials and solvent (if any) is cancelled out in such differential spectra. The two cells used for the measurements must be carefully matched.

(2) Raman

Liquid Raman cells are usually simple glass tubes. Since incident and scattered radiation are in the visible range, no difficulty is present in obtaining cell material. When mercury arc radiation is used, then cells are irradiated along their length and scattered radiation is observed through an end window. Special designs are used to maximize the Raman scattered light entering the detector and to eliminate stray light. The samples must be dust free to prevent an extremely large central component due to "Tyndall" scattering from dust particles.

Absolute measurements can be made with resonable precision using radiation from mercury lamps. Usually carbon tetrachloride is used as a standard for such measurements. The lamps can be designed to be quite stable and the sample can be positioned quite reproducibly. The effects of refractive index, sample color, etc. are difficult to correct for.

Raman laser sources have several advantages, such as being in the form of an intense, polarized, concentrated beam. In order to obtain good absolute measurements, however, it is necessary to reproduce the source-cell geometry very accurately. A "fixed-beam" apparatus makes more accurate absolute measurements possible. Here the incident laser beam and the spectrometer are maintained in exact positions with the use of pinholes [13].

(c) Detection

(1) Infrared

After transmission through the cell, the monochromatic radiation can be focused on some detector in the spectrograph with mirrors or lenses. Various infrared detectors are available [21]. Thermocouples can be used as changes appear in its electrical potential due to heating of the thermocouple junction when IR is focused on it. In "bolometers" the resistance change in materials (thermistors) due to such heating is measured. Detection in a "Golay cell" depends on the distortion of windows due to the expansion of a gas (usually Xenon) arising from an increase in temperature due to absorption of the IR. Photoconducting devices are also available for a range in the IR. These are semiconductors (e.g., antimony-doped germanium) which change their electric conductivity when absorbing quanta of radiation. Often detection is done through an alternating rather than a direct current to utilize resonant circuits and thus minimize background noise. In such cases, the incident radiation is chopped at a specific frequency, and only variation in the signal from the detector at this frequency is further amplified. When double beam spectrometers are used, then the difference in the signal from the reference and the sample cell is measured.

"Fourier spectroscopy" can also be used to obtain $I(\omega)$. In this case radiation from a continuum source is split into two parts in e.g., a Michelson interferometer (Fig. 11.7). The mirror in the reference arm is then moved back and forth in a specific pattern. This gives an "interferogram" $I(x)$ at the detector, where x is the displacement of the mirror. After correction for the background interferogram (i.e., when the specimen is absent), $I(x)$ can be Fourier transformed to obtain $I(\tilde{\nu})$ ($\tilde{\nu}$ in cm^{-1}) and $I(\omega)$. A full discussion can be found in Ref. 22.

(2) Raman

Much of the Raman data obtained using mercury lamps is in the form of a photographic recording. Such a photograph is taken of the scattered light after dispersion by a grating or a prism. Effective use is made of the scattered light in this way, but the film surface is not as effective as a photoelectric surface as when photomultipliers are used. Examples of spectrometers can be found in [23].

Scattered lines quite close to the central Rayleigh line can be detected by a "heterodyne" or "beating" spectrometer. This approach is described in Sec. 14.2(c) instead of here, however, as it is more appropriate for lines closer than in most Raman lines.

12.3. RESULTS FOR SPECIFIC SYSTEMS

(a) Orientational and Vibrational Relaxation

Numerous studies have recently been reported on the shape of IR and Raman lines in pure liquids and solutions. The results for four different systems are briefly discussed here to illustrate problems in data analysis and the types of information attainable. Correlation of the data from IR and Raman with NMR (Chap. 13) and Rayleigh scattering (Chap. 14) data is available for some such systems.

As indicated in (12.15), the isotropically scattered Raman light is independent of the orientational relaxation, but dependent on vibrational relaxation. The anisotropically scattered light is however also dependent on orientational relaxation. The broadening of the Raman lines due to these effects can be expressed in terms of the half-widths $\delta\nu_v$ (or $\delta\tilde{\nu}_v$ if cm^{-1} are used, or $\delta\omega_v$ if rad sec^{-1} are used) and $\delta\tilde{\nu}_{or}$. These two effects can be separated out for the polarized and depolarized lines. The line shape to be analyzed must first be corrected for any instrumental effects.

For depolarized scattering, the line width can be assumed to be of the form

$$\delta\tilde{\nu} = \delta\tilde{\nu}_v + \delta\tilde{\nu}_{or} = \delta\tilde{\nu}_v + \delta\tilde{\nu}_{or,0}\ \exp\left[-\frac{E^{\#}_{or}}{kT}\right] \qquad (12.17)$$

The total line width $\delta\tilde{\nu}$ can be written in the form of a sum as in (12.17) when both the vibrational (intrinsic) and orientational line shapes are assumed Lorentzian (20.52), even though it is due to the convolution of the intrinsic shape with the orientational shape (12.15). The temperature dependence of vibrational relaxation is in (12.17) assumed negligible compared to the Arrhenius form for orientation with an activation energy $E^{\#}_{or}$.

In the case of polarized Raman lines, contributions from both isotropically and anisotropically scattered light are present. The isotropically scattered line shape can then be obtained by correcting the polarized line by subtracting an appropriate amount of the depolarized (12.13). This leads to a knowledge of $\delta\tilde{\nu}_v$. It is not possible to separate $\delta\tilde{\nu}_v$ and $\delta\tilde{\nu}_{or}$ in IR spectra.

(1) Acetonitrile

Both the Raman [12,24] and the IR [25] spectrum of pure liquid acetonitrile (CH_3-CN) have been studied. The results of studies on the C-H stretching (2942 cm^{-1}), C-C stretching (918 cm^{-1}), and C-N stretching (2249 cm^{-1}) bands have been analyzed.

A vibrational width $\delta\tilde{\nu}_v \simeq 2.5\ cm^{-1}$ is obtained in Ref. 12 from analysis of Raman lines leading to a vibrational relaxation time $\tau_v = 1/(2\pi c \cdot \delta\nu_v) \simeq 2.1 \times 10^{-12}$ sec for the CN stretch. It is pointed out in Ref. 24, however, that there is secondary structure in the fundamental band at 2249 cm^{-1}, probably due to some molecular interaction [Sec. 12.3(d)]. This is illustrated in Fig. 12.2 where the band is partially resolved into two Lorentzians. This analysis leads to $\delta\tilde{\nu}_v = 1.6 \pm 0.2\ cm^{-1}$ and $\tau_v \simeq 3.3 \times 10^{-12}$ sec.

According to Ref. 12 the orientational half-widths are $\delta\tilde{\nu}_{or} = 4.0 \pm 0.5\ cm^{-1}$ for the C-C and $\delta\tilde{\nu}_{or} = 3.5 \pm 0.5\ cm^{-1}$ for the C-N band. These numbers refer to the same orientational motion. As can be seen from the large uncertainties in $\delta\tilde{\nu}_{or}$, it is meaningless to try to obtain the exact shape of $G_2(t)$ from the data through Fourier transforming the band shape (12.16).

In Ref. 24 the analysis has been extended to include the vibrational mode at 2942 cm^{-1} which leads to description of the orientational motion perpendicular to the major (N-C-C-) axis. This motion is interpreted in terms of rotational diffusion [Sec. 6.1(e)]. The diffusion coefficient D_r is expressed as $D_r = kT/\zeta$ (6.62) with ζ (6.13) corrected for microviscosity effects. The results obtained are in reasonably good agreement with dielectric and NMR results.

The vibrational orientational relaxation of several bands for acetonitrile can be observed through IR [25]. Bands corresponding to normal modes parallel to the major axis as well as "perpendicular

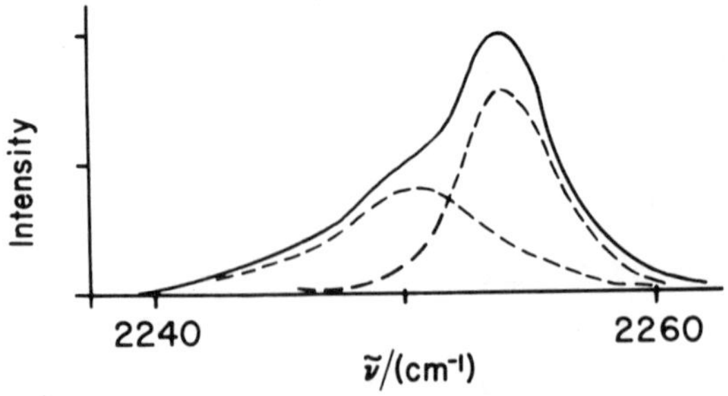

Fig. 12.2. Raman intensity I_{VV} vs $\tilde{\nu}$ for acetonitrile in the region of ν_2 (CN stretching). —— Total intensity; --- two partially resolved components. After Ref. 24.

bands" can be observed. The results for the two parallel bands (918 cm^{-1}, 2249 cm^{-1}) discussed previously indicate that for a short time ($\sim 0.1 \times 10^{-12}$ sec) the correlation function corresponds to free rotor decay with the appropriate moment of inertia as determined from the gas phase spectrum [see also Sec. 14.3(c)]. It thus takes of the order of 0.1×10^{-12} sec for a significant hindering effect to take place in orientations. This corresponds to an angular jump of about 6°.

Vibrational energy transfer seems initially to decay more gradually than exponentially. If an exponential vibrational form with $\tau_v = 2.3 \times 10^{-12}$ sec is assumed, then the rotational correlation calculated is greater than unity. At longer times, the total relaxation is exponential. Assuming $\tau_v = 2.3 \times 10^{-12}$ sec gives then a value of 3.2×10^{-12} sec for τ_r. This is the same as a value reported from dielectric relaxation, and as necessary, larger than the value 1.5×10^{-12} sec for $\tau_{r,2}$ obtained from Raman (6.31).

Far infrared spectra of acetonitrile and its analysis in terms of dipole correlation is discussed in Ref. 26.

(2) Benzene

In the case of benzene, $\delta\tilde{\nu}_{or} \approx 2.0$ cm^{-1} leading to a relaxation time $\tau_{r,2}$ (i.e., relaxation time for the $\ell = 2$ spherical harmonic (6.31)) $\simeq 2.6 \times 10^{-12}$ sec [12]. This is in agreement with NMR and Rayleigh scattering results. The vibrational relaxation time from Raman studies is $\tau_v \simeq 4.4 \times 10^{-12}$ sec. Ultrasonic absorption studies give a value of very different value, 2.7×10^{-10} sec [Sec. 10.3(b)]. This may be because the ultrasonic value refers to vibration-translation relaxation, while τ_v here refers to the relaxation of one mode, i.e., includes vibrational-vibrational.

(3) Alcohols

Analysis of the depolarized Raman lines of alcohol indicate that vibrational relaxation is so rapid [Sec. 10.3(b)] that $\tau_v < \tau_r$, i.e., $\delta\tilde{\nu}_v > \delta\tilde{\nu}_{or}$. For example, in the case of the CH_2 twisting mode of $C_8H_{17}OH$, $\delta\tilde{\nu}_v \approx 8.0$ cm^{-1} as compared to $\delta\tilde{\nu}_{or} \approx 1.6$ cm^{-1}. Thus line broadening studies (both IR and Raman) in such systems are not very useful for observing rotational motion.

Figure 12.3 [25] shows the vibrational correlation function (from Raman, $\tau_v \approx 1.9 \times 10^{-12}$ sec), the vibration rotation function (from IR, $\tau_{vr} \approx 1.4 \times 10^{-12}$ sec), and the rotational function (the difference) for 2-propanol (CH_3-CHOH-CH_3). The vibrational relaxation predominates at longer times, but for $t < 10^{-12}$ sec, the rotational relaxation is predominant.

IR studies of alcohols can be useful from point of view different than from obtaining correlation functions (e.g., [27]). Such aspects are discussed in Sec. (c).

(4) Solutions of Simple Molecules

Several types of systems have received a great deal of attention. Numerous studies have been carried out of the IR and Raman band shapes of transitions in spherical-top molecules, e.g., CCl_4, CH_3I, ClO_3F [28], both pure and in solution. Other numerous studies have been

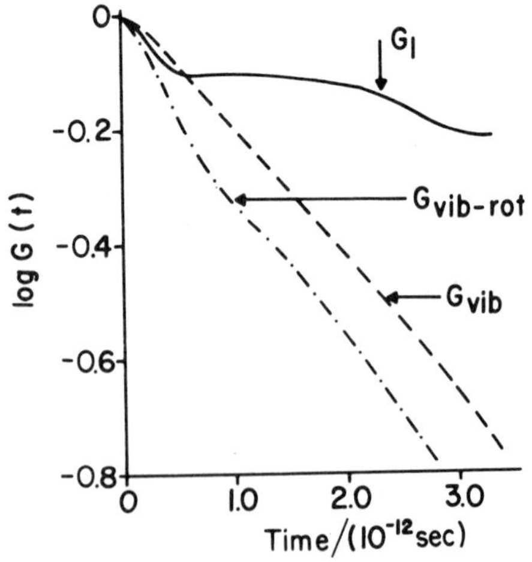

Fig. 12.3. The vibrational-rotational time correlation function —·—·—; the vibrational function ----; and the orientational function —— for 2-propanol. The functions are obtained from the shape of the 816 cm^{-1} (C-C stretch) bands. After Ref. 25.

made on solution of simple molecules such as, e.g., CO, N_2, HCl [29]. The two types of systems should represent the limits of the spectrum of types of orientational motion. The latter types of systems should also be easier to analyze due to the presence of only one normal mode.

Figure 12.4 shows the IR profile of the 0 → 1 vibrational transition band of HCl in CCl_4. The experimental profile is shown fitted by calculated curves. In the calculation, the function $G_1(t)$ is assumed to have one component due to rotational diffusion (6.31) and another due to gas-phase-like motion. The calculated curves correspond to (i) a fraction 0.40 due to diffusional, and (ii) a fraction 0.53 due to diffusional relaxation.

(b) *Collision-Induced Far-Infrared Absorption*

Solutions of methane (CH_4) in liquid argon have been studied by Raman, IR [30] and also far-infrared (20-250 cm^{-1}) [31] spectroscopy. Here the FIR results for this simple case will be discussed, complementary to the discussion of dielectric relaxation of benzene [Sec. 11.3(a)].

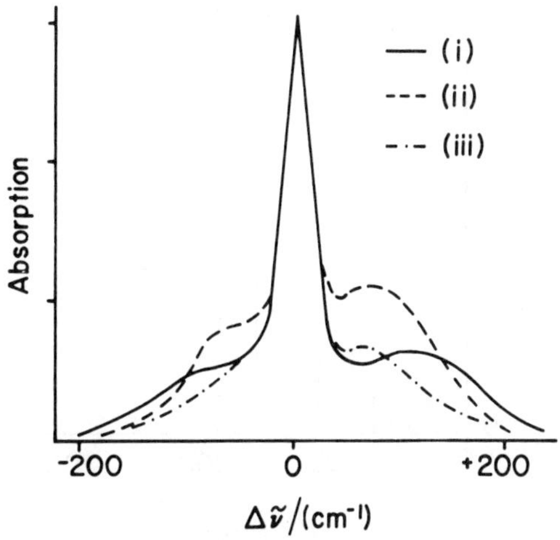

Fig. 12.4. The IR band shape of the 0 → 1 vibrational transition of HCl in CCl_4. (i) —— Experimental; (ii) --- calculated shape with 0.40 rotational diffusion; (iii) —·— calculated shape with 0.53 rotational diffusion. After Ref. 29.

Results for benzene [32] will be discussed after this. The FIR absorption is interpreted in both cases as resulting from collision-induced effects.

As methane is symmetrical, there is no net dipole or quadrupole interaction [Sec. 1.1(b)]. Thus octopolar fields [Sec. 1.1(a)] are responsible for the induced dipoles. Figure 12.5 [31] shows the absorption of CH_4 in liquid argon. The line strengths and positions for the expected rotational spectrum are shown, calculated on the assumption of collision-induced rotational transitions.

The width of these lines was used as adjustable parameters to give the fit shown. It is ~25 cm^{-1}, suggesting that the average collision time is of the order of 2×10^{-13} sec. This assumes the relaxation to be due to collisions of finite time, i.e., existence of the induced dipoles for a finite time.

The measured absolute value of the absorption is only about 15% of the calculated value. The calculations do not take account of

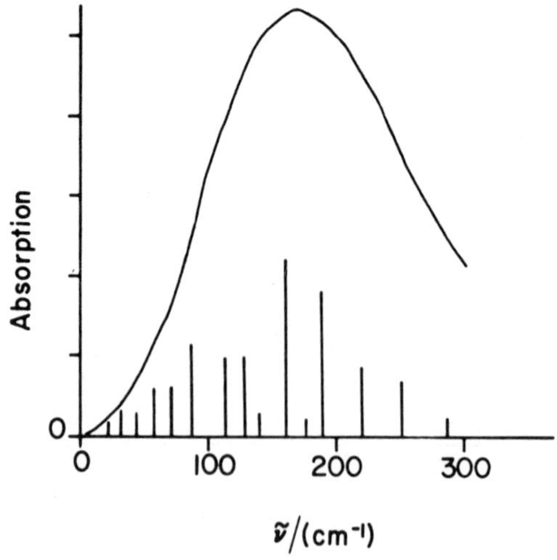

Fig. 12.5. Far IR absorption spectrum of CH_4 dissolved in liquid argon. The vertical lines indicate the positions and strengths of the expected rotational spectrum. After Ref. 31.

"solvent effects" which occur during the binary collision assumed. Other dipoles induced in neighboring molecules would lead to some cancellation. In gases, such cancellation is smaller and collision-induced absorption is more intense [32].

As already noted in 11.3(a), the absorption in the corresponding region in benzene is also interpreted as being collision-induced, but not involving transitions between rotational levels. Figure 12.6 shows the absorption coefficient of benzene, carbon tetrachloride and a solution of benzene in carbon tetrachloride. From these curves and curves for solutions at other concentrations, evidence can be obtained to indicate that the absorption arises from bimolecular collision effects [33].

If it is assumed that bimolecular collisions are the basic cause of the absorption, then the integrated absorption A_{tot} can be expressed as

$$A_{tot} = X_a^2 A_{aa} + X_b^2 A_{bb} + 2X_a X_b A_{ab} \tag{12.18}$$

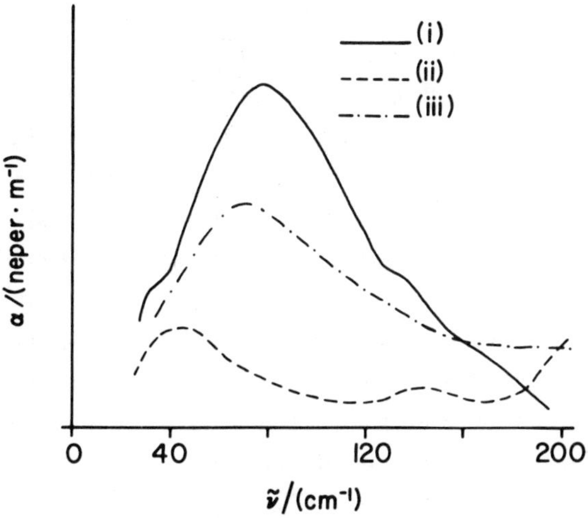

Fig. 12.6. Far IR absorption spectrum of (i) —— benzene (ii) --- CCl_4 (iii) —·— a solution 5.2m CCl_4 in benzene. After Ref. 33.

Here A_{aa} is the integrated absorption due to an A-A interaction etc. This is analogous to Eq. (4.18). It is assumed in analogy to Secs. 4.1(e) and 1.1(e) that $A_{ab} = (A_{aa} A_{bb})^{1/2}$. The agreement between such a calculated A_{tot} vs X_a curve and the experimental is to within experimental limits, indicating the assumption of bimolecular interactions to be reasonable.

In the case of polar molecules, the FIR absorption is believed to be libratory motion in a cage formed by nearest neighbors. Such models are discussed in some detail in Ref. 34.

(c) *Intramolecular Vibrations in Liquid Water*

The IR and Raman spectra of liquid water (H_2O, D_2O, and HDO) have been the subject of numerous investigations. Reviews are given in Refs. 13 and 35. Some of the results will be reviewed in this and the following section. In this section only changes in the intramolecular modes of vibration will be discussed.

Figure 12.7 illustrates the shifting of the central frequency of an IR vibrational band, its increase in intensity, and the coalescing out of its structure as density increases. The data are for the rather extreme case of 400°C, with densities from 0.016 to 0.9 g cm^{-3}.

The O-D stretching mode is displayed, as it is easiest to study intramolecular stretching modes of dilute solutions of HDO in H_2O. Then there is only weak coupling to vibrations in neighboring molecules, and the OD stretch is further removed from the overtone (Δv = 2) of the ν_2 (bending) vibration of water (Sec. 21.5).

The temperature dependence of the isotropic part of the Raman spectum of this same band is shown in Fig. 12.8. This shows that the system does not have an "isosbestic" frequency, contrary to the conclusions reached on examination of earlier data which was not resolved into isotropic and anisotropic components [13]. An isosbestic frequency is a frequency at which the intensity is independent of temperature [or concentration (Fig. 12.11)].

The appearance of an isosbestic phenomenon implies that two components are present in the band, each with a half-width independent

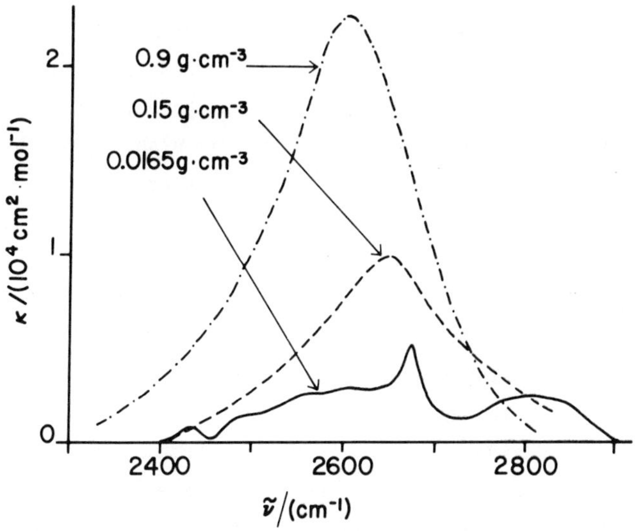

Fig. 12.7. The IR absorption band of the OD stretching region of HOD at 400°C with variation in density. —— 0.0165 g cm^{-3}, ---- 0.15 g cm^{-3}, —·— 0.90 g cm^{-3}. After Ref. 36.

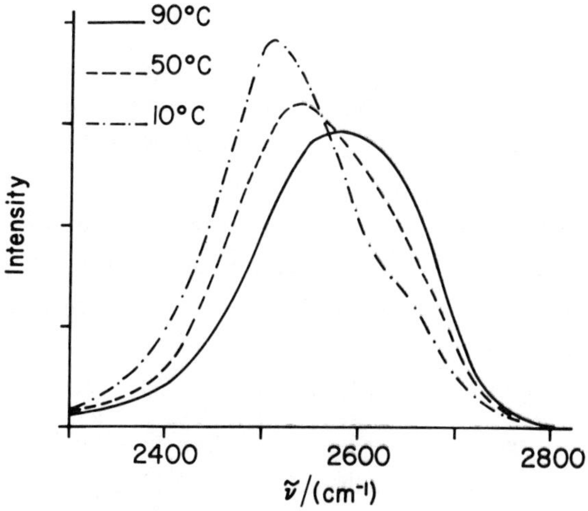

Fig. 12.8. The isotropic part of the Raman spectrum of the OD stretching region of HOD for liquid water at temperatures of —— 90°C, --- 50°C, —·— 10°C. After Ref. 37.

of temperature, but with intensities with opposite temperature dependence. The apparent isosbestic point in water has thus been interpreted as being due to a component arising from hydrogen-bonded O-D bonds, and another from free O-D bonds. As temperature increases, the H-bonded (lower frequency) component diminishes (and the free increases) in intensity [13]. Other authors interpret the band as being due to a broad continuum [35]. These interpretations are discussed in some detail in Ref. 38.

The band shape of a spectrum such as that shown in Fig. 12.8, (or for the corresponding OH stretch in the 3000 to 3800 cm^{-1} range) has been often interpreted as being due to the sum of four Gaussian components [13]. The nonbonded (high $\tilde{\nu}$) and the H-bonded components are further subdivided into two components each. Two subcomponents arise for each bond type due to coupling between stretching vibrations. The subcomponents correspond to the symmetric and antisymmetric stretching modes [ν_1 and ν_3, (Sec. 21.5)] in the isolated water molecule [39].

The presence of four components is supported by stimulated spectra [13], where some of the four components can be preferentially increased by changing the H_2O:D_2O ratios. The line width of the components is also diminished.

Thus this Raman data give support to the existance of two types of OH bonds for times greater than those of vibrational transitions. However, some authors interpret the four bands as being due to vibrations other than those described above [37]. Yet others find it impossible to fit the data to within experimental error using four Gaussian components [40] (see also "Further Recent References").

(d) Intermolecular Vibrations in Liquid Water

IR (see Fig. 11.9) and Raman bands [41] appear in liquid water also at lower frequencies. These bands are usually interpreted using ice as a model [42]. The band in the 200 to 1100 cm^{-1} region is interpreted as being due to the librational motion of water molecules. The Raman spectrum is interpreted as being due to three components with very large half-widths (~220 cm^{-1}) at 425, 500, and 740 cm^{-1}. The IR spectrum shows a maximum absorption at about 700 cm^{-1}, somewhat lower than the corresponding band maximum in ice (795 cm^{-1}). As temperature increases, the frequency shifts downward. As the intensity of the band is low, quantitative studies are difficult.

There are broad weak bands observed in Raman spectra at even lower frequencies, 170 and 60 cm^{-1} [13]. The latter is also observed in neutron scattering [Sec. 16.3(e)]. The intensities of these bands decrease with increasing temperature. An IR band centered at about 170 cm^{-1} is also observed, again at a frequency lower than the corresponding ice band (214 cm^{-1}). Again the frequency decreases as the temperature is increased. These bands are interpreted as being due to intermolecular vibrations (i.e., hindered translations).

All of the intermolecular modes together can be considered as the normal modes of vibration of a 5-molecule H-bonded structure (a tetrahedrally coordinated water) [35]. This complex can be assumed to have the same C_{2v} symmetry as water itself. The normal modes of this 5-unit complex are 3 nonsymmetric deformations about 3 moments of inertia (i.e., the 3 librations); 4 H-bonded stretching modes (at 170 cm^{-1}), and some symmetrical deformations corresponding to H-bond bending (at 60 cm^{-1}).

The decrease in intensity of the intermolecular bands with increase in temperature can then be attributed to breakdown of these structural groups. Such an interpretation yields a satisfactory value of -10.1 kJ mol^{-1} for the ΔH^{θ} of an H bond.

(e) Water in Organic Solvents

In dilute solutions in nonpolar solvents, water shows signs of being in a monomeric form [43]. This is shown in Fig. 12.9, where several spectra are compared. The shift in the frequency shows a correlation with solution dielectric constant [Sec. 12.1(b)].

However, evidence has been obtained for the presence of water dimers in carbon tetrachloride (CCl_4). IR studies of water in dichloroethane ($C_2H_4Cl_2$) [44] have been interpreted in terms of trimers.

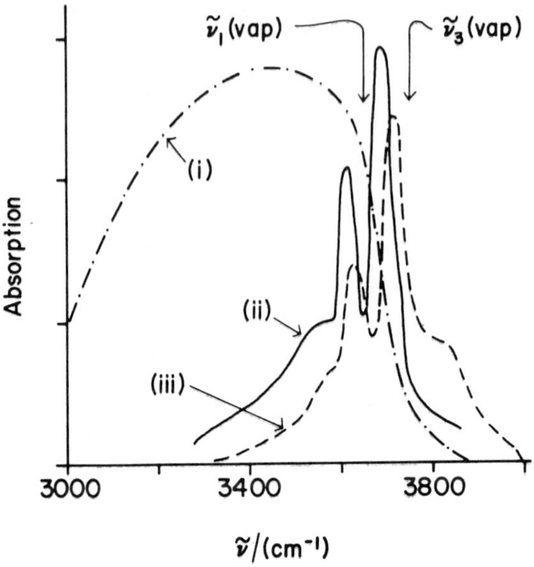

Fig. 12.9. The IR absorption spectrum of the OH stretching region for (i) —·—· liquid water, (ii) —— water in CCl_4, (iii) ---- water in $C_2H_4Cl_2$. After Ref. 43.

This interpretation follows from the concentration dependence of the intensity of the low-frequency shoulder evident in Fig. 12.9(ii). The shoulder is assigned to the stretching mode of bonded O-H.

In various other polar organic solvents, the IR spectrum of water in solution can be interpreted successfully in terms of 1:1 or 1:2 water:solvent complexes [45]. The band corresponding to OH stretching is shifted to longer wavelengths as the water proton becomes more strongly bonded with the solvent, i.e., in more basic solvents. These aspects are discussed further in more general terms in the next section.

(f) Hydrogen Bonding in Solutions

The effect of solvent on the X-H stretching bands has been extensively studied [3]. The large shifts cannot be interpreted on the basis of a continuum solvent model. Specific X-H---Y (i.e., H-bonding to solvent Y) interactions must be postulated in many cases.

Such a shift in the NH stretching bands for dimethylamine ($(CH_3)_2NH$) in carbon tetrachloride (CCl_4) and n-hexane (C_6H_{14}) are shown in Fig. 12.10 [46]. The frequency in CCl_4 is less than in C_6-H_{14} due to the greater complexing ability of CCl_4. This leads to increased polarization of the N-H bond and a lowering of the frequency. The intensity of absorption in CCl_4 solution is also considerably greater than in C_6H_{14} due to this same effect.

The lower frequency bands (3322 cm^{-1} in C_6H_{14}, 3302 in CCl_4 and 3294 in pure $(CH_3)_2NH$) are interpreted as being due to N-H stretching in N-H---N hydrogen-bonded dimers or multimers. The slight lowering of the frequency of this association band with increasing concentration can be explained by the formation of trimers, chainlike associates etc. at higher concentrations. Such multimers possess stronger H bonds, as an increase in the polarization of the NH bond for any reason results in a stronger H bond and a lower frequency [Sec. 1.3 (b)]. Association constants can be calculated from the concentration depencence of the spectra.

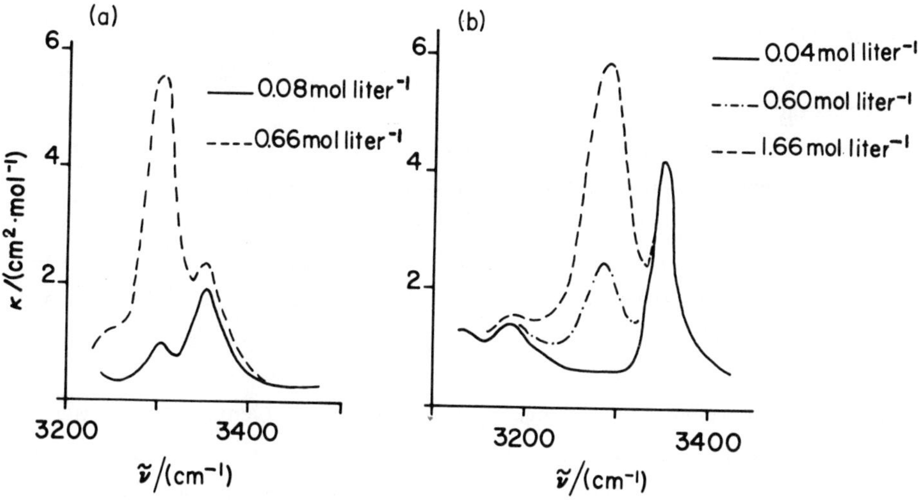

Fig. 12.10. The IR absorption bands (NH stretching) for dimethylamine in (a) hexane solution at two concentrations, and (b) CCl_4 solutions at three concentrations. After Ref. 46.

When the temperature dependence of the spectra is available, then thermodynamic data for the proposed equilibria can be calculated. The ΔH^{θ} for the NH---N bond estimated in this way is -11.5 kJ mol^{-1} in C_6H_{14} and -5.3 kJ mol^{-1} in CCl_4. Vapor pressure data gives a value of -7.6, while excess mixing functions lead to a value of -8.5 [Sec. 8.3(c)]. The value in CCl_4 can be considered to be lower as the more stable solvent complex must be dissociated before an association can occur.

In the case of symmetric hydrogen bonds of the type $(-X-H---X-)^-$, a continuum absorption is obtained in the range 1700 to 3000 cm^{-1}. Examples of systems where such configurations arise are CH_3OK in methanol, KOH in water etc. [47]. The H bond in this case has a double minimum potential well. This makes its polarizability extremely large, and leads to intense IR absorption (12.3).

(g) Ion Solvent Effects

IR bands arising from solvent molecules can be split into two components by the presence of ions. This is illustrated in Fig. 12.11 where the OD stretching of HOD is seen to be split by the presence of $Mg(ClO_4)_2$ [48]. This figure also illustrates the appearance of an isosbestic frequency. Such splitting occurs with anions of the strongest acids.

An interpretation of such a phenomenon is that a new high-frequency mode originates from water molecules in between the cation and anion of a solvent-shared ion pair. In the case of anions of strong acids, no H bond is formed by the anion with the trapped water. Such an effect does not occur in solutions of alkali halides, as the water is H-bonded to the halide ion, so that the OH stretch is similar to that in pure water and no new component arises.

Such phenomena also occur in nonaqueous solvents. Propylene carbonate ($C_4H_6O_3$) is an excellent solvent for cations, but solvates anions poorly. A study of various salts in this solvent showed no variation in the IR absorption with the anion [49]. There was a shift in frequency of the solvent bands (C=O, O-C-O stretches) and

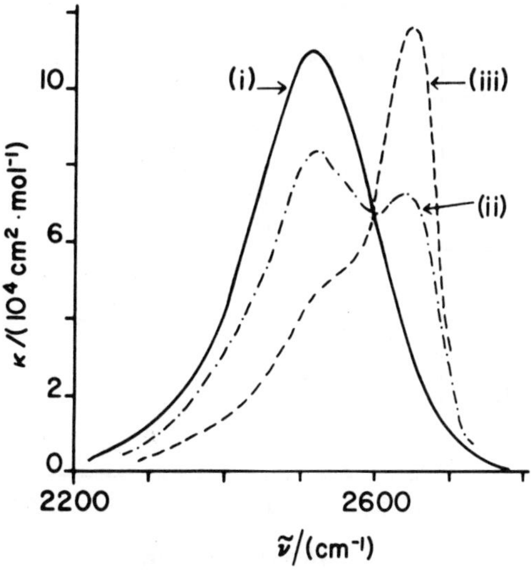

Fig. 12.11. The IR absorption in the OD stretching region of HOD with three ratios of the solute ($Mg(ClO_4)_2$) to solvent (water): (i) —— pure water; (ii) —·— $Mg(ClO_4)_2$:H_2O as .05:1; (iii) ---- $Mg(ClO_4)_2$:H_2O as .15:1. After Ref. 48.

the appearance of a new IR band that was dependent on cations. The shift was greatest for Li and Ag salts, smaller for Na and not noticeable for $(n\text{-Bu})_4N$ salts. No new component appeared for the $(n\text{-Bu})_4N$ salt solutions. Plots of band shift vs mole ratio of solvent to ion showed the relation to have a sharp break at mol ratio 6 for Li, Na, K, and Ag salts independent of anion. This suggests an arrangement of propylene carbonate around cations, with no anion effects even at high concentrations. Thus the ion pairs in the solutions are not likely to be contact ion pairs.

Changes in the spectrum of aqueous solutions of tetraalkylammonium salts can be detected with a difference spectrometer in the near-infrared [50]. An example of such a difference spectrum is given in Fig. 12.12. The spectra are interpreted as being due to components arising from a nonbonded and a bonded OH. A temperature study suggests

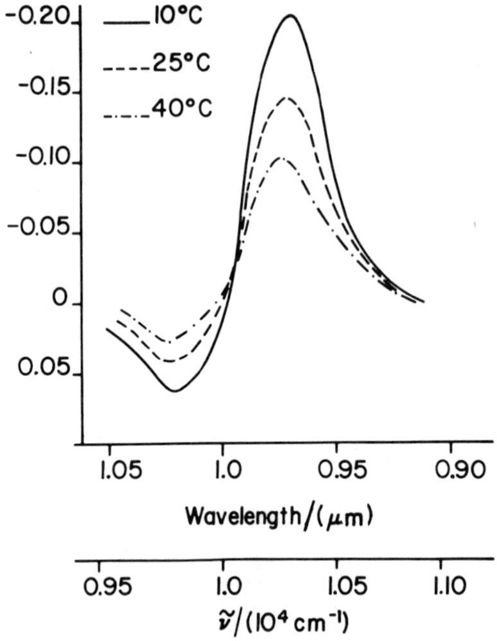

Fig. 12.12. The IR difference spectrum in the 1 μm region between water and a 1m Bu_4NBr solution at —— 10°C, --- 25°C, —·— 40°C. After Ref. 50.

the activation energy for the transition between these two states to be 7.8 kJ mol^{-1}. The introduction of tetraalkylammonium ions shifts the equilibrium towards the bonded OH, i.e., the effect is equivalent to lowering the temperature of pure water. Li^+ and F^- ions have the same effect while the other alkali metal and halide ions have the opposite; i.e., Na^+, Cl^-, etc. ions are "structure breakers" according to the discussion in Secs. 1.3(d), 4.3, and 8.3(h).

Similar studies have been carried out for solutions of salts in liquid ammonia, but using Raman instead of IR [51]. The symmetric bending mode of NH_3 shows strong cation dependence which can be explained on the basis of an electrostatic model.

(h) Ion Pairing in Aqueous Sulfate and Nitrate Solutions

(1) Sulfates

In addition to elucidating ion-solvent interaction, IR and Raman spectroscopy can also be used to study ion pairing phenomena. Some results for aqueous solutions of sulfate and nitrate salts are discussed here to illustrate such studies.

No evidence of the contact ion pairing postulated to be present in $MgSO_4$ solutions [Sec. 10.3(g)] was noted in the first Raman studies on these solutions [52]. The spectra of 0.1 M Na_2SO_4 and $MgSO_4$ solutions show essentially only the very strong band at 982 cm^{-1} due to the symmetrical stretching of the SO_4^{-2} ion. Addition of NaCl to Na_2SO_4 solution did not change the spectrum, suggesting the absence of $NaSO_4^-$ ion pairs at these concentrations. Similar results were obtained for Mg^{+2} solutions. This suggests that any ion pairs present are solvent separated [Sec. 10.3(g)], and that the cation in such solvent separated ion pairs does not interact strongly enough with SO_4^{-2} to change the Raman spectrum of this ion.

On addition of acid (HCl), new lines appeared in the spectrum (Fig. 12.13). A band at 1053 cm^{-1} assigned to the HSO_4^- ion appears. By observing relative intensities of the 1053 and 982 cm^{-1} as a function of temperature, acid dissociation constants can be obtained. The 1053 cm^{-1} band is however less intense when Na^+ or Mg^{+2} is present, the intensity being transferred to the 982 cm^{-1} band. This can be interpreted as indicating that there is a competition for SO_4^{-2} by H^+ and Na^+ or Mg^{+2}. When the SO_4^{-2} is in the form of solvent separated ion pairs, it would contribute to the 982 cm^{-1} band.

The $MgSO_4$ band was however in subsequent work noted to be asymmetric on the high-frequency side (i.e., near 1000 cm^{-1}) when compared to the band in Na_2SO_4 solutions. This has been interpreted as being due to the presence of an additional component ($MgSO_4$ contact ion pair) [53]. The pressure dependence of the relative sizes of the components gives the dependence of the ion pair dissociation constant and a value of ΔV for that equilibrium (17.34). The ΔV value of -20 $cm^3\ mol^{-1}$ obtained differs from that obtained from ultrasonic absorp-

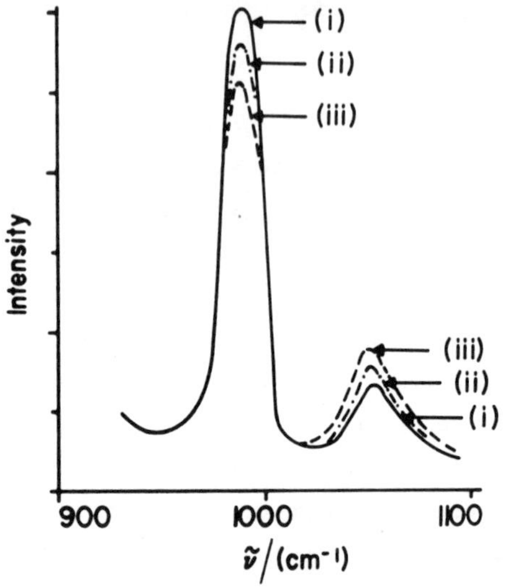

Fig. 12.13. Raman spectra in the 1000 cm^{-1} region of (i) —— a solution 0.1M in Na_2SO_4, 0.1M in HCl and 0.2M in $MgCl_2$; (ii) —·—· 0.1M in Na_2SO_4, 0.1M in HCl and 0.7M in NaCl; (iii) ---- 0.1M in Na_2 SO_4, and 0.1M in HCl. After Ref. 52.

tion and conductivity, as here the ΔV refers to the contact ion pair ⇄ all other configurations, i.e., IV ⇄ I, II, III in (10.55). Conductivity would measure the ΔV for II, III, IV ⇄ I.

(2) Nitrates

Several studies have been made on nitrate systems [54,55]. A change in the spectrum of the NO_3^- ion is noted even in very dilute solutions. This is believed to be due to the splitting of a degenerate normal mode of NO_3^- through perturbation by water. At concentrations where contact ions occur, another doubly degenerate mode of NO_3^- is perturbed enough to give an observed splitting. This can be considered from the point of view that the symmetry of the NO_3^- ion (D_{3h}) is lowered on perturbation by water or cations (to C_{2v} or C_s), leading to a loss of degeneracy.

The splitting of NO_3^- lines indicative of contact ion pairs does not occur in $Mg(NO_3)_2$ solutions until concentrations are reached which correspond to 6 mol water per mol $Mg(NO_3)_2$ [54]. This is a higher concentration than when other divalent cations (Ca^{+2}, Cd^{+2}) are present. It is interpreted as being due to an especially stable hexahydrated ion $(Mg(H_2O)_6)^{+2}$ being present. This prevents $Mg^{+2}\cdot NO_3^-$ contact ions from forming, just as $Mg^{+2}\cdot SO_4^{-2}$ are not easily formed.

Solutions of silver nitrate ($AgNO_3$) have also been studied both by IR and Raman spectroscopy [55]. It is possible in this case to distinguish between lines from bound and solvated nitrate, and to obtain an equilibrium constant for the transition between these two states. The data are consistent with a symmetry for the $Ag^+\cdot NO_3^-$ ion pair species with Ag^+ sitting above the plane of the NO_3^- ion.

REFERENCES

The basic relationships for infrared and Raman spectroscopy can be obtained in [1], [2], and [4]. The book referred to in [3] and [10] gives a recent review of aspects more closely related to liquids. Summaries of time correlation function relationships are available in [5] and [7] (see also Chap. 7).

1. G. Herzberg, Spectra of Diatomic Molecules, 2nd ed., Van Nostrand, New York, 1950.
2. G. M. Barrow, Introduction to Molecular Spectroscopy, McGraw-Hill, New York, 1962.
3. H. E. Hallam, in Infrared Spectroscopy and Molecular Structure (M. Davies, ed.), Elsevier, New York, 1963.
4. G. Herzberg, Infrared and Raman Spectra, Van Nostrand, New York, 1945.
5. R. G. Gordon, Adv. Mag. Resonance, *3*, 1 (1968).
6. E. C. Kemble, Quantum Mechanics, Dover, New York, 1938.
7. W. A. Steele, in Transport Phenomena in Fluids (H. J. M. Hanley, ed.), Marcel Dekker, New York, 1967.
8. S. Bratoz, J. Rios, and Y. Guissani, J. Chem. Phys., *52*, 439 (1970).
9. L. A. Nafie,and W. L. Peticolas, J. Chem. Phys., *57*, 3145 (1972).

10. J. C. Evans, in Infrared Spectroscopy and Molecular Structure (M. Davies, ed.), Elsevier, New York, 1963.

11. R. G. Gordon, J. Chem. Phys., *42*, 3658 (1965).

12. F. J. Bartoli and T. A. Litovitz, J. Chem. Phys., *56*, 404 (1972).

13. G. E. Walrafen in GR7.

14. J. A. Koningstein, Introduction to the Theory of the Raman Effect, Reidel, Boston, 1972.

15. P. Lallemand, in The Raman Effect, Vol. 1 (A. Anderson, ed.), Marcel Dekker, New York, 1971.

16. W. Kaiser and M. Maier, in Laser Handbook, Vol. 2 (F. T. Arecchi and E. O. Schulz-Dubois, eds.), North-Holland, Amsterdam, 1972.

17. A. E. Martin, in Infrared Spectroscopy and Molecular Structure (M. Davies, ed.), Elsevier, New York, 1963.

18. A. Mooradian, in Laser Handbook, Vol. 2 (F. T. Arecchi and E. O. Schulz-Dubois, eds.), North-Holland, Amsterdam, 1972.

19. D. A. Draegert, N. W. B. Stone, B. Curnutte, and D. Williams, J. Opt. Soc. Am., *56*, 64 (1966).

20. P. Rhine, D. Williams, G. M. Hale, and M. R. Querry, J. Phys. Chem., *78*, 238 (1974).

21. R. D. Hudson, Jr., Infrared System Engineering, Wiley-Interscience, New York, 1969.

22. R. J. Bell, Introductory Fourier Transform Spectroscopy, Academic Press, New York, 1972.

23. T. R. Gilson and P. J. Hendra, Laser Raman Spectroscopy, Wiley-Interscience, New York, 1970.

24. J. E. Griffiths, J. Chem. Phys., *59*, 751 (1973).

25. W. G. Rothschild, J. Chem. Phys., *57*, 991 (1972).

26. R. M. Van Aalst, J. van der Elsken, D. Frenkel, and G. H. Wegdam, Faraday Symp. Chem. Soc., No. 6, 94 (1972).

27. C. Bourdéron and C. Sandorfy, J. Chem. Phys., *59*, 2527 (1973).

28. S. Sunder, K. E. Hallin, and R. E. D. McClung, J. Chem. Phys., *61*, 2920 (1974).

29. Y. Guissani and J. C. Leicknam, Can. J. Phys., *51*, 938 (1973).

30. A. Cabana, R. Bardoux, and A. Chamberland, Can. J. Chem., *47*, 2915 (1969).

31. L. Marabella and G. E. Ewing, J. Chem. Phys., *56*, 5445 (1972).

32. H. L. Welsh and R. J. Kriegler, J. Chem. Phys., *50*, 1043 (1970).

33. G. J. Davies and J. Chamberlain, J. C. S. Farad. Trans. II, *69*, 1739 (1973).

34. I. W. Larkin, J. C. S. Farad. Trans. II, *69*, 1278 (1973); ibid, II, *70*, 1457 (1974).

35. GR5.

36. E. V. Franck and K. Roth, Disc. Farad. Soc., *43*, 108 (1967).

37. J. R. Scherer, M. K. Go, and S. Kint, J. Phys. Chem., *78*, 1304 (1974).

38. F. Franks in GR7.

39. M. J. Colles, G. E. Walrafen, and K. W. Wecht, Chem. Phys. Lett., *4*, 621 (1970).

40. W. C. Mundy, L. Gutierrez, and F. H. Spedding, J. Chem. Phys., *59*, 2173 (1973).

41. G. E. Walrafen and L. A. Blatz, J. Chem. Phys., *59*, 2646 (1973).

42. B. R. Lentz, A. T. Hagler, and H. A. Scheraga, J. Phys. Chem., *78*, 1844 (1974).

43. G. R. Choppin and J. R. Downey,Jr., J. Chem. Phys., *56*, 5899 (1972).

44. C. Jolicoeur and A. Cabana, Can. J. Chem., *46*, 567 (1967).

45. O. D. Bonner and Y. S. Choi, J.. Phys. Chem., *78*, 1723, 1727 (1974).

46. H. Wolff and G. Gamer, J. Phys. Chem., *76*, 871 (1972).

47. D. Schiöberg and G. Zundel, J. C. S. Farad. Trans., II, *69*, 771 (1973).

48. Z. Kecki, Adv. Mol. Relax. Proc., *5*, 137 (1973).

49. H. L. Yeager, J. D. Fedyk, and R. J. Parker, J. Phys. Chem., *77*, 2407 (1973).

50. P. R. Philips and C. Jolicoeur, J. Phys. Chem., *77*, 3071 (1973).

51. K. R. Plowman and J. J. Lagowski, J.Phys . Chem., *78*, 143 (1974).

52. F. P. Daly, C. W. Brown, and D. R. Kester, J. Phys. Chem., *76*, 3664 (1972).

53. R. M. Chatterjee, W. A. Adams, and A. R. Davis, J. Phys. Chem., *78*, 246 (1974).

54. M. Peleg, J. Am. Chem. Soc., *76*, 1019 (1972).

55. T. G. Chang and D. E. Irish, J. Sol. Chem., *3*, 175 (1974).

Further Recent References

J. G. Chambers, M. J. Phillips, A. J. Barnes, and W. J. Orville-Thomas, "Analysis of Infrared Band Shapes Derived from Attenuated Reflection (ATR) Measurements", Adv. Mol. Relax. Proc., *7*, 113 (1975).

M. Perrot, J. Devaure, and J. Lacombe, "Influence de la Pression sur les Profils des Bandes de Diffusion Raman Dépolarisée et Rayleigh Dépolarisée du Dioxyde de Carbone Liquide", Mol. Phys., *30*, 97 (1975).

W. G. Rothschild, G. J. Rosasco, and R. C. Livingston, "Dynamics of Molecular Reorientational Motion and Vibrational Relaxation in Liquids. Chloroform", J. Chem. Phys., *62*, 1253 (1975).

L. C. Rosenthal and H. L. Strauss, "Rotational Correlation in Chloroform", J. Chem. Phys., *64*, 282 (1976).

D. Robert and L. Galatry, "Influence of Molecular Nonrigidity on the Infrared Absorption and Raman Scattering Line Shape in Dense Media", J. Chem. Phys., *64*, 2721 (1976).

D. R. Jones, H. C. Andersen, and R. Pecora, "Infrared and Raman Studies of Rotational Correlation Functions in Liquids", Chem. Phys., *9*, 339 (1975).

P. C. M. van Woerkom, J. de Bleijser, M. de Zwart, P. M. J. Burgers, and J. C. Leyte, "Vibrational Relaxation in Liquids: Some Applications of the Isotopic Dilution Method", Ber. Bunsenges. Physik. Chem., *78*, 1303 (1974).

G. J. Davies and M. Evans, "Use of Generalized Langevin Theory to Describe Far Infrared Absorption in Non-dipolar Liquids", J. C. S. Farad. II, *72*, 1194, 1206 (1976).

M. Sceats, S. A. Rice, and J. E. Butler, "The Stimulated Raman Spectrum of Water and its Relationship to Liquid Structure", J. Chem. Phys., *63*, 5390 (1975).

O. D. Bonner and Y. S. Choi, "A Spectroscopic Investigation of the Structure of Alcohol-Water Solutions", J. Sol. Chem., *4*, 457 (1975).

H. Kelm, J. Klosowski, and E. Steger, "The Association in Mixtures of Dimethylsulphoxide and Water as Studied by Raman Spectroscopy", J. Mol. Struct., *28*, 1 (1975).

R. Mierzecki, "The Structure of Chloroform Adducts in Binary Mixtures Determined by Infrared and Raman Intensity Measurements by Means of the Modified Job's Method", Adv. Mol. Relax. Proc., *7*, 61 (1975).

G. Fini and P. Mirone, "Evidence for Short-range Orientation Effects in Dipolar Aprotic Liquids from Vibrational Spectroscopy. Part 2 - Carbonyl Compounds", J. C. S. Farad. II, *70*, 1776 (1974).

D. W. James, R. F. Armishaw, and R. L. Frost, "Structure of Aqueous Solutions. Librational Band Studies of Hydrophobic and Hydrophilic Effects in Solutions of Electrolytes and Nonelectrolytes", J. Phys. Chem., *80*, 1346 (1976).

G. E. Rodgers and R. A. Plane, "A Raman Spectrophotometric Study of the Effect of N,N-dimethylformamide and the Electrolytes $NaClO_4$, $Sn(ClO_4)_2$, $NaNO_3$, and $Zn(NO_3)_2$ on the Structure of Liquid Water", J. Chem. Phys., *63*, 818 (1975).

D. Schiöberg and G. Zundel, "The Influence of Neutral Salts on the Easily Polarizable Hydrogen Bond of $H_5O_2^+$ Groupings in Acid Solutions", Can. J. Chem., *54*, 2193 (1976).

A. G. Briggs, N. A. Hampson, and A. Marshall, "Concentrated Potassium Zincate Solutions Studied Using Laser Raman Spectroscopy and Potentiometry", J. C. S. Farad. II, *70*, 1978 (1974).

C. Barker and J. Yarwood, "Vibrational Spectroscopic Studies on Ion-Molecule Interactions in Non-aqueous Solvents. Part 1. Far Infrared Studies on Tetra-n-butylammonium Chloride in Benzene", J. C. S. Farad. II, *71*, 1322 (1975).

R. G. Baum and A. I. Popov, "Spectroscopic Studies of Ionic Solvation XVIII. Solvation of the Lithium Ion in Acetone and Acetone-Nitromethane Mixtures", J. Sol. Chem., *4*, 441 (1975).

I. S. Perelygin and M. A. Klimchuk, "Infrared Spectra and Structure of Non-Aqueous Electrolyte Solutions VI. Solutions of Sodium and Lithium Iodides in Acetone at Temperatures Ranging from -90° to 45°C", Russ. J. Phys. Chem., *49*, 90 (1975).

T. G. V. Findlay and M. C. R. Symons, "Solvation Spectra Part 50. - Spectrophotometric Studies of the Solvation of Nitrate Ions in Protic and Aprotic Media", J. C. S. Farad. II, *72*, 820 (1976).

Chapter 13

MAGNETIC RESONANCE METHODS

This chapter introduces a break in the natural sequence: dielectric relaxation, IR and Raman spectroscopy, light scattering, X-ray scattering, neutron scattering. It is placed between Chaps. 12 and 14 as the molecular phenomena which it elucidates are most closely related to Raman and Rayleigh scattering. Its position neighboring Chap. 12 is also natural as Chaps. 12 and 13 are the only chapters in part B which are dependent on resonant transitions, i.e., transitions between discrete energy states.

Magnetic resonance relaxation also has analogies to dielectric relaxation. Here the relaxation of the magnetization $\underline{M}$ is discussed, while in Chap. 11 the polarization $\underline{P}$ was considered. While classical considerations were satisfactory for a description of dielectric relaxation, here the discrete orientations of the nuclei in the magnetic field cannot be neglected.

Only brief mention is made here of the line shift analysis which is of such great use in identifying molecules and functional groups. Instead, the discussion deals primarily with relaxation phenomena. The background for electron spin phenomena are not covered here. However, a considerable part of the discussion is applicable to electron as well as nuclear spin phenomena. An example of the use of ESR is given in Sec. 13.3(h).

13.1. THEORETICAL BACKGROUND

(a) *Electromagnetic Properties of Nuclei*

As indicated in Eq. (20.19), electric charge moving effectively as a current in a loop can be considered in terms of a magnetic moment (dipole) $\underline{m}$. Thus nuclei and electrons which have a spin can have a magnetic moment (21.32)

$$\underline{m} = \gamma_N \hbar \underline{I} = g_N \beta_N \underline{I} \qquad \text{or} \qquad \underline{m} = g_e \beta_e \underline{S} \tag{13.1}$$

Here $\underline{I}$ and $\underline{S}$ are the spins, g_N and g_e the "g-factors," and β_N and β_e the "Bohr magnetons" for the nucleus considered and an electron, respectively, and γ_N the gyromagnetic ratio.

For an electron, $S = \frac{1}{2}$ and $g_e = 2.002$. These values can be derived from a relativistic quantum mechanical treatment of the electron. The value of I for a particular nucleus depends on the number of protons and neutrons present in it, and their distribution among nuclear energy states, i.e., analogous to the building up to the electronic spin states of the elements through the periodic table [1]. The value of g_N for a nucleus is obtained experimentally and reflects aspects of the structure of the nucleus. Note that they can be negative in cases, as shown in Table 13.1.

Nuclei with spins of 1 or more (e.g., ^2H, $^{35}Cl \cdots$) can also possess a nuclear electric quadrupole moment Q [Sec. 1.1(a)]. It is described in terms of the charge distribution inside the nucleus, $\rho(r)$, for many nuclei simply as

$$Q = \frac{1}{e} \int \rho(r)(3z^2 - r^2)\, dV = Z\langle 3z^2 - r^2 \rangle \tag{13.2}$$

The z axis is in the direction of spin $\underline{I}$. When there is an electric field gradient present due to, e.g., a distribution of charge outside the nucleus, the potential energy of a nucleus with a non-zero Q is affected. The magnitude of the field gradient (usually denoted by eq) is not readily available. Thus often the quadrupole coupling constant, $e^2Qq/\hbar$, is listed as obtained from experiment.

TABLE 13.1

Electromagnetic Properties of Commonly Used Nuclei

Nucleus	^1H	$^2H(D)$	^7Li	^{13}C	^{17}O	^{19}F	^{23}Na	^{31}P
Spin I	1/2	1	3/2	1/2	5/2	1/2	3/2	1/2
g_N	5.58	0.857	2.17	1.40	-0.76	5.26	1.48	2.26

(b) Energy Levels of Spin States in a Magnetic Field

When a magnetic field $\underline{B}_0$ is applied along the z axis, then the energy of interaction is (21.33):

$$-\underline{m}\cdot\underline{B}_0 = -g_N\beta_N I_z B_0 \qquad (13.3)$$

Here I_z is the z component of the spin vector $\underline{I}$. It can have 2I + 1 values. For nuclei with I = 1/2 (or single unpaired electrons) I_z (or S_z) thus has possible values +1/2 (spin state $|\alpha>$) and -1/2 (spin state $|\beta>$) (21.23). Thus two energy states with an energy difference $g_N\beta_N B_0$ are formed.

The actual field at a nucleus is not identical to the externally applied field. It can generally be written as $(1 - \sigma)B_0$, where σ is the "screening constant." The applied field can induce electric current through its interaction with electrons in the molecules, giving rise to a field $-\sigma B_0$. As the value of σ depends on the environment of a nucleus, the measurement of the difference between the externally applied and the effective field (chemical shift) can be exploited for numerous types of studies [2]. In Sec. 13.3 its use to observe H-bonding and ion solvation is discussed. There a change occurs in the "chemical" (electronic) environment of a nucleus due to intermolecular interactions.

A complicating but also useful aspect in NMR is the appearance of structure in the lines due to splitting of energies arising from spin-spin interaction. This hyperfine structure is not of central importance in this book, but is widely exploited in other types of studies [2-4].

(c) Absorption of Energy by Spin States

For a system containing nuclei with spin 1/2 in a magnetic field B_0, the difference in energy levels is $g_N\beta_N B_0$. A net absorption of energy due to transitions between these energy levels can occur only if there is a population difference between the levels. At equilibrium, the ratio of nuclei in $<\alpha|$ to those in $<\beta|$ is (18.4):

$$\left(\frac{N_\alpha}{N_\beta}\right)_{eq} = \exp\left[\frac{g_N\beta_N B_0}{kT}\right] \tag{13.4}$$

As generally $g_N\beta_N B_0 \ll kT$, the difference in population between $\langle\alpha|$ and $\langle\beta|$ is only about 1 part in 10^5.

When an alternating electromagnetic field at a resonant frequency $\omega_0(\hbar\omega_0 = g_N\beta_N B_0)$ is applied to the system, then absorption of energy can occur. If the difference $N_\alpha - N_\beta$ is written as ΔN, then

$$\frac{d\,\Delta N}{dt} = -2w_{\beta\alpha}\,\Delta N(t) \qquad \text{i.e.,} \qquad \frac{dE}{dt} = -\hbar\omega w_{\beta\alpha}\,\Delta N(t) \tag{13.5}$$

Here $w_{\beta\alpha}$ (= $w_{\alpha\beta}$) is the probability of absorption (emission) due to the presence of the alternating radiofrequency (RF) field (21.4). If at $t = 0$, ΔN is given by the condition (13.4), then continuous application of the RF will according to (13.5) lead eventually to $\Delta N \to 0$, or saturation, where no net absorption occurs. This means the spin "temperature" $\to \infty$ (13.4).

There are, however, other mechanisms of transitions between the two states which try to maintain thermal equilibrium. These are described through a time T_1 characterizing a relaxation process. Thus (13.5) becomes

$$\frac{d\,\Delta N}{dt} = -2w_{\beta\alpha}\,\Delta N(t) - \frac{\Delta N(t) - \Delta N_{eq}}{T_1} \tag{13.6}$$

Here ΔN_{eq} is the population difference at thermal equilibrium.

T_1 is called the "spin lattice" (also longitudinal) relaxation time, and the above process spin-lattice relaxation. "Lattice" is here defined loosely as all degrees of freedom other than those concerned with spin. The magnitude of T_1 determines the steady state population difference possible in the presence of a continuous RF field. In many experiments, saturation ($\Delta N \to 0$) is caused deliberately [Sec. 13.2(b)].

The presence of spin-lattice relaxation makes the lifetime of a spin state finite. Thus a width of a transition line of the order of $1/T_1$ is predicted through the uncertainty condition ($\Delta E\ \Delta t \geq \hbar$).

There are other processes present which cause a variation of the relative energies of the spin levels, however. Thus the total line shape is characterized by another relaxation time T_2 (the "spin-spin" or "transverse" relaxation time). In many cases, for liquids, the condition for the limit of rapid motion is valid, and $T_1 = T_2$.

(d) *Relaxation of Magnetization (Bloch Equations)*

The meaning of T_1 and T_2 can be better understood if a macroscopic picture is taken of the NMR relaxation process. Just as there is orientational polarization ($\underline{P}$) due to electric dipoles, so there is also a magnetization $\underline{M}$ present, with $\underline{M} = (1/V)\sum_N \underline{m}_i$. In this case, unlike (11.4) and (11.5) the orientation of the magnetic dipoles $\underline{m}_i$ are spatially quantized. Thus the relationship is not exactly analogous to (11.6).

When no externally applied magnetic fields are present, then the components of $\underline{M}(M_x,M_y,M_z)$ can be treated equivalently, i.e., $dM_z/dt = -M_z/T_1$, $dM_x/dt = -M_x/T_1$, etc. The instantaneous value of M_z is $g_N\beta_N\ \Delta N/V$ (13.4). If there is equilibrium, then $\Delta N = M_z = 0$ when there is no field.

When now a field $\underline{B}_0$ is applied along the z axis, then neglecting precessional motion,

$$\frac{dM_z}{dt} = -\frac{M_z - M_{z,eq}}{T_1} \qquad \frac{dM_x}{dt} = -\frac{M_x}{T_2} \qquad \frac{dM_y}{dt} = -\frac{M_y}{T_2} \tag{13.7}$$

Here $M_{z,eq}$ is the equilibrium value of M_z when there is a field $\underline{B}_0$ present. From (13.4) it can be approximated as $M_{z,eq} = (N/V)g_N^2\beta_N^2 B_0/kT$. The transverse components are shown decaying with a time T_2. Changes in M_z need an exchange of energy between the spin system and the lattice. Changes in M_x and M_y do not however alter the total (Zeeman) energy of the nuclear spin system.

If the total bulk magnetization is not in line with $\underline{B}_0$, then it precesses about it, governed by the equation $d\underline{M}/dt = \gamma_N(\underline{M} \times \underline{B}_0)$, because there is a torque exerted on a magnetic moment (current loop) by a magnetic field (20.12). The precession is at the "Larmour frequency"

$\omega_0 = \gamma_N B_0$. When this precessional frequency is taken into account, then the "Bloch equations" describing the motion of $\underline{M}$ are obtained

$$\frac{dM_z}{dt} = -\frac{M_z - M_{z,eq}}{T_1} \qquad \frac{dM_x}{dt} = +\omega_0 M_y - \frac{M_x}{T_2} \qquad \frac{dM_y}{dt} = -\omega_0 M_x - \frac{M_y}{T_2} \tag{13.8}$$

Next an alternating (RF) field $\underline{B}_1$ is considered applied in a manner such that it alternates clockwise in the xy-plane i.e., $\underline{B}_1 = B_1(\underline{i} \cos \omega t - \underline{j} \sin \omega t)$ where $\underline{i}$, $\underline{j}$, $\underline{k}$ are unit vectors in the x, y, z directions. It is now best to consider the motion of $\underline{M}$ in a new coordinate system rotating with $\underline{B}_1$ at an angular velocity ω about the z axis (Fig. 13.1). Quantities considered in the rotating frame will be denoted by the subscript r.

The transformations are then $\underline{B}_{1,r} = \underline{i}_r B_1$, $\underline{\omega}_r = -\omega\underline{k}$, $\underline{M}_r = \underline{i}_r M_{x,r} + \underline{j}_r M_{y,r} + \underline{k} M_z$, i.e., $\underline{k}_r = \underline{k}$. The Bloch equations in the rotating frame are then [5,6]

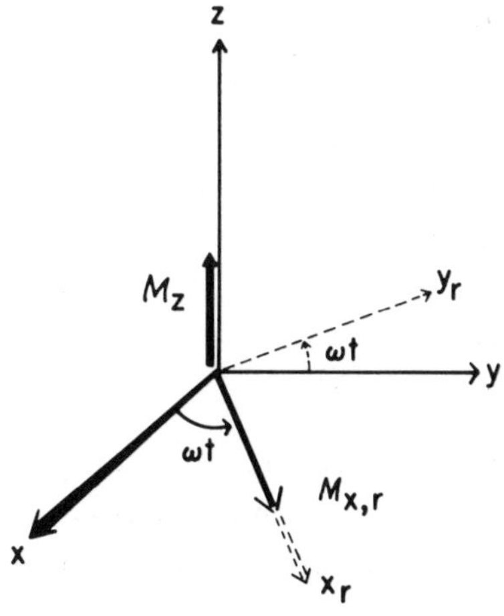

Fig. 13.1. Schematic diagram illustrating the definition of the rotating coordinate system.

$$\frac{dM_z}{dt} = -\gamma_N B_1 M_{y,r} - \frac{M_z - M_{z,eq}}{T_1}$$

$$\frac{dM_{x,r}}{dt} = (\omega_0 - \omega)M_{y,r} - \frac{M_{x,r}}{T_2}$$

$$\frac{dM_{y,r}}{dt} = -(\omega_0 - \omega)M_{x,r} + \gamma_N B_1 M_z - \frac{M_{y,r}}{T_2} \qquad (13.9)$$

The derivation of (13.9) is straightforward but tedious. Its solution for a stationary state is also straightforward and tedious. The results give $M_{x,r}$ and $M_{y,r}$ as functions of time and the parameters (T_1, T_2, ω_0, etc.) characterizing the system. The calculation can also be carried out for a rotating field instead of the oscillating field used in experiments [sec. 13.2(a)]. The results are the same, however, as an oscillating field is the sum of two counterrotating fields.

As in the case of dielectric relaxation, where a complex permittivity was introduced, here a complex permeability $\mu^*(\omega)$ can be introduced to describe the relation between $\underline{B}_1$ and M_x, M_y (20.28). The real part of $\mu^*(\omega)$ is related to $M_{x,r}$ as $M_{x,r} = (\mu'(\omega) - 1)B_1/\mu_0$ while the imaginary part $\mu''(\omega)$ is related to $M_{y,r}$. This imaginary (out of phase with $\underline{B}_1$) component gives rise to energy absorption as in Sec. 11.1(c). Thus from the solution to $M_{y,r}$ for the stationary state problem ($d/dt = 0$) the line shape for energy absorption in continuous NMR experiments is for small fields,

$$I(\omega) = \frac{T_2}{\omega} \frac{1}{1 + T_2^2(\omega - \omega_0)^2} \qquad (13.10)$$

This is a Lorentzian shape (20.52) (Fig. 20.1) with a half width $2T_2$.

A value of T_2 can thus be obtained from line shape studies. However, pulse methods [Sec. 13.2(b),(c)] give more accurate results for both T_2 and T_1 in many cases.

(e) Quantum-Mechanical View of Relaxation

The relaxation times T_1 and T_2 were discussed in terms of macroscopic quantities in Sec. (d) above and in terms of microscopic in Sec. (c). Here these considerations will be combined to relate T_1 and T_2 to properties of the system considered. To do this the Bloch equations for a spin $\underline{I}$ are set up. A constant magnetic field $\underline{B}_0$ along the z-axis is present, but there is no alternating (RF) field as in (13.9). The presence of a zero-average fluctuating field $\underline{B}'(t)$ is however now included. It can arise from several processes (e.g., molecular rotation, translation) which change the field at the nucleus. The effect of $\underline{B}'(t)$ will be to disturb the regular precession of $\underline{I}$ about $\underline{B}_0$ and cause relaxation.

In the fixed frame of reference, the equations are

$$\frac{d\underline{I}}{dt} = \gamma_N \underline{I} \times \underline{B}_0 + \gamma_N \underline{I} \times \underline{B}' \qquad (13.11)$$

In the coordinates x_r, y_r, z_r of the frame rotating at $\omega_0 = \gamma_N B_0$ about the z axis, the equations are thus

$$\frac{dI_{z,r}}{dt} = \gamma_N (I_{x,r} B'_{y,r} - I_{y,r} B'_{x,r})$$

$$\frac{dI_{x,r}}{dt} = \gamma_N (I_{y,r} B'_{z,r} - I_{z,r} B'_{y,r}) \qquad (13.12)$$

where $B'_{x,r} = B'_x \cos \omega_0 t + B'_y \sin \omega_0 t$ etc.

If now at $t = 0$, $I_{z,r}$ has a value $I_{z,r}(0)$ while $I_{x,r}(0) = I_{y,r}(0) = 0$, then from (13.12), $I_{z,r}(t)$ can be written as [6]

$$I_{z,r}(t) = I_{z,r}(0)[1 - \gamma_N^2 \int_0^t dt' \int_0^{t'} (B'_{x,r}(t')B'_{x,r}(t'')$$

$$+ B'_{y,r}(t')B'_{y,r}(t''))\, dt''] \qquad (13.13)$$

The change in $I_{x,r}$ and $I_{y,r}$ have been taken into account in formulating (13.13). The expression in (13.13) can be then rewritten in terms of the fixed coordinate axes.

Now $\mathcal{B}'_x$, $\mathcal{B}'_y$ and $\mathcal{B}'_z$ are assumed uncorrelated, and $<(\mathcal{B}'_x)^2> = <(\mathcal{B}'_y)^2>$. Often it can also be assumed after Sec. 7.2(e) that $<\mathcal{B}'_x(0)\cdot\mathcal{B}'_x(t)>= <(\mathcal{B}'_x)^2> \exp[-t/\tau]$. A solution of (13.13) can then be obtained as

$$I_z(t) = I_z(0)[1 - \gamma_N^2(<(\mathcal{B}'_x)^2> + <(\mathcal{B}'_y)^2>) \int_0^t dt' \int_0^{t'} \cos\omega_0 t'' \cdot\exp\left[-\frac{t''}{\tau}\right] dt'' \tag{13.14}$$

For longer values of t, $I_z(t)$ has the form $I_z(t) = I_z(0)[1 - t/T_1]$, i.e., of the form of (13.8) where

$$\frac{1}{T_1} = \gamma_N^2(<(\mathcal{B}'_x)^2> + <(\mathcal{B}'_y)^2>)\ \frac{\tau}{1 + \omega_0^2\tau^2} \tag{13.15}$$

By a similar analysis, it can be shown that [6]

$$\frac{1}{T_2} = \gamma_N^2\left\{<(\mathcal{B}'_z)^2>\tau + \frac{1}{2}\left[<(\mathcal{B}'_x)^2> + <(\mathcal{B}'_y)^2>\right]\frac{\tau}{1 + \omega_0^2\tau^2}\right\} \tag{13.16}$$

This can be seen to be of the form

$$\frac{1}{T_2} = \frac{1}{T'_2} + \frac{1}{2T_1} \tag{13.17}$$

When $<(\mathcal{B}'_x)^2> = <(\mathcal{B}'_z)^2>$ and $\omega_0\tau << 1$, then $1/T'_2 = 1/2T_1$ [(13.16) and (13.17)]. In such cases, common for liquids, $T_2 = T_1$.

The relationship between T_1 and system parameters can be further examined by referring back to (c). There $1/T_1$ was indicated to be twice the transition probability induced by interactions between the spin and the lattice systems, $\mathcal{W}'_{\alpha\beta}$. These interactions can be described through a perturbation Hamiltonian $\mathcal{H}'(t)$. Thus from (21.41) and (21.42):

$$\mathcal{W}'_{\alpha\beta} = \frac{1}{\hbar^2}\ |\mathcal{H}'|^2_{\alpha\beta} \int_{-\infty}^{\infty} G_{\mathcal{H}'}(t)\ \exp[i\omega_0 t]\ dt \tag{13.18}$$

If now this interaction is due to random forces so that $G_{\mathcal{H}'}(t) = \exp[-t/\tau]$ then

$$W'_{\alpha\beta} = \frac{1}{2T_1} = \frac{1}{\hbar^2}\,|H'|^2_{\alpha\beta}\,\frac{2\tau}{1 + \omega_0^2\tau^2} \tag{13.19}$$

When $H'(t)$ is due to the magnetic field $\underline{B}'(t)$, then as expected

$$|H'|_{\alpha\beta} = \frac{1}{2}\,\gamma_N\hbar(B'_x + iB'_y) \tag{13.20}$$

so that (13.19) and (13.15) are in agreement. Through similar considerations, the analogous relations for T'_2 are

$$\frac{1}{T'_2} = \frac{1}{2\hbar^2}\int_{-\infty}^{\infty}\langle(|H'(t)|_{\alpha\alpha} - |H'(t)|_{\beta\beta})(|H'(0)|_{\alpha\alpha} - |H'(0)|_{\beta\beta})\rangle\,dt$$

$$= \frac{\tau}{\hbar^2}\langle(|H'|_{\alpha\alpha} - |H'|_{\beta\beta})^2\rangle \tag{13.21}$$

In the latter form, the interaction $H'(t)$ is assumed to be due to a random fluctuation, so that $\int_{-\infty}^{\infty} = \langle(|H'|_{\alpha\alpha} - |H'|_{\beta\beta})^2\rangle \int_0^{\infty}\exp[-t/\tau]\,dt$.

From (13.19) and (13.20) it can be seen [see also Sec. (c)] that the broadening of NMR lines (13.10) is due to two reasons. The $1/T'_2$ term in (13.17) shows broadening due to the modulation of the energy of the transition. The $1/2T_1$ term gives the "lifetime broadening" arising from the finite lifetime of the spins.

(f) Mechanisms for Nuclear Relaxation

A number of mechanisms can be responsible for nuclear magnetic relaxation. In general it must be a perturbation of the spin states, $H'(t)$, with a time dependence such that there are frequency components in it with a frequency of the magnitude of ω_0 (21.41). Electronic motions are too rapid to have any effect. Thus molecular rotation and diffusion are usually involved in the case of liquids. Some of the more important mechanisms will be discussed below. Others are discussed in Secs. (g), (h), and (i).

(1) Dipole-Dipole Relaxation

A nucleus with spin $\underline{I}_a$ will be affected by the presence of another nucleus $\underline{I}_b$. The perturbation due to this can be described as (21.34):

$$H'(t) = \frac{1}{4\pi\varepsilon^{\bullet}c^2}\gamma_N^2 \underline{I}_a \cdot \underline{\underline{D}}(t) \cdot \underline{I}_b \qquad (13.22)$$

Here the tensor $\underline{\underline{D}}(t)$ (21.34) is a function of the intermolecular distance vector and its orientation in the magnetic field $\underline{B}_0$. In (13.22) it is assumed A and B are of the same species, so that γ_N is the same. The nuclei need not be identical, however, and can be in the same molecule (intramolecular dipole-dipole coupling) or on different molecules (intermolecular).

In the case of intermolecular dipole-dipole relaxation, it is obvious that rotation or translation of a molecule containing $\underline{I}_a$ relative to its neighbor containing $\underline{I}_b$ will change $\underline{\underline{D}}(t)$. The internuclear distance can change, and also the orientation of the nucleus-nucleus vector can change with respect to $\underline{B}_0$. If these motions have a time dependence such that $H'(t)$ contains a frequency component at ω_0, then the interaction can lead to spin-lattice relaxation.

If the nuclei are within the same molecule, their internuclear distance vector has effectively the same magnitude. Its direction changes with respect to $\underline{B}_0$ on rotation of the molecule, causing $\underline{\underline{D}}(t)$ to change with time.

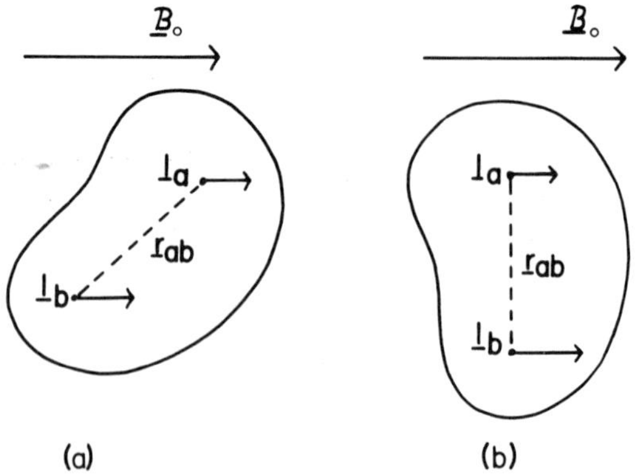

Fig. 13.2. Schematic diagram illustrating intramolecular dipole-dipole relaxation.

Figure 13.2 illustrates how this occurs, by schematically showing two orientations of the molecule in $\underline{B}_0$, assuming $\underline{I}_a$ and $\underline{I}_b$ both to be in the direction of $\underline{B}_0$, and not to have undergone relaxation.

Consideration of a Hamiltonian of the form of (21.34) for intramolecular dipole-dipole relaxation leads to an expression for T_1 [7]:

$$\frac{1}{T_1} = \frac{\gamma_N^4 \hbar^2 I(I + 1)}{\langle r_{ab}^3 \rangle^2} \int_{-\infty}^{\infty} G_2(t)\, dt \qquad (13.23)$$

Here $G_2(t)$ is the function described in (7.40) [see also (12.16)]. $\int_{-\infty}^{\infty} G_2(t)\, dt = \tau_2$ if $G_2(t) = \exp[-|t|/\tau_2]$ is assumed.

The effects of intra- and intermolecular dipole-dipole relaxation are not readily separable. In the case of protons, it can be done by isotopic substitution. The neighbors of the proton containing molecule are deuterated, changing the intermolecular DD coupling constant. The intermolecular relaxation rate can then be shown to decrease by a factor of 24 as the protonated: deuterated ratio → 0. Reference 8 gives an example of such analysis.

(2) Quadrupole Relaxation

For nuclei with $I > 1/2$, the relaxation is most often dominated by nuclear electric quadrupole relaxation. Quadrupole relaxation results in values of T_1 considerably less than the values (of the order of seconds) usual in liquids if dipole-dipole or spin-rotation [Sec. (f)(3) following] are the basic relaxation mechanisms. In the absence of relaxation, the nucleus continues to precess about $\underline{B}_0$ during molecular rotation. As a result the orientation of the nuclear electric quadrupole moment in its intramolecular electric field gradient changes. This causes a time-dependent interaction energy which can result in relaxation.

A form similar to (13.23), i.e., $\propto \int_{-\infty}^{\infty} G_2(t)\, dt$ results for this form of relaxation in the case of a linear molecule, or a nucleus on the axis of a symmetric-top molecule [7]. The usual assumptions of isotropy and noninterference of $\underline{B}_0$ on the molecular motions are present. If a value of $\int_{-\infty}^{\infty} G_2(t)\, dt$ (i.e., essentially a value of τ_2) is to be obtained from an analysis, then it is necessary to know the quadrupole coupling constant. This can be measured in gases and solids, and can be interpolated to be valid for the liquid if the values are not too different. It is also possible to measure the quadrupole coupling constant in liquids if values of T_1 are available for both ^{13}C and ^{2}H [9].

(3) Spin-Rotation Relaxation

The rotation of a molecule results in a molecular magnetic moment as there is a distribution of charge in the molecule. This molecular magnetic moment can then interact with the nuclear magnetic moment, arising from nuclear spin, to give a contribution to $H'(t)$. In this case the angular momentum vector for the molecule, $\hbar\underline{J}$, interacts with the molecule.

A measurement of the relaxation rate $1/T_1$ due to spin-rotation interaction leads to a knowledge of the angular momentum correlation time τ_J. It can be separated from effects due to orientation [Secs. (1) and (2) above], as the correlation times τ_{rot} and τ_J for rotational motion and angular momentum have different temperature dependencies.

As temperature increases, τ_J increases, but τ_{rot} decreases. In the limit of a dilute gas, where there are no collisions, $\tau_J \rightarrow \infty$, while τ_{rot} is quite small. The times can be shown to be related approximately as $\tau_{rot} \cdot \tau_J = I_m/6kT$, where I_m is the moment of inertia of the molecule. Thus the temperature dependence of T_1 can be used to decide which mechanism (spin-rotation or dipole-dipole) is mainly responsible for the relaxation, e.g., Ref 10. Small symmetrical molecules with large possible chemical shifts commonly have significant spin-rotation interactions.

Another mechanism related to SR is that of chemical shift anisotropy. This is rarely of primary importance in liquids and will not be pursued here. Its relative importance can be evaluated by measuring T_1 at different values of B_0. Yet another relaxation mechanism, "scalar relaxation" will also not be discussed here. It can be considered to be a case of the chemical exchange effects outlined in (g) [11].

(g) Line Broadening Due to Chemical Exchange

The discussion to this point has been for the "narrowing region," where the nuclear spin correlation functions decay much more slowly than the molecular (or "lattice") motion. This is not the case for viscous liquids, and it is also not the case when chemical exchange of the nucleus concerned takes place.

In the limit of infinitely slow exchange of a nucleus (e.g., proton) between two different chemical environments, two separate lines are observed, with two different chemical shifts. In the limit of infinitely fast exchange, there is only one average environment as fluctuations in $H'(t)$ due to the exchange are too rapid to contain ω_0 frequency components. At medium rates of exchange, line broadening (i.e., relaxation) can occur due to this mechanism (scalar relaxation of the first kind) [11].

This behavior is illustrated in Fig. 13.3 for values of the

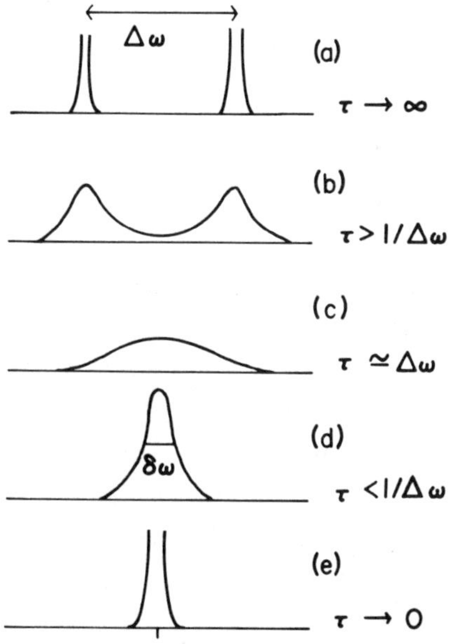

Fig. 13.3. Schematic diagram illustrating the effect of residence time τ on the NMR spectrum.

chemical residence time τ relative to the difference $\Delta\omega$ of the chemical shift due to the two environments in the $\tau \to \infty$ limit. The discussion up to Sec. (g) has been for $\tau << 1/\Delta\omega$. In this region, the line broadening due to chemical exchange is from the uncertainty principle, and gives rise to a line width $\delta\omega = 1/\tau$. A more sophisticated discussion of line broadening due to chemical exchange is given in Ref. 6 in terms of the Bloch equations.

(h) Overhauser Effect

Spins can be coupled together in a way such that the relaxation of one affects the other. When nuclear spins are involved, this can result in "scalar relaxation of second kind" [11]. Dramatic effects can result if the coupling is between electron and nuclear spins.

Unpaired electron spins $\underline{S}$ can be present in solutions of ions, e.g., Mn^{+2}, etc. or free radicals, usually large organic species. In such cases, the "Overhauser effect" can occur, resulting in an increase in the intensity of an NMR line by factors of hundreds, or a "negative absorption," i.e., emission of energy at the NMR frequency. The phenomenon occurring depends on the type of relaxation mechanism present. Overhauser effects can also be observed for nuclear-nuclear coupling. Thus for example the ^{13}C signal from a hydrocarbon can be increased by a factor of nearly 3 on irradiating at the ^{1}H frequency [10].

The measurement of nuclear Overhauser enhancements is used now in many cases to determine the type of coupling responsible for spin-lattice relaxation. Although it is not treated in any detail in Sec. 13.3, the basis of the Overhauser effect will be described somewhat further here. The simple case of a nucleus and an electron with I = S = 1/2 will be considered at it gives most dramatic results.

At thermal equilibrium with a constant applied field $\underline{B}_0$, the population ratio $N_{\beta,e}/N_{\alpha,e}$ between electron spin states $|\beta,e\rangle$ and $|\alpha,e\rangle$ is much greater then $N_{\alpha,N}/N_{\alpha,N}$ as given in (13.4) as $\beta_e >> \beta_N$ (13.1). If the interaction between $\underline{I}$ and $\underline{S}$ is of a scalar form ($H'(t) = C(t)\underline{I}\cdot\underline{S}$) then it can be assumed that the only nonnegligible transition rates are between $|\alpha,e\rangle,|\beta,N\rangle \rightleftarrows |\beta,e\rangle,|\alpha,N\rangle$ and $|\alpha,e\rangle,|\beta,N\rangle \not\rightleftarrows |\beta,e\rangle,|\beta,N\rangle$, $|\alpha,e\rangle,|\alpha,N\rangle \not\rightleftarrows |\beta,e\rangle,|\alpha,N\rangle$.

If then an RF or microwave field is applied to saturate the electron spin system then the above transitions serve to make the nuclear spin population ratio different from that in (13.4). It can be shown [6] that the population ratio becomes

$$\frac{N_{\alpha\alpha} + N_{\beta\beta}}{N_{\alpha\beta} + N_{\beta\beta}} = \exp\left[\frac{(g_N\beta_N + g_e\beta_e)B_0}{kT}\right] \qquad (13.24)$$

an increase by a factor of 659.

Such a large increase does not occur in practise because of incomplete saturation and the idealization of scalar coupling. In the case of dipolar relaxation, instead of an enhancement in absorption, a negative absorption, i.e., emission is predicted.

(i) Effect of Field Gradients

A perfectly homogeneous field $\underline{B}_0$ has been assumed up to now. However, inhomogeneities in $\underline{B}_0$ can lead to an increase in the linewidth, i.e., a decrease in T_2. This effect can be exploited for the measurement of self-diffusion coefficients.

A magnetic field gradient $\underline{G}$ is set up in the system. When a nucleus is displaced due to translational diffusion, the magnetic field it is subjected to changes. Thus its nuclear spin energy changes with time due to diffusional motion, causing a decrease in the transverse relaxation time. The problem can be treated quantitatively by adding a term (6.23) $D^* \nabla^2 \underline{M}$ to the Bloch equations (13.8) and replacing $\underline{B}_0$ by $\underline{B}_0 + \underline{G}\cdot\underline{r}$ [5].

The decay of the tranverse magnetization $M_\perp$ then becomes

$$M_\perp(t) = M_\perp(0) \exp\left[-\frac{t}{T_2}\right] \exp\left[-\frac{1}{12}\gamma_N^2 G^2 D^* t^3\right] \qquad (13.25)$$

instead of the simple exponential decay with time constant T_2, the transverse relaxation time in the absence of a field gradient. The factor $G^2/12$ is usually not available through calculation, but must be obtained through calibration using a system with known values of D* [see, e.g., Sec. 9.3(d)]. Several methods based on (13.25) have been developed for the measurement of D* [e.g., Sec. 13.2(c)].

13.2. EXPERIMENTAL TECHNIQUES

Commercial apparata are available for most measurements of interest with regard to the topics in this book. Thus only a brief overview will be given of the experimental techniques. Many of the techniques are described in length in [11].

(a) Continuous Wave Techniques

A schematic view of a CW apparatus is given in Fig. (13.4). It is of the "crossed coil" type where two RF coils are used: one to supply the other to detect the RF field.

The static field B_0 is quite large, of the order of kilogauss. The transmitter coil supplies RF radiation. When this RF signal is the same as the Larmour frequency $\omega_0 = \gamma_N B_0$, then resonance occurs in the system and a signal is induced in the receiver coil. The latter

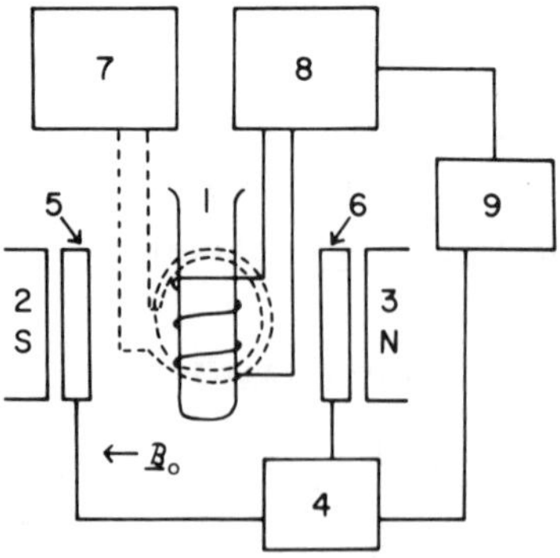

Fig. 13.4. Schematic diagram of a continuous wave NMR apparatus. (1) Sample tube; (2,3) Poles of permanent magnet; (4) Oscilloscope; (5,6) Sweep coils; (7) RF transmitter; (8) RF amplifier; (9) Detector and audio amplifier.

is placed at right angles to minimize stray pickup from the coil. The field strength $\mathcal{B}_0$ is usually such that the RF is of the order of 10s of MHz, usually from 60 to 100 MHz for the ^{1}H work.

To obtain the resonance condition, it is possible to either sweep the RF in a range $\Delta\omega$ about ω_0 or to sweep the field $\mathcal{B}_0$ with fixed RF to vary the Larmour frequency through a range $\Delta\omega$. The latter method is often used, with the strength of $\mathcal{B}_0$ modulated at 60 Hz. Stability of frequencies and field strengths, and the homogeneity of the field are aspects of importance if high resolution is desired.

Such a CW technique is used usually to detect chemical shifts. For protons, it is common to use tetramethylsilane $Si(CH_3)_4$ as a reference. Chemical shifts are then expressed as being parts per million down- or upfield from such a reference.

T_2 can also be obtained from CW techniques through observation of the linewidth. However, more accurate values can be obtained through pulse methods.

(b) Free Induction Decay

Basic to the considerations of pulse methods is the concept of free induction decay following a pulse of a specified time t_p. Such a pulse length time corresponds to a rotation of the magnetization vector through a specific angle. This is shown schematically in Fig. 13.5.

A magnetic field $\mathcal{B}_{1,r}$ is applied in the manner described in Sec. 13.1(d) such that it is along the x_r axis of the frame of reference rotating as ω_0. Such a field interacts with the magnetization $\underline{M}_r$ as $d\underline{M}_r/dt = \gamma_N \underline{M}_r \times \underline{\mathcal{B}}_{1,r}$. This rotates $\underline{M}_r$ in the z_r-y_r plane toward the y axis. If then the $\underline{\mathcal{B}}_{1,r}$ is applied for a time t_p, then will have rotated through an angle

$$\theta = \gamma_N \mathcal{B}_{1,r} t_p \qquad \text{radians} \tag{13.26}$$

Hence the term "90 degree pulse," "180 degree pulse," etc. become meaningful. Generally, $t_p << T_1$ or T_2.

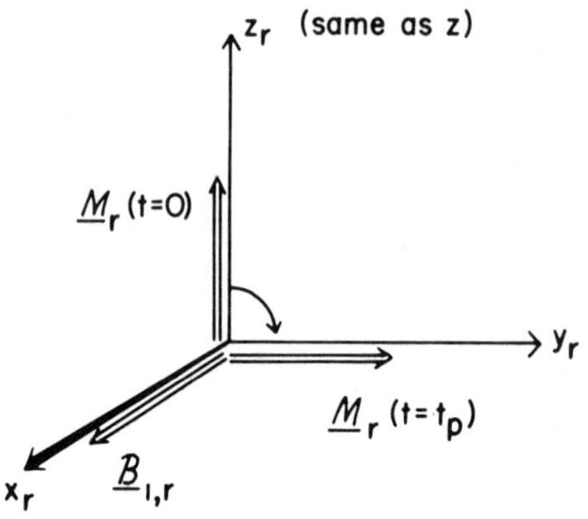

Fig. 13.5. Schematic diagram illustrating the rotation of the vector $\underline{M}$ through $\pi/2$ due to application of a field $\underline{B}_{1,r}$ for a time t_p.

Free induction decay can thus occur in the following simple case. A 90° (or $\pi/2$) pulse of RF is given (i.e., the field $\underline{B}_{1,r}$ is applied for a time t_p such that $\gamma_N B_{1,r} t_p = \pi/2$). Immediately after this pulse, the magnetization $\underline{M}$ is along the y axis. The component of $\underline{M}$ in the xy (or $x_r y_r$) plane will then relax to its equilibrium value with the transverse relaxation time T_2 as shown in (13.8).

The apparatus is usually arranged so that signals induced in a coil about the fixed x or y axis are picked up. The magnitude of $M_\perp$ (or M_{xy}) is thus observed after t_p as an RF signal with the free precession frequency ω_0. This free induction signal decays ideally exponentially with a time T_2, but field inhomogeneities [Sec. 13.1(i)] makes this simplest method a poor way of measuring T_2 [see Sec. 13.2 (c)].

To measure T_1, a pulse sequency π, τ, $\pi/2$ can be applied with various values of τ. Figure 13.6 shows schematically how this results in a T_1 measurement. The π pulse inverts the direction of M_z. In the time τ, M_z diminishes somewhat in relaxing toward its equilibrium value. The $\pi/2$ pulse rotates $\underline{M}$ to the y axis. A free induction signal then results as $M_\perp$ diminishes and $M_z (M_\parallel)$ relaxes toward its equilibrium value. The intensity of the free induction decay signal depends on

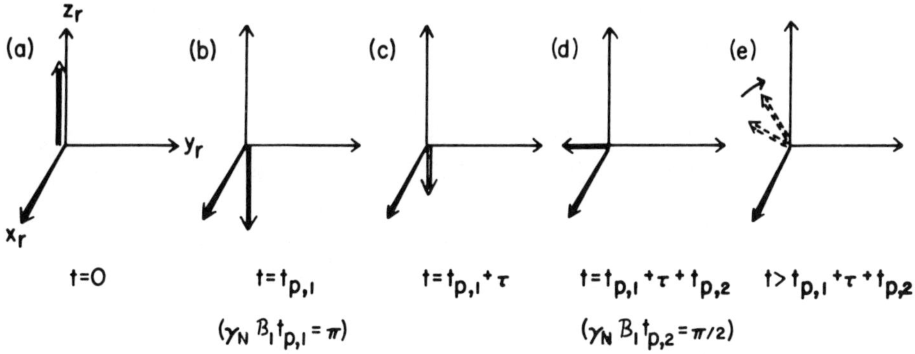

Fig. 13.6. Schematic diagram illustrating a π, τ, π/2 pulse sequence for measurement of T_1.

the degree to which M_z has decayed before the π/2 pulse. Thus by measuring this intensity as a function of τ, the delay between the π and π/2 pulses, it is possible to determine T_1.

(c) Samples of Spin-Echo Techniques

In order to obtain the most accurate values of T_1 and T_2 by methods based on free induction decay, several ingenious pulsing sequences have been developed [11]. Some of the more common ones will be outlined here.

In the Hahn spin-echo technique, a π/2, τ, π sequence is used. First $\underline{M}$ is rotated to the y_r axis. As $\underline{B}_0$ is in practise not completely homogeneous, then nuclei in different parts of the sample precess at different speeds so that a "dephasing" occurs, and $\underline{M}$ can be thought to fan out in the $x_r y_r$ plane. After τ, the π pulse inverts $M_\perp$ and reverses the speeds of precession about the z axis of the individual nuclei. Thus at a time 2τ all the nuclei rephase again along the y_r axis ($t_p \ll \tau$). A "spin-echo" is thus observed. In this way T_2 can be measured from the size of the echo as a function of τ. This value of T_2 is more accurate than that measured as outlined in Sec. 2(b), as effects of inhomogeneities in $\underline{B}_0$ are here minimized.

The Carr-Purcell sequence ($\pi/2$, τ, π, 2τ, π, 2τ,$\cdots$) is an extension of the Hahn technique. Here a train of spin echoes at 2τ, 4τ, 6τ, etc. are obtained. From the decreasing magnitude of these pulses, T_2 can be calculated. Thus a saving in time is obtained. The effects of diffusion can also be minimized. Self-diffusion is operative only during periods of 2τ. Thus with the use of (13.25), the decay of the echo train at time t is given as $\propto \exp[-t/T_2 - \frac{1}{3}\gamma_N^2 G^2 D^* \tau^2 t]$. This is to be compared to

$$\propto \exp\left[-\frac{2\tau}{T} - \frac{2}{3}\gamma_N^2 G^2 D^* \tau^3\right] \qquad (13.27)$$

for the Hahn method. Thus longer relaxation times can more accurately be measured.

The experimental apparatus for spin-echo techniques is discussed in Ref. 3. The major problems are to obtain sources capable of delivering short (1 to 10 x 10^{-6} sec) pulses of intense (100 to 1000 V) RF so that B_1 can be $\approx$100 gauss. Quick recovery times from overloads and electrical isolation of the electronic circuitry are of importance. Both the $\underline{B}_1$ and the $\underline{B}_0$ fields must also be as homogeneous as possible.

In the previous examples, $\underline{B}_1$ has always been applied along the x_r axis. It is of advantage in cases both from the point of view of utilization of apparatus, and the accuracy of the information obtained, to consider changes in the direction of $\underline{B}_1$ in the rotating frame. $\underline{B}_1$ can then be considered to have a role analogous to $\underline{B}_0$ in the previous discussion.

It is thus possible to design "rotating frame" experiments where the phase of $\underline{B}_1$ is changed. In this way it is possible to obtain values of relaxation times for the rotating frame. These are designated at $T_{1,\rho}$, $T_{2,\rho}$. For most liquids, $T_{1,\rho} = T_2$. Rotating frame experiments and relaxation times are discussed in some detail in Ref. 11.

(d) Fourier Transform Methods

The free induction decay following a $\pi/2$ pulse can be shown to be the Fourier transform of the line shape function. In the case of an exponential decay, a Lorentzian shape is obtained (13.10); i.e.,

$$\int_0^\infty \exp\left[-\frac{t}{T_2}\right] \cos\,(\omega - \omega_0)t\;dt = \frac{T_2}{1 + T_2(\omega - \omega_0)^2} \qquad (13.28)$$

Thus a Fourier analysis of the free induction decay signal will provide a continuous wave spectrum, for single or for multispin systems.

The advantage of Fourier transform methods is a more efficient collection of data than in the case of continuous wave (CW) methods. Either more data can be collected in the same time, increasing the signal to noise ratio, or else a saving in time can be effected. Short-lived, transient species can also be observed by this method.

The field $\underline{B}_1$ used for the pulse preceding free induction must be large enough so that $\gamma_N B_1 >> 2\pi \cdot \Delta\omega$, where $\Delta\omega$ is the range of CW frequencies to be covered. Thus $t_p << 1/(4\Delta\omega)$. The time during which the free induction signal is observed cannot be truncated arbitrarily, as then the Fourier analysis gives arbitrary modulation of the transformed (frequency) function. However, with appropriate data manipulation, truncation can be performed with minimal aberration.

Fourier analysis is usually carried out by digital computer. A reasonably well resolved spectrum requires a considerable computer memory. Current commercial instruments can, however, carry out Fourier transforms of free induction decay signals quite routinely.

13.3. RESULTS FOR SPECIFIC SYSTEMS

As indicated in 1, NMR techniques can be used to obtain several different types of information regarding structure and dynamics in liquids. Because of the vast amount of literature dealing with this specific topic, the coverage of possible types of information obtained through NMR techniques is somewhat less thorough than in some of the other chapters of Part B.

(a) Orientational and Angular Momentum Correlation Times

(1) Quadrupole and Spin-Rotation Coupling

The interpretation of nuclear magnetic relaxation is somewhat easier in pure liquids where the molecules contain an atom which has a nucleus with nonzero nuclear electric quadrupole moment. In such cases, the relaxation is due essentially to quadrupole coupling. Thus in liquid chlorine, the relaxation time T_1 (= T_2) of the ^{35}Cl nuclei (spin 3/2) is given by [12]

$$\frac{1}{T_1} = \frac{1}{10} \frac{e^2qQ}{\hbar^2} \tau_Q \qquad (13.29)$$

For this linear molecule the time τ_Q in (13.29) can be equated to τ_2, assuming $G_2(t)$ falls exponentially [Sec. 13.1(f)]. The measured relaxation time T_1 is relatively short (~1.5×10^{-5} sec) when there is quadrupole relaxation present. The temperature dependence shows an activation energy of only 3140 ± 170 J mol^{-1}. The data can be fitted well by several theories for orientational relaxation.

Several other recent investigations of orientation and self-diffusion in liquids are available [13-15]. Some of these [14,15] involve determination of the angular momentum correlation time τ_J, which can be obtained when contributions to relaxation from spin-rotation interactions [Sec. 13.1(f)] can be separated out. This usually necessitates the consideration of intramolecular and intermolecular dipole-dipole contributions, as they are of the same order of magnitude. Intermolecular contributions can be estimated knowing the self-diffusion constant.

In the case of CCl_3F (a symmetric-top molecule) both ^{35}Cl and ^{19}F relaxation can be studied [15]. The ^{35}Cl relaxation is effectively due only to quadrupole interaction; the analysis of this yields τ_2. The ^{19}F relaxation at high temperatures is due primarily to spin-rotation coupling. At these higher temperatures, comparison of τ_J and τ_2 indicate that the reorientation must be described by angular steps of about 1 radian. The "J-diffusion" model [Sec. 7.3(a)] seems more realistic, i.e., both the magnitude and direction of the angular momentum vector are randomized at each collision.

(2) Glycerol

Numerous studies have been carried out on glycerol ($HOCH_2$-CH(OH)-CH_2OH) [16,17]. It is a viscous liquid which supercools, so that the molecular motions in it can be investigated in time scales of a number of experimental techniques. The NMR relaxation of the protons in glycerol is due to both inter and intramolecular contributions. The ^2H relaxation yields essentially purely intramolecular (orientational) information as the relaxation is through quadrupolar mechanism. The ^{13}C relaxation [17] also yields information regarding orientational motion as the major relaxation mechanism involves the protons attached to the ^{13}C.

Both inter and intramolecular relaxation can be studied in glycerol by observing ^1H and ^2H relaxation times as a function of isotopic dilution [16]. Such studies have been carried out as a function of the field strength (i.e., the Larmour frequency). An extensive frequency study is not possible for ^2H due to the small value of g_N for ^2H (Table 12.1). For ^1H, it is possible to have the frequency vary from 6MHz to 180MHz. It is thus possible to obtain a curve of $(1/T_1)$ vs ν for intramolecular relaxation as shown in Fig. 13.7.

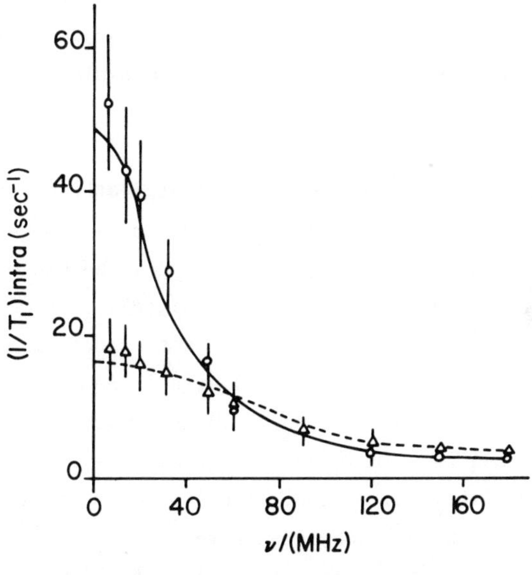

Fig. 13.7. Frequency dependence of the intramolecular relaxation rate $(1/T_1)_{intra}$ for glycerol. ϕ Experimental points and —— Cole-Davidson fit at T = -20°C; Δ Experimental points and ---- Cole-Davidson fit at T = +72°C. After Ref. 16.

It is now possible to test the validity of the assumption of exponential decay of the time correlation function made in arriving at (13.15). From an extension of the discussion in Sec. 13.1(f), it can be shown that if the ^1H relax by dipolar and the ^2H through quadrupolar interaction, then in both cases,

$$\left(\frac{1}{T_1}\right)_{intra}(\omega) = C\left\{\int_0^\infty G_2(t)\ \exp[i\omega t]\ dt + 4\int_0^\infty G_2(t)\ \exp[i2\omega t]\ dt\right\} \tag{13.30}$$

This is the basic form from which (13.29) is obtained, on the assumption of $G_2(t) \propto \exp[-t/\tau]$. The constant C is given by

$$C = \frac{3}{10}\gamma_N^4\hbar^2 r^{-6} \quad \text{for} \quad {}^1H \qquad C = \frac{3}{40}\left(\frac{eqQ}{\hbar}\right)^2 \quad \text{for} \quad {}^2H \tag{13.31}$$

The experimental results cannot be fitted adequately by a single or a double relaxation. A satisfactory fit can, however, be obtained with a Cole-Davidson distribution of relaxation times [Sec. 11.1(d)]. In the ^{13}C study, however [17], it was not found necessary to introduce a distribution of relaxation times to explain the data.

(3) Water

The results of NMR investigation of liquid water are reviewed in [18] and [19]. Only the results of T_1 measurements are outlined in Sec. 13.3(a). Chemical shift (i.e., H-bonding), and proton transfer measurements are discussed in Secs. 13.3(b),(c). The results of NMR self-diffusion measurements [20] will not be described here as they add little to the topics already covered in Sec. 9.3(b).

In the case of ^2H_2O and $H_2^{17}O$, spin-lattice relaxation is due to quadrupole coupling. Thus the relaxation time reflects only intramolecular orientational motion. When proton magnetic relaxation is observed, dipole-dipole coupling is responsible for the relaxation, and both inter and intramolecular motions are involved.

Studies of ^2H_2O and $H_2^{17}O$ [21,22] show a temperature dependence which is non-Arrhenius in behavior. The rotational time involved is about 2.0×10^{-12} sec at 25°C, but the exact nature of the species responsible is not known, as in the case of dielectric relaxation [Sec. 11.3(b)]. It has not been possible with nuclear magnetic relaxation to distinguish a time due to a single relaxation from that describing a continuum of relaxations as in Sec. (2) above. The ratio of the nuclear magnetic relaxation time to the dielectric relaxation time is about 0.27, independent of temperature. The NMR time decreases for water in organic solvents, just as the dielectric time [Sec. 11.3(b)].

In making measurements of relaxation times in water or other liquids, it is important not to have any dissolved oxygen present. The presence of paramagnetic species such as O_2 can lower the relaxation time considerably due to electron spin-nuclear spin coupling.

(b) Hydrogen Bonding in Water and Solutions

(1) Pure Water

Chemical shift studies of pure liquid water can be interpreted to give information regarding the fraction of H-bonded molecules. Figure 13.8 shows that the proton NMR signal in gaseous water is shifted considerably upfield from the liquid value. The value in CCl_4 solution is intermediate. ^{17}O and ^{2}H studies show a similar effect.

The observed chemical shift can be interpreted [19] in terms of

$$\Delta = X_{H--O}\Delta_{H--O} + X_H\Delta_H \tag{13.32}$$

The chemical shift of the H-bonded protons is further down-field. When involved in H-bonding, the proton has a lower electron density about it, i.e., it will be less shielded and will have a shift which is downfield from the non-H-bonded proton, i.e., will require a smaller B_0 to attain resonance. As T increases, the fraction X_H of non-H-bonded protons increases and the chemical shift of the protons is further upfield. The bonded-unbonded environment of a proton alters so rapidly in the time scale of an NMR experiment that only an "average" environment is seen. According to this interpretation, the fraction of non-bonded water molecules increases from 0.15 at 0°C to 0.35 at 100°C.

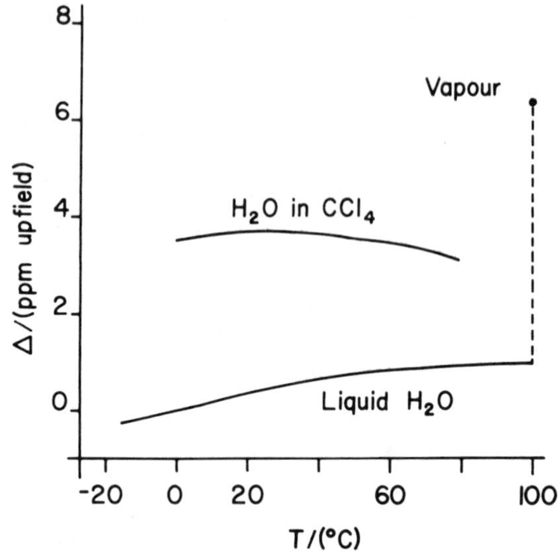

Fig. 13.8. The chemical shift Δ of ^1H in H_2O as a function of temperature in liquid water and in a carbon tetrachloride solution. After Ref. 19.

(2) Solutions of Alcohols in Water

A number of NMR studies have been carried out on water-alcohol mixtures [23-25]. Downfield shifts of the water H take place in dilute alcohol. The observed shift can be considered to be due to effects of the polar (hydrophilic) group and the nonpolar (hydrophobic) group. There seems to be agreement that the polar effects cause a downfield shift [23,24]. There is controversy as to whether nonpolar groups give a downfield shift due to increase in water structuring (i.e., essentially the same effect as lowering the water temperature; see Fig. 13.8). At high temperatures, an upfield shift occurs [25], while the conclusion in Ref. 23 is that such effects cause little if any shift.

(3) Other Solutions

Thermodynamic parameters for the H-bonding of chloroform (CCl_3H) with various species have also been obtained through chemical shift studies [26]. The analysis is carried out essentially as in the case of water, i.e., assuming the chemical shift observed to be due to the sum of a contribution from the "free" chloroform molecule and from a "complexed" species. In this way equilibrium constants for the formation of 1:1 complexes can be obtained. Through the temperature dependence of K, ΔH^θ and ΔS^θ for the complexation equilibria can be derived (17. 34). Reference 26 gives such data for chloroform complexing with 12 different proton acceptors.

Another example of the use of NMR to study association equilibria in solutions is the investigation of t-butyl alcohol in hexadecane ($n\text{-}C_{16}H_{34}$) [27]. The degree of association of the alcohol can be inferred from an analysis of the chemical shift with concentration. If the alcohol is present in the form of an n-mer, then a plot of $(\Delta\nu/(C_{Al})^{n-1})^{1/n}$ vs $\Delta\nu$ should be linear [27]. The C_{Al} refers to the alcohol concentration assuming it to be unassociated. A trimer rather than a dimer seems to be the predominant association form. To explain the NMR data in conjunction with vapor pressure and infrared data, however, it is necessary to postulate other forms of association.

Such studies need not be restricted to proton chemical shift measurements, nor to H-bonding. Thus ^{13}C shifts obtained through Fourier-transform spectroscopy [28] have been used to observe the effect of solvent on various substituted benzenes [e.g., Sec. 11.3(e)]. The results give information regarding the change in the electronic nature of the aromatic ring due to solute-solvent interactions.

Such information can be obtained through other types of NMR measurements than chemical shift measurements. Thus relaxation and self-diffusion as well as chemical shift NMR data on water-dimethylsulfoxide ($(CH_3)_2SO$) [29,30] have been interpreted in terms of the effects of intermolecular interactions (H-bonding) on translational and rotational mobility.

(c) Proton Transfer Studies

(1) Water

The rate of proton exchange in water catalyzed by acids or bases can also be investigated using NMR [see also Sec. (d)]. The presence of the reactions

$$H_3O^+ + H_2O \overset{k_H}{\rightleftarrows} H_2O + H_3O^+$$

$$H_2O + OH^- \overset{k_{OH}}{\rightleftarrows} OH^- + H_2O \tag{13.33}$$

cause a change in T_2 of both H and ^{17}O in $H_2^{17}O$, while T_1 remains unchanged.

When the exchange reactions are faster than molecular reorientation (when pH << 7 or pH >> 7), then $T_2 = T_1$. When the exchange is slow (at pH ≈ 7), then however the "collapsed multiplets" due to ^{17}O-H spin-spin coupling are broader for both ^{17}O and H [Sec. 13.1(g)]. Although T_1 has the same value as at low and high pH, the linewidth is broadened, i.e., T_2 is decreased, due to this effect.

An analysis of T_2 vs pH yields the results $k_H = 7.9 \times 10^9$ mol^{-1} liter sec^{-1}, $k_{OH} = 4.6 \times 10^9$ mol^{-1} liter sec^{-1} at 25°C with $E_H^{\#} = 10.9$ kJ mol^{-1} and $E_{OH}^{\#} = 11.3$ kJ mol^{-1}. Such data is in reasonable agreement with the values of k_H, k_{OH} calculated assuming proton and hydroxyl exchange to be responsible for the anomalously high electrical conductivity of OH^- and H^+ [Sec. 9.3(b)].

(2) Other Systems

Proton exchange studies have been carried out using NMR in a large variety of systems: aqueous solutions of amines and amides [32], alcohols [33], inorganic species [34], carboxylic acids in alcohols [35], and nonaqueous alcohols [36,37]. In the last case both ^{17}O and Overhauser studies [Sec. 13.1(h)] (involving the CH_3 and OH protons in methanol) have been carried out. In most cases, however, the rates are obtained from analysis of traces such as Fig. 13.3.

The variation of NMR CW traces such as Fig. 13.3 with temperature pH, concentration, etc. can yield information regarding the mechanism, of the overall proton exchange occurring in systems. Such exchange in aqueous solutions is generally acid-catalyzed, base-catalyzed or "solvent reaction." In the case of urea solutions [32], the reactions would be

$$NH_2\text{-}CO\text{-}NH\underline{H} + H^+ \rightleftarrows NH_2\text{-}CO\text{-}NH_2\underline{H}^+ \rightleftarrows NH_2\text{-}CO\text{-}NH_2 + \underline{H}^+ \qquad (13.34)$$

(acid catalyzed), or

$$NH_2\text{-}CO\text{-}NH\underline{H} + H_2O \rightleftarrows NH_2\text{-}CO\text{-}NH_2 + H\underline{H}O \qquad (13.35)$$

(solvent reaction).

From NMR studies it can be shown that mechanism (13.35) has a rate constant of only $2 \pm 2 \times 10^{-2}$ liter mol^{-1} sec^{-1} as compared to $3.5 \pm 1.0 \times 10^6$ for (13.34). The uncertainties in these rate constants (~100% and ~30%) are larger than normal for such studies. It is, however, often not possible to achieve accuracies of better than 10% because of various interfering factors, e.g., in the above case coupling with the quadrupole moment of the nitrogen nucleus.

(d) Systems Near the Critical Point

NMR studies near the critical point in one and two-component systems are reviewed in [38]. Measurements of both the self-diffusion coefficient and the spin lattice relaxation time indicate no anomalous behavior near the critical point, The phenomena responsible for phase separation seem to be characterized by such long-range interactions that the short-range dependent NMR phenomena are not affected by this.

Thus in the system aniline-cyclohexane [39] chemical shift and T_1 measurements indicate preference for AA and CC interactions rather than AC interactions. No information regarding ordering beyond nearest neighbors is possible, however. Any such nearest-neighbor interactions are also not strong enough to result in a basic translational motion involving anything but individual molecules. The mutual diffusion coefficient approaches zero at the critical point [Sec. 9.3(e)], but self diffusion coefficients indicate normal behavior.

In one-component systems, an anomaly has been observed in the product $D^*\rho$ [40]. There is a pronounced minimum in this product near T_c in ethane, interpreted as being due to a decrease in D^*. This is the only system in which such a minimum has been found, however.

(e) *Chemical Shift Studies in Electrolyte Solutions*

A review of the use of magnetic resonance in electrolyte solution studies can be found in [41,42]. Again information can be obtained from chemical shift, spin-lattice relaxation and self-diffusion measurements. In this section some examples of chemical shift studies are outlined. The chemical shift observed can be either in the solute (ion) nuclei or in the solvent (e.g., water) nuclei.

(1) Solute Chemical Shifts

References [43-45] show examples where the chemical shift of the ion is investigated. In Ref. 43 the chemical shift of ^{23}Na is measured (relative to aqueous NaCl) for various sodium salts in various solvents. The chemical shift of the perchlorate (ClO_4^-) salt in a number of solvents was found independent of concentration. This indicates that contact ion pairs are not likely to be present. The iodide salt shows a concentration-dependent ^{23}Na chemical shift, suggesting the presence of contact ion pairs.

The chemical shift of halogen nuclei (^{35}Cl, ^{79}Br, ^{127}I) was studied in a variety of solvents and with a variety of cations [44]. An important factor in the change of chemical shift with solvent seems to be interactions involving charge transfer to the solvent. A correlation was observed between the chemical shift and the wavelength of the charge transfer bands observed spectroscopically [Sec. 1.2(c)]. Chemical shift studies of the salts in mixed solvents can also be of use in determining whether preferential solvation is present. In analyzing the NMR results in mixed solvents, however, the activities of the solvent species in the bulk solvent must be taken into account.

In Ref. 45 the shifts of both cations and anions in alkali metal halide solutions were measured in a mixed solvent of water and hydrogen peroxide. "Infinite dilution" shifts were obtained by extrapolating the data to zero salt concentration. The dependence of these infinite dilution shifts on the mol ratio $H_2O:H_2O_2$ can then be analyzed to obtain quantitative data on preferential solvation. The results show Rb^+, Cs^+ and F^- to be preferentially solvated by H_2O_2 and Li^+ by

H_2O. No preference is shown by Na^+. This can be seen from Fig. 13.9 where ^{19}F and ^7Li shifts show deviations from a linear dependence of ^{23}Na in different directions. The free enthalpy of preferential solvation can be obtained from the NMR data and related to ΔG^θ of transfer from one solvent to another [46].

(2) Solvent Chemical Shifts

The chemical shifts of nuclei in the solvent can also be investigated, e.g., water proton shifts in aqueous electrolyte solutions [47]. The observed shift can be considered to be due to a "cation" and an "anion" shift. Estimates of the sizes of these two shifts for a particular salt solution can be made under various assumptions, or by e.g., taking the molal shift for Cl^- as being zero. The results can be explained satisfactorally on the consideration only of primary solvent mole-

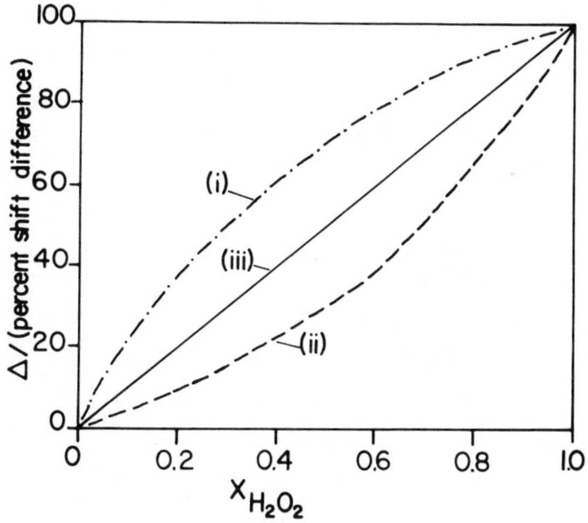

Fig. 13.9. The chemical shifts of (i) ^{19}F (from KF) —•—•; (ii) ^7Li (from LiCl) — —; and (iii) ^{23}Na (from NaCl) —— for 1 aquamolal solutions in hydrogen peroxide-water mixtures as a function of mol fraction peroxide. The shifts are given as a percentage between a shift in pure water and in pure hydrogen peroxide. In the peroxide, the shift of ^{19}F is 25, of ^7Li is 0.5, and of ^{23}Na is 14 ppm relative to the shift in water. After Ref. 45.

cules (i.e., water molecules in contact with the ion). In the case of anions, a correlation between the shift and the pK_A of the conjugate acid is obtained. The greater the basicity of the anion, i.e., the greater its affinity to protons, the more negative is the anion chemical shift of the protons, i.e., the less the protons are shielded. This is the same type of effect as in H-bonding [Sec. 13.3(b)]. The competition of water with the anions in the solvating process must be taken into account.

The study of proton (and other nucleus) chemical shifts in aqueous acid solutions can thus be used to obtain K_A values for acids [48]. Proton and ^{35}Cl shift data on $HClO_4$ thus indicate complete dissociation of the acid up to 6 M concentrations. Raman results [see, e.g., 12.3(h)] on the perchlorate ion also indicates complete dissociation up to at least 6 M.

In solutions of electrolytes in organic solvents, the solvent chemical shift can be measured for either ^1H [49] or ^{13}C [50] present in the solvent. In ^{13}C spectra, the effect of a cation is of the same type as that of the introduction of an electronegative substituent in the molecule. Solvation numbers can be obtained from the integrated intensities of the bound and bulk solvent signals. For $Mg(ClO_4)_2$ in ethanol, a solvation number 5.5 ± 1 was obtained.

(f) Self-Diffusion Studies in Electrolyte Solutions

NMR relaxation provides a convenient method for obtaining self-diffusion coefficients both in solutions and in pure liquids [Sec. 13.1 (i)]. The precision possible is not as high as that for the more time consuming classical methods [Sec. 9.2(b)]. However, self-diffusion coefficients for a number of species can be obtained relatively easily, as, e.g., for both ions and water molecules in a number of of aqueous salt solutions [51].

The self-diffusion coefficient of water $D^*_{H_2O}$ in electrolyte solutions can be considered as being a weighted average of the D^* for cation water, anion water and "free" water [see also Sec. 11.3(h)]. In alkali halides, the main effect is due to the cations, the "anion water" (i.e., that solvating anions) being as mobile as "free" water

The self-diffusion coefficient of Li^+, $D^*_{Li^+}$, in aqueous LiCl solutions is related to the electrical conductivity through the Nernst-Einstein relation (6.66). The value for $D^{*\infty}_{Li^+}$ obtained by extrapolating the experimental data to $c \rightarrow 0$ is in reasonable agreement with the calculated value using Λ_{Li^+}. The concentration dependence of $D^*_{Li^+}$ can be explained reasonable if $D^*_{Li^+}$ is assumed to be the same as $D^*_{H_2O}$(cation), i.e., the Li^+ is assumed to move together with the cation water.

An activation energy for $D^*_{Li^+} = D^*_{H_2O}$(cation) is obtained which is higher than that for $D^*_{H_2O}$ by about 2 kJ mol^{-1}. This is expected for "positive solvation" [52] [Sec. 5.2(c)]. At lower concentration, $D^*_{H_2O}$ shows two activation energies, with $E^{\#}$ for $D^*_{H_2O}$ in the range 0 to 40°C higher than that in the range 40 → 100°C. Above 4 M, the results can be explained with one activation energy for the whole T range, 0 → 100°C. At low concentrations and temperatures, the hydration shell of Li^+ is highly symmetrical resulting in a very low mobility and high $E^{\#}$ for cation water. At higher concentrations and/or temperatures, the symmetry is perturbed and $E^{\#}$ is less.

(g) NMR Relaxation in Electrolyte Solutions

The results outlined in Sec. (f) are also obtained from relaxation measurements. As in Secs. (e) and (f) the relaxation of nuclei in both solute and solvent can be investigated. Such measurements of T_1 allow for a calculation of lifetimes of the water in the hydration shells [53].

Non-aqueous solvents can also be investigated, e.g., Mg^{+2} in methanol [54], where the exchange rate between molecules in the solvation shell of Mg^{+2} and bulk solvent have been obtained. In this particular case, a separate signal was obtained for the solvation shell methanol OH proton. The relative intensity of this signal to free OH protons give a solvation number of 6. For other salts, e.g., Li^+, Ca^{+2}, Sr^{+2}, no separate solvation-shell signal was observed, even at very low temperatures.

Examples of studies of the NMR relaxation of solute ions are given in a series of papers by H. G. Hertz et al. [55]. In the case of Li^+ the relaxation is due to both dipole-dipole and quadrupole coupling, so that measurements of T_1 in both H_2O and D_2O were carried out to separate out the contribution from the Li-proton dipole coupling [50]. This intraparticle coupling is divided up into contributions from the first hydration sphere and that from the remaining waters. The latter interaction is not negligible, contributing nearly 1/4 of the relaxation rate.

The analysis yields a time 2×10^{-11} sec for the residence time of the water in the hydration shell. The time characteristic of the reorientation of the Li^+-H (H in the first solvation shell) is also about 10^{-11} sec. Activation energies for these two times are both $\sim$19 kJ mol^{-1}. This indicates a stable symmetrical first hydration shell for Li^+.

(h) Electron Spin Relaxation in Macromolecules

Much of the background of ESR is the same as for nuclear magnetic resonance. The two topics are treated in common in Ref. 6, while ESR itself is described in detail in [57,58]. ESR experimentals can be carried out only in systems containing unpaired electrons. Few simple molecules have a net electron spin. Thus in many cases, ESR experiments involve solutions of large molecules. These are often biological macromolecules which have a fixed "spin label" on them. The spin label is often a nitroxide group [59].

Macromolecules can have very long orientational relaxation times, with times as high as 2×10^{-5} sec observed [59]. Such long reorientation times can also be obtained for smaller species in very viscous liquids. The rotational motion in this "slow tumbling region" can be examined in some detail by ESR. It is possible not only to obtain a reorientational relaxation time, but also to determine the model of reorientation by matching the electron spin resonance trace with simulation spectra [60].

The motion of the peroxylamine disulfonate (PADS) radical was slowed down sufficiently by using a mixed solvent with 85% glycerol so that the slow tumbling region could be examined. The experimental ESR spectrum for this species was simulated on the basis of three models of rotational motion. The differences between three such simulations are shown in Fig. 13.10. ESR spectra traditionally displayed differently from the NMR spectra as shown in Fig. 13.3. The ESR spectrum is essentially the derivative of the absorption vs frequency (or field strength) spectrum usually shown for NMR.

The three models of reorientation used were (i) Brownian rotational diffusion [Sec. 6.1(e)]; (ii) jump diffusion, where the molecule has a fixed orientation for a time τ_0, and then jumps instantaneously to a new orientation; and (iii) free diffusion, where the molecule reorients freely for a time τ_1 due to inertial motion and then jumps instantaneously to a new orientation [Sec. 7.3(a)]. Matching with experimental spectra show that the motion deviates from Brownian

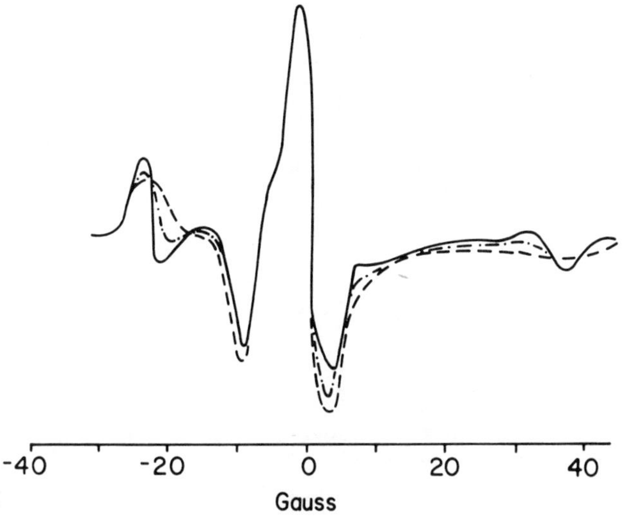

Fig. 13.10. The ESR line shapes for an axial nitroxide assuming (i) ——— Brownian diffusion; (ii) — — — jump diffusion; (iii) —·—· free diffusion. After Ref. 59.

motion at short times (<2 x 10^{-11} sec). The free diffusion model gives the best fit to the experimental spectrum. Consideration of anisotropic reorientation seems necessary to improve the match between experimental and simulated spectra.

REFERENCES

A thorough account of nuclear magnetic relaxation can be found in [5], while [6] gives an account which is complete enough for the purpose of this book. Reference 11 covers several aspects of more recent experimental methods, while a number of examples of uses of magnetic resonance [8,51] are found in the same number of Ber. Bunsenges. as contributions to a symposium, "Molekuläre Bewegungen in Flüssigkeiten."

1. R. D. Evans, The Atomic Nucleus, McGraw-Hill, New York, 1955.
2. F. A. Borey, Nuclear Magnetic Resonance Spectroscopy, Academic Press, New York, 1969.
3. E. D. Becker, High Resolution NMR, Academic Press, New York, 1969.
4. J. B. Stothers, Carbon-13 NMR Spectroscopy, Academic Press, New York, 1969.
5. A. Abragam, The Principles of Nuclear Magnetism, Oxford University Press, New York, 1961.
6. A. Carrington and A. D. McLachlan, Introduction to Magnetic Resolution, Harper and Row, New York, 1967.
7. R. G. Gordon, Adv. Mag. Res., *3*, 1 (1968).
8. H. J. Bender and M. D. Zeidler, Ber. Bunsenges. Physik. Chem., *75*, 236 (1971).
9. H. Saito, H. H. Mantsch, and I. C. P. Smith, J. Am. Chem. Soc., *95*, 8453 (1973).
10. T. C. Farrar, S. J. Druck, R. R. Shoup, and E. D. Becker, J. Am. Chem. Soc., *94*, 699 (1972).
11. T. C. Farrar and E. D. Becker, Pulse and Fourier Transform NMR, Academic Press, New York, 1971.
12. R. T. Obermyer and E. P. Jones, J. Chem. Phys., *58*, 1677 (1973).
13. D. E. O'Reilly, E. M. Peterson, and C. E. Scheie, J. Chem. Phys., *60*, 1603 (1974).
14. R. A. Assink and J. Jonas, J. Chem. Phys., *57*, 3329 (1972).

15. K. T. Gillen, D. C. Douglass, M. S. Malmberg, and A. A. Maryott, J. Chem. Phys., *57*, 5170 (1972).

16. J. P. Kintzinger and M. D. Zeidler, Ber. Bunseng. Physik. Chem., *77*, 98 (1973).

17. L. J. Burnett and S. B. W. Roeder, J. Chem. Phys., *60*, 2420 (1974).

18. GR5.

19. J. A. Glasel in GR7.

20. K. T. Gillen, D. C. Douglass, and M. J. R. Hoch, J. Chem. Phys., *57*, 5117 (1972).

21. J. C. Hindman, A. J. Zielen, A. Svirmickas, and M. Wood, J. Chem. Phys., *54*, 621 (1971).

22. Y. Lee and J. Jonas, J. Chem. Phys., *57*, 4233 (1972).

23. J. Oakes, J. C. S. Farad. Trans. II, *69*, 1311 (1973).

24. W. Y. Wen and H. G. Hertz, J. Sol. Chem., *1*, 17 (1972).

25. M. M. Marciacq-Rousselot and M. Lucas, J. Phys. Chem., *77*, 1056 (1973).

26. G. R. Wiley and S. I. Miller, J. Am. Chem. Soc., *94*, 3287 (1972).

27. E. E. Tucker and E. D. Becker, J. Phys. Chem., *77*, 1783 (1973).

28. G. L. Nelson, G. C. Levy, and J. D. Cargioli, J. Am. Chem. Soc., *94*, 3089 (1972).

29. K. J. Packer and D. J. Tomlinson, Trans. Farad. Soc., *67*, 1302 (1971).

30. T. Tokuhiro, L. Menafra, and H. H. Szmant, J. Chem. Phys., *61*, 2275 (1974).

31. R. E. Glick and K. C. Tewari, J. Chem. Phys., *44*, 546 (1966).

32. D. L. Hunston and I. M. Klotz, J. Phys. Chem., *75*, 2123 (1971).

33. E. K. Ralph and E. Grunwald, J. Am. Chem. Soc., *91*, 2426 (1969).

34. J. Grimaldi, J. Baldo, C. McMurray, and B. D. Sykes, J. Am. Chem. Soc., *94*, 7641 (1972).

35. S. Highsmith and E. Grunwald, J. Phys. Chem., *78*, 2339 (1974).

36. H. Versmold and C. Yoon, Ber. Bunsenges. Physik. Chem., *76*, 1164 (1972).

37. Y. Arata, T. Fukumi, and S. Fujiwara, J. Chem. Phys., *51*, 859 (1969).

38. H. Hamann, C. Hoheisel, and H. Richtering, Ber. Bunsenges. Physik. Chem., *76*, 249 (1972).

39. J. E. Anderson and W. H. Gerritz, J. Chem. Phys., *53*, 2589 (1970).

40. M. Bloom, in Critical Phenomena (M. S. Green and J. V. Sengers, eds.), Natl. Bureau Stand. Misc. Publ., 273 (1966).

41. J. Burgers and M. C. R. Symonds, Quart. Rev., *22*, 276 (1968).

42. M. Szwarc, in Ions and Ion Pairs in Organic Chemistry, Vol. 1 (M. Szwarc, ed.), Wiley-Interscience, New York, 1972.

43. R. H. Erlich and A. I. Popov, J. Am. Chem. Soc., *93*, 5620 (1971); M. S. Greenberg, R. L. Bodner, and A. I. Popov, J. Phys. Chem., *77*, 2449 (1973).

44. T. R. Stengle, Y. C. E. Pan, and H. C. Langford, J. Am. Chem. Soc., *94*, 9037 (1972); J. P. K. Tong, C. H. Langford, and T. R. Stengle, Can. J. Chem., *52*, 1721 (1974).

45. A. K. Covington, T. H. Lilley, K. E. Newman, and G. A. Porterhouse, J. C. S. Farad. Trans. I, *69*, 963 (1973).

46. A. K. Covington, K. E. Newman, and T. H. Lilley, J. C. S. Farad. Trans. I, *69*, 973 (1973).

47. J. Davies, S. Ormondroyd, and M. C. R. Symonds, Trans. Farad. Soc., *67*, 3465 (1971).

48. J. W. Akitt, A. K. Covington, J. G. Freeman, and T. H. Lilley, Trans. Farad. Soc., *64*, 2701 (1968).

49. J. F. Coetzee and W. R. Sharpe, J. Sol. Chem., *1*, 77 (1972).

50. G. W. Stockton and J. S. Martin, Can. J. Chem., *52*, 744 (1974).

51. A. Weiss and K. H. Nothnagel, Ber. Bunsenges. Physik. Chem., *75*, 216 (1971).

52. O. Y. Samoilov in GR6.

53. H. G. Hertz, Prog. NMR-Spectroscopy, Vol. 3, Pergamon, London, 1967.

54. S. Nakamura and S. Meiboom, J. Am. Chem. Soc., *89*, 1765 (1967).

55. H. G. Hertz, M. Holz, G. Keller, H. Versmold, and C. Yoon, Ber. Bunseng. Physik. Chem., *78*, 493 (1974).

56. H. G. Hertz, R. Tutsch, and H. Versmold, Ber. Bunsenges. Physik. Chem., *75*, 1177 (1971).

57. L. T. Muus and P. W. Atkins (eds.), Electron Spin Relaxation in Liquids, Plenum, New York, 1972.

58. A. Carrington, in Molecular Relaxation Processes, Academic Press, New York, 1966.

59. J. S. Hyde and L. Dalton, Chem. Phys. Lett., *16*, 568 (1972).

60. S. A. Goldman, G. V. Bruno, C. F. Polnaszek, and J. H. Freed, J. Chem. Phys., *56*, 716 (1972).

Further Recent References

F. H. A. Rummens, "Intermolecular Interactions in Nuclear Magnetic Resonance X. A Site-Specific Model for the Gas-to-Liquid Shifts of Nonpolar Solutes. Applications to Proton Medium Shifts and the Determination of Cavity Radii", Can. J. Chem., *54*, 254 (1976).

D. L. VanderHart, "Study of Molecular Reorientation: Pressure and Temperature Dependence of Deuterium Relaxation in $CDCl_3$", J. Chem. Phys., *60*, 1858 (1974).

H. Versmold, "NMR Studies of Reorientational Motion in Ethanol and Ethanol Glycerol Mixtures", Ber. Bunsenges. Physik. Chem., *78*, 1318 (1974).

W. Schröer and E. Lippert, "Nahordnung in Flüssigkeiten V. NMR-Verschiebungen, Verdampfungs-Enthalpien und Zusatzfunktionen von Alkanen und Alkylchloriden in Flüssigen Mischphasen", Ber. Bunseng. Physik. Chem., *80*, 267 (1976).

T. J. Rowland, "A ^{14}N Nuclear Relaxation Study of Hydrogen Bonding in Diethylamine-Alcohol Solutions", J. Chem. Phys., *63*, 608 (1975).

J. Jonas, T. DeFries and D. J. Wilbur, "Molecular Motions in Compressed Liquid Water", J. Chem. Phys., *65*, 582 (1976).

H. Strehlow and J. Frahm, "The Influence of Chemical Exchange on NMR Spin Lattice Relaxation", Ber. Bunsenges. Physik. Chem., *79*, 57 (1975).

A. D. Covington and A. K. Covington, "Nuclear Magnetic Studies of Preferential Solvation. Part 5 - Magnesium Perchlorate in Water and Acetone Mixtures at 185K", J. C. S. Faraday I, *71*, 831 (1975).

Y. M. Cahen, P. R. Handy, E. T. Roach, and A. I. Popov, "Spectroscopic Studies of Ionic Solvation XVI. Lithium-7 and Chlorine-35 Nuclear Magnetic Resonance Studies in Various Solvents", J. Phys. Chem., *79*, 80 (1975).

A. I. Mishustin and Yu. M. Kessler, "Ion-Solvent Molecule Interaction in Nonaqueous Solutions: Spin-Lattice Relaxation Time of ^7Li", J. Sol. Chem., *4*, 779 (1975).

L. Simeral and G. E. Maciel, "Fourier Transform Magnesium-25 Nuclear Magnetic Resonance Study of Aqueous Magnesium (II) Electrolytes", J. Phys. Chem., *80*, 552 (1976).

H. G. Hertz, R. Tutsch, and N. S. Bowan, "Intermolecular and Intramolecular Motions in the Solvation Spheres of Some Ions in Methyl and Ethyl Alcohol", J. Phys, Chem., *80*, 417 (1976).

G. R. Stevenson, and A. E. Alegria, "Rates of Ion Pair Formation and Dissociation and of Electron Exchange Between Free Ion and Neutral Molecule in Hexamethylphosphoramide", J. Phys. Chem., *80*, 69 (1976).

D. Hoel and D. Kivelson, "ESR Linewidths in Solution VII. Nondiffusional Anisotropic Spin-Rotational Contributions in Hydrogen Bonding Solvents", J. Chem. Phys., *62*, 4535 (1975).

L-P. Hwang and J. H. Freed, "Dynamic Effects of Pair Correlation Functions on Spin Relaxation by Translational Diffusion in Liquids", J. Chem. Phys., *63*, 4017 (1975).

J. G. Hexem, U. Edlund, and G. C. Levy, "Paramagnetic Relaxation Reagents as a Probe for Translational Motion of Liquids", J. Chem. Phys., *64*, 936 (1976).

Chapter 14

LIGHT SCATTERING

The last three chapters in Part B all deal with scattering phenomena. Thus there is a considerable amount of analogy in the background for these experimental methods. This analogy is not completely exploited, however, as some differences in the approach to the theory in the three chapters is introduced in order to make the development physically most illustrative. Even whithin this single chapter, the problems are approached in a number of ways.

First the total intensity of scattered light is examined neglecting any frequency shifts or polarization changes. A more refined model is next introduced to describe the spectrum of the polarized (or undepolarized) scattered light, and the depolarized light. An explanation of the line shapes of the scattered light requires introduction of the macroscopic (hydrodynamic) motions present (Chap. 6) as well as the motions of individual molecules (Chap. 7).

A summary of the topics discussed in Sec. 14.1 together with a comparison with the scattering processes in Chaps. 15 and 16 is given in Sec. 14.1(g). Light scattering will be seen to be a method for obtaining information about both the structure and the dynamics of liquids. It will also be seen to have close connections with topics discussed in essentially all the chapters in Part B.

14.1. THEORETICAL BACKGROUND

(a) *Scattering from Single Particles*

The scattering of light by single particles has been considered previously [Sec. 12.1(e)] in connection with Raman scattering. In addition to the appearance of Raman lines, Eq. (12.9) predicts Rayleigh scattering, i.e., scattering with no change in the frequency. Such scattering arises due to the presence of an oscillating induced electric dipole. According to (20.5), such a dipole is the source of radiation for which the magnitude of the electric field varies as $1/r$ (20.40), and as $\sin \alpha$, where α is the angle between the direction of polarization of the incident light and the direction of propagation of the scattered light (Fig. 20.2).

The above aspects can be combined to describe scattering from molecules more completely. It is however here useful to picture the molecule as a sphere radius a, where $a \ll \lambda$. Maxwell's equations (20.3) can be solved for this case of a dielectric sphere in an electric field [1]. The sphere has induced in it a dipole moment

$$\underline{p}_{ind} = 4\pi a^3\left(\frac{n^2 - 1}{n^2 + 2}\right) \varepsilon \bullet \underline{E} = \frac{4}{3}\pi a^3 \underline{P} \tag{14.1}$$

Here n is the refractive index of the sphere relative to the medium. By comparison with (20.8), it can be seen that the polarizability $|\underline{\underline{\alpha}}|$ is $\propto a^3$.

When (14.1) is combined with the considerations in the first paragraph, then the intensity of the scattered wave is given by [2]

$$I_{sc} = I_{inc}\,\frac{16\pi^4 a^6}{r^2\lambda^4}\left(\frac{n^2 - 1}{n^2 + 2}\right)^2 \sin^2\alpha = \frac{\pi^2}{r^2\lambda^4}\,|\underline{\underline{\alpha}}|^2 \sin^2\alpha \tag{14.2}$$

Equation (14.2) can be developed further for various special cases, e.g., polarized incident light, unpolarized incident light, observation restricted to a plane ("scattering plane") etc.

If the spatial configuration of the scattering "spheres" is random, then there is no coherence in the light scattered from different particles. In such a case the intensities rather than the amplitudes of contributions from different particles must be added to obtain the total scattered intensity. From (14.2) it can be seen that the scattering is very sensitive to the size of scattering particles (e.g., dust particles, large molecules, etc. in a liquid). The turbidity b [(14.3), the total scattering by a unit volume] can thus be used as a measure of the "coarseness" of scattering material (Tyndall effect). If V_{sc} is the volume of a scattering particle and n_{sc} is the number density of such scatterers, then

$$b = \frac{24\pi^3 n_{sc} V_{sc}^2}{\lambda^4}\left(\frac{n^2 - 1}{n^2 + 2}\right)^2 \qquad T = \frac{I_{sc}}{I_{inc}} = \exp[-b\ell] \tag{14.3}$$

The optical transmission T has also been defined in (14.3) together with b in terms of the pathlength ℓ.

Instead of the turbidity b, scattering can also be described in terms of the Rayleigh ratio, $R(\theta)$, It is the scattering by a unit volume per unit solid angle in the direction given by the scattering angle θ. This is the angle between the wave vectors of the incident and scattered light (see Fig. 14.1).

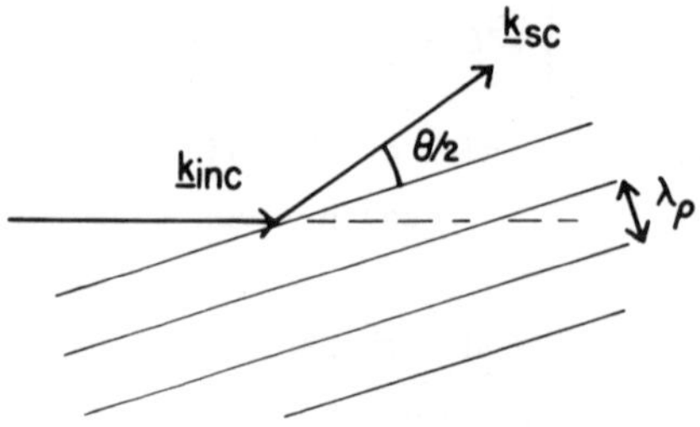

Fig. 14.1. Schematic diagram illustrating Bragg reflection of light from density waves.

$$R(\theta) = \frac{r^2 I_{sc}}{VI_{inc}} = \frac{1}{V}\frac{d\sigma}{d\Omega} \tag{14.4}$$

where σ is the scattering cross-section for the light (20.55). In the case of unpolarized incident light, the Rayleigh ratio can be expressed in terms of turbidity b using (14.2) as

$$R_u(\theta) = \frac{3}{16\pi}\, b(1 + \cos^2\theta) = R_{pol}(\theta) + R_{depol}(\theta) \tag{14.5}$$

In (14.5) the Rayleigh ratio has been subdivided into a polarized (plane of polarization perpendicular to the scattering plane) and a depolarized (plane of polarization in the scattering plane) com ponents. As in the case of Raman scattering [Sec. 12.1(g)], depolarized scattering can be due only to anisotropic parts of the polarizability tensor; polarized scattering can be due to both anisotropic and isotropic (due to the symmetrical part of the polarizability tensor) scattering. These are designated R_{an} and R_{iso}.

In the case of scattering of unpolarized light observed at right angles (i.e., $\theta = 90°$), the relation between R_{iso} and R_{an} can be shown to be

$$R_{iso} = R\,\frac{6 - 7\rho_u}{6 + 6\rho_u} \qquad R_{an} = R\,\frac{13\rho_u}{6 + 6\rho_u} \tag{14.6}$$

Here R is the total measured Rayleigh ratio, and ρ_u is the measured depolarization ratio (R_{depol}/R) for unpolarized incident light. The factor (for 90° only) $(6 + 6\rho_u)/(6 - 7\rho_u)$ is usually called the Cabannes factor C_b. It expresses the factor by which the Rayleigh ratio is enhanced due to the presence of an anisotropy.

It is of interest to note that when a number of molecules (scattering particles) is condensed from gas to a liquid, R_{iso} decreases to only about 5% of its gas-phase value. This is due to pronounced position correlation in the liquid as compared to the gas [see Sec. 14.1(b)]. However, R_{an} does not change much, as the increase in density does not necessarily cause correlation in orientations.

(b) Total Intensity of Scattered Light in Liquids

Since the positions of particles in liquids are by no means random (e.g., Chaps. 2 and 3), then interference effects of light scattered from various parts of the liquid must be taken into account. If the liquid were perfectly homogeneous, then such interference would make the net amplitude of the scattered light at all angles $\theta \neq 0$ disappear. There would in fact then be no scattering. Fluctuations occurring in the liquid give rise to scattering, however.

Such fluctuations can be described by dividing the liquid up into volumes δV. There will then be assumed to be random fluctuations $\delta\varepsilon$ in the permittivity from the average in these volumes. It is sufficient for most cases to assume that the fluctuations $\delta\varepsilon$ arise from random density (and concentration) fluctuations (19.3). These volumes can then be considered as independent scattering particles as in Sec. 14.1(a) with respect to the fluctuation.

A fluctuation $\delta\varepsilon$ in a volume δV can be thought of as giving rise to an induced dipole moment (or polarizability) $\delta \underline{P}$ as in (14.1). According to (20.10),

$$\delta \underline{P} = \delta\varepsilon \cdot \varepsilon^{\bullet} \underline{E} \qquad \delta \underline{p}_{ind} = \delta\varepsilon \cdot \varepsilon^{\bullet} \underline{E} \delta V \tag{14.7}$$

The intensities of the light scattered from the different volumes can be added to get the total scattering as the fluctuations $\delta\varepsilon$ are random. Thus the turbidity b can be obtained directly from (14.3) using (14.1), (14.7), and the following substitutions:

$$n_{sc} \to \frac{1}{\delta V} \qquad V_{sc} \to \delta V \qquad \frac{n^2 - 1}{n^2 + 2} \to \frac{\delta\varepsilon}{3}$$

$$b = \frac{8\pi^3}{3\lambda^4} \langle \delta\varepsilon^2 \rangle \, \delta V \tag{14.8}$$

The result (14.8) must be multiplied by the Cabannes factor C_b, as only isotropic scattering has been allowed for in the argument. For anisotropic scattering, $\delta\varepsilon$ must be considered as a tensor.

Equation (14.8) can be expressed in terms of thermodynamic quantities. If the fluctuations $\delta\varepsilon$ are assumed to be due only to density fluctuations, then using (19.32) to get $\langle \delta V^2 \rangle$, or $\langle \delta\rho^2 \rangle$,

$$b = C_b \frac{8\pi^3}{3\lambda^4} \left(\rho \frac{\partial\varepsilon}{\partial\rho} \right)_T^2 kT\kappa_T$$

or

$$R_u(\theta) = C_b(\theta) \frac{\pi^2}{2\lambda^4} \left(\rho \frac{\partial\varepsilon}{\partial\rho} \right)_T^2 kT\kappa_T (1 + \cos^2 \theta) \tag{14.9}$$

The dependence of $\delta\varepsilon$ on temperature fluctuations has been neglected in (14.9). In two-component systems, fluctuations of $\delta\varepsilon$ due to concentration fluctuations must also be considered. Thus a more complete expression for $\langle \delta\varepsilon^2 \rangle$ would be

$$\langle \delta\varepsilon^2 \rangle = \left(\frac{\partial\varepsilon}{\partial p} \right)_{T,c}^2 \langle \delta\rho^2 \rangle + \left(\frac{\partial\varepsilon}{\partial T} \right)_{\rho,c}^2 \langle \delta T^2 \rangle + \left(\frac{\partial\varepsilon}{\partial c} \right)_{T,\rho}^2 \langle \delta c^2 \rangle \tag{14.10}$$

In (14.10), fluctuations in ρ, T, and c are assumed statistically independent (19.3). Neglect of the second (temperature) term leads to errors of the order of 1% [3]. The third (concentration) term cannot be neglected, especially when $\partial\mu/\partial c$ is small [$\langle \delta c^2 \rangle$ is large (18.44)]. The form of this term has been discussed in Sec. 7.1(f).

(c) Spectrum and Polarization of Scattered Light

In Sec. (b) above the total intensity of scattered light is considered, irrespective of changes in its polarization or its frequency. In this section, a description of the spectrum of undepolarized and depolarized scattered light is given with an emphasis to pointing out the physical basis of the processes. In later parts, more rigorous quantitative descriptions are developed for these phenomena.

As indicated in Sec. (a) above, depolarized scattered light arises from anisotropic parts of the permittivity fluctuations, while undepolarized (or polarized) scattering is due to both isotropic and anisotropic fluctuations. The contributions of the two processes can be separated by subtracting an appropriately scaled amount of the depolarized spectrum from the polarized spectrum to get the isotropic spectrum [e.g., [4], see also Sec. 12.1(g)]. The isotropic scattering and polarized scattering are often considered to be the same, as the correction for depolarized scattering usually is negligible.

(1) Isotropic Scattering

As indicated in Sec. 3.1(c), density fluctuations can be described in terms of the Fourier components. The expansion parameter $\underline{q}$ used can be thought of as being the wave vector corresponding to the dynamical density fluctuations present in a liquid [See Sec. 7.1(d)]. For each $|\underline{q}|$ (in an isotropic medium) there would be a corresponding wavelength $\lambda_\rho = 2\pi q$, a velocity v, a frequency $\nu_\rho = v/\lambda_\rho$. The subscript ρ indicates that the entities refer to the density "waves."

These density variations are at times referred to as "Debye" waves to indicate their analogy to the longitudinal normal vibrations (phonons) present in the Debye theory of solids (18.2). They can also be considered as being spontaneously formed ultrasonic waves, in contrast to the artificially generated ultrasonic waves discussed in Chap. 10. As shown in Sec. (d), there are also present nonpropagating density fluctuations due to the presence of constant pressure density fluctuations as well as the adiabatic (constant entropy) propagating density fluctuations.

As indicated in Sec. 10.2(b), an ultrasonic wave can be considered as being a grating due to the regular compressions and rarefactions present. Light scattering can then be considered to be reflection of light from such a grating when the Bragg reflection condition is fulfilled. At a scattering angle θ as shown in Fig. 14.1 (see page 396) this occurs when (10.50):

$$2\lambda_\rho \sin\frac{\theta}{2} = \lambda_\ell$$

or

$$\omega_\rho = qv = 2\omega_\ell v\left(\frac{n}{c}\right) \sin\frac{\theta}{2} \tag{14.11}$$

In (14.11), the subscript ℓ refers to the light.

In (14.11), it has also been assumed that $|k_{inc}| = |\underline{k}_{sc}|$, i.e., that the change in momentum is essentially due only to change in direction. This means $|\underline{q}| = |\underline{k}_{inc} - \underline{k}_{sc}| = (4\pi \sin\frac{\theta}{2})/\lambda_\rho$. The process can be thought of as being a "photon-phonon" interaction. This also implies an energy exchange is possible, i.e., a shift in frequency of the photon. Such a shift is very small, however, so that $|\underline{k}_{inc}| = |\underline{k}_{sc}|$ is still a good approximation.

The change in frequency can also be viewed as a Doppler effect. The "grating" is moving with a speed v. Thus the lines scattered from this grating have frequencies $\omega_{inc} \pm vq$. A "Mandelshtam-Brillouin" doublet is then expected. Usually such a shift $\Delta\tilde{\nu}_{MB}$ is from 0.1 to 2 cm^{-1}.

Such "gratings" have, however, also a finite lifetime due to the absorption of ultrasonic waves. In Chap. 10, this was described by the pressure absorption coefficient α. In MB scattering it is usually described by the "lifetime" Γ of the wave ($\Gamma = \alpha v^3/\omega^2$). The larger the absorption, the less sharp the "grating" and the broader the MB components.

Thus the isotropic (polarized) spectrum consists of a central Rayleigh line and two MB components. The difference in frequency $\Delta\nu_{MB}$ between the central Rayleigh line and the two MB components depends on the velocity of the spontaneous ultrasonic waves present. The half-width $\delta\nu_{MB}$ depends on the absorption coefficient for these waves. The half-width $\Delta\nu_c$ of the central component is dependent on the thermal conductivity and heat capacity of the liquid [Sec. (d)]. The ratio of intensity between the central and the two MB lines $I_c/2I_{MB}$ is normally given by the Landau-Placzek ratio, $(C_p - C_v)/C_v = (\kappa_T - \kappa_S)/\kappa_S$.

(2) Anisotropic (Depolarized) Scattering

The depolarized scattering is dependent on the orientational properties of the molecules. It generally consists of a broad unshifted line, the "Rayleigh" wing. This can have a half-width $\delta\tilde{\nu}_{RW}$ of the order of 10 cm^{-1}, i.e., of the order of $\Delta\tilde{\nu}_{MB}$. It is thought to arise from the orientational fluctuations of anisotropic molecules. A Rayleigh wing is, however, also present in isotropic molecules(e.g., CCl_4 [5]) due to collision-induced anisotropy. It can be thought of as arising from the spontaneous fluctuation of the polarization, in contrast to the artificially generated polarization as described in Chap. 11.

On top of the Rayleigh wing there can occur a "diffuse line" or sharp component. The origin of this line is believed to be orientational relaxation arising from tumbling of uncorrelated molecules [6]. This is in contrast to the momentary fluctuations from orientational equilibrium giving rise to the broad Rayleigh wing. The interpretation of these two features in depolarized scattering have not been definitively explained as yet, however (see also "Further Recent References").

(d) Scattering in Terms of S(q,ω)

The approach taken by Mountain [7] is outlined here to arrive at the structure factor $S(q,\omega)$ (7.11) for light scattered isotropically. Such a development can also be found in [8]. It is based on a solution of Maxwell's equations (20.3) written for the appropriate situation.

A dipole moment density or polarization $\underline{P}(\underline{r},t)$ can be written for the liquid as (the symbol $\underline{r}$ is used to indicate distance within the scattering volume, $\underline{\mathrm{r}}$ will be used to denote distance from this volume)

$$\begin{aligned}\underline{P}(\underline{r},t) &= \alpha\varepsilon^{\bullet}\underline{E}_{inc}(\underline{r},t)\Sigma\delta(\underline{r}_j(t) - \underline{r}) \\ &= \alpha\varepsilon^{\bullet}\underline{E}_{inc}\cdot n(\underline{r},t) \qquad (14.12)\end{aligned}$$

Here the δ function definition of the density has been used (7.6). This time dependent polarization is then considered as a current, $(1/c)\partial \underline{P}/\partial t$, which is the source term for the scattered field. Application of Maxwell's equations (20.3) then results in the wave equation for the scattered field:

$$\nabla^2 \underline{\mathcal{D}} - \frac{\varepsilon}{c^2}\frac{\partial^2 \underline{\mathcal{D}}}{\partial t^2} = \frac{\varepsilon}{c^2}\frac{\partial^2 \underline{P}}{\partial t^2} \tag{14.13}$$

A non-magnetic system ($\mu = 1$) with no free charges ($\rho = 0$) is assumed.

The incident light is assumed to be in the form of a plane monochromatic wave, i.e.,

$$\underline{E}_{inc}(\underline{r},t) = \underline{E}_{inc} \exp[i\underline{k}_{inc}\cdot\underline{r} - \omega_{inc}t] \tag{14.14}$$

Then the solution is sought for the scattered radiation with frequency ω_{sc} and $k_{sc}^2 = \omega_{sc}\varepsilon/c^2$. As $\underline{E}_{inc}(\underline{r},t)$ varies much more rapidly than $n(\underline{r},t)$, then (14.13) can be written as

$$\nabla^2 \underline{\mathcal{D}} + k_{sc}^2 \underline{\mathcal{D}} = -\frac{\omega_{inc}^2 \varepsilon\varepsilon^\bullet}{c^2} \underline{E}_{inc} \exp[i(\underline{k}_{inc}\cdot\underline{r} - \omega_{inc}t)]\Sigma\delta(\underline{r}_j(t) - \underline{r}) \tag{14.15}$$

A solution of (14.15) can be found for $\underline{E}_{sc}(\underline{r},t)$ at a distance $\underline{r}$ outside the scattering volume:

$$\underline{E}_{sc}(\underline{r},t) = -\frac{\omega_{inc}^2 \alpha\varepsilon^\bullet}{c^2}\frac{\exp[ik_{inc}r]}{4\pi r}\underline{E}_{inc}\Sigma\exp[i(q\cdot\underline{r}_j(t) - \omega_{inc}t)] \tag{14.16}$$

The previous definition of $\underline{q}$ has been used, i.e., $\underline{q} = k_{inc} - \underline{k}_{sc}$; $q \simeq 2k_{inc} \sin\frac{\theta}{2}$.

The observable quantity is the intensity in a frequency interval $d\omega$ and an angle interval $d\Omega$. It can be written as

$$I(\omega)\, d\omega = \left(\frac{\omega_{inc}^2 \alpha\varepsilon^\bullet \sin\alpha}{4\pi r c^2}\right)^2 E_{inc}^2 \langle|E(\omega)|^2\rangle\, d\omega \tag{14.17}$$

Here α is the angle between $\underline{E}_{inc}$ and $\underline{k}_{sc}$ and $\langle|E(\omega)|^2\rangle$ is

$$<|E(\omega)|^2> = \frac{1}{2\pi} \int_{-\infty}^{\infty} <E(0)\cdot E(t)> \exp[-i\omega t]\, dt \tag{14.18}$$

Equation (14.18) can be arrived at through an analysis analogous to that in (21.4).

Combination of (14.18) and (14.16) then leads to a normalized intensity distribution

$$\frac{d\sigma}{d\omega} d\omega = \frac{I(\omega)}{I_{inc}} d\omega = \left(\frac{\omega_{inc}^2 \alpha\varepsilon^{\bullet} \sin\alpha}{4\pi r c^2}\right)^2 \frac{1}{2\pi} \int_{-\infty}^{\infty} \exp[-i(\omega_{sc} - \omega_{inc})t]\, dt$$

$$\cdot <\sum_j \exp[i\underline{q}\cdot\underline{r}_j(0)] \sum_{\ell} \exp[-i\underline{q}\cdot\underline{r}_{\ell}(t)]> d\omega \tag{14.19}$$

When Eqs. (7.1), (7.10) and (7.11) are now introduced, then

$$\frac{d\sigma}{d\omega} = \left(\frac{\omega_{inc}^2 \alpha\varepsilon^{\bullet} \sin\alpha}{4\pi r c^2}\right)^2 S(q,\omega) \tag{14.20}$$

This assumes a value of q as specified by $\sin^2 \alpha$ and $S(q,\omega)$. The dependence of σ on q is described through the $\sin^2 \alpha$.

The above theory is quite general and can also be applied with some modification to X-rays and neutrons. For X-ray and light scattering, the relation between q and θ is simply $q = 2k \sin\frac{\theta}{2}$ as $|\underline{k}_{inc}| \simeq |\underline{k}_{sc}|$. In the case of neutrons the relationship is more complex. It is also not as yet specific to liquids, as no model of the liquid has been introduced.

(e) The Shapes of the CR and MB Components

(1) Density Fluctuations

The scattering law $S(q,\omega)$ for density fluctuations was derived in Sec. 7.1(e) for the case of the hydrodynamic region. Figure 14.2 shows the $S(q,\omega)$ vs $\omega(q = \text{constant})$ for this case (7.15). Here q is small, as hydrodynamic considerations are valid only in the long wavelength region. For the short wavelength region (i.e., as $q \to \infty$) the $S(q,\omega)$ characteristic of gaslike motion is obtained. This is a Lorentzian centered at $\omega = \omega_{inc}$ with a width at half-height $\delta\omega = q\sqrt{kT/m}$.

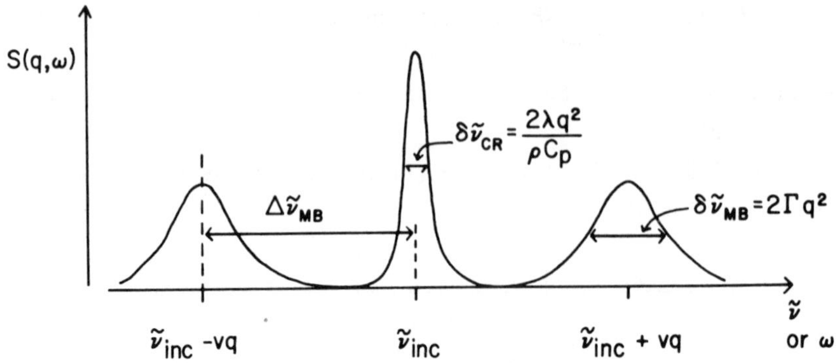

Fig. 14.2. Schematic diagram illustrating the scattering law for isotropic scattering in the hydrodynamic region. $S(q,\omega)$ is shown as a function of ω with q = constant = $(4\pi/\lambda) \sin (\theta/2)$.

(2) Presence of Relaxations

It is often the case that v is dependent upon q. Such a dispersion is indicative of the presence of an equilibrium in the system which has a relaxation frequency in the region of vq. The presence of such an internal relaxation [usually vibrational relaxation; Sec. 10.3(a)] has other effects on the scattering spectrum as well.

The ratio $I_{CR}/2I_{MB}$ becomes greater than $\gamma - 1$ and a broad additional Rayleigh component appears. The half-width of this quasi-elastic component is of the order of $1/\tau$ (for $vq\tau \simeq 1$), where τ is the relaxation time of the process. The shapes of the MB lines also show asymmetry.

(3) Concentration Fluctuations

As indicated in (14.10), concentration fluctuations can also give rise to light scattering. This can result in an increased intensity in the central Rayleigh line as indicated by the simplified argument given below which neglects cross-terms between density and concentration fluctuations.

In Sec. 7.1(f) the form of the scattering law due to concentration fluctuations was obtained (7.18). Such fluctuations contribute to scattering proportional to

$$S_c(q,\omega) = \left(\frac{\partial\varepsilon}{\partial c}\right)^2_{p,T}\left(\frac{kT}{(\partial\mu/\partial c)_{p,T}}\right)\frac{2Dq^2}{(Dq^2)^2 + \omega^2} \tag{14.21}$$

The q dependence of $S_c(q,\omega)$ has not been specified completely [see Sec. 14.3(g)]. The intensities of the MB components are not affected. The width may increase through an increase in Γ, however,[i.e., α; see Sec. 10.3(c)].

Relation (14.21) can be exploited to study critical phenomena in mixtures. There $\langle\delta c^2\rangle$ is larger and concentration fluctuations dominate the central Rayleigh line. The half-width of the CR line should then decrease as T_c is approached [i.e., as $D \to 0$; Sec. 9.3 (e)]. The angular dependence of the half-width would be dependent on $\sin^2 \frac{\theta}{2}$.

Light scattering from concentration fluctuations can also be employed to study the thermodynamics of liquid mixtures. Values of the ratio $I_{CR}/2I_{MB}$ are dependent on $\partial\mu/\partial c$. Thus $\partial\mu/\partial c$ can be determined, as $\partial\varepsilon/\partial c$ can be obtained through independent measurement. If relaxation is present, then the analysis can be complicated [9].

(f) Line Shape for Depolarized Scattering

The major features of the depolarized scattering are a sharp or diffuse line on a very broad background (Rayleigh wing). A dip or "hole" has also been observed in the center in the case of liquids with large polar molecules. An explanation of such structure in terms of a macroscopic, hydrodynamic model as in Sec. 7.1(e) is inadequate. Reorientation of single molecules must be considered if the diffuse line is to be explained.

Numerous explanations have recently been suggested for the shape of the depolarized scattering (e.g., Refs. 7,5,6,10). Here some of the aspects which seem to have reasonably good credibility will be discussed. Many aspects are however not well understood as yet [5].

(1) Anisotropic Molecules

In the case of liquids with anisotropic molecules, the shape of the diffuse (sharp) line is determined as for depolarized Raman scattering.

It could loosely be equated to a type of anisotropic "Raman" scattering without a vibrational transition taking place. The intensity $I(\omega)$ is then [see also Sec. 12.1(h)] the Fourier transform of the time correlation function of the polarizability anisotropy. Assuming that the orientational motions of neighboring molecules are unrelated, the line shape is then given as in Sec. 12.1(h), i.e., as

$$I(\omega) \propto \int_{-\infty}^{\infty} \langle \underline{\underline{\beta}}(0):\underline{\underline{\beta}}(t)\rangle \exp[i\omega t]\, dt \propto \int G_2(t) \exp[i\omega t]\, dt \qquad (14.22)$$

Without the assumption of unrelated motion, the summation in the averaging in (7.40) must also be taken in pairs over all the molecules in the region illuminated.

Thus depolarized light and Raman scattering, and NMR [Sec. 13.1 (f)] all lead to information regarding $G_2(t)$. Knowledge about $G_1(t)$ can be obtained from dielectric relaxation (Chap. 11), and far infrared (Chap. 12) and infrared (Chap. 12) absorption. Some of the inaccuracies which can arise from the simplifying assumptions made in relating data obtained using these methods to $G_1(t)$ and $G_2(t)$ are discussed in Ref. 11. In many cases it is furthermore assumed that $G_1(t)$ and $G_2(t)$ are exponential, with characteristic times τ_1 and τ_2.

The broad background (Rayleigh wing) is possibly due to spontaneous orientational fluctuations. These can then lead to collective orientational modes (shearlike waves) just as spontaneous density fluctuations lead to collective modes (ultrasonic waves). As the lifetime of such orientational modes is very short, then a broad line is expected [12]. An explanation in terms of arguments centered on collisions is given for the broad background in [13].

(2) Isotropic Molecules

Explanation of depolarized scattering from liquids composed of isotropic molecules involves added complications. Collision-induced molecular anisotropy must be considered, but it is usually sufficient to consider only binary collision [5,14]. The processes giving rise to depolarized light scattering are the same as those giving rise to dielectric [Sec. 11.3(a)] and far infrared [Sec. 12.3(b)] absorption in such systems.

The Rayleigh wing can be explained [5] in terms of a collision model. The change in the pair polarizability anisotropy $\underline{\underline{\beta}}$ on a binary head-on collision is set proportional to the repulsive part of the intermolecular force. For a Lennard-Jones potential, then $\beta(t) \propto r^{-13}(t)$, where the time-dependence of β and the intermolecular distance $\underline{r}$ has been emphasized. As $I(\omega)$ is the Fourier transform of the time correlation function of the anisotropy, then [5]:

$$I(\omega) = \int_0^{\infty} \left| \int_{-\infty}^{\infty} \beta(t) \exp[i\omega t]\, dt \right|^2 g(v)\, dv \propto \omega^{12/7} \exp[-\frac{\omega}{\omega_a}] \quad (14.23)$$

$g(v)dv$ is the distribution of head-on collisions with relative velocity v. The frequency ω_a can be calculated from intermolecular potential data. A shift is predicted of the scattered spectrum to higher frequencies as temperature rises (for isotropic molecules) [13].

There are indications that such liquids (e.g., CCl_4) also contain a diffuse line, Lorentzian in shape [5]. This is related to the dielectric relaxation found in such liquids. No explanation is offered for the origin of this feature in isotropic liquids.

(g) Comparison of Scattering Processes

As can be seen from Sec. 14.1(c), scattering can be considered as the transfer of a quantum of momentum $\hbar\underline{q}$ and/or energy $\hbar\omega$ with the system investigated. The general relationship is given in (14.20). A transfer $\hbar\omega$ can be detected by a shift in the energy (frequency) of the incoming radiation. A transfer $\hbar\underline{q}$ can be detected through the scattering angle if $|k_{sc}| \simeq |k_{inc}|$.

The range of momentum transfer possible in a scattering experiment determines the range of distances for which the structure can be elucidated. The range of energy transfer $\hbar\omega$ determines the range of time scale for which the dynamics can be elucidated. This arises from the Fourier transform relationships [Sec. 7.1(d)]. The approximate ranges of $\hbar q$ and $\hbar\omega$ which can experimentally be realized for different types of scattering are summarized in Table 14.1. Some scattering

TABLE 14.1

Comparison of Scattering Processes

Radiation	Incident		Transferred		Information Scale	
	Energy (cm^{-1})	Momentum ($Å^{-1}$)	Energy (cm^{-1})	Momentum ($Å^{-1}$)	Time (sec)	Distance (Å)
Light						
(i) MB	10^5(~10 eV)	10^{-3}	10^{-2}	10^{-3}	10^{-9}	10^4
(ii) CR	10^5(~10 eV)	10^{-3}	10^{-3}	10^{-3}	10^{-8}	10^4
(iii) D	10^5(~10 eV)	10^{-3}	1	10^{-3}	10^{-11}	10^4
(iv) RW	10^5(~10 eV)	10^{-3}	10	10^{-3}	10^{-12}	10^4
X-rays	10^8 (~10 keV)	1	Not observable	1		10
Neutrons as waves	0.1→100 meV 0.8→800 cm^{-1}	5	0.4→800	0.1→10	10^{-11}→10^{-14}	1→100

processes (e.g., electrons, γ-rays) are not included in the table. The data in the table is meant only to give orders of magnitude.

It can be seen that both structure and dynamics in liquids can be investigated through neutron- and light scattering. Highly monochromatic sources and frequency sensitive detectors are now available to measure the small $\hbar\omega$ in light [Sec. 14.2(b),(c)]. However, the energy transferred in X-ray scattering is small as compared to the band width (energy uncertainty) in the incident X-ray. Thus dynamical information cannot be obtained through X-ray scattering. The bandwidth of the incident neutron radiation can be reduced to 0.4 cm^{-1}, allowing for a wide range in study of dynamics.

14.2. EXPERIMENTAL TECHNIQUES

Most of the techniques used for light scattering are described in Ref. 3. Such techniques can be separated into two groups: Those for measuring absolute or relative intensities with no spectral resolution, and those for measuring line shapes and relative line intensities. In all cases the samples must be carefully prepared to prevent Tyndall scattering from dust particles.

(a) Measurement of Total Intensity

Many studies of light scattering are made to obtain simply the Rayleigh ratio at constant scattering angle, usually 90°. In other cases, especially in "classical" studies of critical phenomena, the scattering angle is also allowed to vary. Examples of such a "classical" apparatus, (i.e., where only total intensity is measured) are described in Ref. 3.

A quartz mercury lamp is often used as a light source, but recently constructed apparatus usually have a laser as a light source. When a quartz lamp is used, it is necessary to have a light condenser and a monochrometer. Detection of the scattered light can be made with a photomultiplier or photographic plates.

In highly turbid systems such as mixtures near the critical point, multiple scattering can cause errors in interpretation. To avoid this, the path length of the light in the cell must be minimized. The choice of a long wavelength also reduces the problem, as the scattering is $\propto 1/\lambda^4$.

Absolute values of the intensity of scattered light can be obtained by reference to a calibration standard. An absolute standard can be obtained by, e.g., replacing the scattering cell by a mirror, and measuring the intensity of the reflected light. The incident light can then be attenuated by known amounts. Such a calibration comparison can be made simultaneously with the scattering experiment.

(b) Fabry-Perot Interferometers

A simple method of studying Mandelshtam-Brillouin scattering in particular is through the use of a Fabry-Perot interferometer. The optical pathlength in the interferometer is varied by varying the pressure of the gas within it (usually argon), giving a variation in n. Figure 14.3 shows an example of such an apparatus [15]. The spectrum is scanned as the gas is slowly leaked into the spectrometer.

Other scanning methods are also available, e.g., a piezoelectric scan, where a confocal Fabry-Perot is used. Brillouin scattering has also been studied using gratings or prisms as dispersing media. Photographic detection is also at times used instead of photoelectric [3].

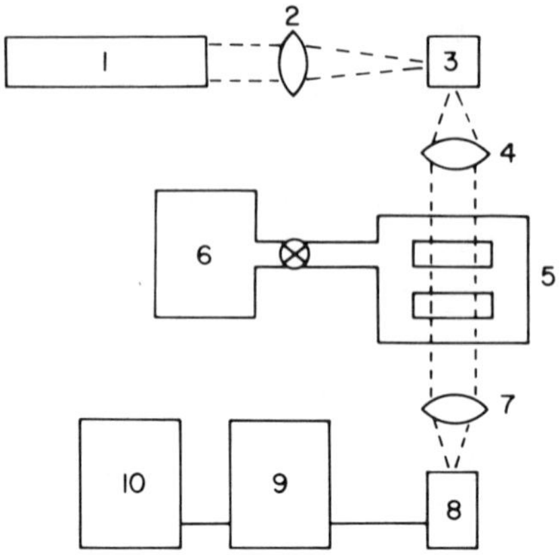

Fig. 14.3. Schematic diagram illustrating a pressure scan Fabry-Perot interferometer. (1) Laser, (2, 4, 7) lenses, (3) sample, (5) plane Fabry-Perot interferometer, (6) gas supply with leak valve, (8) phototube, (9) photon counter, (10) recorder. After Ref. 15.

The pressure swept Fabry-Perot is however the most common type of instrument.

Just as in the case of Raman scattering [Sec. 12.1(h)] it is possible to obtain stimulated Brillouin, central Rayleigh and Rayleigh wing scattering if high power lasers are used [16]. In such experiments, it is usual to use Fabry-Perot interferometers with photographic detection. Such stimulated emission has not been studied quantitatively in many systems [16].

(c) Hetero- and Homodyne Beat Methods

The line shape of the central Rayleigh line cannot be resolved well with the methods mentioned in Sec. (b) above. "Beating" methods have been developed recently which make such high resolution studies possible.

In heterodyne methods, the incident light is split into two. One part is sent directly to the detector (photocell) while the other is sent to the same detector after scattering. The beat (difference) and sum frequencies will then be obtained as the output of the photocell. Thus $\omega_{sc} - \omega_{inc}$ can be obtained directly instead of as the difference between two large quantities.

Figure 14.4 shows such a heterodyne spectrometer [17]. It is somewhat more sophisticated than the simple version described above. The beat frequency would normally be around zero, causing difficulties in detection. Thus the reference line frequency is shifted by a constant amount to make the beat frequency occur in the RF range. Such a shift is caused by sending the light through a "Bragg tank." This is a tank of water into which ultrasonic waves with a frequency in the RF region are passed, causing a "Doppler" effect as indicated in Sec. 14.1(c).

In a homodyne spectrometer, the scattered light alone falls on a phototube. The fluctuations in the current I(t) is then obtained. By a transform (14.18), the spectrum $I(\omega)$ can then be obtained. The theory behind this method is outlined in [18]. Apparata can be constructed which can be operated either as a homo- or heterodyne spectrometer, e.g., [19].

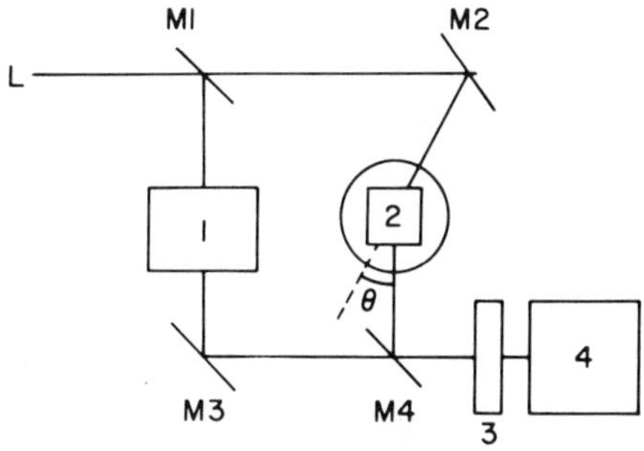

Fig. 14.4. Schematic diagram illustrating a heterodyne spectrometer. (L) Laser (6328Å He-Ne), (M1, M2, M3, M4) mirrors, (1) Bragg tank, (2) sample cell, (3) 6328Å filter, (4) photomultiplier. After Ref. 17.

14.3. RESULTS FOR SPECIFIC SYSTEMS

(a) Total Scattering Intensity in Liquids

Many experimental studies have been made of the Einstein-Smoluchowski-Cabannes (ESC) relation (14.9), especially for water [20,21]. The agreement is within experimental error (±2%) when experimental values of $\partial\varepsilon/\partial\rho$ and κ are used. Other methods of testing (14.9) also lead to good agreement between theory and experiment [2].

The ESC relation assumes scattering only from density fluctuations. Scattering due to fluctuations in the degree of association (at constant temperature) can be considered as an additional source of scattering in H-bonded liquids. This would lead to an elucidation of water structure from light scattering. Calculations show, however, that such an effect would increase the scattering intensity by amounts less than experimental error [21]. Thus no new information about water structure can be obtained from such studies.

The depolarization ratio ρ_u of liquids is intimately related to the polarizability tensor [22] and the Kerr constant [23] for liquids. Thus molecular theories developed for light scattering are also applicable to the Kerr effect [Sec. 11.1(f)]. Thus for nonpolar liquids, the Kerr constant B has contributions from the dielectric anisotropy fluctuation (B_{an}) and from hyperpolarizability. A reasonably reliable [23] relation is available between B_{an} and ρ_u, the depolarization ratio. Thus from measurements of ρ_u and the total Kerr constant, it is possible to obtain values for the hyperpolarizability [Sec. 1.1(c)].

(b) Relaxation in Pure Liquids

As indicated in Sec. 10.3(a), the excess ultrasonic absorption in pure unassociated liquids in the MHz region is believed due to a vibrational-translational equilibrium. In most liquids, the frequency where this process shows relaxation is above the frequencies attainable by standard ultrasonic apparata. Brillouin scattering studies extend the frequency range possible for these studies.

Figure 14.5 shows examples of experimental traces showing MB lines obtained through a pressure-scanned Fabry-Perot [24]. It is

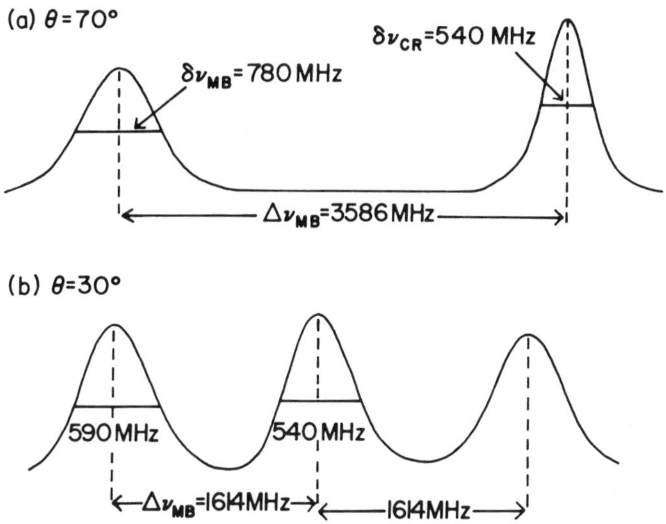

Fig. 14.5. Brillouin spectra in Toluene at 22°C at two scattering angles: (a) 70 deg., (b) 30 deg. The instrumental width is 500 MHz. Only the antistokes MB line is shown in (a), while both antistokes and stokes lines are shown in (b). After Ref. 24.

for liquid toluene at 20°C. The instrumental width contributes about 500 MHz to the line widths, but the increase in $\delta\nu_{MB}$ at higher frequencies (larger scattering angles) is evident.

Such experimental line shapes must be corrected for instrumental linewidth before analysis to obtain v (from $\Delta\nu_{MB}$) and α (from $\delta\nu_{MB}$). An analysis of precise results for CS_2 [25] gives results in agreement with the extensive ultrasonic results available. At the frequencies attainable (1.7 to 6 GHz) no dispersion is seen, and only a very slight decrease in the already low α/ν_ρ^2 with ν_ρ. This indicates that the total vibrational specific heat does indeed relax at lower (~70 MHz) frequencies with a single relaxation time.

Brillouin scattering studies of benzene show that a minimum of two vibrational relaxation times are present. (2.98×10^{-10} and 3.6×10^{-11} sec at 25°C). This is shown in the absorption and dispersion curves in Figure 14.6 where a fit cannot be obtained with single-relaxation equations (10.24). This is an agreement with the results obtained from ultrasonic data [Sec. 10.3(b)].

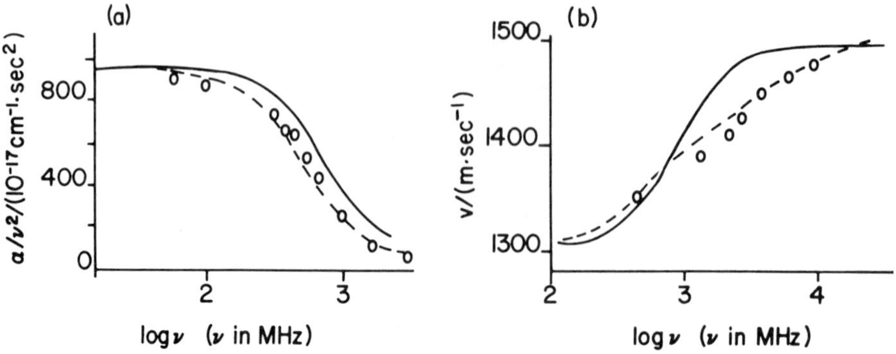

Fig. 14.6. Ultra and hypersonic (a) absorption and (b) dispersion in benzene at 25°C. —— Show fits assuming a single relaxation time (ν_c = 675 MHz) and --- show fits assuming two relaxations at 447 and 4300 MHz. Experimental uncertainty is shown by the size of the points. After Ref. 26.

Results of Brillouin scattering in pure liquids is further discussed in Ref. 27. Vibrational relaxation is also observed in the GHz range for otner unassociated liquids, e.g., CCl_4, C_6H_{12}. A second high frequency relaxation near the GHz range has been found in carboxylic acids [28]. It is believed to be due to a monomer-dimer equilibrium or some other association equilibrium which involves the breaking of only one H-bond. A relaxation observed in acrylic monomers (e.g., cyclohexyl methacrylate) is, however, ascribed to a rotational isomerism equilibrium involving the ester group about a C-C bond [29]. In monatomic liquids such as argon, the velocity of hypersound up to 3 GHz agrees with the velocity of ultrasound as measured at lower frequency. Thus, as expected, no relaxation process with a relaxation time $\gtrsim 10^{-12}$ sec is present [27].

(c) *Orientational Relaxation in Anisotropic Liquids*

The Rayleigh peak of the polarized (VV) scattering shown in Fig. 14.5, also contains contributions from anisotropic scattering (12.13). This is not apparent in Fig. 14.5, but is clearly shown in Fig. 14.7, which shows the polarized (VV) and depolarized (VH) spectra for a liquid made up of highly asymmetric molecules, quinoline (C_9H_7N).

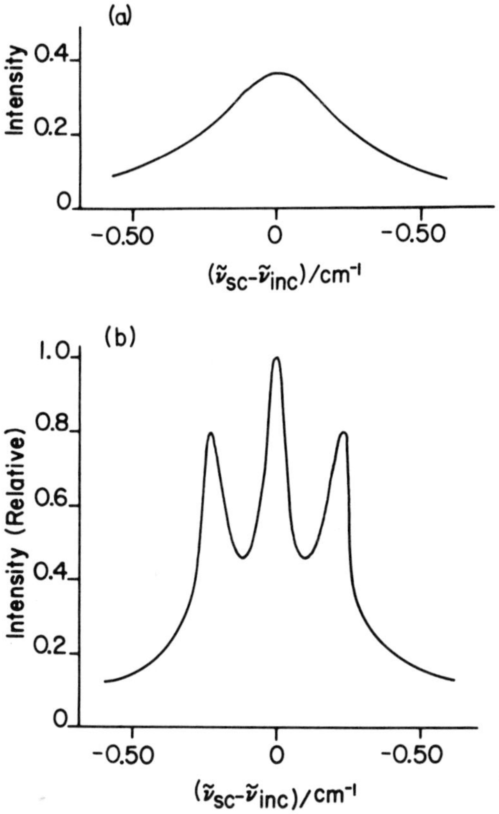

Fig. 14.7. Light scattering spectra from quinoline at 45°C and θ = 90 deg. showing (a) the depolarized (VH) spectrum and (b) the undepolarized (VV) spectrum. The VH spectrum contains a broad background and a diffuse line assumed to be Lorentzian with $\delta\tilde{\nu}$ = .248 cm^{-1}. The VV spectrum has the same two components as in the VH spectrum and, in addition, the central Rayleigh and the Mandelshtam-Brillouin doublet with $\delta\tilde{\nu}_{MB}$ = .012 cm^{-1}. The depolarization ratio for the anisotropically scattered light is according to theory 0.75 (12.13). After Ref. 6.

As indicated in Sec. 14.1(f)(1), the depolarized spectrum is composed of a broad background and a sharp (diffuse) line related to orientational motion. In fairly dilute solutions of anisotropic molecules, the diffuse line is a single Lorentzian, as the orientation is due essentially only to single particle motion. Thus analysis can be made of the line shape to obtain $G_2(t)$ (14.22) or simply the line width to obtain an orientational relaxation time.

In concentrated solutions and pure liquids, correlation of motions of different molecules becomes important and the spectrum becomes more complicated. Typically the spectrum is composed of broad doublets with an intensity minimum at the exciting frequency [30]. Such complications arising in the depolarized spectrum of anisotropic liquids can be explained from two points of view: The microscopic e.g., Refs. 10 and 12, and the hydrodynamic, e.g., in Ref. 7. Experimental results are in reasonable agreement with predictions of both theories [30].

(1) Orientational Relaxation Times in Solutions

Several interesting aspects can be illustrated by a study of solutions of nitrobenzene [31]. The single molecule reorientation correlation time can be obtained by examining the spectrum as a function of concentration and extrapolating to zero concentration. The single-particle correlation time is obtained from NMR spin lattice relaxation no matter what the concentration [Sec. 13.3(a)], but this NMR time may still be concentration dependent due to viscosity or association effects. These are not the same times, however, as the light-scattering time is most heavily weighted by the orientational axis which causes the greatest change in polarization. The ^{13}C spin lattice relaxation is due to intramolecular dipole-dipole (C-H) relaxation, and is most strongly weighted by the axis which reorients the C-H bond most rapidly.

The results of the nitrobenzene study show the relaxation time to vary linearly with solution viscosity. The τ_{NMR} is shorter than τ_{LS} and is less dependent on viscosity. The concentration dependence of τ_{NMR} suggests the presence of dimers with a lifetime of the order of τ_{NMR}, i.e., $\simeq 10 \times 10^{-12}$ sec [31].

The depolarized light-scattering spectrum can also be used to measure rotational diffusion coefficients of macromolecules in solution [32]. Assuming Brownian rotational motion [Sec. 6.1(e)], the half-width of the depolarized (diffuse) line can be interpreted in analogy with translational diffusion (7.18). Analysis of the depolarized spectrum of lysozyme in a sodium-acetate- acetic acid buffer solution thus yields a value $D_r = 17 \times 10^6$ sec. Assuming (6.13) and (6.62) to hold, then an effective size can be calculated for the lysozyme. Experimental values of D, the translational diffusion coefficient, also obtained from linewidth measurements [Eq. (7.18); Sec. 14.3(e)] give another effective size. On the basis of these data, the lysozyme is in solution in the form of a prolate with principal axes 55 Å, 33 Å, 33 Å.

(2) Orientational Time Correlation Functions

If the line shape of the depolarized scattered line is known to sufficient accuracy, then the time correlation function $G_2(t)$ can be obtained as a function of time. Such analysis has been carried out on scattering from liquid benzene [33].

Before Fourier analysis of the depolarized band shape (14.22) the experimental shape must be corrected for instrumental effects. The contributions to the spectrum of collisional effects [Sec. 14.3 (d)] must also be subtracted. Figure 14.8 shows the magnitude of the contribution of the collision effect. The Fourier transform then gives $G_2(t)$ for benzene (Fig. 14.9).

The short-time behavior of $G_2(t)$ approximates a "free rotor" behavior. Departures from this occur at $t \simeq 10^{-13}$ sec, indicating an average angular motion of 15 degrees before an interaction changes the motion considerably. For $t \gtrsim 1.5 \times 10^{-12}$ sec, the motion is rotational diffusion as log $G_2(t)$ is linear with t.

The intermediate time region can be investigated further by constructing an angular velocity correlation function (the transform of $\omega^2 I(\omega)$). A negative peak is observed at $t \simeq 0.2 \times 10^{-12}$ sec for benzene at 76°C. This indicates that collisions are not totally randomizing the angular velocity but are reversing it. Figure 7.3 shows the analogous effect for translational velocity.

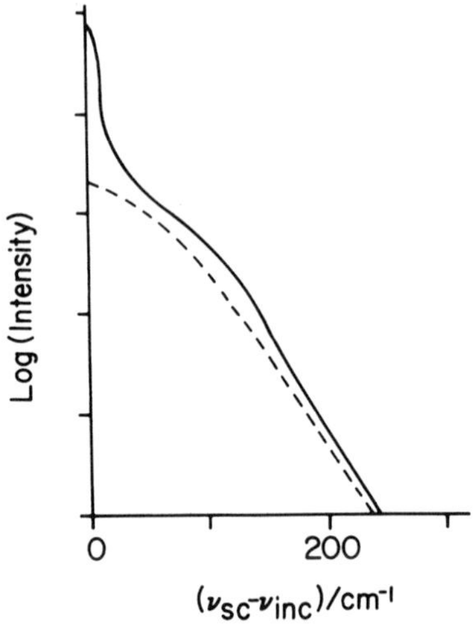

Fig. 14.8. Log (intensity) of the depolarized scattering from benzene at 20°C. —— Experimental spectrum, --- estimated collisional spectrum. After Ref. 33.

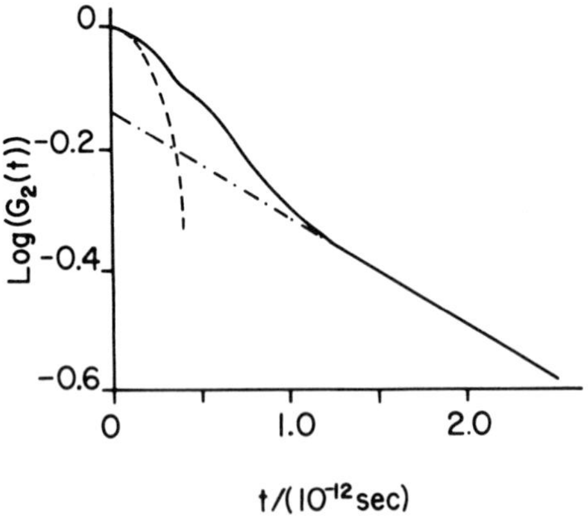

Fig. 14.9. Log $(G_2(t))$ vs t for benzene at 20°C. —— Experimental curve, --- free rotor decay, —·—· exponential decay. After Ref. 33.

(d) Depolarized Scattering in Isotropic Liquids

As indicated in (14.22), the depolarized line shape can be considered as approximating the Fourier transform of the time correlation $G_2(t)$. More generally it can be said to be the time correlation of the anisotropic part of the polarizability. This anisotropy can be permanent, or induced through collisions.

The experimental spectrum for CCl_4 can be resolved into a Lorentzian contribution and a collisional contribution. The Lorentzian is the Fourier transform of an exponential function. Thus it can be thought to represent light scattering from a relaxational process. This would be basically the same process as the dielectric relaxation present in nonpolar liquids, in which case the time correlation of the induced dipole is involved. The process is discussed for benzene in Sec. 11.3(a) (Fig. 11.8). A similar tan δ vs log $\tilde{\nu}$ graph has been obtained for CCl_4 [5] (Fig. 14.10). The collision function $C_2(\omega)$ is given by (14.23), and is calculated by computer.

If dispersion is ignored, then the loss tangent expressed in terms of permanent or collision-induced dipole correlation functions is

$$\tan \delta \propto \left(1 - \exp\left[-\frac{\hbar\omega}{kT}\right]\right) \int_{-\infty}^{\infty} \langle \underline{p}(0)\cdot\underline{p}(t)\rangle \exp[i\omega t]\, dt \qquad (14.24)$$

Thus a comparison of the dipole and the polarizability dynamics involves a comparison of tan δ with $I(\omega) \times (1 - \exp[-\hbar\omega/kT])$ (14.22). This is shown for CCl_4 in Fig. 14.10. The agreement is qualitatively satisfactory. Consideration of intercollisional effects improves the agreement [5].

These phenomena have been further investigated [11,13], mostly by study of the temperature dependence of the spectrum and moment analysis. There does not seem to be complete clarification of the phenomena responsible for depolarized light scattering as yet (see "Further Recent References"). Recent experimental results on five molecular liquids [34] cannot distinguish between the **validity** of the predictions of the theories available [5,14]. However, molecular

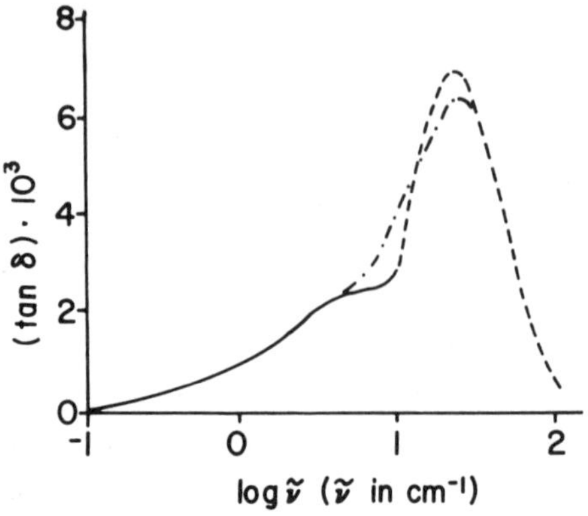

Fig. 14.10. Tan δ vs $\tilde{\nu}$ for carbon tetrachloride at 20°C. —— Microwave (dielectric) absorption, --- infrared absorption, —·—· light scattering. After Ref. 5.

dynamics calculations of collision-induced depolarized light scattering from atomic fluids give agreement with experimental data over a wide range of conditions [35].

(e) *Thermodynamics in Liquid Mixtures*

In pure liquids, light scattering from concentration fluctuations is not present. Such scattering can be the major contribution in the case of solutions, however. As indicated in Sec. 14.1(e), the total intensity of the scattering can be used to obtain thermodynamic information for the systems.

The activity coeficients and excess free energies measured through light scattering are judged to be less accurate than those obtained by vapor pressure measurements [Sec. 8.3(d)]. Thus values of ΔG_m^e for benzene-2-propanol were as much as 16% below vapor pressure data [36]. The reason for this deviation may be due to inaccuracies in calculating the density fluctuation contribution, especially the factor $\partial\varepsilon/\partial\rho$ (or $\partial\varepsilon/\partial p$). Another source of error may be the imprecision of depolarization ratio measurements, at least in the case where nonlaser light sources are employed.

The depolarization ratio and anisotropically scattered light has been subject to special attention [37]. For alcohol-water systems, the experimental anisotropic scattering intensity deviates from calculated curves only slightly. These theoretical curves are calculated assuming random orientation of all molecules (methanol or ethanol and water). The values of anisotropy β^2 were obtained from Kerr constant measurements. Thus the data suggests that there are no dramatic changes in the distribution of mutual orientations in the whole composition range. Anisotropic scattering in liquid mixtures is generally a more monotonous function of concentration, while isotropic scattering can have pronounced maxima. Thus anisotropic scattering seems relatively insensitive to concentration and density fluctuations in the medium.

The isotropic scattering is nearly all due to density rather than concentration fluctuations in alcohol-water systems [37]. Thus activity coefficients cannot readily be obtained from light scattering.

(f) *Dynamics in Liquid Mixtures*

The mutual diffusion coefficient in liquid mixtures can also be studied through light scattering. In this case the linewidth of the central Rayleigh component must be measured. This means the measurement of half-widths of the order of 4 kHz (10^{-7} cm^{-1}). This can be done using a heterodyne method [Sec. 14.2(c)] [19]. The scattering angle determines the value of q which is to be used in (14.21) to obtain D, e.g., if $\theta = 10°$, then $q = 3.0 \times 10^4$ cm^{-1} in the system n-propanol-nitrobenzene.

Diffusion coefficients can be obtained in liquid mixtures correct to about 5%. Values of D obtained for the same system (acetone-CS_2) through light scattering at different angles can, however, show differences (e.g., 2.3×10^{-5} cm^2 sec^{-1} for $\theta = 1°$ vs 1.0×10^{-5} cm^2 sec^{-1} for $\theta = 10°$). The higher value is believed erroneous because of errors introduced when the scattering angle θ is very small.

Translational diffusion coefficients can also be measured for large macromolecules in solution, e.g., human plasma lipoproteins [38]. A homodyne (or self-beat) spectroscopic method is used for this. The scattering is assumed to be due to the macromolecules only, with these molecules undergoing Brownian motion. The noise power spectrum of the time fluctuation of the scattered light is then a Lorentzian with a half-width of about 2 kHz for a scattering angle of 90°. This correspinds to a D of the order of 10^{-7} cm^2 sec^{-1}. Application of (6.63) then gives the dimension of the macromolecule in solution (≃ 80 Å in radius).

(g) Diffusion Near the Critical Temperature

Measurement of mutual diffusion coefficients are of special interest near the critical solution point. There concentration-fluctuation scattering is very intense, and the line should become increasingly narrow as T_c is approached. Figure 14.11 shows both these effects in laser homodyne spectra [17]. The increased noise indicates a greater magnification in the figure, i.e., smaller scattering intensity. The half-width is also proportional to $\sin^2(\theta/2)$ (i.e., q^2) as predicted by (14.21). At $|T - T_c| \simeq .004$K, the half-width is 38 Hz, of which 13 Hz is instrumental width.

The diffusion coefficient as a function of temperature is shown for this same system (cyclohexane-aniline) in Fig. 14.12 [39]. In analogy with the form of D for spheres (6.63), the critical solution can be thought to contain droplets of radius ξ, so that $D = kT/6\pi\eta\xi$. The rapid increase in D is mainly due to a rapid variation of ξ, as neither T nor η varies much in such a small range of T.

The correlation length ξ [similar to L in Eq. (3.60)] is postulated to follow a power law, so that

$$\xi = \xi_0 |T_c/(T - T_c)|^{\nu} \tag{14.25}$$

On the Ornstein-Zernike model, $\nu = 0.5$. The data in Fig. 14.12 can be fitted well if ξ_0 is given a value 2.11 Å and $\nu = 0.59$.

For temperatures very close to T_c, the relation (14.25) must be altered. The half-width is no longer $2Dq^2$, i.e,, the decay rate Γ is not described properly by Dq^2. More complex forms are described in [39] and [40]. It is found that Γ/q^3 vs $q\xi$ is a function independent

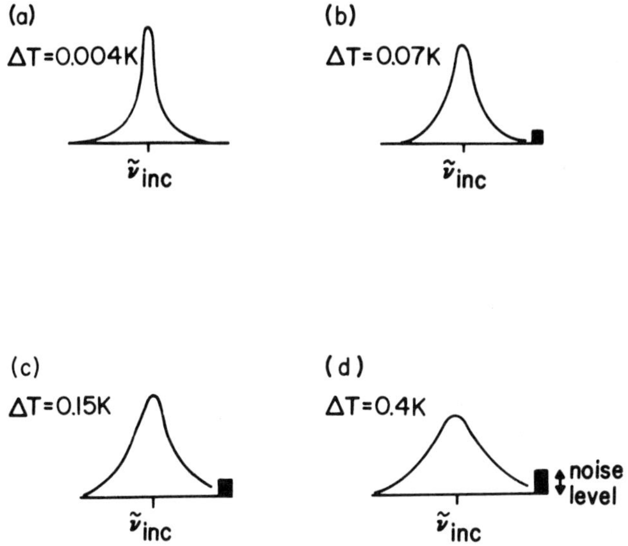

Fig. 14.11. The shape of the central Rayleigh line for cyclohexane-aniline at a scattering angle of 20.5° as obtained from a homodyne light-scattering spectrometer at four temperatures near T_c. The increased intensity at smaller values of $\Delta T = |T - T_c|$ is indicated by the smaller noise level. After Ref. 17.

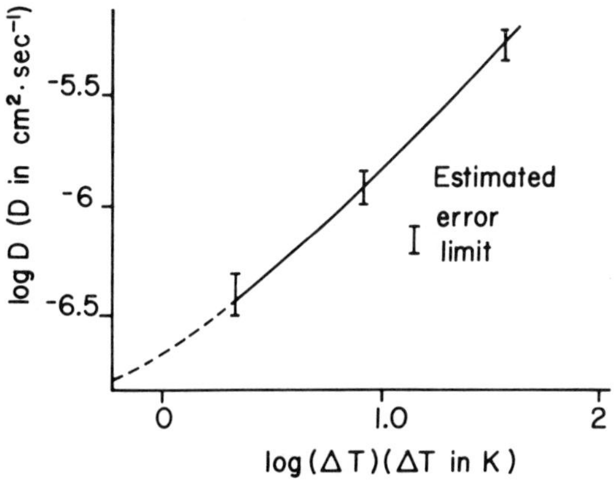

Fig. 14.12. A log-log plot of the mutual diffusion coefficient D vs $\Delta T = |T = T_c|$ for cyclohexane-aniline as determined from the width of the central Rayleigh line. —— Experimental curve with estimated error limits, --- extrapolation for $\Delta T < 2K$. After Ref. 39.

of temperature [39,41]. A review of recent theory is presented in Ref. 42.

Similar studies can be carried out for one-component systems, (e.g., Refs. 18 and 40). It is also predicted that the depolarization ratio should change as a gas-liquid critical point is approached [43]. For xenon it is predicted to increase as ξ^2 due to the increase in the collision-induced effects [Sec. 14.3(d)] in systems with a greater amount of short-range structure.

(h) Total Scattering Intensity Near the Critical Point

The distance parameter ξ_0 is obtained usually from measurement of total scattered intensity rather than from linewidths. The concentration fluctuation scattering as shown in (7.18) is dependent upon $\partial\mu/\partial c$. When δA is expressed in terms of Fourier components $\langle c(q)^2\rangle$ of the concentration fluctuation (4.38), the q dependence of $\partial\mu/\partial c$, and hence $S(q,\omega)$, can be obtained. Combining (4.38) with (3.60), (14.20), and (14.21) leads to the Ornstein-Zernike-Debye equation.

$$I(q) \propto \frac{T/T_c}{(T/T_c) - 1 + q^2L^2/6} \tag{14.26}$$

In these experiments, q can be equated to $(2\pi n/\lambda)\sin\theta/2$. Equation (14.26) predicts that $I(q)^{-1}$ vs $\sin^2(\theta/2)$ will be a straight line with both slope and ordinate temperature-dependent. It can be rewritten as

$$\frac{I(q)}{I(0)} = \frac{\xi^{\eta-2}}{(\xi^{-2} + q^2)^{1-\eta/2}} \simeq \frac{1}{1 + q^2\xi^2} \tag{14.27}$$

Here η is a small number indicating deviation from the OZD equation. The second form is for $\eta = 0$. The OZD plots are linear to within 0.03°C of the critical temperature as shown in Fig. 14.13. Errors due to multiple scattering become greater as $|T - T_c|$ decreases due to increased turbidity [44].

For the system 2,6-lutidine-water shown in Fig. 14.13, η was found to be $\simeq 0$, $\xi_0 \simeq 2.0 \pm .2$ Å and the exponent ν describing the tempera-

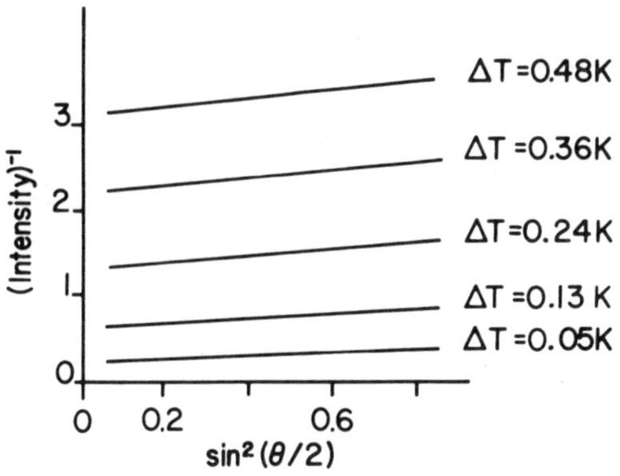

Fig. 14.13. A plot of the reciprocal of the scattering intensity vs $\sin^2(\theta/2)$ for scattering from 2,6 lutidine-water at 5 temperatures near T_c. After Ref. 44.

ture dependence of ξ (14.25) as 0.61 ± .08.

Plots similar to that in Fig. 14.13 are also made in light scattering studies of micelle formation [45]. Thus the sizes of the scattering entities can be obtained in analogy to obtaining a value of ξ. Micelle molecular weights of the order of 10^6 can be obtained in this way. The geometry of the micelles can also be elucidated.

(i) Studies in Electrolyte Solutions

Ultrasonic studies of ion-pairing phenomena [Sec. 10.3(g)] can be extended to higher frequencies making use of MB scattering [46,47]. Accuracies of up to 0.1% in the velocity (from $\Delta\nu_{MB}$) and 2.5% in the absorption (from $\delta\nu_{MB}$) (Fig. 14.2) are attainable. Studies of 2:2 electrolytes [47] show relaxation frequencies for ion pairing equilibria of ~8 x 10^7 Hz for $ZnSO_4$ and ~1.5 x 10^7 Hz for $MnSO_4$ solutions in reasonable agreement with estimates from ultrasonic experiments. The central Rayleigh line in such systems has also been investigated [48] to see if there is any additional light scattering due to the ion pairing association. The spectra could in all cases be accounted for by scattering from diffusional concentration fluctuations [Sec. 14.3(f)].

No excess absorption is found in NaCl and NaBr solutions, even up to 4 M concentration. However, in very concentrated aqueous solutions of LiCl, a relaxation process is observed at low temperatures [49]. This is also observed in low temperature, high concentration studies of $Ca(NO_3)_2$ solutions [50]. It is interpreted as being viscoelastic in origin, rather than due to some ion pairing equilibrium. In addition, an increase in the Landau-Placzek ratio ($I_{CR}/2I_{MB}$) [Sec. 14.1(e)] with a decrease in temperature in LiCl indicates increasing scattering from concentration fluctuations. This in turn indicates the presence of critical solution temperature. The central Rayleigh line is also anomalously intense at higher temperatures. This may be due to light scattering associated with ionic hydration reactions [49].

Depolarized scattering has also been studied in aqueous solutions of KI and $MgSO_4$ [51]. An increase of the intensity in excess of that predicted by the collision-induced theory [5] is explained in terms of structural changes. An increase in depolarized scattering with increase in KI concentration is ascribed to a "structure breaking" effect, while $MgSO_4$ shows signs of "structure making" [Sec. 8.3(h)]. The variation of hypersonic velocity (from $\Delta\nu_{MB}$) with salt concentration is also explained in terms of structural changes in the water caused by the ions, but some controversy remains in the interpretation of the experimental data [52].

REFERENCES

References 2 and 3 give a thorough account of light scattering, while [7] discusses some more recent applications. A good review of light scattering in critical systems can be found in the proceedings of a meeting from which [34] and [35] are taken.

1. W. K. H. Panofsky and M. Phillips, Classical Electricity and Magnetism, Addison-Wesley, Reading, 1962.
2. M. Kerker, The Scattering of Light, Academic Press, New York, 1969.
3. I. L. Fabelinskii, Molecular Scattering of Light, Plenum, New York, 1968.

4. V. S. Starunov, E. V. Tiganov, and I. L. Fabelinskii, Sov. Phys. -JETP Litt., *4*, 176 (1966).

5. J. A. Bucaro and T. A. Litovitz, J. Chem. Phys., *55*, 3585, 3846 (1971).

6. E. Zamir, N. D. Gershon, and A. Ben-Reuven, J. Chem. Phys., *55*, 3397 (1971).

7. R. D. Mountain, CRC Critical Rev. Solid State Science, Vol. 1, 5 (1970).

8. L. D. Landau and E. M. Lifshitz, Electrodynamics of Continuous Media, Plenum, New York (1960).

9. L. Fishman and R. D. Mountain, J. Phys. Chem., *74*, 2178 (1970).

10. T. Keyes and D. Kivelson, J. Chem. Phys., *56*, 1057, 1876 (1972).

11. P. van Konynenburg and W. A. Steele, J. Chem. Phys., *56*, 4776 (1972).

12. A. Ben-Reuven and N. D. Gershon, J. Chem. Phys., *51*, 893 (1969); ibid., *54*, 1049 (1971).

13. H. Dardy, V. Volterra, and T. A. Litovitz, Farad. Symp. Chem. Soc., No. 6, 71 (1972).

14. H. K. Shin, J. Chem. Phys., *56*, 2617 (1972).

15. H. Z. Cummins and P. E. Schoen, Laser Handbook, Vol. 2 (F. T. Arecchi and E. O. Schulz-Dubois, eds.), North Holland, Amsterdam, 1972.

16. W. Kaiser and M. Maier, Laser Handbook, Vol. 2 (F. T. Arecchi and E. O. Schulz-Dubois, eds.), North Holland, Amsterdam, 1972.

17. S. S. Alpert, in Critical Phenomena (M. S. Green and J. V. Sengers, eds.), Nat. Bur. Stand. Misc. Publ., 237 (1966).

18. N. C. Ford, Jr. and G. B. Benedek, Critical Phenomena (M. S. Green and J. V. Sengers, eds.), Nat. Bur. Stand. Misc. Publ., 273 (1966).

19. A. M. Jamieson and A. G. Walton, J. Chem. Phys., *58*, 1054 (1973).

20. G. Cohen and H. Eisenberg, J. Chem. Phys., *43*, 3881 (1965).

21. A. Litan, J. Chem. Phys., *48*, 1052, 1059 (1968).

22. D. J. Coumou, Trans. Farad. Soc., *65*, 2654 (1969).

23. J. V. Champion, G. H. Meeten, and C. D. Whittle, Trans. Farad. Soc., *66*, 2671 (1970).

24. R. Y. Chiao and P. A. Fleury, Physics of Quantum Electronics, McGraw-Hill, New York, 1966.

25. S. Gewurtz, W. S. Gornall, and B. P. Stoicheff, J. Acoust. Soc. Am., *49*, 994 (1971).

26. W. H. Nichols, C. R. Kunsitis-Swyt, and S. P. Singal, J. Chem. Phys., *51*, 5659 (1969).

27. P. A. Fleury, in Physical Acoustics, Vol. 6 (W. P. Mason and R. N. Thurston, eds.), Academic Press, New York, 1970.

28. L. V. Lanshina, M. I. Lupina, and P. K. Habibullaev, Soviet Phys.-Acoustics, *16*, 343 (1971).

29. A. Papayoanou, T. R. Hart, and R. D. Andrews, J. Chem. Phys., *59*, 109 (1973).

30. G. Enright and B. P. Stoicheff, J. Chem. Phys., *60*, 2536 (1974).

31. G. R. Alms, D. R. Bauer, J. I. Brauman, and R. Pecora, J. Chem. Phys., *59*, 5310 (1973).

32. S. B. Dubin, N. A. Clark, and G. B. Benedek, J. Chem. Phys., *54*, 5158 (1971).

33. H. D. Dardy, V. Volterra, and T. A. Litovitz, J. Chem. Phys., *59*, 4491 (1973).

34. J. H. K. Ho and G. C. Tabisz, Can. J. Chem., *51*, 2025 (1973).

35. B. J. Alder, H. L. Strauss, and J. J. Weis, J. Chem. Phys., *59*, 1002 (1973).

36. H. H. Lewis, R. L. Schmidt, and H. L. Clever, J. Phys. Chem., *74*, 4377 (1970).

37. G. D. Parfitt and J. A. Wood, Trans. Farad. Soc., *64*, 2081 (1968).

38. S. K. Davi, J. C. S. Farad. Trans. II, *70*, 700 (1974).

39. B. Volonchine, Ber. Bunseng. Physik. Chem., *76*, 217 (1972).

40. B. Chu, Ber. Bunseng. Physik. Chem., *76*, 202 (1972).

41. R. F. Chang, P. H. Keyes, J. V. Sengers, and C. O. Alley, Phys. Rev. Lett., *27*, 1706 (1971).

42. H. L. Swinney and D. L. Henry, Phys. Rev., *A 8*, 2586 (1973).

43. D. W. Oxtoby and W. M. Gelbart, J. Chem. Phys., *60*, 3359 (1974).

44. E. Gülari, A. F. Collings, R. L. Schmidt, and C. J. Pings, J. Chem. Phys., *56*, 6169 (1972).

45. D. Attwood, J. Phys. Chem., *72*, 339 (1968).

46. C. J. Montrose and K. Fritsch, J. Acoust. Soc. Am., *47*, 786 (1970).

47. Y. Yeh and R. N. Keeler, J. Chem. Phys., *51*, 1120 (1969).

48. J. H. R. Clarke, G. J. Hills, C. J. Oliver, and J. M. Vaughan, J. Chem. Phys., *61*, 2810 (1974).

49. S. Y. Hsich, R. W. Gammon, P. B. Macedo, and C. J. Montrose, J. Chem. Phys., *56*, 1663 (1972).

50. J. H. Ambrus, H. Dardy, and C. T. Moynihan, J. Phys. Chem., *76*, 3495 (1972).

51. M. A. Gray, T. M. Loehr, and P. A. Pincus, J. Chem. Phys., *59*, 1121 (1973).

52. M. Gross, J. Azoulay, and D. Gerlich, J. Chem. Phys., *58*, 5812 (1973); ibid., *60*, 4102 (1974)

Further Recent References

B. Chu, Laser Light Scattering, Academic Press, New York, 1974.

D. Kivelson, T. Keyes and J. Champion, "Theory of Molecular Reorientation Rates, Flow Birefringence, and Depolarized Light Scattering", Mol. Phys., *31*, 221 (1976).

A. K. Burnham, G. R. Alms, and W. H. Flygare, "The Local Electric Field. I. The Effect on Isotropic and Anisotropic Rayleigh Scattering", J. Chem. Phys., *62*, 3289 (1975).

S. R. Aragón and R. Pecora, "Fluorescence Correlation Spectroscopy as a Probe of Molecular Dynamics", J. Chem. Phys., *64*, 1791 (1976).

E. R. Pike, W. R. M. Pomeroy, and J. M. Vaughan, "Measurement of Rayleigh Ratio for Several Pure Liquids using a Laser and Monitored Photon Counting", J. Chem. Phys., *62*, 3186 (1975).

C. J. Montrose, J. A. Bucaro, J. Marshall-Coakley, and T. A. Litovitz, "Depolarized Rayleigh Scattering and Hydrogen Bonding in Liquid Water", J. Chem. Phys., *60*, 5025 (1974).

A. Martinez, B. Peyret, and A. Rousset, "Les Fluctuations de Densité dans les Liquides Visqueux et la Diffusion Moléculaire de la Lumière: Interprétation des Resultats Obtenus avec les Alcools a Basse Températures", J. Chim. Phys., *71*, 1475 (1974).

Y. Y. Huang and C. H. Wang, "Brillouin, Rayleigh, and Depolarized Rayleigh Scattering Studies of Polypropylene Glycol I", J. Chem. Phys., *62*, 120 (1975).

G. D. Enright and B. P. Stoicheff, "Light Scattering from Shear Modes in Liquid Salol", J. Chem. Phys., *64*, 3658 (1976).

J. Rouch, J. P. Chabrat, L. Letamendia, C. Vaucamps, and N. D. Gershon, "Low Frequency Depolarized Light Scattering in the VH Geometry from Quinoline", J. Chem. Phys., *63*, 1383 (1975).

G. M. Searby, P. Bezot, and P. Sixou, "Transverse Collective Modes in Liquid Pyridine by Depolarized Light Scattering", J. Chem. Phys., *64*, 1485 (1976).

P. van Konynenburg and W. A. Steele, "Molecular Rotation in Some Simple Fluids", J. Chem. Phys., *62*, 2301 (1975).

A. M. A. da Costa, M. A. Norman, and J. H. R. Clarke, "Reorientational Molecular Motion in Liquids: A Comparison of Raman and Rayleigh Scattering", Mol. Phys., *29*, 191 (1975).

G. D. Patterson and J. E. Griffiths, "Raman and Depolarized Rayleigh Scattering in the Liquid State: Reorientational Motions and Correlations in Orientation for Symmetric Top Molecules", J. Chem. Phys., *63*, 2406 (1975).

J. F. Dill, T. A. Litovitz, and J. A. Bucaro, "Molecular Reorinetation in Liquids by Rayleigh Scattering: Pressure Dependence of Rotational Correlation Functions", J. Chem. Phys., *62*, 3839 (1975).

D. R. Bauer, G. R. Alms, J. I. Brauman, and R. Pecora, "Depolarized Rayleigh Scattering and ^{13}C NMR Studies of Anisotropic Molecular Reorientation of Aromatic Compounds in Solution", J. Chem. Phys., *61*, 2255 (1974).

C. K. Cheung, D. R. Jones and C. H. Wang, "Single Particle Reorientation and Pair Correlations of Methyl Iodide Solutions Studied by Depolarized Rayleigh and Raman Scattering", J. Chem. Phys., *64*, 3567 (1976).

J. Schroeder, C. J. Montrose, and P. B. Macedo, "Kinetics of Concentration Fluctuations in a Binary Alkali-Silicate System", J. Chem. Phys., *63*, 2907 (1975).

D. L. Carle, W. G. Laidlaw, and H. N. W. Lekkerkerker, "Spectral Analysis of the Light Scattered from a Chemically Relaxing Fluid: A Ternary Mixture", J. C. S. Faraday II, *71*, 1448 (1975).

D. Thiel, B. Chu, A. Stein, and G. Allen, "Light Scattering from a Binary Liquid Mixture above its Critical Consolute Point", J. Chem. Phys., *62*, 3689 (1975).

G. A. Miller, "Brillouin Spectra of Solutions IV. Aqueous Magnesium Sulfate", J. Phys. Chem., *80*, 775 (1976).

Chapter 15

X-RAY SCATTERING

As indicated in Sec. 14.1(g) X-ray scattering can presently be used to study only the structure, and not the dynamics, of liquids. The transfers of energy from X-rays to the liquid are so small relative to the total X-ray photon energies that they cannot be experimentally detected.

The theoretical basis for X-ray scattering is approached here from a microscopic point of view, considering individual electrons. This is done to give an alternative way of approaching scattering phenomena. It could be derived from the results of Sec. 14.1(d), however, as the density $n(\underline{r})$ can be expressed in microscopic (non-continuum) terms as a sum of δ functions. This latter approach is taken in Chap. 16 for neutron scattering.

Special nomenclature has arisen in the various specialties described in Part B. Here a nomenclature consistent with Chap. 14 is used. This is somewhat different from the usual nomenclature in X-ray scattering literature. There s is usually used instead of the symbol q used here, and the scattering angle is designated as 2θ instead of θ as used here.

15.1. THEORETICAL BACKGROUND

(a) The Debye Equation for X-ray Scattering

Scattering of electromagnetic radiation from electrons has been discussed in Sec. 20.5, where a scattering cross section is arrived at in (20.56). Here scattering of unpolarized electromagnetic radiation with λ in the X-ray region (~1 Å) will be discussed. The electric field and intensity of the scattered radiation will be expressed in terms of "electron units" rather than in absolute units. Thus the scattering intensity $I_{eu}(\theta)$ is the intensity relative to that calculated for a single electron. A proportionality sign will be used initially for conciseness.

The electric field $\underline{E}_{sc}(\underline{r},t)$ due to scattering from an atom with atomic number Z would be expected to be Z times that due to scattering from a single electron. The electrons in an atom are, however, distributed in space over distances which are not negligible as compared to the X-ray wavelength. Thus interference effects between radiation scattered from electrons in different parts of the atom makes $\underline{E}_{sc}(\underline{r},t)$ due to an atom = $f \cdot \underline{E}_{sc,eu}(\underline{r},t)$ where $\underline{E}_{sc,eu}(\underline{r},t)$ is the electric field at $\underline{r}$ due to scattering from a single electron. The "atomic structure factor" or "scattering factor" f is a number less than Z, and is generally dependent on the scattering angle θ (i.e., on q) (Fig. 15.1). As $q \to 0$, $f \to Z$, as the optical path from source to detector is the same for all electrons. It can be obtained if the electronic structure of the atom is known, e.g., from quantum-mechanical calculations of electron density [1].

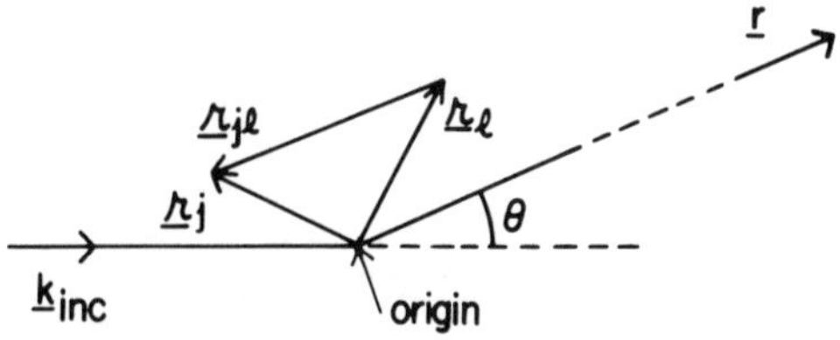

Fig. 15.1. Schematic diagram illustrating the geometry of X-ray scattering. The vectors $\underline{r}_j$ and $\underline{r}_\ell$ give the positions of scatterers within the scattering system.

Consider next a group of atoms distributed about the origin, with the jth atom $\underline{r}_j$ from the origin. Scattering from this system is is observed at a point at $\underline{r}$ from the origin, where $\underline{r} \gg \underline{r}_j$. The incident wave vector of the X-rays is $\underline{k}_{inc}$, while the scattered vector is $\underline{k}_{sc}$, with the same direction as $\underline{r}$ (Fig. 15.1). As before $\underline{q} = \underline{k}_{inc} - \underline{k}_{sc}$; $|\underline{q}| = q = 2k_{inc} \sin(\theta/2) = (4\pi/\lambda)\cdot\sin(\theta/2)$.

The phase of the radiation scattered from the atom at $\underline{r}_j$ is different from that scattered from the atom at the origin by $\underline{r}_j\cdot(\underline{k}_{inc} - \underline{k}_{sc}) = \underline{r}_j\cdot\underline{q}$. Thus if the incident radiation is plane monochromatic, i.e., if $\underline{E}_{inc}(\underline{r},t) = \underline{E}_{inc}(\underline{r})\cdot\exp[i\omega t]$, then the electric field at $\underline{r}$ due to scattering from the atom at $\underline{r}_j$ is, relative to the origin atom,

$$\underline{E}(\underline{r},t) \propto f_j \exp[i(\omega t - \underline{r}_j\cdot\underline{q})] \tag{15.1}$$

A static situation is assumed here so that there are effectively no frequency shifts due to "Doppler effects" etc. Equation (15.1) can be generalized for any number of atoms by summing over j.

The intensity can be obtained by multiplying the amplitude of $\underline{E}(\underline{r},t)$ by its complex conjugate. Thus

$$\begin{aligned} I(\underline{r}) &\propto \langle \sum_j f_j \exp[-i\underline{r}_j\cdot\underline{q}]\cdot\sum_\ell f_\ell \exp[+i\underline{r}_\ell\cdot\underline{q}]\rangle \\ &\propto \langle \sum_{j\ell} f_j f_\ell \exp[-i\underline{q}\cdot(\underline{r}_j - \underline{r}_\ell)]\rangle \\ &\propto \langle \sum_{j\ell} f_j f_\ell \exp[iqr_{j\ell}\cos\gamma]\rangle \end{aligned} \tag{15.2}$$

In the last form γ refers to the angle between $\underline{q}$ and $\underline{r}_j - \underline{r}_\ell$.

In the case of an isotropic liquid, $\underline{r}_j - \underline{r}_\ell$ takes on all positions in space at random, so that γ takes on all values at random. Integration over γ gives then

$$I(q) \propto \sum_{j\ell}\sum f_j f_\ell \frac{\int \langle \exp[iqr_{j\ell} \cos \gamma] \rangle \, d\Omega}{\int d\Omega}$$

or

$$I_{eu}(\theta) = \sum_{j\ell}\sum f_j f_\ell \left\langle \left\{ \frac{\sin qr_{j\ell}}{qr_{j\ell}} \right\} \right\rangle \qquad (15.3)$$

(15.3) is often referred to as the Debye equation. It connects the angular dependence of the scattered X-ray intensity, as expressed in electron units, with the geometry of the liquid from which the scattering takes place.

(b) Scattering from Monatomic Liquids

In the case of a monatomic liquid, all the structure factors are identical. The summation indicated in (15.3) can then be carried out by summing over the distances from one atom placed at the origin. Each atom in turn is considered to be the origin atom. This gives

$$I_{eu} = Nf^2 \left\{ 1 + \sum_{j'} \left\langle \frac{\sin q \cdot r_j}{q \cdot r_j} \right\rangle \right\} \qquad (15.4)$$

In (15.4), N is the total number of atoms, and j' indicates a summation over all atoms, except the origin atom. The summation over atoms with respect to themselves leads to the term 1 in the curly brackets as $\sin qr/qr \to 1$ as $r \to 0$.

If now the distribution of atoms is assumed to be described by a radial density function $n(\underline{r})$ [Sec. 3.1(a)], then

$$I_{eu} = Nf^2 \left\{ 1 + \int_0^\infty 4\pi r^2 n(r) \frac{\sin qr}{qr} \, dr \right\}$$

$$= Nf^2 \left\{ 1 + \int 4\pi r^2 (n(r) - n) \frac{\sin qr}{qr} \, dr \right\} \qquad (15.5) \qquad (15.5)$$

In (15.5) the integration has been taken to ∞ instead of to the radius of the liquid sample. The function $n(r)$ rapidly approaches the average value n, and it can be shown the integral of $\int_0^\infty r^2(\sin qr/qr)dr = 0$. This is the reason for expressing the density as the deviation from the average density as indicated in the second form.

The second form in (15.5) can be written in a more convenient form as

$$q\, i(q) = \int_0^\infty 4\pi r^2(n(r) - n) \sin qr\, dr \tag{15.6}$$

Here the "structurally sensitive intensity function" $i(q) = [I_{eu}(q)/Nf\ ] - 1$ has been introduced. A Fourier transform of (15.16) leads to the form commonly used to obtain distribution functions from experimental data:

$$4\pi r^2 n(r) = 4\pi r^2 n + \frac{2r}{\pi} \int_0^\infty q \cdot i(q) \sin qr\, dq \tag{15.7}$$

Equation (15.7) can be thought of as being a generalization of the Bragg reflection law. In solids, the discrete distances between planes of atoms are obtained from the intensity at discrete angles θ (i.e., values of q). In liquids, both $n(r)$ and $i(q)$ are continuous functions, so that an intensity distribution $i(q)$ is seen instead of reflections at discrete Bragg angles [Secs. 10.2(b) and 15.1(c)].

Relation (15.7) can also be obtained in a concise elegant way from (14.20). The derivation outlined here is meant to complement the more abstract derivation in Sec. 14.1(d) and give more physical insight into interference effects occurring in scattering processes.

(c) Scattering from Molecular Liquids

In the case of molecular liquids, different types of atoms are present. Thus (15.3) cannot be written as (15.4), but instead must be expressed as

$$I_{eu} - \sum_{j=1}^{N} f_j^2 = \sum_{j=1}^{N} \sum_{\ell \neq j=1}^{N} f_j f_\ell \left\langle \frac{\sin qr_{j\ell}}{qr_{j\ell}} \right\rangle \tag{15.8}$$

Instead of a single density function $n(r)$, functions $n_{\alpha\beta}(r)$ must now be introduced, where $n_{\alpha\beta}(r)$ is the function giving the density of distinct pairs of atoms of type α and β separated by a distance r [see also Secs. 4.2(c) and 5.2(a)]. For water, there would be three functions $n_{HH}(r)$, $n_{OO}(r)$, and $n_{OH}(r)$.

The atoms in the liquid can also be considered in structural units of m atoms, each structural unit being, for example, a molecule. There are then N/m structural units (molecules) present in the volume of liquid considered.

The scattering intensity i(q) is for this case defined as

$$i(q) = I_{eu}(q)\cdot\frac{m}{N} - \sum_{j=1}^{m} f_j^2(q)$$

$$= \sum_{\alpha=1}^{m}\sum_{\beta=1}^{m} f_\alpha f_\beta \int_0^\infty 4\pi r^2 (n_{\alpha\beta}(r) - n)\,\frac{\sin qr}{qr}\,dr \qquad (15.9)$$

The summation is over all distinct pairs in the structural unit. In general, the functions $n_{\alpha\beta}(r)$ cannot be individually obtained. However, if the system is made up of only one kind of spherically symmetric molecule with no orientational correlation, then a molecular radial density function can be obtained [Sec. 15.3(c)].

An overall X-ray density function $g_X(r)$ can be obtained from the Fourier transform of (15.9). This $g_X(r)$ is a sum of components $g_{\alpha\beta,X}(r)$. These are related to the true distribution functions $g_{\alpha\beta}(r)$ through relations which can be calculated in practice [3].

$$g_{\alpha\beta,X}(r) = \frac{1}{r}\int_{-\infty}^{\infty} r' g_{\alpha\beta}(r) T_{\alpha\beta}(r' - r)\,dr'$$

where

$$T_{\alpha\beta}(r) = \frac{1}{\pi}\int_0^\infty f_\alpha f_\beta M(q)\cos qr\,dq \qquad (15.10)$$

The function $M(q) = [\sum_{\alpha=1}^{m} f_\alpha]^{-2}$ for $q < q_{max}$, and 0 for $q > q_{max}$, the maximum experimentally accessible value of q. The atomic structure factors or scattering amplitudes f_α are all dependent on q. Only if independent experiments are made which involve different scattering factors (e.g., isotope substitution) can the $g_x(r)$ be decomposed into the $g_{\alpha\beta,x}(r)$.

In many cases the atom pair correlation functions for a single molecule can be obtained from molecular data, assuming the same molecular structure as that present in the vapor. Models of the liquid structure can then be constructed using these model molecules as structural units. From the liquid models, the radial distribution and hence intensity functions can be calculated. These calculated functions can then be compared with experimentally observed data.

(d) Small Angle Scattering

In the limit of small angles ($q \to 0$), I(q) approaches a value which is determined by the long-range fluctuations of $n_{\alpha\beta}(r)$ from n. Thus I(0) is quite large near the critical point. An explanation of this requires consideration of the macroscopic properties of liquids [2] [Sec. 3.1(c) and Eq. (3.38)].

The scattering factors f_j, f_ℓ in (15.3) can for the low-angle region be replaced by $\rho_j\, dV_j$, $\rho_\ell\, dV_\ell$, where ρ_j is the average electron density in the volume element dV_j. Thus

$$I \propto \iint \rho_j \cdot \rho_\ell \frac{\sin q r_{j,\ell}}{q r_{j,\ell}} dV_j\, dV_\ell \tag{15.11a}$$

$$\propto \iint \frac{\delta\rho_j}{\rho} \cdot \frac{\delta\rho_\ell}{\rho} \frac{\sin q r_{j,\ell}}{q r_{j,\ell}} dV_j\, dV_\ell \tag{15.11b}$$

$$\propto \left(\frac{\delta\rho}{\rho}\right)^2 V \int h(r) \frac{\sin qr}{qr} 4\pi r^2\, dr \tag{15.11c}$$

In (b) the electron densities have been expanded as $\rho_j = \rho + \delta\rho/\rho$ and the negligibly small integrals have been removed. In (c), the density correlation function h(r) (3.6) has been introduced as (3.17)

$$< \frac{\delta\rho_j}{\rho} \cdot \frac{\delta\rho_\ell}{\rho} > = <\left(\frac{\delta\rho}{\rho}\right)^2 > h(r) \tag{15.12}$$

The correlation length L^2 (3.59) can then be obtained from small angle X-ray scattering as for $q \to 0$ [2]

$$\frac{I(q)}{I(0)} = 1 - \frac{q^2L^2}{6} \tag{15.13}$$

Relation (15.13) is useful only for systems near a critical point. In other cases, I(q) increases rather than decreases with q (e.g., Fig. 3.1). The similarity of (15.13) to the OZD equation for light scattering should be noted [Sec. 14.3(h)].

The zero angle scattering intensity can be calculated from thermodynamics (3.19) as

$$I(0) = kT\kappa_T\rho(NF^2) \tag{15.14}$$

Here F is the number of electrons per molecule (i.e., = Z for monatomic species) and N the number of molecules in the sample.

15.2. EXPERIMENTAL TECHNIQUES

Experimental techniques for X-ray scattering are reviewed in Ref. 3 and described more completely in [4,5]. Here a brief review of the apparatus and some of the major experimental sources of error are outlined.

The source of the X-ray beam is an X-ray tube in which a beam of electrons are impinging on the metal target. The metal emits electromagnetic radiation in the X-ray region with a spectrum characteristic of the metal. Discrete lines are present in this spectrum, corresponding to transitions of the core electrons of the metal atoms. The wavelength used must be one removed from any resonant transitions in the atoms present in the scattering system. The 0.7107 Å line emitted from molybdenum is often used.

A system of slits serve to define both the incident and the scattered beams. The scattering often takes place from the open surface of the liquid held in some container. Any effects from sample holder absorption or scattering can be eliminated by a proper slit system. In cases, the liquid must be completely enclosed, e.g., when under pressure. A beryllium container is often used in such cases. The scattering from the liquid is then determined from two separate scattering measurements: with the cell filled, and with the cell empty [8].

Before entering the detector, the scattered beam is normally reflected by a monochromator. Such a monochromator is simply a crystal (e.g., NaCl) positioned so that Bragg reflection occurs from a plane in it. It can be shaped so that it also focuses the radiation into the detector. It is also possible to use filters to eliminate unwanted radiation.

The detector is usually a scintillation or proportional counter. Photographic detection can also be used, but in this case the monochromator is used for the incident rather than the scattered beam.

Some of the major experimental inaccuracies can be due to sample absorption, multiple scattering, polarization of the X-ray beam (assumed unpolarized) fluorescence and Compton scattering. In large angle scattering, where the process can be thought of as being much like reflection off the surface with only some penetration, Compton scattering is the major effect which must be accounted for.

Compton scattering can be considered as the result of collision between the X-ray photon and a less tightly bound electron. This results in a wavelength shift in the Compton-scattered photon. The amount of this shift is dependent upon the scattering angle, as both momentum and energy are conserved in the collision. Such scattering is incoherent, and should be subtracted from the total scattered intensity to get the structurally sensitive part of the scattering intensity (see Fig. 15.5). A correction for this effect involves a consideration of the resolution of the monochromator as the wavelength shift is angle-dependent.

Small angle scattering is usually measured in transmission geometry from a thin sample. To achieve the smallest scattering angles, the beam must be well collimated. In such cases, the major correction factors to be applied are for sample absorption and for multiple scattering. The zero angle scattering $I(0)$ can be obtained by extrapolation of the data or from thermodynamics (15.13).

Some aspects of data reduction and model construction [Sec. 15.1 (c)], which can be considered as parts of experimental technique, are mentioned in Sec. 15.3.

15.3. RESULTS FOR SPECIFIC SYSTEMS

(a) Distribution Function of Argon

The radial distribution function $g(r)$ [Eq. (3.1)] can be obtained experimentally through X-ray scattering quite accurately for monatomic liquids such as Argon etc. The results can then be used as a test for various aspects of theories of simple liquids as outlined in Sec. 3.2. For this reason, X-ray scattering in argon has been widely studied [6].

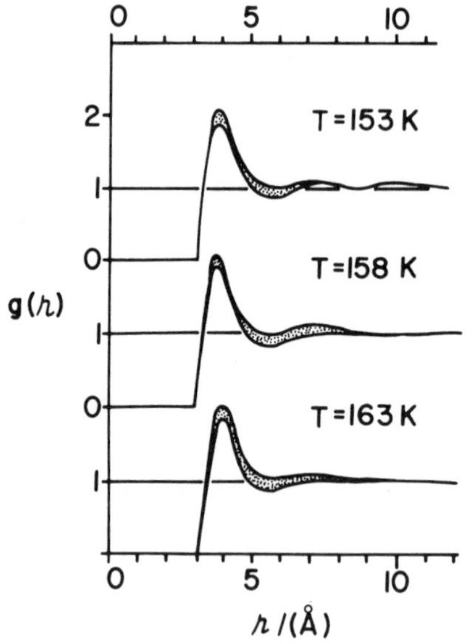

Fig. 15.2. The radial distribution function of liquid argon at three temperatures with $\rho = .536$ g cm^{-3} as measured by X-ray scattering. The experimental uncertainty is shown by the width of the lines. After Ref. 6.

Figure 15.2 shows some resulting curves for $g(r)$ at three temperatures. The uncertainty in the results as indicated is due to experimental factors, but also in part to the error introduced in truncating of the Fourier transform (15.7). Experimental data for the curves in Fig. 15.2 were available for $0.3 < q < 8$ Å^{-1}.

As can be seen from the curves, the position and height of the first maximum remains approximately constant with temperature. The height of the second maximum decreases markedly as temperature is increased. The reduction in the size of the second maximum is also noted when density is decreased, while temperature is held constant.

The effective pair potential for argon can be calculated from the experimental X-ray results assuming various liquid theories. This aspect is discussed in Sec. 3.2(d). A comparison between the PY and HNC theories [5] indicates that both theories are inadequate. Either the number of terms included in the theories must be increased, or else the neglect of many-body interactions [Sec. 1.1(g)] introduces considerable error.

Tests of theories of liquids can also be carried out in terms of "artificial liquids" [7]. Polystyrene latex systems are at times also used to study instrumental distortion effects. Such a system of spheres (radius ~1240 Å) suspended in a latex can be used to simulate liquids at different densities. The results show the number of nearest neighbors to be ~9.4, in reasonable agreement with real simple liquids (e.g., Ar, Ne).

When analysed in terms of the PY equation [Sec. 3.2(b)] the results for systems composed of such spheres lead to a physically unsatisfactory pair potential function. An analysis in terms of the HNC equation gives a potential function $v(r)$ which shows an attractive part at a reasonable distance. The magnitude and r-dependence of $v(r)$ are characteristic of dispersion forces [Sec. 1.1(d)]. Such forces would have to originate in the surface layers of the particles when the particles are so large.

(b) Structure of Benzene and Other Molecular Liquids

A unique analysis of X-ray scattering data from molecular liquids is much more difficult than that from atomic liquids. Normally a structure for the liquid must be proposed, and the intensity from the proposed model calculated. If there is agreement, then the model corresponds to a possible structure for the liquid, but is not necessarily the only possible structure.

An example of such an analysis is shown in Figs. 15.3 and 15.4 for the case of benzene [8]. The model of benzene used to calculate $q \cdot i(q) \cdot M(q)$ is one in which the geometry of the benzene molecule is assumed as indicated from spectroscopic and other data. The arrangement of molecules proposed is similar to that in solid benzene. It is assumed that each molecule sees only its 12 closest neighbors, the rest being distributed randomly. The size of the unit cell is assumed that necessary to achieve the experimental density. With these assumptions, the arrangement is described in terms of five distance variables (intermolecular C-C distances).

The five distances mentioned above and several other parameters were varied to give the best fit for $q\ i(q)$ as shown in Fig. 15.3. A thermal factor was also included in the calculation, taking into account the distribution of instantaneous interatomic distances due to thermal motion. The thermal (or Debye-Waller) factor can be written as $\exp[-\frac{1}{2}\langle\zeta^2\rangle q^2]$ where $\langle\zeta^2\rangle$ is the mean square variation of the interatomic distance due to thermal motion. The net result gave a model of the liquid quite similar to the solid. This is a time-average static model, and gives no information about the ease with which the molecules can move relative to each other, or any other dynamical data.

The X-ray distribution function $g_X(r)$ shows several aspects which can be interpreted on the basis of the structure of the benzene molecule. The maxima at 1.41, 2.44, and 2.82 are in the ratio $1:\sqrt{3}:2$, and describe the para, meta, and ortho C-C distances in the regular hexagonal structure. Scattering from carbon atoms contributes substantially more than that from H-atoms, as the atomic number (and thus the scattering factor) for carbon is higher.

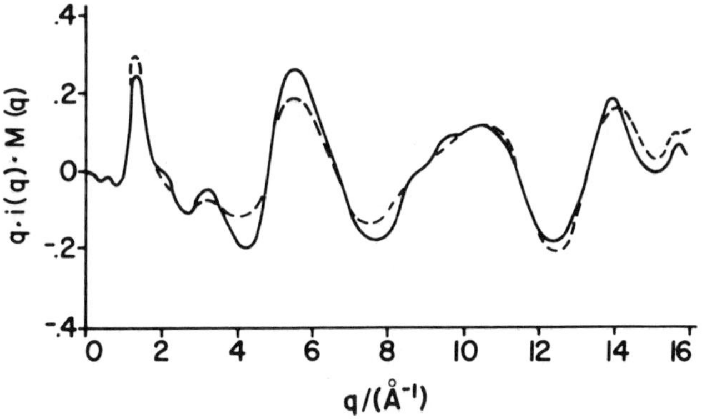

Fig. 15.3. Experimental --- and calculated —— X-ray scattering functions for benzene at 25°C. The calculated curve assumes a time average structure of liquid benzene quite similar to the solid. After Ref. 8.

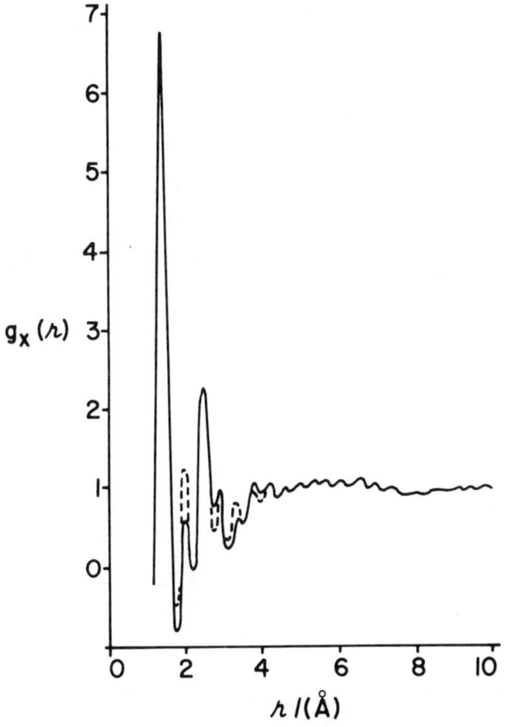

Fig. 15.4. The experimental --- and calculated —— curves of $g_x(r)$ corresponding to the scattering functions in Fig. 15.3. After Ref. 9.

Other examples of elucidation of structure in molecular liquids through X-ray scattering can be found in Refs. 9 and 10. In Ref. 9, liquid ammonia is investigated together with ammonia-water mixtures. In Ref. 10, liquid carboxylic acids are studied. The results in Ref. 10 can be interpreted best when allowance is made for 2 H bonds per molecule. This suggests the presence of ring dimers of chain-type associates [Sec. 14.3(b)].

(c) Structure of Water

X-ray studies of the structure of water are reviewed in Ref. 3. In order to arrive at $g_X(r)$ the experimental data must be corrected for various effects to obtain q·i(q)·M(q) and then Fourier analyzed. An example of the total scattering intensity functions are shown in Fig. 15.5. The curves in Fig. 15.6 are obtained from such data. It shows

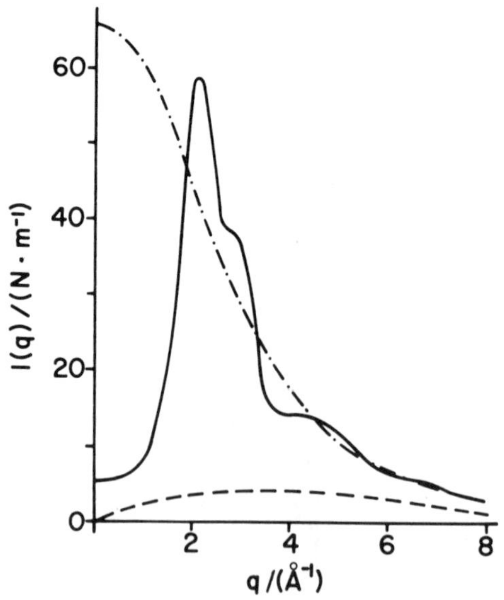

Fig. 15.5. X-ray scattering from liquid water at 25°C showing: —·—· independent atom scattering; --- Compton scattering passed by the monochromator; and —— structurally sensitive scattering (15.8) for water. After Ref. 3.

that self-scattering and Compton scattering contribute considerably to the total scattering intensity.

The X-ray correlation functions $g_x(r)$ for water at several different temperatures are shown in Fig. 15.6. The 200°C curve is for a system at its equilibrium vapor pressure; the other curves at atmospheric pressure. The peak near 1 Å must be due to intermolecular OH distances, while the peak near 2.9 Å is due to intermolecular nearest neighbor O-O distances. The distance between nearest neighbors increases somewhat with increasing temperature. The number of nearest neighbors, as obtained from the area under this maximum, remains approximately constant at 4.4 with temperature.

The function $g_x(r)$ beyond 2 Å corresponds fairly closely to the distribution function for molecular centers (i.e., essentially $g_{OO}(r)$). Most of the scattering intensity is due to the O atom, and the electron density of a water molecule is very nearly spherically symmetric

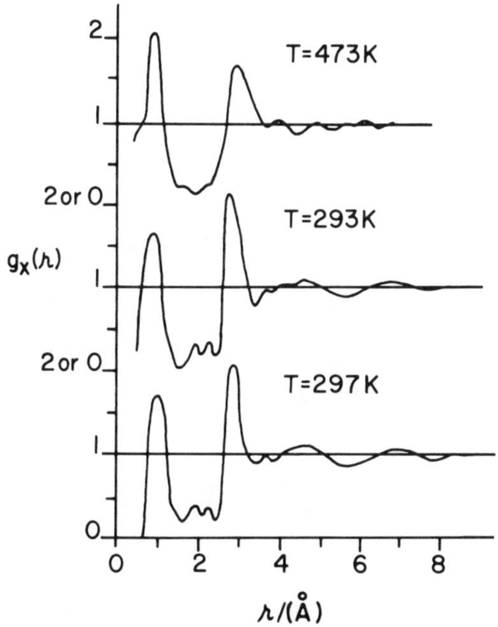

Fig. 15.6. X-ray correlation functions $g_x(r)$ for water at three temperatures. After Ref. 3.

[11]. Orientational correlation is thus not observed well by X-rays. The positional correlation can be seen to extend to about 8 Å.

In order to obtain the three distribution functions $g_{OO}(r)$, $g_{OH}(r)$, and $g_{HH}(r)$, three separate scattering experiments are needed. However, when knowledge of the geometry of the H_2O molecule, neutron scattering data of D_2O, and X-ray data are combined (Sec. 16.3), then the three curves (for D_2O) shown in Fig. 15.7 can be obtained [12]. Orientational correlation is described by $g_{OD}(r)$ and $g_{DD}(r)$. It can be seen to be restricted essentially to nearest neighbors. The tetrahedral "pentamer" model [Sec. 13.3(e)] seems to fit such a short-distance orientational correlation well.

Many other proposed models of liquid water are incompatible with the data in Figs. 15.6 and 15.7. Scattering functions calculated from such models do not fit the experimental function. A compatible model

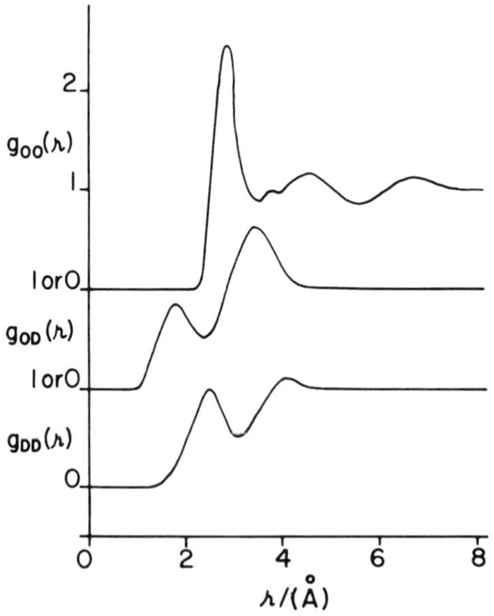

Fig. 15.7. Atom pair correlation functions for water at 25°C as determined from X-ray and neutron scattering. After Ref. 12.

(but not necessarily the only one) is one in which water is a mixture of "network" or "H-bonded" molecules and "cavity" or "monomer" molecules. There are present H-bonded networks similar to an expanded ice-I lattice structure. Such networks are short lived ["flickering clusters"; Sec. 5.2(b)], although this aspect cannot of course be studied by X-rays. There are cavities in this open network, some of which are (randomly) occupied by randomly oriented molecules.

(d) X-ray Scattering Near the Critical Point

Low-angle X-ray scattering from systems near the critical point is of interest in the study of long-range density or composition fluctuations. The theoretical background and interpretation of the results is much the same as for light scattering [Sec. 14.3(h)]. Thus the OZD theory predicts plots of $(i(q))^{-1}$ vs q^2 to give straight lines from which a correlation (or "persistence") length L^2 can be obtained. The agreement between X-ray and light scattering results is not always good, however [13]. The reason for this may often be in experimental inaccuracies rather than in faults in the models used for interpretation.

The effect of gravity on behavior of systems near the critical point has recently been investigated for X-rays [2,14]. In disagreement with the OZD theory [Sec. 14.3(h)], the scattering intensity at constant q does not reach a maximum at T_c [14]. In the system perfluoroheptane-isooctane, this results in a calculated value of L which reaches its maximum value about 1° away from T_c, as shown in Fig. 15.8. Analogous effects have been noted in ultrasonic [Sec. 10.3(f)] and dielectric [Sec. 11.3(g)] studies.

There seems thus to be a relatively large transition region present in two-component liquid mixtures when critical solution phenomena occur. It is not expected to be so large in one-component systems [14]. Experimental X-ray investigations at the small $|T - T_c|$ values and small scattering angles needed to detect such effects in one-component systems would be quite inaccurate.

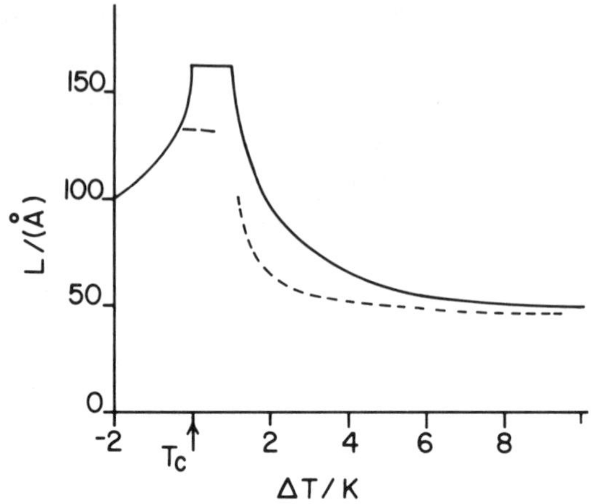

Fig. 15.8. The persistent length L as a function of temperature for —— 40 percent perfluoroheptane in isooctane, and --- 30 percent as determined from X-ray scattering. T_c marks the temperature at which two phases appear for the 40 percent mixture (23.78°C). After Ref. 2.

(e) Structure in Ionic Solutions

X-ray radial distribution functions for ionic solutions can be interpreted to obtain structural information [15,16]. Such solutions must be quite concentrated if differences from the background scattering of the solvent itself (usually water) are to be noted. Thus $g_X(r)$ for tetra-n-butylammonium fluoride-water solutions with a mole ratio 1:41 is nearly the same as that for water itself [15]. The number of nearest neighbors is 3.8 compared to 4.4 for water itself, and the nearest neighbor distance 2.80 Å compared to 2.85 Å. A model of water such as in Sec. 15.3(c) gives a reasonable fit to the experimental data. The F^- and $-\overset{|}{\underset{|}{N}}{}^{+}-$ atoms are part of the H-bonded network in the expanded ice-I lattice, while the butyl chains are located in the cavities.

Studies of inorganic electrolyte solutions have also been carried out to determine hydration numbers and ion associations [16]. From integration of appropriate peaks in $g_X(r)$, the concentration of ion-solvent and ion-ion interactions can be obtained. The various maxima in the $g_X(r)$ must of course be properly interpreted to make this approach valid.

REFERENCES

Thorough reviews of X-ray scattering can be found in [4] and [5]. A review of aspects of particular interest to liquids is given in [3].

1. J. Berghuis, I. M. Haanappel, M. Potters, B. O. Loopstra, C. H. McGillavary and A. L. Veenendaal, Acta Cryst., *8*, 478 (1955).
2. G. W. Brady, J. Appl. Cryst., *4*, 367 (1971).
3. A. H. Narten and H. A. Levy in GR7.
4. H. Brumberger (ed.), Small Angle X-ray Scattering, Gordon and Breach, New York, 1967.
5. A. Guinier, X-ray Diffraction, W. H. Freeman, San Francisco, 1963.
6. P. G. Mikolaj and C. J. Pings, J. Chem. Phys., *46*, 1401, 1412 (1967). C. J. Pings, Disc. Farad. Soc., *43*, 89 (1967).
7. G. W. Brady and C. C. Gravatt, Jr., J. Chem. Phys., *55*, 5095 (1971).
8. A. H. Narten, J. Chem. Phys., *48*, 1630 (1968).
9. A. H. Narten, J. Chem. Phys., *49*, 1962 (1968).
10. T. V. Gorbunova, V. V. Shilov, and G. I. Batalin, J. Struc. Chem., *14*, 388 (1973).
11. A. H. Narten and H. A. Levy, J. Chem. Phys., *55*, 2263 (1971).
12. A. H. Narten, J. Chem. Phys., *56*, 5681 (1972).
13. H. Brumberger, in Critical Phenomena (M. S. Green and J. V. Sengers, eds.), NBS Misc. Publ., 273 (1966).
14. B. C. Dobbs and P. W. Schmidt, J. Chem. Phys., *56*, 2421 (1972).
15. A. H. Narten and S. Lindenbaum, J. Chem. Phys., *51*, 1108 (1969).
16. G. W. Brady, J. Chem. Phys., *33*, 1079 (1960); *29*, 1371 (1958).

Further Recent References

A. H. Narten, C. G. Venkatesh, and S. A. Rice, "Diffraction Pattern and Structure of Amorphous Solid Water at 10 and 77°K", J. Chem. Phys., *64*, 1106 (1976).

R. Triolo and A. H. Narten, "Diffraction Pattern and Structure of Aqueous Hydrochloric Acid Solutions at 20°C", J. Chem. Phys., *63*, 3624 (1975).

Chapter 16

NEUTRON SCATTERING

Neutron scattering is in principle the most versatile of the scattering methods discussed in Part B (Table 16.1). A considerable range is possible in both the energy and momentum transfers between the neutrons and the liquid. Thus both the spatial arrangement of atoms and their dynamics can be studied by neutron scattering. The spatial range which can be probed is from ~1 to 100 Å, while the range in time is from ~10^{-14} to 10^{-11} sec. Thus many of the aspects regarding liquids discussed previously in other chapters in Part B can also be elucidated through neutron scattering.

Even though neutrons are not electromagnetic waves, the theoretical background for neutron scattering has many analogies to that discussed in Secs. 14.1 and 15.1. To explain the interference effects in neutron scattering, a wave optics approach must be taken. The neutron is thus viewed through the wave-particle duality as a wave motion with wavelength $\lambda = \hbar/p$, with the momentum given through $p^2 = 2m_{ne}E_{ne}$. The speed of the neutrons is thus related to the wavelength and energy, and not constant as assumed in scattering of electromagnetic waves.

In experiments elucidating liquid structure, low energy ("thermal" or "cold") neutrons are used. Thus the discussion in this chapter will be restricted to this case, where $\lambda \sim 1$ Å and $E_{ne} \sim kT$ ($T \approx 300$ K).

A wavelength of the order of interatomic spacings is needed if interatomic structure is to be probed. It is also easier to obtain good energy resolution with low-energy neutrons, as the energy transferred with the liquid $|\Delta E|$ is appreciable in size with the incident neutron energy E_{inc}. The incident energy is so low in cases, that only transfers of energy from the liquid to the neutrons can be observed ($E_{sc} > E_{inc}$, "antistokes" scattering).

Unlike the case with light and X-rays, the momentum transfer $\hbar q$ is not fixed by the scattering angle only. For neutrons, $|\underline{k}_{sc}| \approx |\underline{k}_{inc}|$ is no longer a valid approximation, and

$$q = \underline{k}_{inc} - \underline{k}_{sc}$$

$$q^2 = \frac{2m_{ne}}{\hbar^2}\left\{E_{inc} + E_{sc} - 2(E_{inc}E_{sc})^{1/2}\cos\theta\right\}$$

$$\hbar\omega = |\Delta E| = |E_{inc} - E_{sc}| = \left|\frac{\hbar^2}{2m_{ne}}(k_{inc}^2 - k_{sc}^2)\right| \qquad (16.1)$$

As the liquids are assumed isotropic, then both q and ω will be taken as positive scalars.

16.1. THEORETICAL BACKGROUND

(a) Interaction of Neutrons with Atoms

Although the neutron has no net charge, it does have a spin and a magnetic moment. Thus if the atoms are not diamagnetic, but possess electronic magnetic moments, then there will be an interaction between the neutron and the whole atom. In the case of diamagnetic materials assumed throughout this chapter, the interaction between neutron and atom occurs only through neutron-nucleus interactions.

The neutron is scattered by the nucleus primarily because of a specific nuclear interaction which gives rise to a nuclear force field [1]. Intermediate excited nuclei can also be formed during the scattering process. Because of the presence of a magnetic dipole in the neutron, there would also be interactions between the neutron and electromagnetic fields due to the nucleus. The magnitude of the total interaction cannot be calculated a priori, but must be obtained as an experimental entity for each species of nucleus.

The neutron-nucleus interaction can be described by a scattering cross section σ [e.g., (20.55)]. The differential cross section $d^2\sigma/d\Omega\, d\omega$ or $d^2\sigma/d\Omega\, dE$ is usually used to describe the angular and energy dependence of σ. In the case of scattering of slow neutrons from the nucleus of a bound atom, the angular dependence of σ can be expressed as

$$d\sigma = b^2\, d\Omega = b^2(2\pi \sin\theta\, d\theta) \tag{16.2}$$

The "scattering length" or "scattering amplitude" b is for slow neutrons independent of the scattering angle θ and the incident energy E_{inc}. This is the case as the energy of the neutrons is << resonant energies, and as λ >> b. In such a case $\sigma = 4\pi b^2$. This is in contrast to X-ray scattering, where the analogous quantity, the scattering amplitude f, is dependent on θ (i.e., on q). In the case of X-rays, however, the inequality λ >> size of the scattering center does not hold. Both X-rays and slow neutrons have $\lambda \approx 1$ Å (10^{-8} cm), but the scattering of X-rays is from the electron cloud of the atom (radius $\approx 10^{-8}$ cm), while for neutrons it is from the nucleus (radius

$\approx 10^{-12}$ cm). Also in contrast to X-rays, the magnitude of b cannot be calculated, and it has no simple relation to Z or the mass number A of the nucleus (see Table 16.1).

An interaction potential energy $v(\underline{r})$ can be constructed for the neutron-nucleus interaction in terms of b. It can be approximated as the "Fermi pseudopotential"

$$v(\underline{r}) = \frac{2\pi\hbar^2}{m_{ne}} \cdot b \cdot \delta(\underline{r}) \tag{16.3}$$

Where $\delta(\underline{r})$ is simple a δ function describing the position of the nucleus.

(b) Coherent and Incoherent Scattering

The scattering length b (or the cross section σ) is made up of two parts, i.e., $b^2 = b^2_{coh} + b^2_{incoh}$. The first term describes scattering in which phase relations of the neutron wave are not randomized in the scattering process. Thus at the point of observation the amplitude of the scattered radiation is obtained by summing the amplitudes of the neutron waves scattering from all the scattering centers (nuclei). Examples of coherent scattering processes are given in Chaps. 14 and 15.

In incoherent scattering, the intensities rather than the amplitudes of the waves scattered from the nuclei must be added at the point of observation. No interference effects occur as there exists no constant phase relationship between the waves scattered from the nuclei. Examples of incoherent scattering are discussed in Sec. 14.1 for the case of scattering from a gas, or from liquid elements where there is a random fluctuation in $\delta\varepsilon$.

The magnitude of b_{incoh} can be described in terms of the degree of randomization of the individual scattering processes. If for all neutron-nucleus interaction the value of b is the same, then $\langle b^2\rangle = \langle b\rangle^2$. In this case there is no incoherent scattering, and $b^2_{coh} = \langle b\rangle^2$. However, if there is a variation in b, then $\langle b^2\rangle > \langle b\rangle^2$, and the incoherent scattering is given by $b^2_{incoh} = \langle b^2\rangle - \langle b\rangle^2$, with $b^2_{coh} = \langle b\rangle^2$.

In the case of neutrons, incoherent scattering (i.e., a fluctuation in b) can arise either due to isotope or spin effects. Different isotopes of an element have different neutron scattering amplitudes. Thus if there is a random distribution of different isotopes in the liquid, then incoherent scattering results. This source of incoherence can be eliminated through choice of monoisotopic liquids.

If the nuclei have a spin, then this spin can have random orientations. As the neutron scattering is dependent on the spin states of the nuclei, then some randomization of the scattering from the nuclei is introduced, and incoherent scattering results. Here the incident neutron beam is assumed unpolarized. With a polarized neutron beam and orientation of the nuclear spins through a magnetic field, this source of incoherence can also be controlled. Incoherence due to "neutron spinflip" cannot be eliminated, however. In this case the incoherence is caused by a change in the neutron (and thus the nuclear) spin on collision leading to scattering.

Incoherent scattering can give information only about individual scattering centers, and no direct information about collective motions. Coherent scattering gives information about collective motion and structure present in the liquid. From a particle view, coherent scattering can be likened to be due to collision of the neutron with a collective motion, such as the thermal waves in Sec. 14.1(c).

Table 16.1 gives values of b_{coh} and b_{incoh} for a number of more common nuclei. Some nuclei are pure coherent scatterers, while others, e.g., H, are essentially pure incoherent. While coherent scattering leads in principle to more information, it is easier to interpret the results of pure incoherent scattering. Interpretation of scattering results in which there is a mixture of coherent and incoherent scattering is more difficult, as separation of the two types of scattering is necessary. Refs. 2 and 3 give more complete lists. The cross sections listed are for bound nuclei. In the case of the free nuclei [3(d)], the reduced mass of the nucleus-neutron collision system must be used instead of the neutron mass. Thus $\sigma_{free} = \sigma_{bound} \cdot A/(A + 1)$. It should be noted that ^1H has by far the largest scattering cross section.

TABLE 16.1

Neutron Scattering Cross Sections for Selected Nuclei

Nucleus	$\sigma_{coh} = 4\pi b_{coh}^2$ /(10^{-24} cm^2 or barn)	σ_{incoh}/(barn)	$\sigma_{tot} = 4\pi(b_{coh}^2 + b_{incoh}^2)$
^{1}H	1.79	79.7	81.5
^{2}H(D)	5.4	2.2	7.6
^{16}O	4.2	~0	4.24
^{20}Ne	2.41	~0.05	2.5
^{27}Al	1.5	0	1.5
^{40}Ar	0.5	0.4	0.9
^{12}C	5.5	~0	5.5
^{23}Na	1.55	1.8	3.4

(c) Scattering Described in Terms of S(q,ω)

A derivation of the expression relating $d^2\sigma/d\Omega\, dE$ to $S(q,\omega)$ is given in Ref. 4. A qualitative analogy can be made with the derivation in Sec. 14.1(d). There the incident electromagnetic radiation induced dipoles in the molecules. These induced dipoles were then sources for scattered waves which were then superposed at the point of observation. Here each nucleus can be thought to be a source of scattered neutron waves which are then superposed at the point observation, adding amplitudes for coherent and intensities for incoherent scattering.

A rigorous approach involves the solution of the time-dependent Schrödinger wave equation (Sec. 21.1). The total wave function at some point $\underline{r}$ at some time t can be written as

$$\Psi(\underline{r},t) = \Psi_{inc}(\underline{r},t) + \Psi_{sc}(\underline{r},t) = \exp[i(\underline{k}_{inc}\cdot\underline{r} - \omega_{inc}t)] + \Psi_{sc}(\underline{r},t) \qquad (16.4)$$

The Hamiltonian would be of the form

$$\hat{H} = -\frac{\hbar^2}{2m_{ne}}\nabla^2 + \sum_j \frac{2\pi\hbar^2}{m_{ne}} b_j \cdot \delta(\underline{r} - \underline{r}_j(t)) \qquad (16.5)$$

Here the total potential energy has been expressed using (16.3) introducing the time dependent δ function [see, e.g., Eqs. (14.12) and (7.1)].

An expression for $\Psi_{sc}(\underline{r},t)$ can then be obtained using first order perturbation theory [e.g., Sec. 21.3(a)]. It is written in terms of a Fourier expansion $\Psi_{sc}(\underline{r},t) = \sum_{\omega}\Psi(\underline{r},\omega_{sc}) \exp[-i\omega_{sc}t]$. The first order perturbation gives after simplification

$$\Psi_{sc}(\underline{r},\omega_{sc}) = \frac{i}{\hbar t}\int_0^t \exp[-i\omega_{sc}t']\, dt' \cdot \sum b_j \int \delta(\underline{r} - \underline{r}_j(t)) \exp[i\underline{q}\cdot\underline{r}]\, d\underline{r} \tag{16.6}$$

The number of neutrons passing through the area $r^2 d\Omega$ relative to unit incident flux is

$$d\sigma = \frac{v_{sc}}{v_{inc}} r^2\, d\Omega \sum_{\omega} |\Psi_{sc}(\underline{r},\omega_{sc})|^2 \tag{16.7}$$

From this the differential cross section can be shown to be

$$\frac{d^2\sigma}{d\Omega\, dE} = \frac{v_{sc}}{v_{inc}} r^2\, d\Omega \left\{ \frac{1}{r^2} \frac{dE}{2\pi\hbar^2} \int_{-\infty}^{\infty} \sum_{j,\ell} b_j^* b_\ell \cdot \exp[i\underline{q}\cdot\underline{r}_\ell(t)] \right.$$
$$\left. \cdot \exp[-i\underline{q}\cdot\underline{r}_j(0)] \exp[-i\omega_{sc}t]\, dt \right\} \frac{1}{d\Omega\, dE} \tag{16.8}$$

The expression in curly brackets gives the expression for $\sum|\Psi_{sc}(\underline{r},\omega_{sc})|^2$. Further simplification using (7.1) and (7.11) leads to the basic relation

$$\frac{d^2\sigma}{d\Omega\, dE} = \frac{b^2 k_{sc}}{2\pi\hbar k_{inc}} S(q,\omega) \tag{16.9}$$

The total cross section in (16.9) is calculated assuming only coherent scattering in monoisotopic fluids. If a variation in b is allowed, then

$$\frac{d^2\sigma}{d\Omega\, dE} = \frac{d^2\sigma_{coh}}{d\Omega\, dE} + \frac{d^2\sigma_{incoh}}{d\Omega\, dE}$$

where

$$\frac{d^2\sigma_{coh}}{d\Omega\ dE} = \frac{b^2_{coh}}{2\pi\hbar}\frac{k_{sc}}{k_{inc}} S(q,\omega) \qquad (b^2_{coh} = \langle b\rangle^2)$$

$$\frac{d^2\sigma_{incoh}}{d\Omega\ dE} = \frac{b^2_{incoh}}{2\pi\hbar}\frac{k_{sc}}{k_{inc}} S_s(q,\omega) \qquad (b^2_{incoh} = \langle b^2\rangle - \langle b\rangle^2) \tag{16.10}$$

The scattering law $S_s(q,\omega)$ refers only to the self-correlation function $G_s(r,t)$ (7.4), while $S(q,\omega)$ refers to the total van Hove function (7.3).

(d) Incoherent Scattering: Quasielastic

Measurements of $S_s(q,\omega)$ leads to knowledge of $G_s(r,t)$. If diffusive motion as described by Fick's law is present, then (7.8) holds and the form of $S_s(q,\omega)$ would be

$$S_s(q,\omega) = \frac{1}{\pi}\frac{Dq^2}{\omega^2 + D^2q^4t} \tag{16.11}$$

This predicts $S_s(q,\omega)$ vs ω to be a Lorentzian (Fig. 20.1) with a width at half height given by $2Dq^2$, i.e., the same as in (14.21). In this case q cannot be assumed to be given simply by the scattering angle (14.1). This simple diffusion model leads to a slight energy width and gives rise to the "quasielastic" scattering. In solids, where $D \to 0$, it is refered to as the "elastic" scattering.

The actual quasielastic peak observed is different from that predicted by (16.11) because of inadequacies of the macroscopic diffusion model assumed to describe motion at short times. At the shortest times probed by neutron scattering ($\to 10^{-14}$ sec) the particle nature of the surroundings of the atom must be considered. The motion can be thought of as being "gaslike" for very short periods of time during which it is carrying out a random jump of length ℓ [Sec. 6.2 (a)]. The time τ_{res} at a site between jumps can then be expressed as (e.g., Ref. 5)

$$\tau_{res} \approx \frac{m_{eff}D}{kT} \quad \text{or} \quad \tau_{res} \simeq \frac{\langle\ell^2\rangle}{6D} \quad (\tau_{res} \simeq 2 \times 10^{-12}\ \text{sec}) \tag{16.12}$$

Here m_{eff} is an effective mass about 30 times the actual mass.

Inclusion of such refinement to the diffusion model predicts the value of D as obtained from (16.11) to be equal to the macroscopic (Fick's law) D only as $q \rightarrow 0$. There the values of $\underline{r}$ sampled are considerably greater than the mean jump distances, and macroscopic theory should apply. At higher values of q, the experimental half width can be considerably less than that predicted from the simple diffusion model, i.e., the "effective D" is smaller than expected. This is an example of the liquid acting more like a solid at short distances (and short times).

The motion of an atom in a molecular liquid will be due both to a motion of the molecule center of mass and a rotational motion. This introduces considerable complexities into the interpretation of the quasielastic $S_s(q,\omega)$ [6,7]. The half-width leads to a value $2(D_{tr} + D_{rot})$ as $q \rightarrow 0$ in this case.

The intensity of $S_s(q,\omega)$ is also affected by the Debye-Waller factor [Sec. 15.3(b)], $\exp[-q^2\langle\zeta^2\rangle/6]$ just as for X-rays. This is due to the nucleus appearing as a "thermal cloud" due to the thermal motion. It is thus effectively spread out over a volume characterized by the mean square displacement $\langle\zeta^2\rangle$. From a classical point of view, there is a phase modulation of the scattered wave due to the Doppler effect associated with nuclei in thermal motion. The angular dependence can be best interpreted from the wave point of view, in analogy with the q dependence of f in X-rays. The decrease in the effective b_{incoh} with angle, i.e., with q, is thus interpreted as being due to interference between the neutron wave scattered from different parts of the "thermal cloud."

(e) Incoherent Scattering: Inelastic

The total motion of the atom in the liquid contains both "diffusive" and "vibrational" components [Sec. 7.2(d)]. The whole motion can be expressed generally through the velocity time correlation function (7.2). This velocity correlation function is related to $S_s(q,\omega)$ as [5]

$$\omega^2\left\{\frac{S_s(q,\omega)}{q^2}\right\}_{q\to 0} = \frac{1}{2\pi}\int_{-\infty}^{\infty}\langle \underline{u}(0)\cdot\underline{u}(t)\rangle \exp[-i\omega t]\, dt$$

$$= G_v(\omega) \qquad (16.13)$$

The normalized Fourier transform is

$$G_v'(\omega) = \frac{m_{eff}}{3kT} G_v(\omega)$$

$$\int_{-\infty}^{\infty} G_v'(\omega)\, d\omega = 1 \qquad (16.14)$$

The quasielastic scattering is due to the diffusive components (see, e.g,, Fig. 7.3). The vibrational components of $G_v(\omega)$ give rise to inelastic scattering. In crystalline solids, such scattering can be thought of as interactions of neutrons with phonons. Motion in liquids at short times should not differ greatly from solids. $S_s(q,\omega)$ for crystals can be expressed in terms of the distribution $g_{ph}(\omega)$ of phonons [e.g., the Debye distribution, (18.17)]. Thus

$$S_s(q,\omega) = \exp\left[-\frac{q^2\langle\zeta^2\rangle}{6}\right]\left\{\delta(\omega^2) + \frac{kT}{m}\frac{g_{ph}(\omega)}{\omega^2} + \left(\frac{kT}{m}q^2\right)^2\int\frac{g_{ph}(\omega-\omega')g_{ph}(\omega)}{2(\omega-\omega')^2\omega^2}\,d\omega'\right\} + \cdots \qquad (16.15)$$

The first term in curly brackets gives the Debye-Waller term for solids. There is effectively no diffusion in solids; hence the "quasi-elastic" peak is "elastic" as indicated by the δ function. The second term in curly brackets is the single-phonon interaction term, the third in curly brackets a two-phonon term. Higher order multi-phonon interactions are not included in (16.15).

As seen in Sec. 14.1(c) such "phonons" or thermal waves in liquids have a much shorter life-time and pathlength than in crystalline solids. The maintenance of transverse waves in liquids is especially difficult. Thus (16.15) can only be expected to give a very qualitative picture of the inelastic scattering spectrum.

(f) Coherent Scattering

The coherent scattering is related to $S(q,\omega)$ as defined in (7.11). The shape of the function $S(q,\omega)$ can thus be anticipated to reflect the shape of $G(r,t)$ as suggested in Fig. 7.1. For $q \to 0$, the form of $S(q,\omega)$ would be expected to be approximated by the hydrodynamic limit. Thus for q fixed $S(q,\omega)$ vs ω would be expected to have the shape shown in Fig. 14.2.

The $q \to \infty$ limit corresponds to the dynamics of spatial arrangements with very small distances, i.e., of the order of interatomic distances. In this case a "gaslike" time dependence would be expected. The half-width of the large q curve can be obtained from (16.12) as $\delta\omega = q\sqrt{kT/m_{eff}}$. At intermediate values of q the $S(q,\omega)$ vs ω would be more complex.

Often the "zeroth moment" of $S(q,\omega)$ is taken, This occurs when energy resolution is not taken into account. This "zeroth moment" is simply

$$S(q) = \int_{-\infty}^{\infty} S(q,\omega)\, d\omega$$

$$= 1 + \frac{1}{2\pi} n\int (g(\underline{r}) - 1) \exp[i\underline{q}\cdot\underline{r}]\, d\underline{r} \tag{16.16}$$

Relation (3.14) has been used to express $S(q)$ in terms of $g(r)$. $S(q)$ can be seen to be essentially the same function as the "structurally sensitive" X-ray scattering function $i(q)$ (15.6) (see also Fig. 3.1).

A common approximation relating $S(q,\omega)$ to $S_s(q,\omega)$ is to write

$$S(q,\omega) = S_s(q,\omega)\cdot S(q) \tag{16.17}$$

More sophisticated models replace the function $S(q)$ with a more realistic function [8]. The model leading to (16.17) does not prevent atoms from "penetrating" each other as time progresses (the "convolution error"). The quasielastic coherent scattering can be seen from (16.17) to be appreciable only for values of q where $S(q)$ is appreciable. The coherent quasielastic scattering is with the assumption of (16.17) and the simple diffusion model (16.11) given as

$$\frac{Dq^2}{(Dq^2/S(q))^2 + \omega^2} \tag{16.18}$$

It is not always possible to choose liquids and conditions so that the scattering is all essentially coherent or all incoherent. Thus for a mixed scatterer, the quasielastic scattering is from (16.11) given as

$$b^2S(q,\omega) = b^2_{incoh}\frac{Dq^2}{(Dq^2)^2 + \omega^2} + b^2_{coh}\frac{Dq^2}{(Dq^2/S(q))^2 + \omega^2} \tag{16.19}$$

(g) Moment Analysis

Instead of describing the shape of $S(q,\omega)$ explicitly, it can also be described in terms of "moments", $S^{(n)}(q)$, as

$$S^{(n)}(q) = (-1)^n \int_{-\infty}^{\infty} \omega^n S(q,\omega)\, d\omega \tag{16.20}$$

The zero order moment has already been indicated to be $S(q)$ (16.16). Such moments can be viewed from the point of view of the intermediate scattering function $I(q,t)$. The moments correspond actually to an expansion of $I(q,t)$ in powers of t. Thus $S^{(n)}(q) = I^{(n)}(q,0)$, where $I^{(n)}$ stands for the nth order time derivative of $I(q,t)$.

Through such an analysis, expressions can be obtained for the various moments: These are, e.g.,

$$I_s(q,0) = 1 \qquad I(q,0) = S(q)$$

$$I^{(1)}(q,0) = \frac{\hbar q^2}{2m} \qquad I^{(1)}(q,0) = \frac{\hbar q^2}{2m} \tag{16.21}$$

$$I_s^{(2)}(q,0) = -\frac{q^2kT}{m} \qquad I^{(2)}(q,0) = \frac{q^2kT}{mS(q)}$$

In the form for $I^{(2)}(q,0)$, the variation of the area under $S(q,\omega)$ with $S(q)$ has been taken into account. The consistency of experimental data can be checked through these moment relations, as they must hold independent of the model used for interpretation.

16.2. EXPERIMENTAL TECHNIQUES

The apparatus and techniques used for neutron scattering are discussed in Refs. 9 and 10. A brief outline will be given here of sources, monochromators, energy analysis, and detectors for thermal neutrons.

The source for thermal neutrons is usually a continuous nuclear reactor with beam tubes built to reach into various parts of the reactor. A continuous beam of neutrons with a distribution of velocities can thus be obtained. The greater the collimation of the beam, however, the smaller is the flux of neutrons in the beam. Pulsed reactors and electron linear accelerators are also possible sources. In the latter, the absorption of high energy electrons by a target of e.g., lead produces γ rays which in turn are absorbed to produce neutrons through a nuclear reaction.

Two types of "monochromators" are possible. In a crystal monochromator, the neutron beam is diffracted by a crystal and the neutrons with the correct Bragg wavelength are selected out, i.e., with $n\lambda = 2d \sin \frac{\theta}{2}$, where d is the spacing between crystal planes and $n = 1, 2, 3, \cdots$. A mechanical monochromator can be used to select neutrons with only one such wavelength, i.e., with only one velocity or energy. This can be a type of screw with axis of rotation parallel to the neutron beam. Such a device lets through only neutrons which can travel in the groove of the screw. A continuous neutron beam is obtained in this way.

Another monochromator producing pulses of neutrons (usually about 10^{-6} sec long) consists of two rotating slits. A pulse of neutrons is allowed through the first slit when its direction coincides with the neutron beam. This pulse widens out as it travels toward a second rotating slit because of a range of velocities in the neutrons. The second slit selects out neutrons with velocities such that they reach the second slit when it is parallel to the neutron beam. Thus pulsed beams are obtained.

Energy analysis of continuous beams can be obtained through Bragg reflection from an analyzing crystal. In the case of pulsed beams energy, i.e., velocity, analysis can also be carried out through a time of flight analysis. A neutron undergoing a change in energy (speed) on scattering will reach a detector at a time different from an elastically ($\Delta E = 0$) scattered neutron. An analysis of the shape of the pulse of neutrons some distance (e.g., 1-5 m) away from the scattering sample yields thus an analysis of the energy transfer in the scattering. This "time of flight" method is most commonly used for liquids where the function $S(q,\omega)$ does not vary very strongly.

Thermal neutrons can be detected only through secondary reactions arising from absorption of neutrons by nuclei. ^{10}B, ^{9}Li, and ^{3}He have large absorption cross sections and are usually employed. Boron in the form of BF_3 is commonly used. For ^{10}B, the reaction making detection possible is

$$^{1}n + {}^{10}B \rightarrow {}^{7}Li + {}^{4}He + \gamma\text{-ray } (0.48 \text{ MeV})$$

The recoil particles of the nuclear reactions are detected by the usual means, e.g., through ionization in a gas or light produced in a scintillating material.

Numerous considerations must be taken into account in order to obtain the best possible experimental results. The resolution in both scattering angle and energy must be arranged to be as great as possible under the condition that greater resolution leads to a smaller number of neutrons to be averaged in obtaining $d^2\sigma/d\Omega\, d\omega$ in the space $d\Omega\, d\omega$. Corrections must also in cases be made for multiple scattering, as in the case of light scattering.

16.3. RESULTS FOR SPECIFIC SYSTEMS

(a) Structure in Atomic Liquids

The function $S(q)$ as obtained from neutron scattering should lead to the same information as the function $i(q)$ from X-ray scattering. This is true for atomic liquids only. In the case of molecular liquids, more than one type of atom is present, and the ratio of f_a/f_b is not the same as b_a/b_b. The equivalence of X-ray and neutron diffraction in obtaining $g(r)$ for monatomic liquids has been demonstrated in [11] for liquid gallium. Neutron (λ = 1.10 Å) and X-ray (λ = 0.71 Å) data give identical results for $g(r)$. The data at $q \rightarrow 0$ is also in agreement with the limit predicted from thermodynamics to within 1%.

Distribution functions for liquid neon have been obtained from neutron scattering [12]. The results are much like the X-ray results of argon [Sec. 15.3(a)]. The interatomic pair potential obtained from $g(r)$ with either PY or HNC theories [Sec. 3.2(b)] is unsatisfactory. In obtaining S(q) for neon from neutron scattering, corrections to the total scattering intensity as a function of angle must be made for multiple scattering, incoherent scattering (see Table 16.1), and contributions from energy changes to the magnitude of q.

(b) Dynamics in Monatomic Liquids

The dynamics in monatomic liquids has often been measured for metals. It is possible to obtain pure coherent scattering liquid metals (e.g., Aℓ), and under the proper condition, effectively completely incoherent scatterers such as liquid sodium. Liquid metals will not be discussed here, but instead the results obtained from argon and neon.

(1) Argon

Both incoherent and coherent scattering laws can be obtained for liquid argon [13]. The coherent scattering can be obtained from ^{36}Ar. A mixture of ^{40}Ar and ^{36}Ar scatters predominantly incoherently, and corrections for coherent contributions can be made with the ^{36}Ar results. Here the incoherent scattering law for Ar will be discussed. Coherent scattering in monatomic liquids will be discussed using the results for neon [14].

The incoherent scattering law for argon is shown in Fig. 16.1 as $S_s(q,E)$ for four values of E. The range of variation in q is 1 to to 4.4 $\mathring{A}^{-1}$. The energy spectrum of scattered neutrons at various scattering angles is observed through time of flight experiments. After correction of experimental data for sample holder scattering, multiple scattering, spectrometer resolution and contributions from coherent scattering, the results can be replotted as in Fig. 16.1 with the aid of relations (16.1). Thus the four curves in the figure are four slices of a 3-D diagram ($S_s(q,E)$ as a function of q and E).

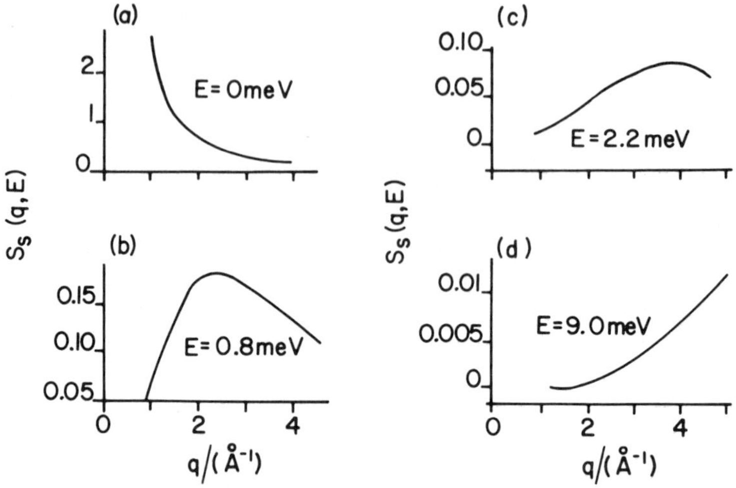

Fig. 16.1. Incoherent scattering law $S_s(q,E)$ as a function of q for liquid argon at 85.2 K at four values of E; (a) E = 0 meV; (b) E = 0.8 meV; (c) E = 2.2 meV; (d) E = 9.0 meV. After Ref. 13.

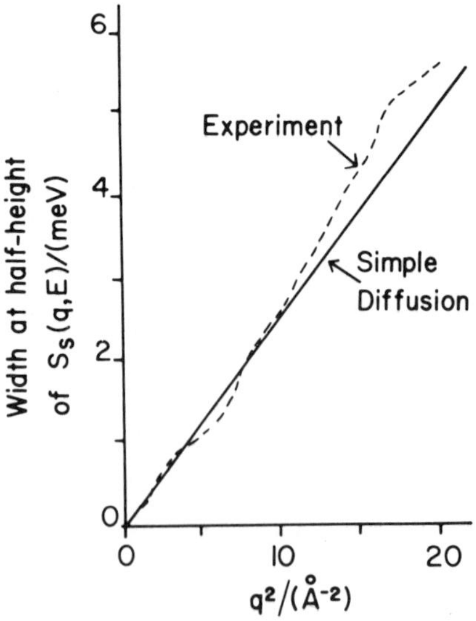

Fig. 16.2. The half-width of the incoherent scattering law as a function of q^2 for argon at 85.2 K. --- experiment; —— simple diffusion ($\delta E = 2\hbar Dq^2$). After Ref. 13.

$S_s(q,E)$ is a monotonically decreasing function of E at all values of q. This can be seen by the scale changes in Fig. 16.1. Examples of such curves for neon are shown in Fig. 16.3. Diffusive modes dominate the spectrum, and vibrational modes are heavily damped. Thus it is not possible to divide the spectrum between diffusion and vibrational modes [Sec. 16.1(e)] as quasielastic and inelastic scattering cannot be separated. The half-width of $S_s(q,E)$ when plotted (Fig. 16.2) as a function of q^2 gives the diffusion coefficient under hydrodynamic assumptions (16.11). The width at half-height is compared to the hydrodynamic prediction ($D = 1.94 \times 10^{-5}$ cm^2 sec^{-1}). With q in the range 1 to 3 Å^{-1}, the half-width is below that predicted by hydrodynamics, in agreement with molecular dynamics calculations [15].

Such molecular dynamics calculations show that $S_s(q,E)$ [and thus $G_v(t)$ (16.13)] is quite sensitive to the form of the intermolecular potential function. If a repulsion softer than the 6-12 potential is used, then the vibrational part of $G_v(t)$ becomes more predominant. Thus the vibrational part of $S_s(q,E)$ becomes more pronounced and persists to larger values of q. This seems to be the case in liquid metals, where the inelastic scattering is more pronounced.

Neutron scattering data for liquid argon has been interpreted in terms of the presence of "longitudinal phonons," e.g., see Ref. 6. This interpretation does not seem to be valid, however, in the range of q sampled by neutrons [16]. Vibrational modes can appear at lower q ranges investigated by light scattering (Chap. 14).

(2) Neon

Figure 16.3 shows curves of the scattering law for coherent scattering from liquid neon displayed scattering intensity for four values of q [14]. This gives the basic shape of $S(q,\omega)$ [(16.1), (16.9)]. Here the energy shift is expressed in frequency (THz = 10^{12} Hz). The integral of $S(q,\nu)$ with respect to ν gives a point on the S(q) vs q curve (16.16). The total intensity at $q = 2.4$ Å^{-1} is thus very high, as S(q) for neon has a high value at $q = 2.4$ Å^{-1} (Fig. 3.1). At $q = 1.4$ Å^{-1} S(q) has a value lower by about a factor of 20. Measurements were made for a range $0.8 < q < 12.5$ Å^{-1}.

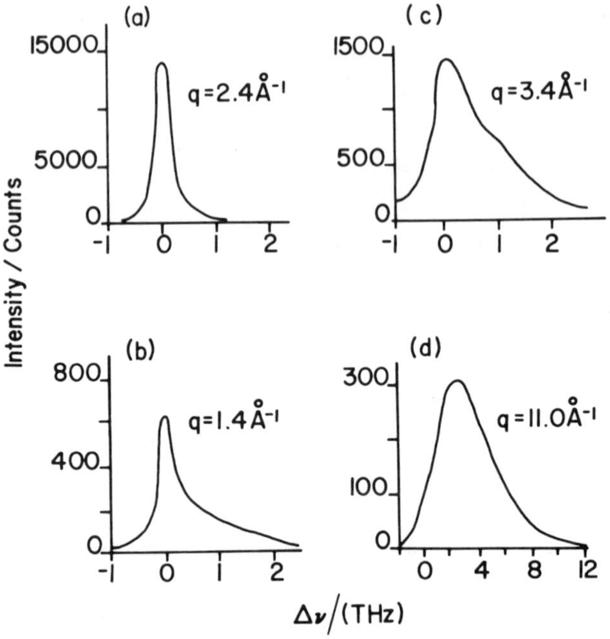

Fig. 16.3. Constant q coherent neutron scattering from liquid neon at 26.9K at four q values. Correction for sample holder scattering has been made. The instrumental resolution is about 0.3 THz. At q = 11 $\mathring{A}^{-1}$ the free recoil frequency ($\hbar q^2/4m\pi$) is 3 THz. After Ref. 14.

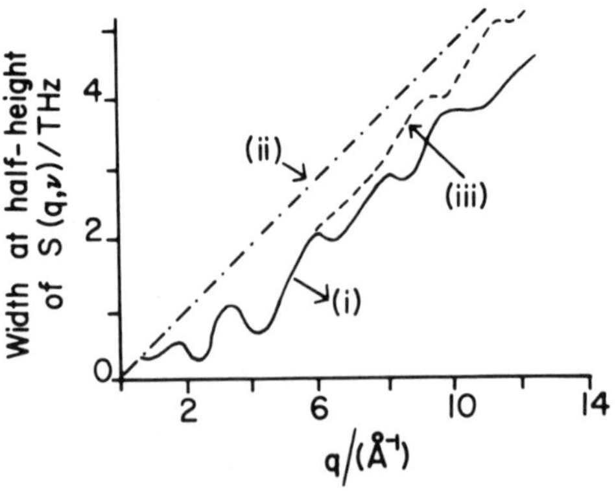

Fig. 16.4. Half-width of the coherent scattering law as a function of q for neon at 26.9K. (i) —— Experimental; (ii) —·—· impulse approximation; (iii) --- including inhibition of recoil (for q > 5.0 $\mathring{A}^{-1}$). After Ref. 14.

There is no evidence of any phonon-like excitation in liquid neon for the q range investigated, as no well-defined inelastic scattering is observed. At much lower q values (0.002 $\AA^{-1}$) a very well-defined Brillouin peak is observed, however [17].

The half-width and the frequency of displacement of the scattering both show oscillations when plotted against q. This is shown in Fig. 16.4 compared with two theoretical predictions. The impulse approximation shown should be valid at $q \to \infty$; the scattering atom is assumed to recoil as if it were free and the scattering function is simply the Doppler profile of the initial velocity (Maxwellian distribution). The second theory takes account of the partial inhibiting of the atom recoil by interatomic forces. If this inhibition were complete then $S(q,\omega)$ would be a δ function in ω.

(c) Rotational Motion in Liquids

(1) Methane

Because of the high incoherent scattering cross section of ^1H (Table 16.1), hydrogenic liquids (i.e., liquids in which the molecules contain many hydrogens) are especially useful in studies of molecular dynamics. The neutron scattering is essentially completely incoherent, so that $S_s(q,\omega)$ can be obtained from the experimental data with few approximations. Interpretation of $S_s(q,\omega)$ for nonmonatomic liquids is complicated by the presence of both center of mass and rotational motion for molecules.

Methane is commonly studied as the moment of inertia is small. This results in large rotational frequencies ($\omega_{rot} \simeq \sqrt{kT/I}$ for unhindered classical rotation), producing an inelastic spectrum arising from rotational motion well removed from the quasielastic (diffusion broadened) peak. This is illustrated in Fig. 16.5, where the experimental data is compared with the model of Sears [7].

The model assumes that rotational and translational (center of mass) motions can be treated separately. This leads to a self-scattering law for the protons of the form:

$$S_s(q,\omega) = \int_{-\infty}^{\infty} S_{rot}(q,\omega - \omega')S_{tr}(q,\omega')\, d\omega' \qquad (16.22)$$

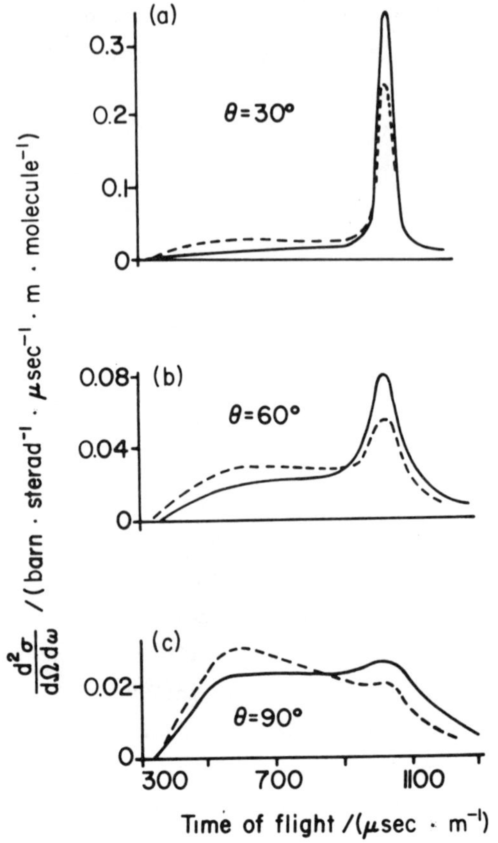

Fig. 16.5. Time of flight neutron scattering spectra for liquid methane at 98K at three scattering angles. ---Experimental; —— calculated following the theory in Ref. 7. After Ref. 18.

The rotational motion can be described in terms of a total angular correlation function which is expanded in terms of spherical harmonics. This leads to

$$S_{rot}(q,\omega) = \sum_{\ell=0}^{\infty} (2\ell + 1)J_{\ell}(qa)^2 S_{\ell}(\omega) \tag{16.23}$$

Where $J_{\ell}(qa)$ is the ℓth order spherical Bessel function, a is the distance between the proton and the center of mass, and $S_{\ell}(\omega)$ is the Fourier transform of the ℓth order orientational relaxation function

(7.3). The functions $S_1(\omega)$ and $S_2(\omega)$ can be obtained from infrared and Raman spectra, respectively. The solid lines in Fig. 16.5 are the calculated values including S_1, S_2, S_3, and S_4, the two latter functions being assumed Gaussian in form. The center of mass motion ($S_{tr}(q,\omega)$) was assumed of a simple diffusion type [Sec. 16.1(d)] [18].

Studies of more complex liquids have also been made, and more sophisticated models for analysis suggested [19-22]. Most of the experimental and theoretical studies are concerned with $S_s(q,\omega)$ in molecular liquids. Investigation of cooperative rotational motion has however also lately been investigated [21,22].

(2) Benzene

The rotational and vibrational motion of benzene has also been studied with neutron scattering [23]. The distribution of frequencies of proton motion present in liquid benzene as determined by neutron scattering [(16.13), (16.14)] is shown in Fig. 16.6. This distribution of frequencies can be compared with that obtained from Raman and IR spectroscopy.

The Raman spectrum of liquid benzene resembles that of the solid, where lines are found at 35, 63, 69, and 105 cm^{-1}, with an IR line at

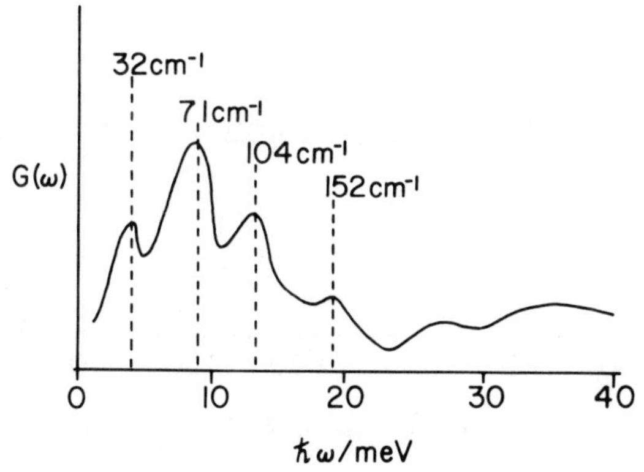

Fig. 16.6. Spectral density function G( ) for benzene at 313K as obtained from neutron scattering. After Ref. 23.

160 cm^{-1}. The frequencies noted in neutron scattering can be matched to these lines to give the following assignments: 32 cm^{-1}, rotational oscillations with axis in the plane of benzene; 71 cm^{-1}, rotational oscillations with axis perpendicular to the plane; 104 cm^{-1}, as for 71 cm^{-1}, 152 cm^{-1}, benzene ring deformation. The contributions of these various types of motion to the total motion is proportional to the area under the respective peaks.

(d) Isotopic Substitution Techniques

A valuable method for obtaining experimental data on molecular liquids is through isotopic substitution. As can be seen in Table 16.1, the neutron scattering characteristics of two isotopes of the same element can be very different. This is illustrated in Fig. 16.7 for three different isotopic forms of methanol [19]. A scattering angle is fixed at 63°.

From the variation of the bandwidth and intensity of the quasi-elastic peak, values can be found for the effective diffusion coefficient [δE vs q^2, (16.11)] and the value of ζ^2 [log area vs q^2; Sec. 16.1(d)]. For methanol, such plots give $D = 2.3 \times 10^{-5}\ cm^2\ sec^{-1}$ and $\langle\zeta^2\rangle = 0.73$ Å.

The isotopic substitution indicates that the inelastic scattering is due mainly to the methyl group. When it is deuterated, the

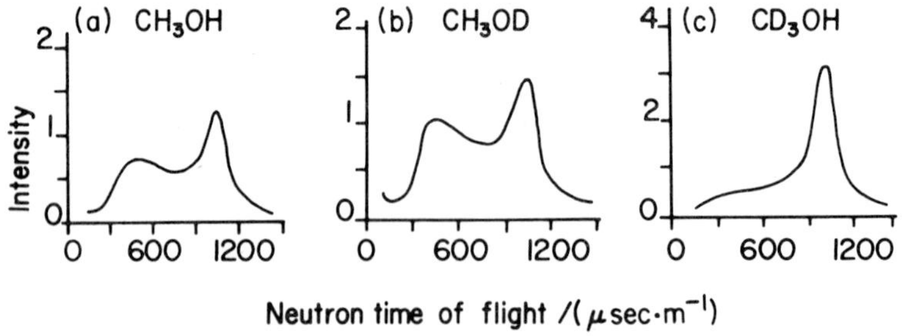

Fig. 16.7. Neutron time of flight spectra at a scattering angle of 63 deg. for three methanol isotopes at 295K. (a) CH_3OH; (b) CH_3OD; (c) CD_3OH. After Ref. 19.

inelastic intensity decreases due to the smaller σ of ^2H. The inelastic peak at ~500 μsec time of flight (120 cm^{-1}) is attributed to being due to rotation of the methyl group. A higher energy peak present in CD_3OH but absent in CH_3OD at ~550 cm^{-1} is assigned to motion of the hydroxyl group. It should be noted that if it is assumed that all the scattering is incoherent and due to ^1H (only ~73% in reality), and if the scattering from methyl and hydroxyl protons is additive, then the CH_3OH spectrum should be attained by adding the CH_3OD and the CD_3OH spectra weighted as 3:1. This gives good agreement, except at large q values and in the quasielastic region where coherent scattering becomes noticeable.

The rotational motion of hydrogenated molecules can also be studied through isotopic substitution and the measurement of total scattering cross section vs incident neutron wavelengths [20]. At low values of λ_{inc}, (<0.5 Å) the neutron energy is considerably greater than energy states in the proton, and the cross section σ is that for the free proton, i.e., $81.5/\mu^2 = 20.4$ barn, where $\mu = 2$ is the

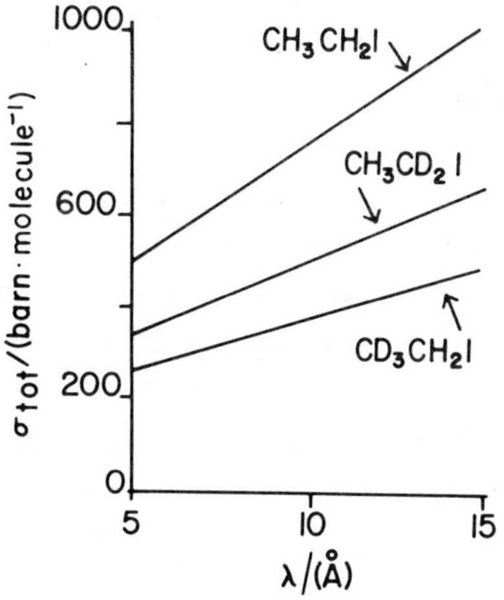

Fig. 16.8. Neutron scattering cross section as a function of the incident neutron wavelength for three ethyl iodides. After Ref. 20.

reduced mass of the proton-neutron collision. At $\lambda \approx 4$ Å, $\sigma \simeq 81$ barn, the bound proton cross section (Table 16.1).

At higher values of λ (cold neutron region), σ can increase to yet higher values. Such an increase occurs due to energy gain in the neutrons from dynamical processes of the protons, in particular internal motions. The slope of σ vs λ gives then information about the internal rotations of methyl groups. The greater the slope, the more free the rotation. For CH_3 groups, the increase in σ for $5 < \lambda < 15$ Å is linear with a slope of ~10 barn Å^{-1} per proton. A comparison of CH_3CH_2I, CH_3CD_2I, and CD_3CH_2I (Fig. 16.8) indicates that all the hydrogens, whether $-CH_3$ or $-CH_2-$, participate equally in internal rotation.

(e) Water

Neutron scattering in water is reviewed in Ref. 24. Most of the experimental work is on light water, as in this case the incoherent scattering from protons is predominant. As noted in Sec. (c) above, this makes it possible to arrive as $S_s(q,\omega)$ and $G_v(\omega)$ without making numerous assumptions. Some of the early experimental results for light water are shown in Fig. 16.9. Peaks are identified by the authors at 61, 21, 8, 5, and 0.5 meV [25]. Closely corresponding peaks appear in the functions $G_v(\omega)$ for water as obtained by applying (16.13) and (16.14) to later experimental work. Two such curves obtained from neutron scattering [26,27] are shown in Fig. 16.10.

Peak I near 65 meV (500 cm^{-1}) is assigned to a librational mode, but there is uncertainty about the resolution of the spectrum below 50 meV. One of the spectral density functions $G_v(\omega)$ for protons in water shown in Fig. 16.10 shows this region as having two peaks, at 22 and 12.5 meV. The peak at 22 meV is interpreted as due to hindered translation (i.e., intermolecular vibration). The low energy region is discussed more fully in Sec. 12.3(e).

The regions in $G_v(\omega)$ due to intramolecular vibrations are not shown fully in Fig. 16.10. The peak at 200 meV arising from the bending modes has been obtained from neutron scattering [26], and is

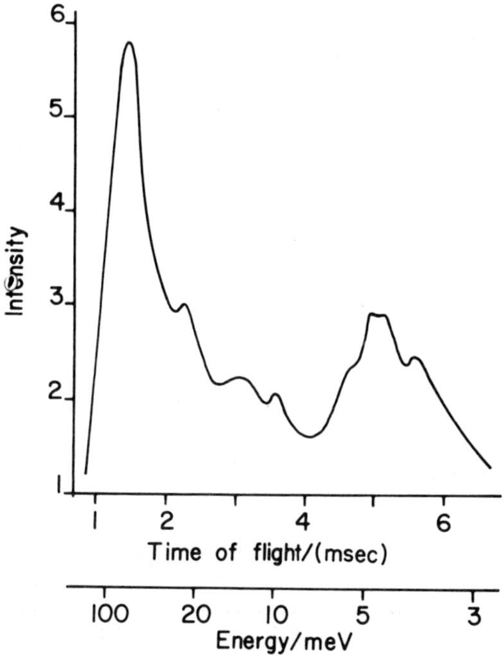

Fig. 16.9. Time of flight spectrum of neutrons scattered by H_2O at 295K with θ = 90 deg. The incident peak is at 5.0 meV. The antistokes spectrum is shown at E > 5.0 meV and the stokes at E < 5.0 meV. The spectrum is not corrected for passage through aluminum in the reactor structure, which contributes a peak at 4 meV. After Ref. 25.

in agreement with infrared data [Sec. 12.3(d)]. The higher energy vibrations at 450 and 530 meV (not shown in Fig. 16.10) are somewhat different as obtained by neutron scattering from the shapes predicted from IR data. These two modes are expected to have a total "weight" in the normalized $G_V(\omega)$ curve of ~0.27, compared to a weight of ~0.13 for the 200 meV mode and ~0.6 for intermolecular modes.

No information regarding S(q), i.e., $g(r)$ can be obtained from light water neutron scattering due to the absence of any appreciable coherent scattering. Measurements on heavy water have also been made [28]. As for the case of neon, the experimental neutron results must be analyzed to correct for change in q due to change in energy as well

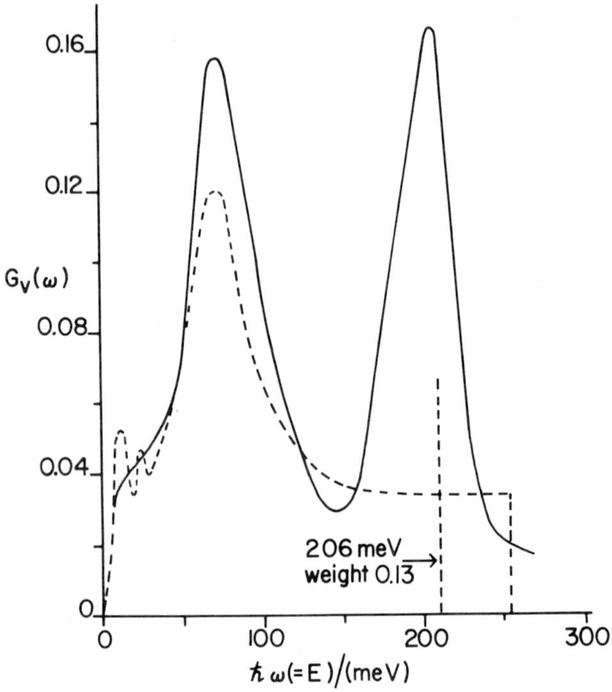

Fig. 16.10. Spectral density function $G(\omega)$ for H_2O at 299K as obtained from neutron scattering. —— $G(\omega)$ as obtained from Ref. 26; --- $G(\omega)$ as obtained from Ref. 27. After Ref. 26.

as in scattering angle (Placzek correction). The results are discussed in combination with X-ray scattering in Sec. 15.3(b).

(f) Mixtures and Solutions

Several studies have been carried out of neutron scattering in mixtures and solutions [29-32]. Diffusive behavior in aqueous solutions can be investigated through the half-width of the quasielastic peak [30,31]. The diffusion of water is detected if light water is used as solvent [30]. If heavy water is used as a solvent and the solute contains many ^1H nuclei, then solute motion can also be studied [31].

When ^1H_2O is used as solvent, then it is possible to obtain self-diffusion coefficients of water in these solutions from plots of the width at half-height vs q^2 (e.g., Fig. 16.2). Such neutron scattering studies show that Cs^+ acts as a "structure breaker," making diffusion of water in the solution easier. La^{+3}, Mg^{+2} are, however, "structure makers" [Sec. 5.1(b)]. These observations are in agreement with NMR [Sec. 13.3(f),(g)] and viscosity [Sec. 9.3(h)] results.

For concentrated solutions, the curves of δE vs q are linear in the whole q range. This indicates that "jump diffusion" has become negligible as compared to "hydrodynamic" diffusion (16.11). This would be the case when the majority of the H_2O are tied up in the primary hydration layers, restricting any "jump diffusion" motion.

Solute diffusion can be observed from the quaielastic line width in the case of solutes such as tetramethylammonium bromide ($(CH_3)_4NBr$) in heavy water. In a 3 M solution, the ion scatters 8.5 times as much as the solvent [31]. The diffusion coefficient for $(CH_3)_4N^+$ measured by neutron scattering was found to be greater than that measured by other methods. This is conceivably due to rotational motion influencing the quasielastic linewidth when the observation times are as small as in neutron scattering [Sec. 16.3(c)]. Such effects of rotational diffusion cannot be detected for water, however. This may be that the rotational diffusion spectrum is for H_2O too broad so that it appears as an almost flat background for the center of mass quasielastic spectrum.

Neutron scattering can also be used to study chemical reactions [32]. Proton transfer reactions such as $CF_3COOH \rightleftarrows CF_3COO^- + H_3O^+$ can be studied, as diffusion-controlled reactions take place in the time scales accessible through neutron scattering (10^{-11} to 10^{-8} sec) [Sec. 10.3(i)]. Association reactions involving carboxylic acids [e.g., Sec. 14.3(b)] should also be detectable with neutron scattering.

REFERENCES

Neutron scattering as a whole is covered well in [1], [3], and the books referred to in [4] and [10]. A number of articles concerning liquids [6,15,19] can be found in a Faraday Discussion, and others [18,20,30,31] in a Bunsengesellschaft meeting summary.

1. I. I. Gurevich and L. V. Tarasov, Low-Energy Neutron Scattering, North-Holland, Amsterdam, 1968.

2. Neutron Diffraction Commission, Acta Cryst., *A25*, 391 (1969).

3. G. E. Bacon, Neutron Diffraction, Oxford University Press, New York, 1962.

4. W. M. Lomer and G. G. Low, in Thermal Neutron Scattering (P. A. Egelstaff, ed.), Academic Press, New York, 1965.

5. P. A. Egelstaff, An Introduction to the Liquid State, Academic Press, New York, 1967.

6. K. E. Larsson, Farad. Symp. Chem. Soc., *6*, 122 (1972).

7. V. F. Sears, Can. J. Phys., *44*, 1279, 1299 (1966); *45*, 237 (1967).

8. K. E. Larsson, in Neutron Inelastic Scattering, 397, Int. At. En. Ag. (1968).

9. S. J. Cocking and F. J. Webb, in Thermal Neutron Scattering (P. A. Egelstaff, ed.), Academic Press, New York, 1965.

10. G. C. Stirling, in Chemical Applications of Thermal Neutron Scattering (B. T. M. Willis, ed.), Oxford University Press, New York, 1973.

11. A. H. Narten, J. Chem. Phys., *56*, 1185 (1972).

12. L. A. de Graaf and B. Mozer, J. Chem. Phys., *55*, 4967 (1971).

13. K. Sköld, J. M. Rowe, G. Ostrowski, and P. D. Randolph, Phys. Rev., A *6*, 1107 (1972).

14. W. J. L. Buyers, V. F. Sears, P. A. Lonngi, and D. A. Lonngi, in Neutron Inelastic Scattering, 399, Int. At. En. Ag. (1972).

15. L. Verlet, Farad. Symp. Chem. Soc., *6*, 116 (1972).

16. R. A. Cowley, A. E. C. L. Rep., 3189 (1968).

17. P. A. Fleury and J. P. Boon, Phys. Rev., *186*, 244 (1969).

18. K. E. Larsson, Ber. Bunseng. Physik. Chem., *75*, 352 (1971).

19. B. K. Aldred, G. C. Stirling, and J. W. White, Farad. Symp. Chem. Soc., *6*, 135 (1972).

20. C. O. Fischer, Ber. Bunseng. Physik. Chem., *75*, 361 (1972).

21. K. E. Larsson, J. Chem. Phys., *59*, 4612 (1973).

22. P. A. Egelstaff, J. Chem. Phys., *53*, 2590 (1970).

23. V. Trepadus, S. Rapeanu, I. Padureanu, V. A. Parfenov, and A. G. Novikov, J. Chem. Phys., *60*, 2832 (1974).

24. D. I. Page in GR7.

25. D. J. Hughes, H. Palevsky, W. Kley, and E. Tunkelo, Phys. Rev., *119*, 872 (1960).

26. O. K. Harling, J. Chem. Phys., *50*, 5279 (1969).

27. B. C. Haywood, J. Nucl. Energy, *21*, 249 (1967).

28. A. H. Narten, J. Chem. Phys., *56*, 5681 (1972).

29. G. J. Safford, P. C. Schaffer, P. S. Leung, G. F. Doebbler, G. W. Brady, and E. F. X. Lyden, J. Chem. Phys., *50*, 2140 (1969).

30. G. J. Safford and P. S. Leung, Ber. Bunseng. Physik. Chem., *75*, 366 (1971).

31. J. W. White, Ber. Bunseng. Physik. Chem., *75*, 379 (1971).

32. J. C. Lassegues and J. W. White, in Molecular Motion in Liquids, (J. Lascombe, ed.), Reidel, Boston, 1974.

Further Recent References

L. Blum and A. H. Narten, "Dynamic Corrections for Neutron Scattering from Molecular Fluids", J. Chem. Phys., *64*, 2804 (1976).

K. Carneiro and J. P. McTague, "Dynamics of Liquid N_2 at T = 66.4K Studied by Neutron Inelastic Scattering", Phys. Rev., A *11*, 1744 (1975).

A. M. Hecht and J. W. White, "Inelastic Neutron Scattering by Water in an Ordered Tobacco Mosaic Virus Solution", J. C. S. Faraday II, *72*, 439 (1976).

Part C

SUMMARY OF BACKGROUND MATERIAL

This part of the book contains basic topics which are not specific to liquids. Many of these topics will have been covered in a standard physical chemistry curriculum. Thus it can be used as a review for those topics which the reader has covered previously, or as a guide for studying unfamiliar topics. The discussion is not comprehensive enough to be used alone for study of unfamiliar topics. References to more thorough discussions are included.

Mathematical methods are not reviewed here. The methods commonly encountered are those involving Fourier transforms and series, spherical harmonics and other orthonormal sets of functions, matrix and vector operations, special functions and series expansions, complex numbers, partial differentials, etc. They are for the most part covered in standard advanced mathematics texts, e.g., H. Margenau and G. M. Murphy, "The Mathematics of Physics and Chemistry," 2nd ed., van Nostrand (1956), or T. A. Bak and J. Lichtenberg, "Mathematics for Scientists," Benjamin (1966).

Chapter 17

THERMODYNAMICS

17.1. BASIC DEFINITIONS AND LAWS

Thermodynamics deals with the bulk properties of systems in equilibrium. In such considerations, the definition of the system is often vitally important. A specification of the independent variables of the system define the system. Thus isolated systems are specified by the internal energy U, and the volume V; closed isothermal systems by the temperature T, and either pressure p or V depending on whether the system is isobaric or has constant volume.

The thermodynamic variables (properties, functions) considered can be of two types, extensive and intensive. Intensive properties are independent of the mass of the system, e.g., T, p; while extensive properties are directly proportional to the mass of the system, e.g., U, V. A relation equating properties must equate extensive to extensive.

An equilibrium state of a system can be defined as a state which is stable with respect to infinitesimal changes in conditions. Changes which proceed through a continuous series of equilibrium states are said to be "reversible." Spontaneous changes in systems from non-equilibrium towards equilibrium states are not reversible, and cannot be treated quantitatively through conventional thermodynamics (Chap. 19). Changes in systems can occur in various ways. Two important cases are isothermal change, occurring at constant T; and adiabatic change, occurring with no heat exchange with the surroundings.

The internal (total) energy U can be considered to be one of the fundamental variables of a system. It is the sum of the kinetic and potential energies of the particles present. The first law of thermodynamics (conservation of energy) states that a change dU in the sum of the heat absorbed by the system from the surroundings, dq, and the work done on it by external forces, dw, i.e.,

$$dU = dq + dw \tag{17.1}$$

The work dw can be separated into two parts. When a system changes its volume by dV under a pressure p, then the work done on it is -p dV. If dw' is used to denote work done by forces other than pressure, e.g., electrical, then

$$dw = -p\ dV + dw' \tag{17.2}$$

When the change is carried out reversibly, then the symbols dq_{rev} dw'_{rev} will be used.

Another fundamental variable of a system is the entropy S. It is defined through the second law of thermodynamics as

$$TdS = dq_{rev} \tag{17.3}$$

Entropy can be considered to be a measure of the state of disorder in a system, while T is a measure of its "hotness." The direction of heat flow between systems on contact is determined by the relative magnitudes of the temperatures. A physical interpretation of S and T can be better obtained through statistical mechanics.

The function S, unlike q, is a state function. U and V are also state functions, i.e., their values depend only on the state of the system and not on the way in which the system achieved that state.

Other state functions are introduced through the following definitions:

$$H = U + pV \qquad A = U - TS \qquad G = H - TS \tag{17.4}$$

H is the enthalpy (heat content), A the Helmholtz free energy and G the Gibbs free energy (thermodynamic potential). The functions H and G are convenient when the independent (natural) variables are the number of moles of component i, n_i, T, p; this is the usual case for experiments. U and A are, on the other hand, convenient when n_i, T, V are the natural variables, as in theoretical calculations.

The combination of the first and second laws [(17.1),(17.3)] gives the relationship

$$dU = T\,dS - p\,dV + dw'_{rev} \tag{17.5}$$

Often the non-p work term dw'_{rev} is zero. When the total differentials of H, A, G are taken (17.4), then with the aid of (17.5),

$$dH = dU + p\,dV + V\,dp = T\,dS + V\,dp + dw'_{rev}$$

$$dA = -S\,dT - p\,dV + dw'_{rev} \tag{17.6}$$

$$dG = -S\,dT + V\,dp + dw'_{rev}$$

Relationships (17.6) lead to a description of the meaning of A and G. For constant T, p it is seen that dG is the work, other than that done by pressure, done on a system in a reversible change. Hence the term "free energy." When $dw'_{rev} = 0$, then $(dG)_{T,p} = 0$ and $(dA)_{T,V} = 0$ for systems in equilibrium. In the case of irreversible change in a nonequilibrium system, the second law states that $dG < 0$, $dA < 0$ for the appropriate isothermal systems, while $T\,dS > dq$ in an isolated system.

17.2. FURTHER RELATIONSHIPS

A number of relationships can immediately be obtained from (17.6) (for $dw'_{rev} = 0$).

$$\left(\frac{\partial U}{\partial V}\right)_S = \left(\frac{\partial A}{\partial V}\right)_T = -p$$

$$\left(\frac{\partial H}{\partial p}\right)_S = \left(\frac{\partial G}{\partial p}\right)_T = V$$

$$\left(\frac{\partial A}{\partial T}\right)_V = \left(\frac{\partial G}{\partial T}\right)_p = -S \tag{17.7}$$

Thus if $G(T,p,n_i)$ is known, then the other variables can be obtained from it through appropriate differentials. When second differentials are taken, "Maxwell's relations" are obtained:

$$\left(\frac{\partial S}{\partial V}\right)_T = -\frac{\partial^2 A}{\partial V \partial T} = -\frac{\partial^2 A}{\partial T \partial V} = \left(\frac{\partial p}{\partial T}\right)_V$$

$$\left(\frac{\partial V}{\partial T}\right)_p = -\left(\frac{\partial S}{\partial p}\right)_T \qquad \left(\frac{\partial T}{\partial V}\right)_S = -\left(\frac{\partial p}{\partial S}\right)_V \qquad \left(\frac{\partial T}{\partial p}\right)_S = \left(\frac{\partial V}{\partial S}\right)_V \tag{17.8}$$

Several of the derivatives of the functions introduced are of a sufficient importance to have a symbol and name themselves. The more important are:

$-1/V(\partial V/\partial p)_T = \kappa_T$, the isothermal compressibility
$-1/V(\partial V/\partial p)_S = \kappa_S$, the isentropic (adiabatic) compressibility
$1/V(\partial V/\partial T)_p = \alpha$, the thermal expansion
$(\partial U/\partial T)_V = T(\partial S/\partial T)_V = C_V$, the heat capacity at constant V
$(\partial H/\partial T)_p = T(\partial S/\partial T)_p = C_p$, the heat capacity at constant p

It is often convenient to work with only intensive quantities. Thus partial molar quantities are defined as, for example, $(\partial V/\partial n_i)_{T,p,j} = V_i$, the partial molar volume of component i. The subscript j in the differential indicates that n_j for $j \neq i$ is constant. Similarily H_i, U_i, S_i can be formed. A particularly important partial molar quantity is $(\partial G/\partial n_i)_{T,p,j} = (\partial A/\partial n_i)_{T,V,j} = G_i = A_i = \mu_i$, the chemical potential. Derivatives of μ_i form relations such as, $(\partial \mu_i/\partial T)_p = -S_i$ etc., following (17.7).

Other thermodynamic relationships can be obtained by simple mathematical transformations. The general form and a particular example are

$$\left(\frac{\partial x}{\partial y}\right)_z = -\frac{(\partial z/\partial y)_x}{(\partial z/\partial x)_y} \qquad \left(\frac{\partial V}{\partial T}\right)_p = -\frac{(\partial p/\partial T)_V}{(\partial p/\partial V)_T} \tag{17.9}$$

Jacobian transformations are also possible, e.g.,

$$\left(\frac{\partial S}{\partial T}\right)_p \equiv \frac{(\partial S/\partial T)_V(\partial p/\partial V)_T - (\partial S/\partial V)_T(\partial p/\partial T)_V}{(\partial p/\partial V)_T} \tag{17.10}$$

Yet other useful relationships can be obtained using Euler's theorem. If, for example, U is U(T,V,n), then

$$V\left(\frac{\partial U}{\partial V}\right)_{T,n} + n\left(\frac{\partial U}{\partial n}\right)_{T,V} = 0 \tag{17.11}$$

This theorem can be used to obtain the relations

$$G = \Sigma n_i \mu_i \qquad V = \Sigma n_i V_i \qquad \text{etc.} \tag{17.12}$$

17.3. CHEMICAL POTENTIAL

Introduction of chemical potential makes it also possible to discuss change in composition and open systems. In such cases, (17.6) is written as

$$dG = -S\ dT + V\ dp + \Sigma\mu_i\ dn_i \tag{17.13}$$

The differential of (17.12) gives $dG = \Sigma n_i\ d\mu_i + \Sigma\mu_i\ dn_i$. Combining this with (17.13) and keeping T,p constant, gives the "Gibbs-Duhem" equation,

$$\Sigma n_i d\mu_i = 0 \qquad \text{or} \qquad X_A\ d\mu_A = -X_B\ d\mu_B \tag{17.14}$$

The second form of (17.14) (two-component system with mole fractions X_A, X_B) is written to indicate how through (17.14) it is possible to obtain $d\mu_A$ through a measurement of $d\mu_B$.

The meaning of chemical potential is essentially the same as that of free energy, i.e., a measure of the ability of the system to do work other than pressure work. If there is a phase equilibrium in a system, e.g., liquid-vapor, then the chemical potential of a component must be the same in both phases, i.e., $\mu_{i,g} = \mu_{i,l}$. Otherwise, the component will spontaneously move toward the phase where μ_i is lower, so that

$$dG = \Sigma(\mu_{i,g}\, dn_{i,g} + \mu_{i,1}\, dn_{i,1}) = \Sigma(\mu_{i,g} - \mu_{i,1})\, dn_{i,g} < 0 \qquad (17.15)$$

Thus knowledge of $\mu_{i,g}$ leads to $\mu_{i,1}$ as well.

In the case of an ideal gas, the value of G(p,T) at some pressure p referred to a value $G^{\theta}(p^{\theta},T)$ at some standard state pressure p^{θ} is given as (17.6):

$$G = G^{\theta} + \int_{p^{\theta}}^{p} dG = G^{\theta} + \int_{p^{\theta}}^{p} V\, dp' = G^{\theta} + \int_{p^{\theta}}^{p} \frac{nRT}{p'}\, dp'$$

$$= G^{\theta} + nRT \ln \frac{p}{p^{\theta}} \qquad (17.16)$$

The change from p^{θ} to p is carried out reversibly here, with the volume always at nRT/p. Thus

$$\mu(T,p) = \left(\frac{\partial G}{\partial n}\right)_{T,p} = \mu^{\theta}(T) + RT \ln \frac{p}{p^{\theta}} = \mu^{\theta}(T) + RT \ln p \qquad (17.17)$$

In (17.17), p is dimensionless in the last form, where the standard state pressure is chosen to be unity. When there is a mixture of ideal gases present, then

$$\mu_i(T,p,n_i) = \mu_i^{\theta}(T) + RT \ln p_i = \mu_i^{\theta}(T) + RT \ln X_{i,p}p \qquad (17.18)$$

In (17.18), the partial pressure p_i is given by the mole fraction $X_{i,p}$ in the vapor times the total pressure p.

When real gases are considered, then (17.18) is written as

$$\mu_i(T,p,n_i) = \mu_i^{\theta}(T) + RT \ln p_i^{\#} \qquad (17.19)$$

where $p_i^{\#}$ is the fugacity or "effective pressure" of the gas. As $p \to 0$, then the gaseous mixture approaches ideality and $p_i^{\#} \to p_i$. Standard states other than that at unit pressure can be chosen. Thus if comparison of $\mu_{i,g}$ and $\mu_{i,1}$ are to be made, the same standard state must be chosen, e.g., the vapor pressure of pure i.

In general the chemical potential of a component in a real solution is given as

$$\mu_i(T,p,n_i) = \mu_i^\theta(T,p) + RT \ln a_i \tag{17.20}$$

Equation (17.20) defines the activity a_i of the component. In liquids and solids, μ_i is rather insensitive to pressure. Thus, besides T, the major variable is the concentration. In an ideal solution, $a_i = X_i$, i.e.,

$$\mu_i(T,p,n_i) = \mu_i^\theta(T,p) + RT \ln X_i \tag{17.21}$$

where X_i is the mole fraction of i present in the solution. The standard state is in this case pure component i.

Three different standard states are commonly used due to the use of three different concentration scales.

$$\mu_i = \mu_i^\theta + RT \ln a_i = \mu_i^\theta + RT \ln f_i X_i$$
$$= \mu_i^{\theta\prime} + RT \ln y_i c_i = \mu_i^{\theta\prime\prime} + RT \ln \gamma_i m_i \tag{17.22}$$

Here X_i is the mole fraction, c_i the molarity (mole liter^{-1}), m_i the molality (mole per kilogram solvent). For dilute aqueous solutions, $m_i \simeq c_i$; molarity is more commonly used, but unlike molality, it is dependent on T and p. The symbols f_i, y_i, and γ_i stand for activity coefficients defined on different concentration scales. They are often referred to as the rational, molar, and molal (or practical) activity coefficients.

In the rational system, $f_i \to 1$ as $X_i \to 1$. The standard state is the pure liquid, i.e.,

$$\mu_{i,l}^\theta(p,T) = \mu_{i,l}^\bullet = \mu_{i,g}^\theta(T) + RT \ln p_i^{\bullet\#} \tag{17.23}$$

where $\mu_{i,g}^\theta(T)$ is the chemical potential of the gas at unit fugacity (17.17) and $p_i^{\bullet\#}$ is the fugacity at the vapor pressure. The activity scales for y and γ are defined in both cases by y, $\gamma \to 1$ as c, $m \to 0$. Thus these scales are more useful for dilute solutions. The standard states are (hypothetical) solutions of unit activity.

In electrolyte solutions, single-ion chemical potential are defined as

$$\mu_+ = \mu_+^\theta + RT \ln a_+ \qquad \mu_- = \mu_-^\theta + RT \ln a_- \tag{17.24}$$

However, it is possible experimentally only to obtain the overall chemical potential,

$$\mu = \mu^{\theta} + (\nu_+ + \nu_-)RT \ln \gamma_{\pm} m_{\pm}$$

$$\gamma_{\pm} = (\gamma_+^{\nu_+} \gamma_-^{\nu_-})^{(1/(\nu_+ + \nu_-))} \qquad m = (m^{\nu_+} m^{\nu_-})^{(1/(\nu_+ + \nu_-))} \tag{17.25}$$

Here $\gamma_{\pm}$ and $m_{\pm}$ are mean activity coefficient and the mean ionic molality. For symmetric electrolytes, i.e., $\nu_+ = \nu_-$, $\gamma_{\pm} = \sqrt{\gamma_+\gamma_-}$; $m_{\pm} = \sqrt{m_+m_-}$

The effects of an electrical potential ϕ are also sometimes included in μ to form the electrochemical potential,

$$\mu_i^{\dagger} = \mu_i + z_i F\phi \tag{17.26}$$

The charge on a mole of species i is $z_i F$, where F is the Faraday constant.

17.4. EQUILIBRIUM

A general equilibrium of the form

$$0 \rightleftarrows \Sigma_i \nu_i I \qquad -\nu_A A - \nu_B B - \cdots \rightleftarrows \nu_X X + \nu_Y Y + \cdots \tag{17.27}$$

has defined for it an equilibrium constant,

$$K = \frac{a_X^{\nu_X} \cdot a_Y^{\nu_Y}}{a_A^{\nu_A} \cdot a_B^{\nu_B}} = \Pi(a_i)^{\nu_i} \tag{17.28}$$

The ν_i are stoichiometric coefficients for the components i. When concentrations are used instead of activities, the symbol K_c is used, and when pressures are used, K_p.

A progress variable ξ can be defined for the equilibrium such that

$$d\xi = \frac{dn_A}{\nu_A} = \frac{dn_B}{\nu_B} = \cdots \tag{17.29}$$

At equilibrium $(dG)_{T,p} = \Sigma\mu_i\ dn_i = 0$. Substitution of (17.29) then leads to the relation

$$\Sigma\nu_i\mu_i\ d\xi = 0 \qquad \text{or} \qquad \Sigma\nu_i\mu_i = 0 \tag{17.30}$$

since $d\xi$ is an arbitrary change.

In general the sum $-\Sigma\nu_i\mu_i$ is called the "affinity" A of the re- librium. It can also be defined as

$$A = -\Sigma\nu_i\mu_i = -\left(\frac{\partial G}{\partial \xi}\right)_{T,p} \tag{17.31}$$

and can be used in expressions as other parameters. The rate of re- action. It can also be defined as

When (17.20) is substituted into (17.30), then the result when equilibrium exists is

$$\Sigma\nu_i\mu_i^\theta = -RT\ \ln\ \Pi(a_i)_{eq}^{\nu_i} = -RT\ \ln\ K \qquad .32)$$

The sum $\Sigma\nu_i\mu_i^\theta$ is simply the G of the products in their standard states less that of the reagents in their standard states and is given the symbol ΔG^θ, the standard free energy of reaction. Similarly $\Delta H^\theta = \Sigma\nu_i H_i^\theta$ is the standard heat of reaction, $\Delta S^\theta = \Sigma\nu_i S_i^\theta$, $\Delta V^\theta = \Sigma\nu_i V_i^\theta\cdots$. A symbol such as $\Delta H = \Sigma\nu_i H_i$ refers to a heat of reaction calculated for other than standard conditions. In analogy to (17.31) these can be expressed as $\Delta H = (\partial H/\partial\xi)_{T,p}$ etc.

These quantities of reaction can be related using (17.6) as

$$\Delta G = \Delta H - T\Delta S \qquad \Delta G^\theta = \Delta H^\theta - T\ \Delta S^\theta \tag{17.33}$$

When (17.7) is used, then

$$\left(\frac{\partial\ \ln\ K}{\partial T}\right)_p = -\frac{\partial}{\partial T}\left(\frac{\Delta G^\theta}{RT}\right) = \frac{\Delta H^\theta}{RT^2} \tag{17.34}$$

$$\left(\frac{\partial\ \ln\ K}{\partial p}\right)_T = \frac{\Delta V^\theta}{RT} \qquad (17.34)$$

Such quantities of reaction are not restricted to chemical reactions, but are also valid for phase changes, mixing processes, etc.

REFERENCES

There are a large number of texts on general thermodynamics. Some of these are listed below. The general references at the end of Chap. 5 should be referred to for a more thorough discussion of problems specific to electrolyte solutions.

1. R. Kubo, Thermodynamics, North-Holland, Amsterdam, 1968.
2. E. A. Guggenheim, Thermodynamics, 5th ed., North-Holland, Amsterdam, 1967.
3. M. W. Zemansky, Heat and Thermodynamics, McGraw-Hill, New York, 1957.
4. A. D. Buckingham, The Laws and Applications of Thermodynamics, Pergamon, New York, 1964.

Chapter 18

STATISTICAL MECHANICS

18.1. CANONICAL PARTITION FUNCTION

Most experimental work is done under conditions where N, p, T are the independent variables. In such cases, the Gibbs free energy G is the basic thermodynamic function.

Theoretically, it is easier to construct models with V rather than p as an independent variable. In such cases, A is the basic thermodynamic function. Thus many calculations give as a result A as a function of N (generally N_a, $N_b \cdots$), V and T.

Such calculations with N, V, T specified are adequate to describe a large number of phenomena. Thus most of this chapter assumes a closed isothermal system. Some cases are, however, better dealt with considering open isothermal systems, i.e., with μ_a, μ_b,$\cdots$V, T as the independent variables. These cases are considered in Sec. 5 of this chapter.

Statistical mechanics relates the macroscopic thermodynamic properties of a system to the microscopic properties of the particles involved in the system. When N, V, T are the independent variables, this connection can be made through consideration of the "canonical ensemble."

A canonical ensemble is an imaginary collection of a large number of systems which each have the same N, V, and T, but which differ on the molecular level. The "ensemble average" value of a variable is then postulated to equal the "time average" value of the variable in the actual system.

The quantitative connections between the molecular level properties involved in the ensemble description and thermodynamic properties of the actual system are available through the relationship:

$$A(N,V,T) = -kT \ln Q(N,V,T) \tag{18.1}$$

Here Q is the "canonical partition function". By use of relationships such as $\mu_i = (\partial A/\partial n_i)_{V,T,j}$; $p = -(\partial A/\partial V)_{N,T}$, etc. (Chap. 17), a complete thermodynamic description of the system is available if the partition function Q is known as a function of N, V, and T.

It is easier to consider the meaning of Q if a quantum-mechanical description is assumed, in so far as the existence of discrete energy levels is accepted. In this case Q can be expressed as

$$Q = \Sigma \exp\left[-\frac{E_i}{kT}\right] \tag{18.2}$$

Where the summation is over all possible energy states of the system, or

$$Q = \Sigma \Omega_j \exp\left[-\frac{E_j}{kT}\right] \tag{18.3}$$

where the summation is over all possible energy levels of the system. Ω_j is the statistical weight, or degeneracy, of the jth energy level. The energy levels E_j are dependent on the values of V and N, but not T.

The probability that the system has an energy E_j can then be expressed in terms of Q as

$$w_j = \Omega_j \frac{\exp[-E_j/kT]}{Q} \tag{18.4}$$

Assuming a continuous distribution of energy, the probability that the system has an energy in the interval dE about E is

$$w(E)\ dE = \Omega(E) \frac{\exp[-E/kT]\ dE}{Q} \tag{18.5}$$

Equations (18.4) and (18.5) follow from another postulate of statistical mechanics, known often as the "ergodic hypothesis" or the "principle of a priori equal probabilities" and describes the distribution of systems in an ensemble. These expressions are not valid for all systems. At low temperatures and for light particles, quantum mechanical effects become nonnegligible. Thus an electron gas must be treated by "Fermi-Dirac" statistics, and helium by "Bose-Einstein" statistics. For sufficiently high temperatures, both F-D and B-E statistics approach the "Boltzmann" statistics for which (18.4) and (18.5) are valid.

The fluctuation in E, $\langle \delta E^2 \rangle$ can be calculated from (18.4) by noting that

$$\langle \delta E^2 \rangle = \Sigma w_i (E_i - \langle E \rangle)^2 = \langle E^2 \rangle - \langle E \rangle^2 \tag{18.6}$$

This energy E can be equated to the thermodynamic internal energy U. From (18.4) it can be seen that

$$\langle E \rangle = U = \Sigma w_i E_i = -\frac{1}{Q} \frac{\partial Q}{\partial(1/kT)} \tag{18.7}$$

while

$$\langle E \rangle^2 = \Sigma w_i E_i^2 = \frac{1}{Q} \frac{\partial^2 Q}{(\partial(1/kT))^2} = \langle E \rangle^2 - \frac{\partial \langle E \rangle}{\partial(1/kT)} \tag{18.8}$$

Combining these results gives

$$\langle \delta E^2 \rangle = \langle \delta U^2 \rangle = kT^2 C_V \tag{18.9}$$

A further discussion of fluctuations follows in this chapter. In addition, Chap. 19 also contains a section on fluctuations.

18.2. CRYSTALS

The "Einstein crystal" is an example of a system composed of independent, distinguishable subsystems. The model assumes each of the N atoms in a crystal to oscillate about their equilibrium positions. Each atom thus has three vibrational degrees of freedom, each assumed independent of the others.

The total Hamiltonian for the system can then be written as

$$H = H_{a,1} + H_{a,2} + H_{a,3} + \cdots H_{N,3} \tag{18.10}$$

where $H_{k,j}$ is the Hamiltonian of a "subsystem" composed simply of the jth vibrational degree of freedom for the kth atom. When the subsystems are independent and there are no cross-terms in (18.10), then the total energy E can be shown also to be of the form

$$E = E_{a,1} + E_{a,2} + E_{a,3} + \cdots E_{N,3} \tag{18.11}$$

The partition function Q can then be written as

$$Q = \Sigma \exp\left[-\frac{E_i}{kT}\right] = \left(\Sigma \exp\left[-\frac{(E_{a,1})_i}{kT}\right]\right)\left(\cdots\right)\cdots\left(\Sigma \exp\left[-\frac{(E_{N,3})_i}{kT}\right]\right) \tag{18.12}$$

Here $(E_{a,1})_i$ is the ith energy state for the first degree of freedom of atom a. Equation (18.12) can be simplified to

$$Q = q_{a,1} \cdot q_{a,2} \cdots q_{N,3} \tag{18.13}$$

where $q_{a,1}$ is the partition function for the subsystem a,1, i.e.,

$$q_{a,1} = \Sigma \exp\left[-\frac{(E_{a,1})_i}{kT}\right] \tag{18.14}$$

In the Einstein crystal, the vibrations are assumed to be simple harmonic. Thus the partition function for a single degree of vibrational freedom is (21.22)

$$q_{vib} = \Sigma_v \exp\left[-\frac{(v + 1/2)h\nu}{kT}\right] = \frac{\exp[-\theta_e/2T]}{1 - \exp[-\theta_e/T]} \tag{18.15}$$

where θ_e is $h\nu/k$ and has units of temperature.

When all the 3N vibrational degrees of freedom are equivalent, then $Q = q_{vib}^{3N}$. This, however, assumes the zero of energy to be the atoms at rest in the crystal. To make the zero of energy that of the atoms at rest in the gas phase infinitely far apart, it is necessary to write

$$Q = \exp\left[-\frac{V(0)}{kT}\right]\cdot q_{vib}^{3N} \tag{18.16}$$

where $V(0)$ is the appropriate potential energy.

The Debye model of the crystal follows from (18.16). In the Debye model, the 3N degrees of freedom are not assumed to have the same frequency ν. Instead the crystal is assumed to have a distribution of "normal" frequencies or modes. These are collective motions of the atoms such that H can be written in the form with no cross-products, [i.e., as in (18.10)] in terms of the "normal coordinates."

A frequency distribution, or spectral density function $G(\nu)$ is introduced. $G(\nu)\,d\nu$ is the number of normal modes with a frequency in the range $d\nu$ about ν. In the Debye theory, this function is assumed to have the form

$$G(\nu)\,d\nu = \frac{3N\nu^2\,d\nu}{\nu_d^3} \qquad \text{for} \qquad 0 < \nu < \nu_d \tag{18.17}$$

This is shown in Fig. 18.1, together with the δ function (21.5) frequency distribution assumed in the Einstein model, where the 3N normal modes all have the same $\nu = \nu_e$. The Debye $G(\nu)$ has a value 0 for $\nu > \nu_d$ so that the total number of normal modes is still 3N, i.e., $\int_0^\infty G(\nu)\,d\nu = 3N$.

The partition function can then be written as

$$-\ln Q = \frac{V(0)}{kT} + \int_0^\infty \left\{\ln\left(1 - \exp\left[-\frac{h\nu}{kT}\right]\right) + \frac{h\nu}{2kT}\right\} G(\nu)\,d\nu \tag{18.18}$$

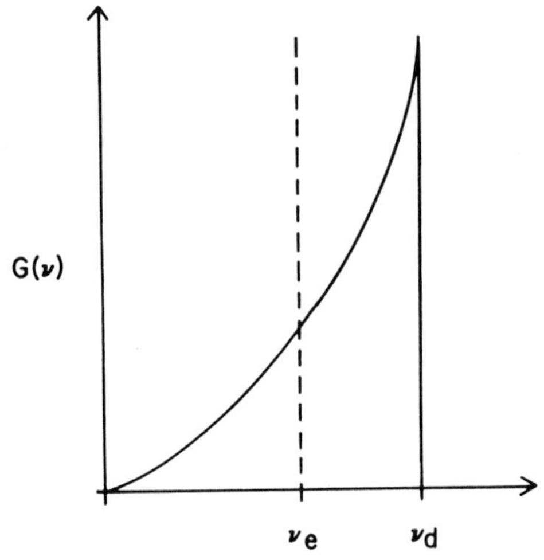

Fig. 18.1. Schematic illustration of the spectral density functions for the Debye and Einstein theories of solids.

18.3. IDEAL GASES

In a crystal the atoms are distinguishable. In a gas, however, they are indistinguishable. Thus in this case, Q is of a different form than (18.13),

$$Q = \frac{q^N}{N!} \tag{18.19}$$

where q is the partition function for a single molecule. When the various modes of motion of a molecule are assumed independent of each other, then

$$q = q_{tr} \cdot q_{rot} \cdot q_{vib} \cdot q_{el} \tag{18.20}$$

where q_{tr} is the translational partition function, q_{rot} the rotational, q_{vib} the vibrational, q_{el} the electronic.

The translational partition function can be obtained by considering the particle in a 3-D box. The energy levels there are given by (21.19):

$$E_{nx,ny,nz} = \frac{h^2}{8mV^{2/3}} (nx^2 + ny^2 + nz^2) \tag{18.21}$$

where the nx, ny, nz are = 1, 2, 3···. The formulation of q_{tr} is not as straightforward as for q_{vib} (18.15), due to the presence of degeneracy. The result is

$$q_{tr} = \left(\frac{2\pi mkT}{h^2}\right)^{3/2} \cdot V = \frac{V}{\Lambda^3} \tag{18.22}$$

$\Lambda = h/(2\pi mkT)^{1/2}$ is often called the "thermal de Broglie wavelength."

For an ideal monatomic gas, $q = q_{tr}$, and assuming $q_{el} = 1$,

$$Q = \frac{(q_{tr})^N}{N!} = \frac{1}{N!}\left(\frac{V}{\Lambda^3}\right)^N = \left(\frac{Ve}{\Lambda^3 N}\right)^N \tag{18.23}$$

Stirlings formula must be used to express ln N!, to get the result shown in the last form.

The partition function for q_{rot} of a heteronuclear diatomic molecule is simply (21.2):

$$q_{rot} = \Sigma_J(2J + 1) \exp\left[-\frac{J(J + 1)hc^{\bullet}B}{kT}\right] \tag{18.24}$$

When the summation is replaced by an integration, then

$$q_{rot} = \frac{T}{\theta_{rot}} \tag{18.25}$$

where

$$\theta_{rot} = \frac{hc^{\bullet}B}{k} = \frac{h^2}{8\pi^2 Ik}$$

For more complex molecules, the general result is

$$q_{rot} = \frac{\sqrt{\pi}}{\sigma}\left(\frac{T^3}{\theta_a\theta_b\theta_c}\right)^{1/2} \tag{18.26}$$

where θ_a, θ_b, θ_c are the "temperatures" (18.25) corresponding to the principal moments of inertia of the molecules, and σ is the "symmetry number." Equations (18.25) and (18.26) assume free rotation. When there is a totally hindered rotation, then the rotational degree of freedom is of a vibrational nature.

The partition function for a vibrational degree of freedom has been discussed earlier (18.15). q_{el} will not be of interest in this context, as generally only ground electronic states are considered. Then q_{el} = degeneracy of the ground electronic state if the zero of energy is taken as the molecule in its lowest energy state.

It should be noted that when the heat capacity C_V is calculated from the partition function, then the contribution per translational and rotational degrees of freedom is $R/2$. This assumes $\theta_{rot} \ll T$. It can, however, reach a value of R per degree of freedom of vibration or totally hindered rotation as T becomes large, i.e., as $T \gg \theta_{vib}$. This is because the Hamiltonian for the latter two cases contain two terms of the form $\frac{1}{2} p_x^2$ or $\frac{1}{2} X^2$ (see Chap. 21), while in translation and rotation there is no potential term.

18.4. NONIDEAL SYSTEMS

(a) Configuration Integral

The partition function for a system of N identical indistinguishable molecules can be expressed in terms of classical mechanics as:

$$Q = \frac{1}{N!h^{3N}} \int \exp\left[-\frac{H(\underline{r},\underline{p})}{kT}\right] d\underline{r}_a \cdots d\underline{p}_N \tag{18.27}$$

The integration is over all of phase space with respect to the 3N position and 3N momentum coordinates.

When H is of the form

$$H(\underline{r},\underline{p}) = \frac{1}{2m}(p_{a,x}^2 + p_{a,y}^2 + \cdots p_{N,z}^2) + V(\underline{r}_a,\underline{r}_b \cdots \underline{r}_N) \tag{18.28}$$

then the integrations over the momentum coordinates can be carried out immediately. The result is then

$$Q = \frac{1}{N!}\frac{1}{\Lambda^{3N}} Z_N \tag{18.29}$$

where Z_N is the "classical configuration integral,"

$$Z_N = \int_V \exp\left[-\frac{V(\underline{r}_a,\underline{r}_b \cdots \underline{r}_N)}{kT}\right] d\underline{r}_a\, d\underline{r}_b \cdots d\underline{r}_N \tag{18.30}$$

When there are no intermolecular forces present, as in an ideal gas, then $V(\underline{r}) = 0$. In this case $Z_N = V^N$ and (18.30) reduces to (18.23).

(b) Cluster Integrals

When $V(\mathbf{r}_a, \mathbf{r}_b \cdots \mathbf{r}_N)$, (written as $V\{N\}$) can be expressed as a sum of pair interactions, i.e.,

$$V\{N\} = \sum_{i>j} v(r_{ij}) \qquad r_{ij} = |\mathbf{r}_i - \mathbf{r}_j| \tag{18.31}$$

then the integrand of the configuration can be expressed as

$$\exp\left[-\frac{V}{kT}\right] = \prod_{i>j} \exp\left[-\frac{v(r_{ij})}{kT}\right] \tag{18.32}$$

With the introduction of the Mayer f functions,

$$f_{ij} = \exp\left[-\frac{v(r_{ij})}{kT}\right] - 1 \tag{18.33}$$

Equation (18.32) can be further expressed as

$$\exp\left[-\frac{V}{kT}\right] = \prod_{i,j} (1 + f_{ij}) = 1 + \Sigma f_{ij} + \Sigma\Sigma f_{ij} f_{kl} + \Sigma\Sigma\Sigma \cdots \tag{18.34}$$

Each term in the expansion in (18.34) is a product of a certain number of f functions. This can be represented in terms of "cluster diagrams." Figure 18.2 shows four examples of such clusters. Each

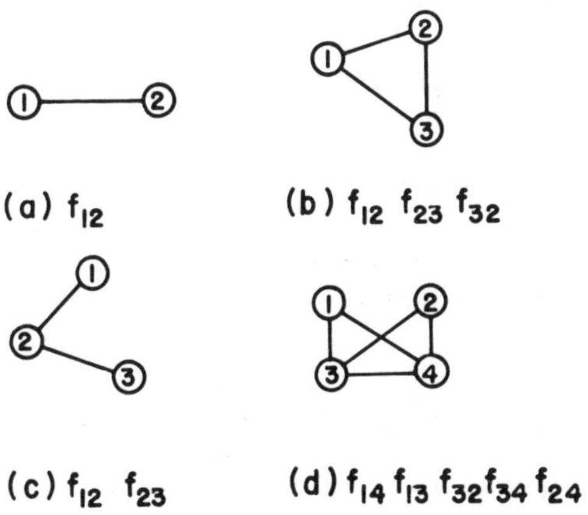

Fig. 18.2. Examples of cluster diagrams representing products of Mayer f functions.

diagram represents a term in Eq. (18.34), (1, 2··· instead of a, b··· are used as subscripts).

It has been shown that there is one to one correspondence between terms in (18.34) and a set of such graphs or cluster diagrams. Of particular importance are "irreducible" clusters. These are clusters which have a mapping in which each point is connected to at least two other points. A cluster of 2 points is also considered irreducible.

The reason for this is that the integral over a configuration such as (c) in Fig. 18.2 can be broken down by an appropriate change of coordinates. Thus, if $\underline{r} = \frac{1}{3}(\underline{r}_1 + \underline{r}_2 + \underline{r}_3)$ and $\underline{r}_{12} = \underline{r}_1 - \underline{r}_2$, then

$$\int f_{12} f_{23}\, d\underline{r}_1\, d\underline{r}_2\, d\underline{r}_3 = \int f_{12} f_{23}\, d\underline{r}_{12}\, d\underline{r}_{23}\, d\underline{r} \tag{18.35}$$

As $\int f_{12}\, dr_{12} = \int f_{23}\, dr_{23} = \int f_{ij}\, dr_{ij} = \beta_1$, then (18.35) gives simply $\beta_1 V$. Here β_1 is an irreducible cluster integral. The integral over mapping (b) would give another, (d) yet another etc.

Such cluster integrals can be useful in various calculations (see, e.g., Chaps. 3 and 5). As an example, the equation of state can be written in terms of them as

$$\frac{p}{\rho kT} = \left(1 - \Sigma_j \frac{j}{j+1} \cdot \beta_j \rho^j\right) \tag{18.36}$$

where β_j are the irreducible cluster integrals.

(c) Principle of Corresponding States

The evaluation of the configuration integral can be simplified in many cases through application of the "principle of corresponding states." In this case Z_N can be obtained as a universal function of "reduced parameters" T_{red}, V_{red}. Thus the calculations can be made for all systems in terms of T_{red}, V_{red} instead of being repeated for each individual system in terms of T, V and the parameters for the system.

In order to make use of this simplification, $v(\underline{r})$ must be assumed a sum of pair interactions as in (18.31). In addition, the intermolecular pair potential function must be of the same form for all the species considered. This can be the 6-12 form (Chap. 1) or more generally,

$$v(r) = \varepsilon \cdot \phi\left(\frac{r}{\sigma}\right) \tag{18.37}$$

Here ϕ is a universal function, and ε and σ energy and distance parameters, respectively, for the species considered.

A set of reduced variables are then introduced,

$$T_{red} = \frac{kT}{\varepsilon} \qquad V_{red} = \frac{V}{\sigma^3 N}$$

$$X_{i,red} = \frac{X_i}{\sigma}, \text{ etc.} \qquad d\underline{r}_{i,red} = \frac{d\underline{r}_i}{\sigma^3} \tag{18.38}$$

In this case,

$$V\{N\} = \varepsilon\Phi(\underline{r}_{1,red}, \underline{r}_{2,red} \cdots) \tag{18.39}$$

where Φ is a universal function, and

$$\begin{aligned} Z_N(T,V) &= \int \exp\left[-\frac{V}{kT}\right] d\underline{r}_1 \cdots d\underline{r}_N \\ &= \sigma^{3N} \exp\left[-\frac{\Phi}{T_{red}}\right] d\underline{r}_{1,red} \cdots d\underline{r}_{N,red} \\ &= \sigma^{3N} Z_{N,red}(T_{red}, V_{red}) \end{aligned} \tag{18.40}$$

In (18.40), $Z_{N,red}$ is a universal function.

Once $Z_{N,red}$ is evaluated then universal functions can also be formulated for A and for the equation of state.

18.5. GRAND CANONICAL ENSEMBLE

The grand canonical partition function Ξ is defined as

$$\Xi(\mu,T,V) = \Sigma_N \exp\left[\frac{N\mu}{kT}\right] \cdot Q_N(T,V)$$

$$= \Sigma_N \exp\left[\frac{N\mu}{kT}\right] \Sigma_E \exp\left[-\frac{E}{kT}\right] \Omega(E) \tag{18.41}$$

The summation has been continued to indicate how the three commonly used partition functions are related. The probability of observing N particles in the system is then

$$\omega(N) = \exp\left[\frac{N\mu}{kT}\right] \cdot \frac{Q_N(T,V)}{\Xi} \tag{18.42}$$

In analogy with the discussion of the fluctuation in U, $\langle\delta N^2\rangle$ can be written as (18.43), where the Σ is not over components, but microscopic states.

$$\langle\delta N^2\rangle = \sum_i \omega_i (N_i - \langle N\rangle)^2 = \langle N^2\rangle - \langle N\rangle^2 \tag{18.43}$$

After appropriate manipulation, this can be shown to be

$$\langle\delta N^2\rangle = kT \left(\frac{\partial\langle N\rangle}{\partial\mu}\right)_{T,V} \tag{18.44}$$

In the case of a one-component system, Euler's theorem (Chap. 17) can be used to give the result

$$\left(\frac{\partial\mu}{\partial\langle N\rangle}\right)_{T,N} = -\frac{V}{\langle N\rangle}\left(\frac{\partial\mu}{\partial V}\right)_{T,\langle N\rangle} = -\frac{V^2}{\langle N\rangle^2}\left(\frac{\partial p}{\partial V}\right)_{T,\langle N\rangle} = \frac{V}{\langle N\rangle^2}\frac{1}{\kappa_T} \tag{18.45}$$

Thus the relative fluctuation is

$$\frac{\langle\delta N^2\rangle}{\langle N\rangle^2} = \frac{kT\kappa_T}{V} \tag{18.46}$$

The fluctuation in energy for such an open system is somewhat more complex than derived in (18.9),

$$\langle\delta U^2\rangle = kT^2C_V + \left(\frac{\partial\langle U\rangle}{\partial\langle N\rangle}\right)^2_{T,V}\langle\delta N^2\rangle \tag{18.47}$$

REFERENCES

The above is a brief review of the aspects of statistical mechanics needed in discussion of the topics considered. There are numerous books to which the reader can refer for thorough discussions. References 1 and 2 begin coverage at an introductory level. More advanced treatments can be found in Refs. 3 and 4, while 5 covers aspects relevant to liquids rigorously.

1. T. L. Hill, Introduction to Statistical Thermodynamics, Addison-Wesley, Reading, Mass., 1960.
2. N. Davidson, Statistical Mechanics, McGraw-Hill, New York, 1962.
3. R. Kubo, Statistical Mechanics, North-Holland, Amsterdam, 1971.
4. L. D. Landau and E. M. Lifshitz, Statistical Physics, 2nd ed., Pergamon, London, 1959.
5. S. A. Rice and P. Gray, Statistical Mechanics of Simple Liquids, Wiley, New York, 1965.

Chapter 19

NONEQUILIBRIUM THERMODYNAMICS AND STATISTICAL MECHANICS

19.1. CONSERVATION EQUATIONS

(a) Mass

In formulating relationships dealing with time-dependent quantities, certain equations of conservation must be obeyed in all cases. The specific case of conservation of mass of component i will be considered first. This component can be formed or can disappear in the system due to chemical reactions.

It is assumed that there are k chemical reactions, with $\nu_{i\ell}$ denoting the moles of i produced (or removed) per mole of reaction ℓ. The "progress variable" of the reaction is ξ_ℓ; thus $d\xi_\ell/dt$ is simply the chemical reaction rate of reaction ℓ expressed as moles of reaction per unit time per unit volume. The change in the mass concentration ρ_i will be

$$\sum_{\ell=1}^{k} \nu_{i\ell} \frac{d\xi_\ell}{dt} \cdot M_i = \phi_i \tag{19.1}$$

where M_i is the molecular weight of i. This term ϕ_i is often referred to as the "source term."

The change in component i in some volume V can then be expressed as

$$\int_V \frac{\partial}{\partial t} \rho_i \cdot dV = \int_V \phi_i \, dV - \int_A \rho_i \underline{u}_i \cdot \underline{dA} \tag{19.2}$$

The last term accounts for the net flow of i (with velocity $\underline{u}_i$) out of V through its surface. The integration over the surface can be replaced by an integration over the volume by use of Gauss' theorem. The resulting expression then becomes

$$\int_V \frac{\partial \rho_i}{\partial t} \cdot dV + \int_V \underline{\nabla} \cdot (\rho_i \underline{u}_i) \, dV - \int_V \phi_i \, dV = 0 \tag{19.3}$$

Because the volume V is arbitrary, then if $\int_V$(something) = 0, it must follow that (something) = 0. Substituting (19.1) for ϕ_i then gives the conservation equation for component i,

$$\frac{\partial \rho_i}{\partial t} + \underline{\nabla} \cdot (\rho_i \underline{u}_i) - M_i \sum_{\ell=1}^{k} \nu_{i\ell} \frac{d\xi_\ell}{dt} = 0 \tag{19.4}$$

The equation for total mass conservation can be written immediately from (19.4). The source term must vanish, i.e., $\Sigma_i \phi_i = 0$ as total mass is conserved. Thus

Thus

$$\frac{\partial \rho}{\partial t} + \underline{\nabla} \cdot (\rho \underline{u}) = 0 \tag{19.5}$$

Equation (19.5) can be rewritten in terms of the "substantial" derivative,

$$\frac{d}{dt} = \frac{\partial}{\partial t} + \frac{\partial x}{\partial t}\cdot\frac{\partial}{\partial x} + \frac{\partial y}{\partial t}\cdot\frac{\partial}{\partial y} + \frac{\partial z}{\partial t}\cdot\frac{\partial}{\partial z} \tag{19.6}$$

The substantial derivative should be interpreted as the time derivative taken at the center of mass of a volume element dV moving at a velocity $\underline{u}$ with respect to the external axes. Combining (19.6) and (19.5) gives the "equation of continuity."

$$\frac{d\rho}{dt} + \rho\underline{\nabla}\cdot\underline{u} = 0 \tag{19.7}$$

(b) Momentum

The equation for conservation of momentum is simply the equation of motion, or Newton's second law. The forces acting on the arbitrary volume will be made up of forces $\underline{F}_i$ acting on the components i, and a surface force described by $\underline{\underline{\sigma}}\cdot\underline{dA}$. This is the force transmitted across area $\underline{dA}$, where $\underline{\underline{\sigma}}$ is the stress tensor.

For a fluid at equilibrium, the shear stresses $\sigma_{ij} = 0$, and $\sigma_{xx} = \sigma_{yy} = \sigma_{zz} = -p$, the equilibrium hydrostatic pressure. This can be considered to be a way of describing a fluid at rest. For a fluid not in equilibrium,

$$p = -\frac{1}{3}\,\mathrm{Tr}(\underline{\underline{\sigma}}) = -\frac{1}{3}\,(\sigma_{xx} + \sigma_{yy} + \sigma_{zz}) \tag{19.8}$$

The form of the stress tensor $\underline{\underline{\sigma}}$ is discussed in some more detail in Sec. 6.1(a).

The conservation of momentum, $\rho\underline{u}$, can be obtained by considering steps (19.2)-(19.4). The source term is given by the forces, as force is the rate of change of momentum. Thus

$$\frac{\partial}{\partial t}(\rho\underline{u}) + \underline{\nabla}\cdot(\rho\underline{u}\underline{u}) - \Sigma\rho_i\underline{F}_i - \underline{\nabla}\cdot\underline{\underline{\sigma}} = 0 \tag{19.9}$$

The expression $\underline{u}\underline{u}$ is a dyadic product. Equation (19.9) can also be written in terms of the substantial derivative (19.6).

(c) Energy

The derivation of this conservation equation in its useful form is more complicated. The assumption of local equilibrium must be introduced, so that it is possible to discuss, in a nonequilibrium system, thermodynamic functions such as internal energy U, chemical potential μ_i, etc. The laws of equilibrium thermodynamics are also assumed to hold locally. Thus (Chap. 17),

$$\mu_i = U_i + pV_i - TS_i$$

$$dU = T\,dS - p\,dV + \Sigma\mu_i\,dn_i \quad -S\,dT + V\,dp = \Sigma n_i\,d\mu_i \tag{19.10}$$

are all assumed to be correct.

The assumption of local equilibrium and the other postulates of nonequilibrium thermodynamics which follow seem to be valid if the gradients of the thermodynamic functions are small, or if their time variation is slow as compared to the relaxation times of the system. These conditions seem to be satisfied in most cases if turbulence and shock waves are not involved.

Derivation of the energy conservation equation is also complicated because three types of energy flow through the surface must be considered: diffusive, convective, and conductive. The first two energy flows involve material flow. Thus the loss of energy due to flow out is

$$\int_A \left\{ \Sigma\rho_i \left(\frac{U_i}{M_i} + \frac{1}{2}\,\underline{u}_i \cdot \underline{u}_i \right) \underline{u}_i + \underline{q}' \right\} \cdot \underline{dA} \tag{19.11}$$

Both potential and kinetic energy are considered. Here $\underline{q}'$ is the heat conduction current density. It can be considered as being due to particles transmitting energy across $\underline{dA}$ without themselves moving across.

The energy source is simply the rate of work

$$\int_V \Sigma\underline{u}_i \cdot \rho_i \underline{F}_i\,dV + \int_A \underline{u} \cdot \underline{\underline{\sigma}} \cdot \underline{dA} \tag{19.12}$$

The basic energy conservation equation is then

$$\int \frac{\partial}{\partial t} \left\{ \Sigma \rho_i \left(\frac{U_i}{M_i} + \frac{1}{2} \underline{u}_i \cdot \underline{u}_i \right) \right\} dV = -\text{Eq. (19.11)} + \text{Eq. (19.12)} \tag{19.13}$$

The changing of (19.13) into the form required for later use, (19.14), will not be covered here. It requires straightforward but laborious substitutions of several variables, with the use of the relations given in (19.10). Detailed descriptions of these steps can be found in Refs. 1 and 2. The form useful for later work is

$$\rho \frac{dU}{dt} = \underline{\underline{\sigma}}:\underline{\nabla}\ \underline{u} - T\underline{\nabla}\cdot\underline{j}_s - \underline{q}\cdot\underline{\nabla} \ln T - \Sigma \underline{j}_i\cdot\underline{\nabla}_T\mu_i^{\dagger} - \Sigma\mu_i\underline{\nabla}\cdot\underline{j}_i \tag{19.14}$$

Here $\mu_i^{\dagger}$ is the chemical potential of i, including the external forces $\underline{F}_i$, and $\underline{\nabla}_T$ indicates the removal of temperature dependence of μ_i, i.e.,

$$\underline{\nabla}_T\mu_i^{\dagger} = \underline{\nabla}\ _i - \underline{F}_i - \frac{\partial \mu_i}{\partial T} \cdot \underline{\nabla}T \tag{19.15}$$

The heat flux $\underline{q} = \underline{q}' - \Sigma \underline{j}_i pV_i$, and $\underline{j}_i$ is the diffusion current of component i, $\underline{j}_i = \rho_i(\underline{u}_i - \underline{u})/M_i$. The current $\underline{j}_s$ is given by $\underline{j}_s = \underline{q}/T + \Sigma \underline{j}_i S_i$, and expresses the entropy current density.

19.2. POSTULATES OF NONEQUILIBRIUM THERMODYNAMICS

Equilibrium thermodynamics gives a description only of reversible processes, where for a closed system dS = dq/T. For nonequilibrium thermodynamics it states only that dS > dq/T. This basis of nonequilibrium thermodynamics is to quantify this inequality. It is thus written as

$$dS = (dS)_{eq} + (dS)_{ir} = \frac{dq}{T} + (dS)_{ir} \tag{19.16}$$

Here $(dS)_{ir}$ is the entropy production within the system.

Expressions for $(dS)_{ir}$ can be obtained by using the above conservation equations, and on introducing some further postulates. In Sec. 1, it has already been assumed that there is "local equilibrium," i.e., that thermodynamic quantities and laws are meaningful in very small regions, even in a nonequilibrium system.

The general conservation equation for entropy can be obtained in analogy to (19.2)-(19.4):

$$\rho \frac{dS}{dt} = \frac{\Phi}{T} - \underline{\nabla}\cdot\underline{j}_S \tag{19.17}$$

The entropy production term is thus Φ/T, where Φ is referred to as the "dissipation function." Under the assumption of local equilibrium, the second law holds locally, Its time derivative in the case of unit volume gives thus

$$\rho \frac{dS}{dt} = \frac{\rho}{T}\cdot\frac{dU}{dt} - \frac{p}{T}\cdot\frac{d\rho}{dt} - \frac{\rho}{T}\cdot\Sigma\mu_i \frac{dc_i}{dt} \tag{19.18}$$

Here μ_i does not include the potential of the forces $\underline{F}_i$.

It now remains to substitute into (19.18) as follows: (19.17) for $\rho\ dS/dt$; (19.14) for $\rho\ dU/dt$; (19.7) for $d\rho/dt$; and (19.4) for $d\rho_i/dt$ (= $M_i\ dc_i/dt$). The net result is that the entropy production term Φ can be written as $\Phi = \Phi_1 + \Phi_2 + \Phi_3 + \Phi_4$:

$\Phi_1 = (\underline{\underline{\sigma}} + p\underline{\underline{1}}):\underline{\nabla}\ \underline{u}$, Entropy production due to viscous flow.

At equilibrium, $\underline{\underline{\sigma}} = -p\underline{\underline{1}}$, as seen from (19.8), and $\Phi_1 = 0$;

$\Phi_2 = -\Sigma A_\ell \cdot d\xi_\ell/dt$, Entropy production due to chemical reactions.

A_ℓ is defined for the ℓth reaction as $\Sigma\nu_{i\ell}\mu_i$ and is called the "affinity" of the reaction (17.31). At equilibrium, $\Sigma\nu_{i\ell}\mu_i = 0$.

$\Phi_3 = -\Sigma\underline{j}_i\cdot\underline{\nabla}_T\mu_i^\dagger$, Entropy production due to isothermal diffusion.

$\Phi_4 = -\underline{q}\cdot\underline{\nabla}\ \ln T$, Entropy production due to heat flow.

It is next assumed that the entropy production is given by the expression $\Phi = \Sigma J_i X_i$, where J_i and X_i are conjugate "flux-force" pairs. As shown in Sec. 19.4, this statement need not be taken as an assumption, but can be derived from statistical-mechanical considerations of fluctuations.

Inspection of the four terms above gives the following tabulation of flux-force pairs

Flux	Force	
$\underline{\underline{\sigma}} + p\underline{\underline{1}}$	$\underline{\nabla}\ \underline{u}$	(a)
$d\xi_\ell/dt$	$-A_\ell$	(b)
$\underline{j}_i$	$-\underline{\nabla}_T\mu_i^\dagger$	(c)
$\underline{q}$	$\underline{\nabla}\ \ln T$	(d)

(19.19)

Phenomenological coefficients L_{ij} are introduced through a postulate stating that the fluxes J_i are linear homogeneous functions of the forces X_i, i.e., $J_i = \Sigma L_{ij}X_j$. This postulate can be made using experimental transport laws such as Fourier's, Fick's, and Ohm's as guides, or by consideration of basic relationships (Sec. 19.4).

Several interesting results can immediately be derived by using this postulate on (19.19). The stress is linearly proportional to the velocity gradient; the rate of reaction is linearly proportional to the affinity, etc. It also follows that at equilibrium, all forces and fluxes are zero.

A restriction is present in the values of L_{ij} in the case of isotropic systems. Vector forces of fluxes can interact among themselves, but not with scalars or tensors. Thus heat flow and diffusive flow cannot couple with viscous flow or chemical reactions through the phenomenological coefficients.

Yet another postulate known as the "Onsager reciprocal relationship" is introduced into nonequilibrium thermodynamics. It states that $L_{ij} = L_{ji}$. This postulate can be rigorously proven for some cases using statistical mechanics, and applying the principle of microscopic reversibility.

On the basis of the conjugate flux-force pairs (19.19), the postulates described above, and the conservation equations, it is possible to develop a complete set of generally applicable transport equations.

19.3. FLUCTUATIONS

A nonequilibrium state can arise in a system due to some external perturbation. Fluctuations from the mean value can also occur in a system in equilibrium, as shown in (18.5) and (18.42). Here a more general approach is used to describe fluctuations. This approach is then extended to discuss the time dependence of fluctuations as well.

In an isolated system, the basic equation of Boltzmann relates the entropy and the statistical weight Ω of a system as

$$S = kT \ln \Omega \tag{19.20}$$

Let now ζ denote some quantity in the system such that its mean value $\langle\zeta\rangle = 0$. The meaning of ζ is further illustrated in Sec. 19.4. The probability $w(\zeta)d\zeta$ that ζ has a value in the interval ζ to $\zeta + d\zeta$ is given considering (19.20) by

$$w(\zeta)\ d\zeta = \text{const} \times \exp[S(\zeta)]\ d\zeta \tag{19.21}$$

The constant in (19.21) must be chosen so that $w(\zeta)$ is normalized.

The entropy has a maximum at $\zeta = \langle\zeta\rangle = 0$ so that $S(\zeta)$ can be expanded as

$$S(\zeta) = S(0) + \left(\frac{\partial S}{\partial \zeta}\right)_0 \cdot \zeta + \frac{1}{2}\left(\frac{\partial^2 S}{\partial \zeta^2}\right)_0 \cdot \zeta^2 = S(0) - \frac{1}{2}\beta\zeta^2 \tag{19.22}$$

where β is a positive constant. When (19.22) is set into (19.21) and the result is normalized, then

$$w(\zeta)\ d\zeta = \frac{\sqrt{\beta}}{2\pi} \exp[\frac{1}{2}\beta\zeta^2]\ d\zeta \tag{19.23}$$

This is a Gaussian distribution, with a mean square fluctuation $\langle\zeta^2\rangle = 1/\beta$. Thus (19.23) can be rewritten as

$$w(\zeta)\ d\zeta = \frac{1}{\sqrt{2\pi\langle\zeta^2\rangle}} \exp\left[-\frac{\zeta^2}{2\langle\zeta^2\rangle}\right] d\zeta \tag{19.24}$$

A graph showing the shape of such a Gaussian distribution is included in Fig. 19.1, compared to the Lorentzian distribution, which also appears commonly in the discussion in this book [e.g., (20.52)].

In the case of systems which are not isolated, (19.21) can be generalized to give the probability of a fluctuation in terms of minimum work δw_{rev} (17.2) required for the change to occur:

$$w \propto \exp\left[-\frac{\delta w_{rev}}{kT}\right] \propto \exp\left[-\frac{\delta U - T\ \delta S + p\ \delta V}{kT}\right] \tag{19.25}$$

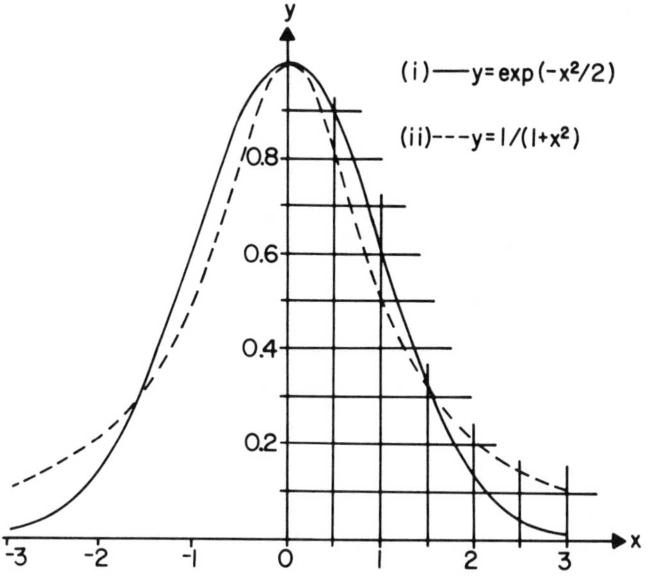

Fig. 19.1. The basic Gaussian distribution compared to the Lorentzian distribution.

Here δU, δS, and δV are the changes in U, S, and V, respectively, in the part of the system under fluctuation. T and p are understood in (19.25) to refer to the mean values in the system. It is assumed that no fluctuations in numbers occurs, i.e., $\mu\delta N = 0$. For fluctuations occurring at constant T, p, (19.25) leads to (17.32), as (17.6):

$$\delta w_{rev} = \delta U - T\,\delta S + p\,\delta V = \delta G \tag{19.26}$$

The exponent in (19.25) can be simplified if only small deviations in U are considered. In this case, U can be considered as a function of S and V, and can be expanded, keeping the first few terms

$$\delta U = \frac{\partial U}{\partial S}\cdot\delta S + \frac{\partial U}{\partial V}\cdot\delta V + \frac{1}{2}\left\{\frac{\partial^2 U}{\partial S^2}\;(\delta S)^2 + \frac{2\partial^2 U}{\partial S\partial U}\cdot\delta S\delta V + \frac{\partial^2 U}{\partial V^2}\cdot(\delta V)^2\right\} + \cdots \tag{19.27}$$

Now $\partial U/\partial S = T$, $\partial U/\partial V = -p$ can be substituted into (19.27) together with

$$\delta T = \delta \frac{\partial U}{\partial S} = \frac{\partial^2 U}{\partial S^2} \delta S + \frac{\partial^2 U}{\partial S \partial V} \delta V \tag{19.28}$$

etc. The result can be expressed as

$$\delta U - T\ \delta S + p\ \delta V = \frac{1}{2} (\delta T \cdot \delta S - \delta p \cdot \delta V) \tag{19.29}$$

When V and T are taken as the independent variables, and δp, δS expanded in terms of them, then

$$\delta S = \left(\frac{\partial S}{\partial T}\right)_V \partial T + \left(\frac{\partial S}{\partial V}\right)_T \delta V = \frac{C_V}{T} \delta T + \left(\frac{\partial p}{\partial T}\right)_V \delta V \qquad \text{etc.} \tag{19.30}$$

The fluctuation (19.25) can then be set into the form

$$w(\delta T, \delta V) \propto \exp\left[- \frac{C_V}{2kT^2} (\delta T)^2 + \frac{1}{2kTV\kappa_T} (\delta V)^2\right] \tag{19.31}$$

The notation and relationships used can be found in Chap. 17.

Inspection of (19.31) gives two results: (i) Fluctuations in V and T are independent, i.e., $\langle \delta T \delta V \rangle = 0$, as the exponent in (19.31) separates into two factors, one dependent on δT only, the other on δV only. (ii) By comparing with the Gaussian form of w (19.24),

$$\langle \delta T^2 \rangle = \frac{kT^2}{C_V} \qquad \langle \delta V^2 \rangle = -kTV\kappa_T \tag{19.32}$$

When instead S and p are taken as independent variables, then the following results can be obtained in an analogeous manner: (i) Fluctuations in p and S are independent. (ii) The mean fluctuations are

$$\langle \delta p^2 \rangle = \frac{kT}{V\kappa_S} \qquad \langle \delta S^2 \rangle = kC_p \tag{19.33}$$

Fluctuations in N can be considered by adding terms $\mu_A \delta N_A$, etc. to δw_{rev} (Refs. 3 and 4). The same results for $\langle \delta N^2 \rangle$ can be obtained more easily by another method, however, (18.4). The fluctuation $\langle \delta V^2 \rangle$ has been obtained elsewhere [(18.9),(18.47)].

19.4. TIME DEVELOPMENT OF FLUCTUATIONS

(a) The Linear Relationship

This rather abstract section is included to indicate what some of the postulates of nonequilibrium thermodynamics are equivalent to at a more basic level. The discussion starts with a generalization of the model introduced in Sec. 3 above. Thus ζ_1, ζ_2, $\zeta_3 \cdots$ denote thermodynamic quantities of a system or part of it. These are all as in Sec. 19.3 defined as deviations from equilibrium, i.e., $\langle\zeta_1\rangle = \langle\zeta_2\rangle = 0$.

The rate of variation of ζ_i is then given as

$$\frac{d\zeta_i}{dt} = \text{function}(\zeta_1, \zeta_2 \cdots) = -\sum_k \lambda_{ik}\zeta_k \tag{19.34}$$

It will be assumed that for small deviations from equilibrium, it is sufficient to keep only linear terms in the expansion of $d\zeta_i/dt$. This assumption (at times referred to as the "linear rate hypothesis") is basic to the considerations that follow.

When only one variable ζ is considered, then (19.34) leads directly to a solution,

$$\zeta(t) = \zeta(0) \exp[-\lambda t] \tag{19.35}$$

For (19.35) to be valid, however, it is necessary for ζ to be large as compared to the mean fluctuation in ζ, even though small on the total scale.

Derivatives of the form

$$X_i = -\frac{\partial S}{\partial \zeta_i} = \sum_k \eta_{ik}\zeta_k \tag{19.36}$$

are also assumed linearly dependent on the ζ_k, as at equilibrium, $X_i = 0$. The η_{ik} are thus second derivatives of S [see (19.22)]; thus $\eta_{ik} = \eta_{ki}$. The time derivatives (19.34) can then also be expressed in terms of the X_i as

$$\frac{d\zeta_i}{dt} = -\Sigma\gamma_{ik}X_k = -\frac{\partial \mathit{f}}{\partial X_i} \tag{19.37}$$

Here $\mathfrak{f}$ is a "generating function,"

$$\mathfrak{f} = \frac{1}{2}\sum\sum\gamma_{ik}X_iX_k \tag{19.38}$$

and the γ are "kinetic coefficients." They can also be shown to be symmetrical, except in the case where external magnetic fields or uniform rotation is involved (Refs. 2,3,6, and 7).

The time derivative of the entropy is thus simply given as

$$\frac{dS}{dt} = \sum \frac{\partial S}{\partial \zeta_i}\cdot\frac{d\zeta_i}{dt} = \sum -X_i\frac{d\zeta_i}{dt} = \sum X_i\frac{\partial \mathfrak{f}}{\partial X_i} = 2\mathfrak{f} \tag{19.39}$$

Thus $\mathfrak{f}$ and dS/dt and the entropy production term Φ (19.17) are proportional to each other. The flux J_i in the postulate $\Phi = \sum J_iX_i$ is then proportional to $d\zeta_i/dt$ as seen in (19.39).

From (19.37), it can be seen that the relationship $J_i = \sum L_{ik}X_k$ can also be derived from this discussion. The reciprocal relations $L_{ik} = L_{ki}$ hold if $\gamma_{ik} = \gamma_{ki}$ hold. The proper sets of fluxes and forces must be chosen if the relations $\Phi = \sum J_iX_i$ and $J_i = \sum L_{ik}X_k$ are to be valid.

The actual time development of the variables ζ is conveniently described in terms of time correlations functions. The properties of such functions are however described in Chap. 7, as they are of importance for the topics of that chapter.

(b) Fluctuation-Dissipation Theorem

Another way in which the time development of fluctuations can be considered is through the "fluctuation-dissipation theorem" [9]. It can be interpreted as stating that when there is an external disturbance of a system, then the dissipative process involves an interaction between this disturbance and the system. The disturbance can be considered to give rise to an energy coherently associated with only a few degrees of freedom. On interaction, this energy is incoherently distributed among the many modes of the dissipative system due to the random fluctuations generated by the system and acting on the disturbance.

The fluctuations thus cause the dissipation of the disturbance according to the above view. This relation can be expressed mathematically [9]. One approximate form for an especially simple case is

$$\langle F^2(\omega)\rangle = \frac{2kT}{\pi}\cdot R(\omega) \qquad (19.40)$$

Here $\langle F^2(\omega)\rangle$ is the Fourier transform concerning the effective forces that describe the spontaneous fluctuations in a system, and $R(\omega)$ is the resistance of the system to an outside disturbance. Through (19.40), relationships for Brownian motion (Chap. 7) can be obtained from Stokes law (6.11). The resistance R given by (6.11) is $6\pi\eta a$. Thus the spectral density of effective forces describing the spontaneous, stochastic motions in Brownian motion for a particle size a have a spectral density for the force [see Eqs. (7.29) and (7.27)].

$$\langle F^2(\omega)\rangle \simeq 12\eta a kT \qquad (19.41)$$

19.5. TRANSITION STATE THEORY

The transition state theory of chemical (and physical) processes can be formulated in a number of ways. It can be quite concisely introduced by extending the discussion of fluctuations from (19.26).

A reaction of the type

$$\mathrm{I} \rightleftarrows (\#) \rightleftarrows \mathrm{II} \qquad (19.42)$$

will be considered. The difference in free energy in the reaction is designated (per unit reaction) as

$$\Delta G = G(\mathrm{II}) - G(\mathrm{I}) \qquad (19.43)$$

The difference in free energy between the standard states of reagent and of the "transition state" or "activated state" complex, (#) is given by the free energy of activation

$$\Delta G^{\#} = G^{\theta}(\#) - G^{\theta}(\mathrm{I}) \qquad (19.44)$$

If the reaction from the transition state to state (II) is for the moment neglected, then the probability of state (I) being in a state of fluctuation such that it is in the activated state is by (19.25) and (19.26) given through

$$\frac{C_{\#}}{C_I} = \exp\left[-\frac{\Delta G^{\#}}{kT}\right] \tag{19.45}$$

The rate of formation of II is then taken to be $C_{\#} \cdot \nu^{\#}$, where $\nu^{\#}$ is the rate of breaking up of (#) to form (II) per unit concentration. This rate can be shown to be equivalent to kT/h when the motion of (#) along the reaction coordinate is considered. The reaction coordinate can be considered as a normal coordinate of (#) which has a negative force constant.

When the process (#) → (II) described above is assumed slow enough so that the "equilibrium" (19.45) is not disturbed significantly, then the overall rate (I) → (II) is given by

$$C_I \frac{kT}{h} \exp\left[-\frac{\Delta G^{\#}}{kT}\right] \tag{19.46}$$

The rate can also be expressed in terms of a rate constant as

$$k = \frac{kT}{h} \cdot \exp\left[-\frac{\Delta G^{\#}}{kT}\right] = A \exp\left[-\frac{E^{\#}}{kT}\right] \tag{19.47}$$

The Arrhenius activation energy $E^{\#}$ and the preexponential factor A have been introduced in (19.47).

When (19.45) is assumed to be a true equilibrium, then other activation parameters such as $\Delta V^{\#}$, $\Delta S^{\#}$, $\Delta H^{\#}$, $C_p^{\#}$, etc. can be introduced. $E^{\#}$ can then be expressed in terms of these variables. When a model of the transition state complex is assumed, then these parameters can be calculated through standard statistical mechanical methods (Chap. 18).

REFERENCES

References 1, 2, 6, and 7 and several chapters in Ref. 8 give thorough discussions of nonequilibrium thermodynamics. Fluctuations are well covered in Refs. 3 and 4.

1. D. D. Fitts, Non-Equilibrium Thermodynamics, McGraw-Hill, New York, 1962.
2. S. R. de Groot and P. Mazur, Non-Equilibrium Thermodynamics, North-Holland, Amsterdam, 1962.

3. L. D. Landau and E. M. Lifshitz, Statistical Physics, Pergamon, London, 1969.

4. R. Kubo, Statistical Mechanics, North-Holland, Amsterdam, 1971.

5. N. Davidson, Statistical Mechanics, McGraw-Hill, New York, 1962.

6. A. Katchalsky and P. F. Curran, Non-Equilibrium Thermodynamics in Biophysics, Harvard Univ. Press, Cambridge, 1967.

7. S. R. de Groot, Thermodynamics of Irreversible Processes, North-Holland, Amsterdam, 1966.

8. H. J. M. Hanley (ed.), Transport Phenomena in Fluids, Dekker, New York, 1969.

9. H. B. Callen, in Fluctuation, Relaxation and Resonance in Magnetic Systems (D. ter Haar, ed.) Oliver and Boyd, London, 1962.

Chapter 20

ELECTROMAGNETISM

20.1. BASIC LAWS AND DEFINITIONS - ELECTROSTATICS

There are several sets of units used to describe electromagnetism. Here the set recommended for SI units will be used. Thus the permeability of a vacuum $\mu^{\bullet}$ is defined as being exactly $4\pi \times 10^{-7}$ H m^{-1} and the permittivity of free space $\varepsilon^{\bullet} = \mu^{\bullet -1} c^{\bullet -2}$ F m^{-1} where $c^{\bullet}$ is the speed of light in vacuum. Other sets of units are discussed in Ref. 1.

In this set of units, Coulomb's law describing the force on a static charge Q' a distance $\underline{r}$ from another charge Q in vacuum is given by

$$\underline{F} = Q'\underline{E} = \frac{Q'Q\underline{r}}{4\pi\varepsilon^{\bullet} r^3} = \frac{QQ'}{4\pi\varepsilon^{\bullet}\underline{\nabla}(1/r)} \tag{20.1}$$

Equation (20.1) also serves to define the electric field intensity vector $\underline{E}$. Coulomb's law can be expressed in differential form. The integral over a surface A of $\underline{E}\cdot\underline{dA}$ gives through the use of Gauss' theorem

$$\int_A \underline{E}\cdot\underline{dA} = \int_V \underline{\nabla}\cdot\underline{E}\, dV = \frac{Q}{\varepsilon^\bullet} \qquad \underline{\nabla}\cdot\underline{E} = \frac{\rho}{\varepsilon^\bullet} \tag{20.2}$$

Here ρ is the charge density at the point where the field has a value $\underline{E}$.

It also follows from (20.1) that $\underline{E}$ can be expressed as

$$\underline{E} = -\underline{\nabla}\,\phi \qquad \underline{\nabla} \times \underline{E} = 0 \tag{20.3}$$

where ϕ is a scalar potential. The second relation follows as $\underline{\nabla} \times \underline{\nabla}\phi = 0$. It is important to note that (20.3) is correct only if the charge Q is not in motion. The scalar potential is for a point charge Q in vacuum given as [see (20.1)]:

$$\phi = \frac{Q}{4\pi\varepsilon^\bullet r} + \text{constant} \tag{20.4}$$

The constant can be chosen according to convenience, and is usually set to zero. Combination of (20.3) and (20.2) results in Poisson's equation

$$\underline{\nabla}\cdot\underline{\nabla}\phi = \nabla^2\phi = -\frac{\rho}{\varepsilon^\bullet} \tag{20.5}$$

Relation (20.5) applies only in a vacuum. In a material medium some "polarization" can occur and (20.5) can be expressed instead as

$$\nabla^2\phi = -\underline{\nabla}\cdot\underline{E} = -\frac{\rho + \rho_p}{\varepsilon^\bullet} \tag{20.6}$$

Here ρ_p is the "polarization" charge density present due to the electrostatic field, while ρ is the true, free charge as previously. The charge ρ_p can be expressed as

$$\underline{\nabla}\cdot\underline{P} = -\rho_p \tag{20.7}$$

where $\underline{P}$ is the electric polarization.

The polarization can be thought to arise from the presence of electric dipole moments $\underline{p}_{\text{ind}}$ induced in the particles present due to the presence at a molecule of an effective field $\underline{E}_{\text{eff}}$. If the induced dipole is proportional to the field, then

$$\underline{p}_{\text{ind}} = \alpha\varepsilon^{\bullet}\underline{E}_{\text{eff}} \tag{20.8}$$

where α is the polarizability, here assumed a scalar quantity [see Sec. 1.1(c)]. In such a case,

$$\underline{P} = \frac{\alpha N\varepsilon^{\bullet}\underline{E}_{\text{eff}}}{V} \tag{20.9}$$

where N/V gives the number of molecules per unit volume. Another term must be added to (20.9) when the molecules contain permanent dipoles (11.7). The discussion of polarization is continued in Chap. 11 and Sec. 1.1.

Equation (20.6) can be written in a simpler form by introducing another vector, the electric displacement $\underline{D}$. Thus

$$\underline{\nabla}\cdot\left(\underline{E} + \frac{\underline{P}}{\varepsilon^{\bullet}}\right) = \frac{\rho}{\varepsilon^{\bullet}} \qquad \underline{\nabla}\cdot\underline{D} = \rho \tag{20.10}$$

where $\underline{D} = \varepsilon^{\bullet}\underline{E} + \underline{P}$. In the special case where $\underline{P}$ is proportional to $\underline{E}$, $\underline{D}$ can be written as $\varepsilon\varepsilon^{\bullet}\underline{E}$, where $\varepsilon\varepsilon^{\bullet}$ is the permittivity of the medium. The relative permittivity (or dielectric constant) ε then also becomes meaningful. The force between two particles in a medium is proportional to $\underline{E}$. As $\underline{E}$ is proportional to $1/\varepsilon$, then it follows that the force between particles in a dielectric medium is less than that in a vacuum, and proportional to $1/\varepsilon$.

When the medium conducts electricity, then an electric current density j will be set up. In many cases $\underline{j}$ is given by Ohm's law as (see also Chap. 19):

$$\underline{j} = \sigma\underline{E} \tag{20.11}$$

where σ is the electrical conductivity.

20.2. BASIC LAWS AND DEFINITIONS - MAGNETISM

The physically fundamental magnetic quantity corresponding to $\underline{E}$ is the magnetic induction (also called the magnetic field) $\underline{B}$. Often the magnetic field intensity $\underline{H}$ is indicated as being fundamentally more significant than $\underline{B}$ because $\underline{H}$ appears mathematically as analogous to $\underline{E}$ in the electromagnetic field equations. This mathematical analogy does not correspond to a physical analogy, however.

A definition of $\underline{B}$ can be obtained by a generalization of (20.1) to the force on a charge Q moving with a velocity $\underline{u}$. In this case

$$\underline{F} = Q(\underline{E} + \underline{u} \times \underline{B}) \tag{20.12}$$

The expression for magnetism analogous to Coulomb's law is somewhat more complex as there is no magnetic equivalent to point charges. The closest in analogy can be considered to be the expression giving the force between two current carrying elements. In the case of volume currents in vacuum the relations are given by the Biot and Savart law:

$$\underline{F} = \int (\underline{j} \times \underline{B})\, dV \qquad \underline{B} = \frac{\mu^\bullet}{4\pi} \int \frac{\underline{j} \times \underline{r}}{r^3}\, dV' \tag{20.13}$$

The analogy to (20.1) can be seen through (20.12) considering that $\rho\underline{u} = \underline{j}$ if there is a charge density ρ instead of a discrete charge Q.

It is also possible to obtain an expression analogous to (20.2). In this case a line integral $\oint$ about a closed path must be constructed and Stokes theorem used to give the results

$$\oint \underline{B}\cdot\underline{d\ell} = \int_A (\underline{\nabla} \times \underline{B})\cdot\underline{dA} = \mu^\bullet I \qquad \underline{\nabla} \times \underline{B} = \mu^\bullet \underline{j} \tag{20.14}$$

In analogy to (20.3) it can be shown that

$$\underline{B} = \underline{\nabla} \times \underline{A} \qquad \underline{\nabla}\cdot\underline{B} = 0$$

Here $\underline{A}$ is a vector potential. From (20.13) it can be shown to be

$$\underline{A} = \frac{\mu^\bullet}{4\pi} \int \frac{\underline{j}}{r}\, dV' + \text{a function} \tag{20.16}$$

The function in (20.16) can be arbitrarily chosen with the restriction that its curl, i.e., $\underline{\nabla} \times$, is zero.

When the magnetic field is in some medium, then in addition to the "true" current $\underline{j}$ associated with the flow of true charge, there can also exist polarization currents $\partial \underline{P}/\partial t$ due to the change in polarization charge with time [see (20.7)]. In addition, magnetization currents, $\underline{j}_m$, can be present in the medium.

When a particular volume (e.g., a molecule) contains a current $\underline{j}_m$, then the magnetic moment $\underline{m}$ of that volume is defined as

$$\underline{m} = \frac{1}{2} \int (\underline{\xi} \times \underline{j}_m)\ dV \tag{20.17}$$

Here $\underline{\xi}$ indicates the coordinates within the molecule. When $\underline{j}_m$ is due to a charge density ρ moving with a velocity $\underline{u}$, then

$$\underline{m} = \frac{1}{2} \int \rho (\underline{\xi} \times \underline{u})\ dV \tag{20.18}$$

When there is a current I flowing in a loop enclosing a surface $\underline{A}$, then $\underline{m}$ is simply $I\underline{A}$ according to (20.18).

The mechanical angular momentum $\underline{L}$ of a system of particles with a mass m and charge Q is related to $\underline{m}$ as

$$\underline{m} = \Gamma\, \underline{L} \qquad\qquad \Gamma = \frac{Q}{2m} \tag{20.19}$$

Here Γ is the "gyromagnetic ratio." For more complex distributions of charged objects and for nonclassical cases, Γ is written as

$$\Gamma = g\, \frac{Q}{2m} \tag{20.20}$$

where the "g factor" defines the magnetic structure.

The magnetic moment $d\underline{m}$ of a volume dV can be related to the magnetization $\underline{M}$ as

$$d\underline{m} = \underline{M}\ dV \tag{20.21}$$

It can then be shown, either by using (20.21) and (20.17), or by going back and considering the vector potential $\underline{A}$ [1], that

$$\underline{j}_m = \underline{\nabla} \times \underline{M} \tag{20.22}$$

The total current j_{tot} can then be written as

$$\underline{j}_{tot} = \underline{j} + \frac{\partial \underline{P}}{\partial t} + \underline{\nabla} \times \underline{M} \tag{20.23}$$

This current must obey the continuity equation (19.7) to conserve charge. Thus

$$\underline{\nabla} \cdot \underline{j} + \underline{\nabla} \cdot \frac{\partial \underline{P}}{\partial t} + \underline{\nabla} \cdot (\underline{\nabla} \times \underline{M}) + \left(\frac{\partial \rho}{\partial t} \right)_{tot} = 0 \tag{20.24}$$

A relation for $(\partial\rho/\partial t)_{tot}$ can be obtained from (20.6). The result is effectively to add a term $\varepsilon^{\bullet}(\partial \underline{E}/\partial t)$, a vacuum displacement current, to $\underline{j}_{tot}$ in (20.23) to give a "solenoidal" current $\underline{j}_{ts}$, i.e., $\underline{\nabla} \cdot \underline{j}_{ts} = 0$. The current $\underline{j}_{ts}$ is the effective current for defining the magnetic induction $\underline{B}$ through (20.14). Thus

$$\underline{\nabla} \times \underline{B} = \mu^{\bullet} \left(\underline{j} + \frac{\partial \underline{P}}{\partial t} + \underline{\nabla} \times \underline{M} + \varepsilon^{\bullet} \frac{\partial \underline{E}}{\partial t} \right) \tag{20.25}$$

When (20.10) is used to introduce $\underline{D}$, then (20.25) can be rewritten as

$$\underline{\nabla} \times (\underline{B} - \mu^{\bullet}\underline{M}) = \mu^{\bullet} \left(\underline{j} + \frac{\partial \underline{D}}{\partial t} \right) \tag{20.26}$$

Further simplification in the mathematical form can be achieved if the magnetic field vactor $\underline{H}$ is introduced as $\underline{H} = \underline{B}/\mu^{\bullet} - \underline{M}$. In this case

$$\underline{\nabla} \times \underline{H} = \underline{j} + \frac{\partial \underline{D}}{\partial t} \tag{20.27}$$

When $\underline{M}$ is assumed to proportional to $\underline{B}$, then the relation between $\underline{B}$ and $\underline{H}$ simplifies to

$$\underline{B} = \mu\mu^{\bullet}\underline{H} = \mu^{\bullet}(1 + \chi_m)\underline{H} \tag{20.28}$$

Here $\mu\mu^{\bullet}$ is the permeability of the medium, μ the relative permeability and χ_m the magnetic susceptibility.

Equations (20.27), (20.15), and (20.10) are three of Maxwell's electrodynamic field equations, and are valid for media at rest. The fourth equation completing this set is an extended form of (20.3). In case of moving charges,

$$\underline{E} = \underline{\nabla}\phi - \frac{\partial \underline{A}}{\partial t} \qquad\qquad \underline{\nabla} \times \underline{E} = -\frac{\partial \underline{B}}{\partial t} \tag{20.29}$$

The extra terms from (20.29) can be derived from Faraday's law of induction.

With the use of Stokes theorem, (20.29) can be written as

$$\oint \underline{E}\cdot\underline{d\ell} = \int_A (\underline{\nabla} \times \underline{E})\cdot\underline{dA} = -\int_A \frac{\partial \underline{B}}{\partial t}\cdot\underline{dA} \tag{20.30}$$

Thus (20.30) reduces to the experimentally observed "flux rule," that the electromotive force in a circuit $\oint \underline{E}\cdot\underline{d\ell}$ equals minus the rate of change of magnetic flux through the circuit, $-\partial/\partial t \int \underline{B}\cdot\underline{dA}$. This law is basic to design of electric motors and generators.

20.3. PROPAGATION OF ELECTROMAGNETIC WAVES

The laws governing electromagnetism, Maxwell's equations, are in summary:

$$\underline{\nabla}\cdot\underline{D} = \rho \qquad\qquad \underline{\nabla}\cdot\underline{B} = 0$$

$$\underline{\nabla} \times \underline{E} = -\frac{\partial \underline{B}}{\partial t} \qquad\qquad \underline{\nabla} \times \underline{H} = \underline{j} + \frac{\partial \underline{D}}{\partial t}$$

In isotropic media, the following relations may also be valid:

$$\underline{D} = \varepsilon\varepsilon^{\bullet}\underline{E} \qquad\qquad \underline{B} = \mu\mu^{\bullet}\underline{H} \qquad\qquad \underline{j} = \sigma\underline{E}$$

The above laws can be combined to give a general wave equation describing the space and time dependence of $\underline{E}$. In a region where $\rho = 0$, this is

$$\nabla^2\underline{E} - \mu\mu^{\bullet}\sigma\frac{\partial \underline{E}}{\partial t} - \frac{\varepsilon\mu}{c^{\bullet 2}}\frac{\partial^2 \underline{E}}{\partial t^2} = 0 \tag{20.31}$$

When the time variation of $\underline{E}$ is assumed periodic with a frequency ω, i.e.,

$$\underline{E}(\underline{r},t) = \underline{E}(\underline{r}) \exp[-i\omega t] \tag{20.32}$$

then, noting that $\mu^{\bullet}\varepsilon^{\bullet}c^{\bullet 2} = 1$, (20.31) can be written as

$$\nabla^2\underline{E} + \left(1 + \frac{i\sigma}{\varepsilon\varepsilon^\bullet\omega}\right)\frac{\mu\varepsilon\omega^2\underline{E}}{c^{\bullet 2}} = 0 \qquad (20.33)$$

The ratio $\varepsilon\varepsilon^\bullet/\sigma$ is often written as τ, the relaxation time of the medium. For a nonconducting medium, $\tau \to 0$.

In the case of sinusoidally varying plane waves in a nonconducting medium, the fields $\underline{E}$ and $\underline{B}$ are in directions transverse to the direction of propagation. They are perpendicular to each other and differ $\pi/2$ in phase. All these results can be obtained from Maxwell's equations ($\rho = 0$, $\underline{j} = 0$).

A general form of the solution to satisfy these equations and (20.33) is

$$\underline{E} = \underline{E}_0 \exp[i(\underline{k}\cdot\underline{r} - \omega t)] \qquad (20.34)$$

Here $\underline{k}$ is the wave vector of the wave motion,

$$\underline{k} = \frac{2\pi\underline{c}}{\lambda c} \qquad (20.35)$$

where $\underline{c}$ is the velocity of propagation and λ the wavelength, $\lambda = 2\pi c/\omega$. The speed is given through

$$\frac{c^\bullet}{c} = n = \sqrt{\varepsilon\mu} \qquad (20.36)$$

where n is the index of refraction. The magnetic field is given as

$$\underline{B} = \underline{k} \times \frac{\underline{E}}{\omega} \qquad (20.37)$$

Such an electromagnetic wave contains an energy density. The time average of this energy density, $\langle U\rangle$ is given as

$$\langle U\rangle = \frac{1}{2}\langle(\underline{E}\cdot\underline{D} + \underline{B}\cdot\underline{H})\rangle = \frac{1}{2}\varepsilon\varepsilon^\bullet E_0^2 \qquad (20.38)$$

The magnetic and electric fields contribute equally to $\langle U\rangle$. An explanation of the appearance of the term $\frac{1}{2}\underline{E}\cdot\underline{D}$ is given in Sec. 1.1(c). The magnetic term is obtained in analogy. This mean energy is related directly to the "Poynting vector" $\underline{N}$ as

$$\underline{N} = \underline{E} \times \underline{H} = \langle U\rangle\underline{c} \qquad (20.39)$$

20.4. EQUATION OF MOTION OF AN ELECTRON

When a charge, e.g., an electron, is accelerated, then a radiative electromagnetic field is produced. The scalar and vector potentials of the electron are given as shown in (20.4) and (20.15). In this case $\underline{j}$ is simply $e\underline{v}$. The forms shown in (20.4) and (20.16) are appropriate only for $\underline{v} \ll c$. This will be the case assumed throughout. The fields $\underline{E}$ and $\underline{B}$ can then be obtained from (20.29) and (20.15). When operating with $\underline{\nabla}$, it is necessary to consider the motion of the particle. Thus $\underline{\nabla}$ is replaced by $\underline{\nabla} - (\underline{r}/rc)\partial/\partial t$ [1].

The fields calculated in this way have two components. One is a nonradiative one present for a nonaccelerating charge. It does not contribute to energy flow over an infinitely distant surface as it varies as $1/r^2$. The second component describes the radiation fields:

$$\underline{B}_{rad} = \frac{e}{4\pi\varepsilon^{\bullet}c^3r^2}(\underline{\dot{v}} \times \underline{r}) \qquad \underline{E}_{rad} = \frac{e}{4\pi\varepsilon^{\bullet}c^2r^3}\underline{r} \times (\underline{r} \times \underline{\dot{v}}) \tag{20.40}$$

Here $\underline{\dot{v}}$ is the acceleration of the electron. The angular distribution of the fields is given by (20.40). They are seen to be 0 in the direction of $\underline{\dot{v}}$ and to have maxima in directions transverse to $\underline{\dot{v}}$.

The Poynting vector can now be calculated from (20.40). When it is integrated over a spherical surface, then the rate of loss of radiated energy is found to be

$$-\frac{dU}{dt} = \frac{e^2\dot{v}^2}{6\pi\varepsilon^{\bullet}c^3} \tag{20.41}$$

In order for energy to be conserved, the loss due to radiation must be compensated by some reaction force $\underline{F}_r$ on the electron such that

$$\underline{F}_r \cdot \underline{v} + \frac{e^2\dot{v}^2}{6\pi\varepsilon^{\bullet}c^3} = 0 \tag{20.42}$$

No solution for $\underline{F}_r$ can be obtained which satisfies (20.42) every instant. On a time average, however, energy is conserved if $\underline{F}_r$ is given by

$$\underline{F}_r = \frac{e^2\underline{\ddot{v}}}{6\pi\varepsilon^{\bullet}c^3} \tag{20.43}$$

There is also a force present due to the presence of an effective "electromagnetic mass" demanded by the conservation of momentum relations [1,2]. It will be later merged into the rest mass, however, and will thus not be discussed here.

The equation of motion for the electron in the presence of an external force $\underline{F}_{ext}$ can be written as

$$\underline{F}_{ext} = m\dot{\underline{v}} - \frac{e^2\ddot{\underline{v}}}{6\pi\varepsilon^\bullet c^3} \tag{20.44}$$

20.5. APPLICATION OF EQUATIONS OF MOTION

(a) Radiative Damping in Emission

In this case a model can be constructed with an electron bound with a harmonic force $\underline{F} = -\mathfrak{f}\underline{x}$ traveling along the x coordinate. It would then have a frequency of natural motion $\omega_0 = \sqrt{\mathfrak{f}/m}$. The equation of motion from (20.44) with $F_{ext} = -\mathfrak{f}x$ and $v = \dot{x}$ is then

$$\ddot{x} + \omega_0^2 x - \frac{e^2\dddot{x}}{6\pi\varepsilon^\bullet c^3 m} = 0 \tag{20.45}$$

The last term can be simplified if it is assumed to be small so that $\dddot{x} \simeq -\omega_0^2\dot{x}$. The result is

$$\ddot{x} + \gamma\dot{x} + \omega_0^2 x = 0 \tag{20.46}$$

where $\gamma = 2\tau_0\omega_0^2 = e^2\omega_0^2/6\pi\varepsilon^\bullet c^3 m$.

A solution for small γ is

$$x = A\exp[-i\omega_0 t]\exp\left[-\frac{\gamma t}{2}\right] \tag{20.47}$$

The potential and kinetic energies of the oscillator can then be calculated. Averaged over a cycle, the rate of loss is

$$-\frac{dU}{dt} = \gamma U = \frac{e^2\omega_0^4 A^2}{12\pi\varepsilon^\bullet c^3}\exp[-\gamma t] \tag{20.48}$$

Equation (20.48) also gives the rate of radiation averaged over one cycle. The "lifetime" of radiation is $1/\gamma$.

When an electric dipole moment $\underline{p} = e\underline{x}$ is defined, then the rate of radiation can also be written as

$$-\frac{dU}{dt} = \frac{1}{6\pi\varepsilon^{\bullet}c^3}\left|\frac{d^2}{dt^2}\underline{p}(t)\right|^2 = \frac{\omega_0^4}{6\pi\varepsilon^{\bullet}c^3}|\langle\underline{p}(t)\rangle|^2 \tag{20.49}$$

This gives the same result as (20.48) when the time variation due to the γ term is very small compared to that of ω term. The average $|\langle\underline{p}(t)\rangle|^2$ denotes

$$|\langle\underline{p}(t)\rangle|^2 = \left|eA\frac{1}{\sqrt{2}}\exp\left[-\frac{\gamma t}{2}\right]\right|^2 \tag{20.50}$$

Because of this radiative damping, the radiation emitted by the electron is not monochromatic. The linewidth can be obtained by Fourier analysis of the field. Thus

$$E(t) = E_0 \exp[-i\omega_0 t]\exp\left[-\frac{\gamma t}{2}\right] = \int_{-\infty}^{\infty} E(\omega)\exp[-i\omega t]\,d\omega \tag{20.51}$$

and

$$E(\omega) = \frac{1}{2\pi}\int_0^{\infty} E(t)\,dt = \frac{E_0}{2\pi}\frac{1}{i(\omega - \omega_0) - \gamma/2}$$

The radiation intensity corresponding to $E(\omega)$ at ω expressed normalized to the total intensity I_0 is then

$$I(\omega) = \frac{I_0\gamma}{2\pi}\frac{1}{(\omega - \omega_0)^2 + \gamma^2/4} \tag{20.52}$$

This gives a frequency width at half intensity of $\Delta\omega = \gamma$. The relationship in (20.52) is the Lorentz function, which appears often, as it is essentially the Fourier transform of the exponential function. It is displayed in Fig. 20.1 together with a related function which often occurs with it [e.g., Sec. 11.1(c)].

(b) Forced Oscillations

Next the case of an harmonically bound electron disturbed by an external electric field is considered. The effect of the magnetic field can be neglected for slow-moving electrons. Thus for a plane

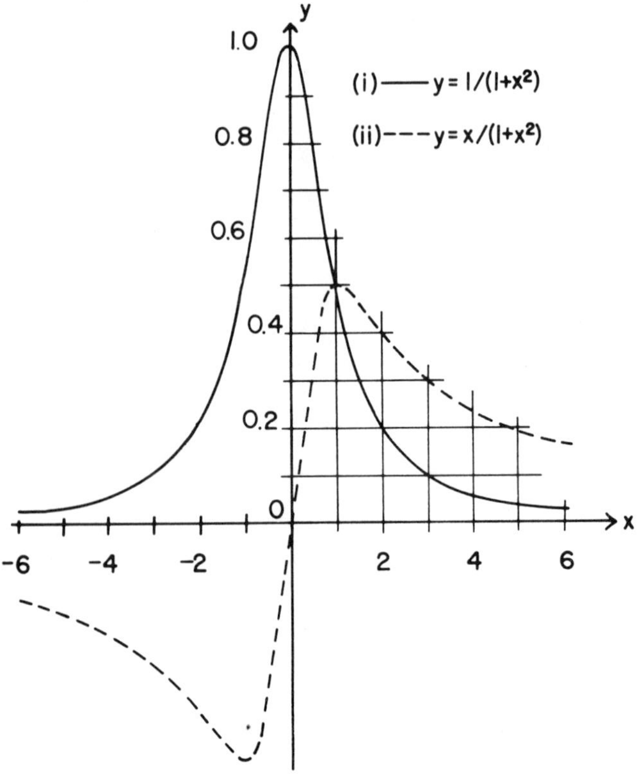

Fig. 20.1. The Lorentz function (——), and the related function $x/(1 + x^2)$ (---).

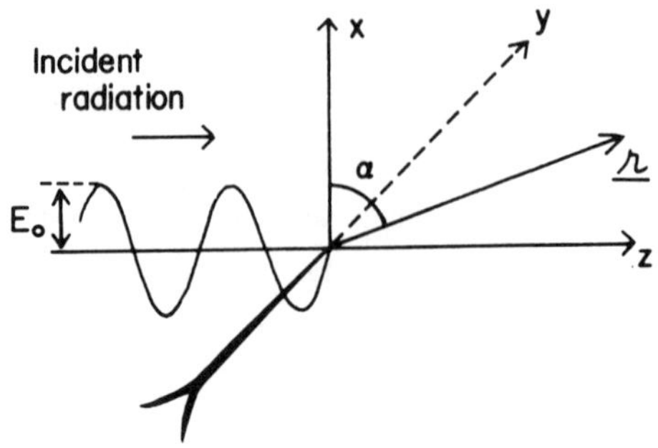

Fig. 20.2. Definition of the scattering angle α.

polarized incident field $\underline{E} = \underline{E}_0 \exp[-i\omega t]$, with $\underline{E}$ in the x direction, the equation of motion is:

$$m(\ddot{x} + \gamma\dot{x} + \omega_0^2 x) = eE_0 \exp[-i\omega t] \tag{20.53}$$

The same approximations as before have been used to obtain the γx term, except now $\gamma = 2\tau_0\omega^2/3$.

The steady state solution of (20.53) is then

$$\underline{x} = \frac{e}{m}\left(\frac{1}{\omega_0^2 - \omega^2 - i\omega\gamma}\right)\underline{E} \qquad \underline{\ddot{x}} = \frac{e}{m}\left(\frac{-\omega^2}{\omega_0^2 - \omega^2 - i\omega\gamma}\right)\underline{E} \tag{20.54}$$

Relation (20.54) can be applied to consider problems in scattering, absorption and dispersion.

In the case of scattering, the acceleration $\ddot{x}$ as indicated in (20.54) gives rise to an electric field (20.40). With an incident wave polarized to have only an E_x component, the scattered wave will also have a component only in the x direction. The magnitude of the field of the scattered wave is the same in all directions in the yz plane, but varies with the angle α as indicated in Fig. 20.2 as sin α [see (20.40)].

The rate of reradiation of energy can be found from (20.54), (20.40), and (20.39) to be

$$-\frac{dU}{dt} = I_0\sigma \tag{20.55}$$

where I_0 is the intensity of the incoming radiation, and σ is the effective scattering cross section per electron. For a free electron, $\gamma = 0$, $\omega_0 = 0$ and σ_0 is given by

$$\sigma_0 = \frac{8\pi r_0^2}{3} = \frac{8\pi}{3}\left(\frac{e^2}{4\pi\varepsilon^\bullet mc^2}\right)^2 \tag{20.56}$$

Here r_0, the "classical electron radius," has been defined.

For bound electrons,

$$\sigma = \sigma_0 \frac{\omega^4}{(\omega_0^2 - \omega^2) + (\gamma\omega)^2} \rightarrow \sigma_0\left(\frac{\omega}{\omega_0}\right)^4 \tag{20.57}$$

Thus for $\omega \ll \omega_0$, $\gamma \ll \omega_0$, the scattering intensity varies as ω^4.

REFERENCES

Reference 1 contains a complete, rigorous description of classical electrodynamics. Other such treatments can be found in Refs. 3 and 4. Many of the phenomena discussed are also found in Ref. 2. The references following Chaps. 11 to 15 give references to more specific topics involving electromagnetism.

1. W. K. H. Panofsky and M. Phillips, Classical Electricity and Magnetism, Addison-Wesley, Reading, Mass., 1962.
2. R. P. Feynmann, R. B. Leighton, and M. Sands, The Feynmann Lectures on Physics, Vol. II, Addison-Wesley, Reading, Mass., 1964.
3. J. A. Stratton, Electromagnetic Theory, McGraw-Hill, New York, 1941.
4. L. D. Landau and E. M. Lifshitz, Electrodynamics of Continuous Media, Addison-Wesley, Reading, Mass., 1960.

Chapter 21

QUANTUM MECHANICS

21.1. QUANTUM-MECHANICAL OPERATORS

A general approach using density matrices and bracket notation is taken in this chapter, as this makes discussion of several phenomena elegant and easy to relate to current literature. The Schrödinger representation is used throughout, except in the last section.

(a) Hamiltonian Operator

The most common operator used in quantum mechanics is the Hamiltonian operator $\hat{H}$. Its classical counterpart is the Hamiltonian function H. In a conservative system, where time does not enter into the expression for H, it describes the instantaneous total energy of the system in terms of coordinates $\underline{r}_i$, momenta $\underline{p}_i$ of the particles involved, as well as any external forces.

The operator $\hat{H}$ can be obtained from the function H by replacing in H all the momentum variables $p_{1,x}$ $\cdots$ etc. by $-i\hbar\partial/\partial x_1$ $\cdots$ etc. Thus in general, H and $\hat{H}$ are for the time-independent case

$$H = \sum^{3N} \frac{p_i^2}{2m_i} + V\{N\} \qquad \hat{H} = -\sum^{N} \frac{\hbar^2}{2m_i} \nabla_i^2 + V\{N\} \tag{21.1}$$

The first summation is over the 3N coordinates x_1, y_1, $\cdots z_N$, while in the second, ∇^2 is the operator $\partial^2/\partial x^2 + \partial^2/\partial y^2 + \partial^2/\partial z^2$ (in Cartesian coordinates). $V\{N\}$ indicates a potential energy term which is a function of the coordinates of the N particles, i.e., $V(\underline{r}_1, \underline{r}_2 \cdots \underline{r}_N)$. Operators corresponding to other classical quantities can be obtained in an analogous manner.

The state of a quantum-mechanical system is described by the appropriate wavefunction Ψ. The physical significance of Ψ is that $\Psi\cdot\Psi^*(\{N\},t)$ gives the probability of finding the system in the state $\{N\}$ at time t. Ψ^* is the complex conjugate of Ψ. Ψ is related to $\hat{H}$ through the time-dependent Schrödinger wave equation

$$i\hbar \frac{\partial \Psi}{\partial t} = \hat{H}\Psi \tag{21.2}$$

This equation can be obtained through the "wave particle duality" (i.e., a particle with momentum p has corresponding to it a wave motion with wavelength $\lambda = \hbar/p$). Equation (21.2) results when the differential equation governing propagation of wave motion (Chap. 20) is adapted using the wave-particle duality [1].

When the system is in some stationary state described by Ψ_j, carrying out a periodic motion with a frequency $\nu_j = E_j/h$, then the time dependence of Ψ can be expressed as $\exp[-iE_j t/\hbar]$. A time-independent wavefunction $\psi_j\{N\}$ can then be defined for this stationary state as

$$\Psi_j(\{N\},t) = \psi_j\{N\} \exp\left[-\frac{iE_j t}{\hbar}\right] \tag{21.3}$$

On substitution into (21.2), the Schrödinger time-independent equation is obtained.

$$\hat{H}\psi_j = E_j\psi_j \qquad \text{or} \qquad \hat{H}|j\rangle = E_j|j\rangle \tag{21.4}$$

Here the notation $|j\rangle$ is used for ψ_j, $\langle j|$ will be used for ψ_j^*. The functions $|j\rangle$ are in this case eigenfunctions (eigenvectors, quantum states) of the operator $\hat{H}$, with corresponding eigenvalues (energies) E_j. States $|j\rangle$, $|k\rangle$ are "degenerate" if $E_j = E_k$. The quantum states of a system as defined by (21.4) are an orthonormal set of functions which can be used as a basis set for expansion of other functions. Thus

$$\int\psi_j^*\psi_k \, d\{N\} = \langle j|k\rangle = \delta_{j,k} \tag{21.5}$$

Here $\delta_{j,k}$ is the "δ function", i.e., $\delta_{j,k} = 1$ if $j = k$, $\delta_{jk} = 0$ if $j \neq k$.

(b) Expectation and Average Values of Observables

An expectation value Q_j of some quantity Q can be obtained for a system in a state $|j\rangle$ as

$$Q_j = Q_{jj} = \langle j|\hat{Q}|j\rangle = \int\psi_j^*\hat{Q}\psi_j \, d\{N\} \tag{21.6}$$

Q_{jj} is called a matrix element of the operator $\hat{Q}$. When $|j\rangle$ is an eigenfunction of the operator [e.g., as in (21.4)], then the expectation value has an exact value,

$$\langle H\rangle = \langle j|\hat{H}|j\rangle = E_j\langle j|j\rangle = E_j \tag{21.7}$$

The equilibrium statistical value $\langle Q\rangle$ of an observable is given as

$$\langle Q\rangle = \Sigma w_j Q_{jj} = \Sigma w_j\langle j|\hat{Q}|j\rangle \tag{21.8}$$

Here ω_j gives the probability of finding the system in the state j. It can be seen from Chap. 18 that in a closed isothermal system,

$$\omega_j = \frac{\exp[-E_j/kT]}{Q} \tag{21.9}$$

In (21.9), Q refers to the partition function, not to the general quantity Q in (21.6).

It is often convenient to express the state of a system in terms of some other orthonormal set of functions $|n\rangle$, $|m\rangle \cdots$ instead of the the set $|j\rangle \cdots$ defined by the quantum states of the system. Thus

$$|j\rangle = \Sigma c_{jn}|n\rangle \qquad c_{jn} = \langle n|j\rangle$$

$$|n\rangle = \Sigma b_{nj}|j\rangle \qquad b_{nj} = \langle j|n\rangle = c^*_{jn} \tag{21.10}$$

In this case,

$$Q_{jj} = \sum_{n,m} c^*_{jm} c_{jn} Q_{mn} = \sum_{n,m} \langle j|m\rangle\langle n|j\rangle Q_{mn} \tag{21.11}$$

$$\langle Q\rangle = \Sigma \omega_j Q_{jj} = \sum_{n,m} Q_{mn} \sum_j \omega_j \langle j|m\rangle\langle n|j\rangle \tag{21.11}$$

In order to simplify the expression for $\langle Q\rangle$, a density matrix $\underline{\underline{\rho}}$ is defined through elements

$$\rho_{nm} = \sum_j \omega_j \langle j|m\rangle\langle n|j\rangle \tag{21.12}$$

The density matrix is considered as an operator, $\hat{\rho}$, such that

$$\langle Q\rangle = \sum_{mn} \hat{\rho}_{nm} Q_{mn} = \sum_m (\hat{\rho}\underline{\underline{Q}})_{mm} = \mathrm{Tr}\ (\hat{\rho}\underline{\underline{Q}}) \tag{21.13}$$

Some supplementary relations for $\underline{\underline{Q}}$ and $\hat{\rho}$ are

$$\mathrm{Tr}\ (\hat{\rho}) = 1 \qquad \mathrm{Tr}\ (\underline{\underline{Q}}\hat{\rho}) = \mathrm{Tr}\ (\hat{\rho}\underline{\underline{Q}}) \tag{21.14}$$

When the set $|n\rangle$, $|m\rangle \cdots$ corresponds to the set $|j\rangle \cdots$, then (21.13) reduces to (21.8).

The time development of the density matrix is governed by (21.2). It can be shown [1] to be governed by the equation

$$\frac{\partial\rho}{\partial t} = -i\hbar(\hat{H}\hat{\rho} - \hat{\rho}\hat{H}) = -i\hbar[\hat{H},\hat{\rho}] \tag{21.15}$$

Here $[\hat{H},\hat{\rho}]$ is the "commutator" of the two operators. A solution for (21.12) is given as

$$\hat{\rho}(t) = \exp\left[-\frac{i\hat{H}t}{\hbar}\right]\hat{\rho}(0)\exp\left[+\frac{i\hat{H}t}{\hbar}\right] \tag{21.16}$$

The variation of Q with time is thus given as

$$\langle Q(t)\rangle = \mathrm{Tr}\ (\hat{\rho}(t)\cdot \underline{\underline{Q}}) \tag{21.17}$$

Equations (21.13) and (21.14) will be returned to in Sec. 21.6, when the Heisenberg representation is introduced.

21.2. STATIONARY STATES FOR SIMPLE SYSTEMS

The operator $\hat{H}$ for a molecule containing N particles (nuclei and electrons) is quite complex (21.1). A solution of the total wavefunction ψ through (21.4) would thus be difficult even for the simplest systems. A great simplification can be made, however, by separating out nuclear and electronic motion, i.e., by setting $\psi = \psi_{el}\cdot\psi_{nuc}$.

This adiabatic or Born-Oppenheimer approximation is possible as the mass of an electron is much smaller than the mass of nuclei. Thus for the sake of obtaining ψ_{el}, the positions of the nuclei can be considered fixed. As nuclear positions vary, the ψ_{el} can adjust nearly instantaneously to the variation of nuclear positions, as the motion of electrons is much faster than the variation in nuclear coordinates.

The total nuclear motion can itself be approximated as being due to 3 separate translational modes, 3 (2 for linear molecules, 0 for atoms) rotational modes, and 3N-6 (5 for linear) vibrational modes. Each of these types of motions can be described by a relatively simple, yet reasonable model. Translation through a particle in a box, rotation through a rigid rotator, and vibration through a harmonic oscillator.

In the case of translational motion (the particle in the box), the operator $\hat{H}$ is simply

$$\hat{H} = -\frac{\hbar^2}{2m}\nabla^2 \qquad \text{or} \qquad \hat{H} = -\frac{\hbar^2}{2m}\frac{\partial^2}{\partial x^2} \quad \text{in} \quad \text{1-D} \tag{21.18}$$

Here m is the total mass of the molecule. The energy $V = 0$ for motion of m inside the box (length L) and ∞ outside.

The solution of (21.4) with $\hat{H}$ in the 1-D form in (21.18) is quite simple. Physically realistic wavefunctions (single-valued, finite) with the proper boundary conditions ($\psi = 0$ at the edges where $V = \infty$) for this system are the sine functions.

$$\psi_n = |n> = \sqrt{\frac{2}{L}} \sin \frac{n\pi x}{L} \qquad n = 1, 2 \cdots \qquad (21.19)$$

These form an orthonormal set of functions. The corresponding eigenvalues are $E_n = n^2h^2/8mL^2$. The 3-D case leads to the results in (18.21). From this, the translational partition function (18.22) can be obtained. This in turn can be used to obtain the Maxwell-Boltzmann distribution of velocities, etc.

Rotational motion when described in terms of a rigid rotator can be equated to the motion of a point mass I (moment of inertia) over the surface of a sphere radius 1. In this case $\hat{H}$ is in the first form of (21.18), i.e., $V = 0$. Spherical polar coordinates should be used to express ∇^2, with $\hbar = 1$. Solutions of (21.4) can then be obtained giving physically realistic eigenfunctions and corresponding eigenvalues.

The eigenfunctions obtained are the spherical harmonics $Y_{\ell,m}(\theta,\phi)$. The eigenvalues are $E_\ell = \ell(\ell + 1)\hbar^2/2I$, i.e., independent of the quantum number m. As there are $2\ell + 1$ possible values of m for every ℓ, i.e., $2\ell + 1$ eigenfunctions $Y_{\ell,m}$ for every eigenvalue E_ℓ, then each energy level E_ℓ is $2\ell + 1$ fold "degenerate." The results lead to the rotational partition function (18.24).

In the case of vibration, the potential energy function V can for a vibrational mode be written as

$$V(\chi) = V(0) + \chi\left(\frac{\partial V}{\partial \chi}\right)_{\chi=0} + \frac{1}{2}\chi^2\left(\frac{\partial^2 V}{\partial \chi^2}\right)_{\chi=0} + \cdots \qquad (21.20)$$

$$\simeq \frac{1}{2} f\chi^2$$

Here χ is the deviation of the vibrational (normal) coordinate from the equilibrium position and f a force constant. Thus the Hamiltonian is

$$\hat{H} = -\frac{\hbar}{2\mu}\frac{\partial^2}{\partial\chi^2} + \frac{1}{2}\,\delta\chi^2$$

$$= -\frac{\hbar}{2}\frac{\partial^2}{\partial\xi^2} + \frac{1}{2}\lambda\xi^2 \tag{21.21}$$

Here μ is the reduced mass for the vibrational motion. It has been incorporated into the variable ξ, which is the "normal" coordinate for the vibrational mode (Sec. 21.5).

The solution of (21.4) and (21.21) leads to the energy levels as indicated for the Einstein crystal,

$$E_v = (v + \tfrac{1}{2})h\nu \qquad \text{where} \qquad \nu = \frac{1}{2\pi}\sqrt{\frac{\delta}{\mu}} \qquad v = 0,1,2\cdots \tag{21.22}$$

The wavefunctions ψ_v are shown schematically in Fig. 21.1. They will be discussed further to point out some additional aspects of quantum mechanics.

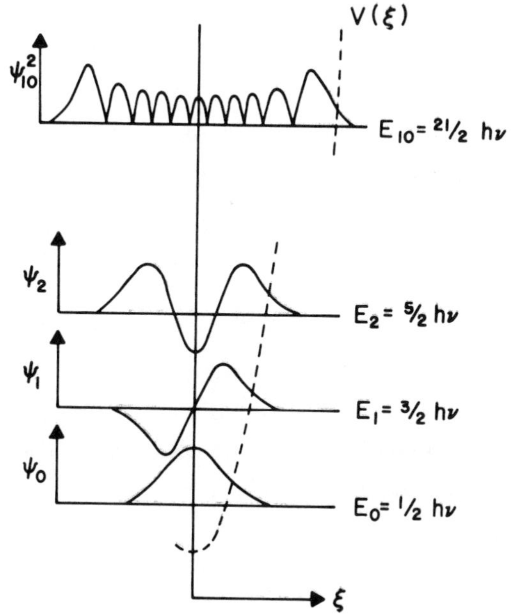

Fig. 21.1. Plots of ψ_0, ψ_1, ψ_2, and ψ_{10}^2 vs χ for a harmonic oscillator. The plots are superposed on a plot of *V* vs χ for the harmonic oscillator with abscissae at the eigenvalues E_0, E_1, E_2, and E_{10}. (After Ref. 6.)

There is a "zeropoint energy" ($\frac{1}{2} h\nu$) present in a vibration. This is in agreement with the Heisenberg uncertainty principle, which states that the product of the uncertainties $\delta\chi$ and $\delta p_{\chi} \geqslant \hbar$ (also $\delta E \cdot \delta t \geqslant \hbar$). When the "quantum number" v is even, then ψ_v is symmetric about $\chi = 0$; when v is odd, then ψ_v is antisymmetric (i.e., $\psi_v(\chi) = -\psi_v(-\chi)$). At high values of v, the probability distribution ψ_v^2 begins to resemble the classical probability distribution (e.g., ψ_{10}^2). This is an example of the "Bohr correspondence principle."

Spin can also be considered as a case of the solution of (21.4). The spin angular momentum for a particle is $\hbar \underline{I}$ with an absolute value of $h\sqrt{I(I + 1)}$, where I is the spin quantum number for the particle. The symbol I is used for spin in this case, as nuclear spin will be of more concern in the book.

There are 2I + 1 possible orientations of the spin vector $\underline{I}$. These orientations are determined by the operator I_z operating on the spin eigenfunctions $|\alpha\rangle$ to give the value of the z component of $\underline{I}$, M_I, as the eigenvalue. There are 2I + 1 possible values of M_I, with $M_I = I, I-1, \cdots, -I$.

For the common case of I = 1/2 (e.g., proton), there will for a single particle be two nuclear spin functions $|\alpha\rangle$ and $|\beta\rangle$. Thus

$$\hat{I}_z|\alpha\rangle = +\frac{1}{2}|\alpha\rangle \qquad \hat{I}_z|\beta\rangle = -\frac{1}{2}|\beta\rangle \tag{21.23}$$

21.3. APPROXIMATE METHODS

Few realistic problems in quantum mechanics can be solved exactly. In most cases, approximate methods such as the perturbation or variation method must be used. The perturbation method is first discussed, followed by a brief outline of the variation method.

(a) Perturbation Method

The symbol $\hat{H}^\circ$ will be used to designate the "unperturbed" system, such as one of those discussed in Sec. 21.2. The energies E_j° and wave functions $|j^\circ\rangle$ are available for this system. For the perturbed system, $\hat{H}$ is written as $\hat{H} = \hat{H}^\circ + \lambda\hat{H}'$, and

$$E_j = E_j^\circ + \lambda E_j' + \lambda^2 E_j'' + \cdots$$

$$|j\rangle = |j^\circ\rangle + \lambda|j'\rangle + \lambda^2|j''\rangle + \cdots \qquad (21.24)$$

The function $|j'\rangle$ can be expressed as an expansion over the orthonormal set $|j^\circ\rangle$ as

$$|j'\rangle = \sum_k a_{jk}|k^\circ\rangle \qquad (21.25)$$

Equation (21.4) can then be written as

$$(\hat{H}^\circ + \lambda\hat{H}')|j\rangle = E_j|j\rangle \qquad (21.26)$$

with $|j\rangle$ and E_j as in (21.24). The coefficients of specific powers of λ, i.e., λ^0, λ^1, $\lambda^2\cdots$ on the two sides of the expanded forms of (21.26) can be equated. If the net coefficient of λ in (21.26) is nonzero, then a polynomial in λ results which is satisfied only for discrete values of λ. Yet (21.26) is to be valid for all values of λ.

The relationship obtained from the coefficients of λ^0 simply regenerates (21.4) for the unperturbed state. When the coefficients of λ^1 are taken, then

$$E_j' = \langle j^\circ|\hat{H}'|j^\circ\rangle = H_{jj}' \qquad (21.27)$$

is obtained. In addition, $|j'\rangle$ can be shown to be

$$|j'\rangle = \sum \frac{H_{jk}'}{E_j^\circ - E_k^\circ}|k^\circ\rangle \qquad (21.28)$$

Equation (21.28) is valid only in the case of nondegenerate states, i.e., where E_j° has only one eigenvector $|j^\circ\rangle$.

When the coefficients of λ^2 are considered, then the second order perturbation energy is obtained,

$$E_j'' = \langle j^\circ|\hat{H}'|j'\rangle = \sum \frac{|H_{jk}'|^2}{E_j^\circ - E_k^\circ} \qquad (21.29)$$

In the case of degenerate systems, where $|1^\circ\rangle\cdots|m^\circ\rangle$ have the same energy E°, the degeneracy can be removed. The values of E' can be shown to be given by the m roots of the equation.

$$\begin{vmatrix} H'_{11}-E' & H'_{12} & \cdots & H'_{1m} \\ \vdots & & & \vdots \\ H'_{m1} & \cdots & \cdots & H'_{mm}-E' \end{vmatrix} = |H'_{ij} - \delta_{ij}E'| = 0 \tag{21.30}$$

Common simple perturbation terms $\hat{H}'$ are charge-charge interactions $QQ'/4\pi\varepsilon^{\bullet}r$; anharmonicity terms $f'\chi^3$; or $\underline{p}\cdot\underline{E}$ describing the interaction energy due to an electric dipole $\underline{p}$ in an electric field $\underline{E}$, etc.

An analogous term (the "Zeeman" term) is valid for a magnetic dipole $\underline{m}$ in a magnetic field $\underline{B}$, i.e., $\underline{m}\cdot\underline{B}$. When the magnetic dipole is due to a particle mass m, charge e with an orbital angular momentum $\underline{r} \times \underline{p} = \hbar\underline{L}$, then the $\hat{H}'$ is given by (20.19):

$$\hat{H}' = \frac{e\hbar}{2m}\,\underline{B}\cdot\underline{L} \tag{21.31}$$

When e, m refer to an electron, then $e\hbar/2m$ is a "Bohr magneton" β_e, when to a proton, it is a "nuclear magneton" β_N. In general, the magnetic dipole due to nuclear spin is given by (20.20):

$$\underline{m} = g_N\beta_N\underline{I}$$

Thus if the field $\underline{B}$ is in the z direction, the perturbation term is given by

$$\hat{H}' = -g_N\beta_N|\underline{B}|I_z \tag{21.33}$$

Another common perturbation is that due to interactions between two dipoles. The expression for magnetic dipoles is the same as that for electrical dipoles given in (1.11). Thus when interactions of protons with spins $\underline{I}_a$, $\underline{I}_b$ is considered,

$$\hat{H}' = \frac{1}{4\pi\varepsilon^{\bullet}c^2}\,g_N^2\beta_N^2\left\{\frac{\underline{I}_a\cdot\underline{I}_b}{r^3} - \frac{3(\underline{I}_a\cdot\underline{r})(\underline{I}_b\cdot\underline{r})}{r^5}\right\} = \frac{1}{4\pi\varepsilon^{\bullet}c^2}\,g_N^2\beta_N^2\underline{I}_a\cdot\underline{\underline{D}}\cdot\underline{I}_b \tag{21.34}$$

Here the matrix $\underline{\underline{D}}$ has components which are functions of the internuclear distance r and x, y, z.

Following the discussion in Sec. 1.1, other interactions are possible. Interaction between a nuclear quadrupole moment and the electric field gradient has some importance in NMR relaxation [Sec. 13.1(f)].

(b) Variation Method

Another approximate method used in the book is the variation method. It makes use of the variational theorem, which in essence states that

$$E = \frac{\int \phi^* \hat{H} \phi \; d\{N\}}{\int \phi^* \phi \; d\{N\}} > E_0 \qquad (21.35)$$

Here $\hat{H}$ is the Hamiltonian for the system, E_0 its true ground state (lowest) energy, and Φ a trial function. If $E \to E_0$, then $\phi \to \psi_0$ the true ground state function for the system.

The function ϕ is usually chosen such that it contains some adjustable parameters γ_j. The value of E is then minimized with respect to these parameters. A common choice of ϕ is to set $\phi = \Sigma\gamma_j|j>$, where $|j>$ are known wavefunctions.

The use of the variational theorem is not restricted to quantum mechanical calculations [see e.g., Sec. 3.2(c)].

21.4. CHANGES IN QUANTUM STATES

(a) Time-Dependent Perturbation

The simple case of a system with unperturbed Hamiltonian $\hat{H}^\circ$ and two unperturbed stationary states $|j^\circ>$, $|f^\circ>$ with $E_j^\circ \neq E_f^\circ$ will be examined. When a time-dependent perturbation $\hat{H}'(t)$ acts on the system, then as shown in Sec. 21.3, the energies of the states $|j>$ and $|f>$ will to a first approximation vary as $E_j^\circ + (H'(t))_{jj}$; $E_f^\circ + (H'(t))_{ff}$.

This time-dependent perturbation can however also induce changes in the system. To allow for this, the time-dependent wavefunction for the system can be written as

$$\psi = c_j(t)|j> \exp\left[-\frac{iE_jt}{\hbar}\right] + c_f(t)|f> \exp\left[-\frac{iE_ft}{\hbar}\right] \qquad (21.36)$$

This function must obey (21.2), i.e.,

$$(\hat{H}^\circ + \hat{H}'(t))\Psi = -\frac{\hbar}{i}\frac{\partial}{\partial t}\Psi \tag{21.37}$$

An expression for $\partial c_f/\partial t$ can be obtained if (21.36) is substituted into (21.37). The resultant expression shown in (21.38) is for the simplified case where $|j\rangle$ is assumed equal to $|j^\circ\rangle$; $|f\rangle$ to $|f^\circ\rangle$, and where the system initially is in state $|j\rangle$, i.e., $c_j(t) \simeq 1$; $c_f(t) \simeq 0$. Thus the transition $f \to j$ is ignored

$$i\hbar\frac{\partial c_f}{\partial t} = \exp\left[\frac{i(E_f - E_j)t}{\hbar}\right]\langle f|\hat{H}'(t)|j\rangle \tag{21.38}$$

The probability that the system has made a transition to $|f\rangle$ at time t is $c_f(t)c_f^*(t)$. Thus the rate of transitions per unit time per system is assumed to be $w_{j\to f} = c_f(t)c_f^*(t)/t$. Thus from (21.37)

$$c_f = \frac{1}{i\hbar}\int_0^t \langle f|\hat{H}'(t')|j\rangle \exp\left[\frac{i(E_f - E_j)t'}{\hbar}\right] dt' \tag{21.39}$$

This makes

$$c_f(t)c_f^*(t) = \frac{1}{\hbar^2}\int_0^t dt' \int_0^t (H'(t'))_{fj}(H'(t''))_{jf} \cdot \exp\left[\frac{i(E_f - E_j)(t' - t'')}{\hbar}\right] dt''$$

$$= \frac{1}{\hbar^2}|H'|_{fj}^2 \int_0^t dt' \int_{-t'}^{t-t'} \delta(t')\delta(t' + t'') \cdot \exp\left[\frac{i(E_f - E_j)t'''}{\hbar}\right] dt''' \tag{21.40}$$

Here $|H'|_{fj}^2$ is the mean square value of $|H'(t)|_{fj}^2$ so that $|\delta(t)|^2 = 1$.

A time correlation function can be introduced to describe the time development of $(H'(t))_{fj}$. Thus in analogy with the functions in Chap. 7, $G_{H'}(t) = \langle\delta(0)\cdot\delta(t)\rangle$, where it is understood that $\delta(t)$ can be a vector quantity as $\langle f|\hat{H}'(t)|j\rangle$ can be a vector.

Equation (21.40) can be simplified when the case of $t \to \infty$ is considered, and $\hbar\omega = E_f - E_j$. In this case the integral over dt''' becomes essentially independent of value of t, as $G_{H'}(t)$ approaches 0 quite rapidly. The first integral over dt' gives a factor t, so that

$$w_{j\to f} = \frac{c_f(t)\cdot c_f^*(t)}{t} = \frac{|H'|^2_{fj}}{\hbar^2} \int_{-\infty}^{\infty} G_{H'}(t) \exp[i\omega t]\, dt \tag{21.41}$$

Expression (21.41) can be further simplified with the introduction of the Fourier transform $G_{H'}(\omega)$ (7.17)

$$G_{H'}(\omega) = \frac{1}{2\pi} \int_{-\infty}^{\infty} G_{H'}(t) \exp[i\omega t]\, dt \tag{21.42}$$

(b) Dipole Transitions

The most common case of transitions between states occurs when $H'(t)$ is due to be the interaction of an electric dipole with an electromagnetic field, i.e., $H'(t) = \underline{p}\cdot\underline{E}$. The dipole $\underline{p}$ can be expressed as $\Sigma e_i \underline{r}_i$ (Chap. 1), where the sum is over all particles (electrons, nuclei) present. The field $\underline{E}$ is usually assumed periodic with a frequency ω_0, i.e., $E_x = E_{x,0} \cos \omega_0 t$ etc.

For a periodically varying $\hat{H}'(t)$, the correlation function $G_{H'}(t)$ is a δ function, in particular [see (21.45) for definition of m_x]

$$|H'|^2_{jf} G_{H'}(\omega) = \{E^2_{x,0}|m_{x,jf}|^2 + E^2_{y,0}|m_{y,jf}|^2 + E^2_{z,0}|m_{z,jf}|^2\} \quad \text{for } \omega = \omega_0 \tag{21.43}$$

When the radiation is isotropic, then $E^2_{x,0} = E^2_{y,0} = \cdots = (2\pi/3)\rho(\nu)$. Here $\rho(\nu)$ is the energy density of the radiation field. In this case [4],

$$w_{j\to f} = \frac{2\pi}{3\hbar^2} \rho(\nu_{jf}) |\underline{m}_{jf}|^2 \tag{21.44}$$

The matrix elements $m_{x,jf}\cdots$ of the matrix $\underline{m}_{jf}$ are components of the "transition dipole moment matrix,"

$$m_{x,jf} = \langle f|\Sigma e_i x_i|j\rangle \qquad \underline{m}_{jf} = \langle f|\Sigma e_i \underline{r}_i|j\rangle \tag{21.45}$$

The concept can be generalized if more than two states are involved. These elements can be zero due to the symmetry properties of the functions $|j\rangle$, $|f\rangle$ involved. In this case the transition $j \rightarrow f$ is forbidden, i.e., $w_{j\rightarrow f} = 0$.

An example of such "selection rules" can be illustrated for vibration. The function $\Sigma e_i \underline{r}_i$ is an antisymmetric function. Thus electric dipole transitions for a harmonic oscillator are forbidden for cases where $|v'\rangle$ (i.e., $|j\rangle$) and $|v''\rangle$ (i.e., $|f\rangle$) are related as $v'' - v'' = 2, 4 \cdots$. When $|v'\rangle$ and $|v''\rangle$ are both of the same symmetry type (e.g., antisymmetric, v', v'' odd), then the matrix elements $\langle v''|\Sigma e_i \underline{r}_i|v'\rangle$ will be zero, as $\int_{(\text{space})}$ of an antisymmetric function $= 0$. Other selection rules can be derived for other types of transitions. In real molecules, $\Delta v = 2$ dipole transitions can be observed as the potential is not exactly harmonic.

(c) *Einstein Transition Probabilities*

$w_{j\rightarrow f}$ in (21.43) gives the rate of transitions per unit molecule (system) induced by radiation. This rate is also given by the "Einstein transition probability" $B_{j\rightarrow f}\rho(\nu_{jf})$. The other Einstein probabilities $A_{f\rightarrow j}$ (spontaneous emission) and $B_{f\rightarrow j}$ (induced emission) are related to $B_{j\rightarrow f}$. The relationship can be obtained by considering the Planck radiation law for $\rho(\nu_{jf})$ at equilibrium.

When $|j\rangle$ has a degeneracy g_j and $|f\rangle$ one of g_f, then

$$g_f B_{f\rightarrow j} = g_j B_{j\rightarrow f} \qquad \text{and}$$

$$A_{f\rightarrow j} = \frac{8\pi h \nu_{jf}^3}{c^3} B_{f\rightarrow j} = \frac{32\pi^3}{3\hbar c^3} \nu_{jf}^3 |\underline{m}_{jf}|^2 \tag{21.46}$$

Thus only one of the three Einstein coefficients needs to be known to get the other two.

21.5. NORMAL VIBRATIONS

In a (nonlinear) molecule composed of N atoms, the internal motions can be described in terms of 3N - 6 "normal vibrations." In each normal mode of vibration, each nucleus carries out periodic motion with the same frequency. Any internal motion of the molecules can be expressed as a superposition of motion along normal coordinates defining the normal vibrations.

The normal coordinates can mathematically be obtained by a linear transformation such that the potential and kinetic energies can be expressed as

$$V = \frac{1}{2}\Sigma\eta_i\xi_i^2 \qquad\qquad T = \frac{1}{2}\Sigma\frac{d^2\xi_i}{dt^2} \qquad (21.47)$$

Each vibrational normal mode can thus be treated separately according to the model of the harmonic oscillator. Thus wavefunctions are obtained for normal vibrations of the same type as before, with appropriate energies.

As an example of such normal vibrations, the normal modes of the H_2O molecule are schematically shown in Fig. 21.2. The arrows show the phases and the relative amplitudes of the motions of the atoms in each mode. The center of mass remains fixed at all times. The $\tilde{\nu}_{vap}$ indicate the energies of the $1 \leftrightarrow 0$ transitions.

Each molecule can be placed in a "point group" according to its structural symmetry. For each point group, there exists a number of symmetry operations, e.g., inversion (i), reflection in a plane (σ), a rotation by an angle $360/p$ ($p = 1,2,3\cdots$) about some axis (C_p), a rotation reflection (S_p). H_2O belongs in the point group C_{2v}, which contains the symmetry elements C_2, σ_v', σ_v''. The $C_2(z)$ axis is through the O bisecting the HOH angle, the σ_v' is in the HOH (xz) plane, the σ_v'' in the yz plane.

Each point group contains a number of "species," "symmetry types" or "irreducible representations." Each species defines a combination of symmetry properties which is possible. A character table showing the species is thus available for each point group. For C_{2v} it is:

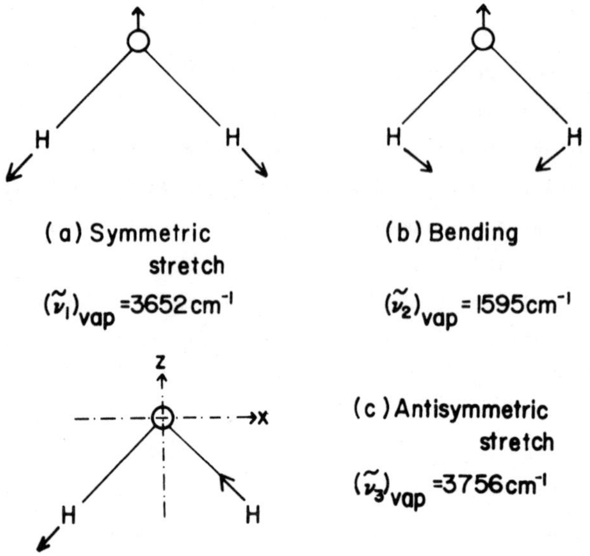

Fig. 21.2. Schematic illustrations of the normal vibrations of H_2O.

	$I(i)^2$	$C_2(z)$	$\sigma_v'(xz)$	$\sigma_v''(yz)$		
A_1	1	+1	+1	+1	T_z	ν_1, ν_2
A_2	1	+1	-1	-1	R_z	
B_1	1	-1	+1	-1	T_x, R_x	ν_3
B_2	1	-1	-1	+1	T_y, R_x	

As can be seen from Fig. 21.2, the normal vibrations ν_1, ν_2 (and their wavefunctions for v odd) are of species A_1. All the symmetry operations leave the vibrations unchanged. This is also true of the "non-genuine" vibration, translation in the z direction, T_z. Vibration ν_3 is, however, of species B_1, as there is a change of sign in the vibrational state on operations $C_2(z)$ and $\sigma_v''(yz)$. Translation in the x direction (T_x) and rotation about the y axis (R_y) are of the same species.

Such tables of species are available for all point groups. The C_{2v} group is somewhat simpler than the general case as it contains no degenerate symmetry types.

The advantage of such analysis using character tables is that selection rules can be predicted from them. The components of the dipole function $\Sigma e_i x_i, \cdots, \Sigma e_i z_i$ have the same symmetry properties as the nongenuine vibrations T_x, T_y, T_z. To have a nonzero transition dipole moment, the species of $\psi_{v'} \cdot \psi_{v''}$ must be the same as at least one of T_x, T_y, T_z.

When the normal coordinate is symmetric to a symmetry operation, then its vibrational wavefunction $\psi_v(\xi)$ is symmetric to that operation for all values of v. If, however, the normal coordinate is antisymmetric, then $\psi_v(\xi)$ is antisymmetric for v odd, but symmetric for v even (Fig. 21.2). Thus the characters of the species which represents a vibrational state v can be obtained by multiplying the character of the species of the normal vibration concerned to the v'th power. The simple case of transitions concerning only one normal mode is referred to above.

In Raman spectra, transitions are allowed if any one of the matrix elements $(\alpha_{xx})_{v'v''}$, $(\alpha_{xy})_{v'v''}$ etc. is nonzero. This occurs if the product $\psi_{v'}\psi_{v''}$ has the same species as one of α_{xx}, α_{xy} $\cdots$. The polarizability elements α_{xx}, α_{yy}, α_{zz} can be shown to have the species A_1 in the C_{2v} point group, while α_{xy}, α_{xz}, α_{yz} have A_2, B_1, B_2 respectively.

If a molecule is distorted through some interaction, then the change in its symmetry properties can result in changes in the selection rules operative. These selection rules also are not always strict due to the presence of anharmonicities and due to transitions other than those due to electric dipole interaction.

21.6. HEISENBERG REPRESENTATION

Equation (21.17) describes the time development of the equilibrium value of an observable $\langle Q \rangle$. It is written in the Schrödinger Representation, where the density matrix $\hat{\rho}(t)$ is time dependent (21.14). The operators $\hat{Q}$ and $\hat{H}$ are in (21.17) assumed time-independent. Reference 7 considers the case $\hat{Q}(t)$, $\hat{H}(t)$.

An equally good representation of the problem leading to the same final description of the values of observables is the Heisenberg representation (picture), in which $\hat{\rho}$ is independent of time, and $\hat{Q} = \hat{Q}_H(t)$ is time dependent. The equation describing the time dependence of $\hat{Q}_H(t)$ is for $\hat{Q} \neq \hat{Q}(t)$

$$\frac{d}{dt}\hat{Q}_H = \frac{i}{\hbar}[\hat{H},\hat{Q}_H] \tag{21.48}$$

The solution for the case of $\hat{H} \neq \hat{H}(t)$ is simply

$$\hat{Q}_H(t) = \exp\left[\frac{i\hat{H}t}{\hbar}\right]\hat{Q}_H(0)\exp\left[-\frac{i\hat{H}t}{\hbar}\right] \tag{21.49}$$

Here $\hat{Q}_H(0) = \hat{Q}$. Thus at $t = 0$, the Heisenberg and Schrödinger representations have the same $\hat{Q}$ and the same $\hat{\rho}$.

The use of the Heisenberg representation is of an advantage in interpreting spectra of complicated systems. Here the assignment of transitions to specific states, and the nature of these states is not of central importance. Instead the Heisenberg picture of spectroscopy focuses on the time-development of the system, and leads to consideration of the spectrum as the Fourier transform of a time-correlation function (Chaps. 7 and 12).

The Heisenberg picture is also useful in consideration of spectroscopy, as it makes it possible to arrive easily at expressions for emission of radiation through use of the Bohr correspondence principle [4].

Other representations (pictures) are possible in quantum mechanics. One such useful one is the "interaction representation." It can be considered as being a time-dependent perturbation of the Heisenberg representation. Here the operator $\hat{H}$ is written as $\hat{H} = \hat{H}^\circ + \hat{H}'(t)$, where $\hat{H}^\circ$ does not explicitly depend on t.

An operator $\hat{Q}$ is in this representation given by

$$\hat{Q}_I(t) = \exp\left[\frac{i\hat{H}^\circ t}{\hbar}\right]\hat{Q}\exp\left[-\frac{i\hat{H}^\circ t}{\hbar}\right] \tag{21.50}$$

and the wavefunctions:

$$\psi_{j,I}(t) = \exp\left[\frac{i\hat{H}^\circ t}{\hbar}\right]\psi_{j,S}(t) = \exp\left[\frac{i(\hat{H}^\circ - \hat{H})t}{\hbar}\right]|j\rangle \tag{21.51}$$

If $\hat{H}' = 0$, then $\hat{Q}_I(t) = \hat{Q}_H(t)$, and $\Psi_I(t) = \Psi_H$, i.e., the wavefunctions (state vectors) would be constant with time as in the Heisenberg picture. For $H'(t) \neq 0$, both the operators and the state functions change with time.

In this way some of the advantages of both the Heisenberg and the Schrödinger representations can be combined.

REFERENCES

There are numerous books on basic and advanced quantum mechanics. Only three are directly referred to in the list below (Refs. 1, 4, and 7). References 5 and 6 give descriptions of the use of group theory in spectroscopy.

1. L. I. Schiff, Quantum Mechanics, 3rd ed., McGraw-Hill, New York, 1955.
2. V. Fano, Rev. Mod. Phys., *29*, 74 (1957).
3. A. Carrington and A. D. McLachlan, Introduction to Magnetic Resonance, Harper and Row, New York, 1967.
4. E. C. Kemble, Quantum Mechanics, Dover, New York, 1937.
5. E. B. Wilson, Jr., J. C. Decius, and P. C. Cross, Molecular Vibrations, McGraw-Hill, New York, 1955.
6. G. Herzberg, Infrared and Raman Spectra, Van Nostrand, New York, 1945.
7. E. Merzbacher, Quantum Mechanics, 2nd ed., Wiley, New York, 1961.

GENERAL REFERENCES

Books Dealing with Liquids in General

GR1. F. Kohler, The Liquid State, Verlag Chemie, Weinheim, 1972.

GR2. P. A. Egelstaff, An Introduction to the Liquid State, Academic Press, New York, 1967.

GR3. J. S. Rowlinson, Liquids and Liquid Mixtures, 2nd. ed., Butterworths, London, 1969.

GR4. J. O. Hirschfelder, C. F. Curtiss, and R. B. Bird, Molecular Theory of Gases and Liquids, Wiley, New York, 1954.

Books Dealing with Water and Aqueous Systems

GR5. D. Eisenberg and W. Kauzmann, The Structure and Properties of Water, Oxford University Press, Oxford, 1969.

GR6. R. A. Horne (ed.), Structure and Transport Processes in Water and Aqueous Solutions, Wiley-Interscience, New York, 1972.

GR7. F. Franks (ed.), Water: A Comprehensive Treatise, Vol. 1, Physics and Physical Chemistry of Water, Plenum Press, New York, 1972.

GR8. F. Franks (ed.), Water: A Comprehensive Treatise, Vol. 2, Water in Crystalline Hydrates; Aqueous Solutions of Simple Nonelectrolytes, Plenum Press, New York, 1973.

GR9. F. Franks (ed.), Water: A Comprehensive Treatise, Vol. 3, Aqueous Solutions of Simple Electrolytes, Plenum Press, New York, 1973.

Other Recent General References and Proceedings of Conferences

Ion-Ion and Ion-Solvent Interactions, Faraday Symposium, September 1977.

Newer Aspects of Molecular Relaxation Processes, Faraday Symposium, December 1976.

J. F. Coetzee and C. D. Ritchie (eds.), Solute-Solvent Interactions, Vol. 2, M. Dekker, New York, 1976.

W. A. Adams, G. Greer, J. E. Desnoyers, G. Atkinson, G. S. Kell, K. B. Oldham, and J. Walkeley (eds.), Chemistry and Physics of Aqueous Gas Solutions, The Electrochemical Society, Princeton, 1975.

E. Wyn-Jones (ed.), Chemical and Biological Applications of Relaxation Spectrometry, D. Reidel, Dordrecht, 1975.

J. P. Riley and G. Skirrow (eds.), Chemical Oceanography, 2nd. ed., Vol. 1, 2, Academic Press, New York, 1975.

I. Prigogine and S. A. Rice (eds.), Non-Simple Liquids, Wiley-Interscience, New York, 1975.

D. T. Hawkins, Bibliography on the Physical and Chemical Properties of Water, 1969 - 1974, J. Sol. Chem, *4* (1975).

W. A. P. Luck (ed.), Structure of Water and Aqueous Solutions, Verlag Chemie, Weinheim, 1974.

J. Lascombe (ed.), Molecular Motions in Liquids, D. Reidel, Dordrecht, 1974.

A. Ben-Naim, Water and Aqueous Solutions. Introduction to a Molecular Theory, Plenum Press, New York, 1974.

R. L. Kay (ed.), The Physical Chemistry of Aqueous Systems, Plenum Press, New York, 1974.

A. K. Covington and T. Dickinson (eds.), Physical Chemistry of Organic Solvent Systems, Plenum Press, New York, 1973.

Kritische Erscheinungen, Ber. Bunsenges. Physik. Chem., *76*, No. 3, 4, (1972).

Molecular Motion in Amorphous Solids and Liquids, Faraday Symposium No. 6, 1972.

Molekülare Bewegungen in Flüssigkeiten, Ber. Bunsenges. Physik. Chem., *75*, No. 3, 4 (1971).

GLOSSARY OF SYMBOLS

The glossary lists most of the symbols used in this book, giving a brief definition and the equation or page where its meaning is best illustrated. When a symbol corresponds to a physical constant, then the value of the constant is also given. The symbols have been chosen to correspond as much as possible to the recommended SI symbols. The units are also to a large extent those recommended as SI units, but the practical units used in the various specialities have been maintained in many cases.

Symbol	Meaning	Equation or Page
A	Amplitude factor	20.47
A	Helmholtz free energy	17.4
A	Pre-exponential factor	19.47
$\underline{A}$	Vector potential	20.15
A	Amount of material in diffusion	6.24
A	Integrated absorption	12.18
A	Mass number of nucleus	454
A	Constant in conductivity equation	9.1
A,B	Parameters in ultrasonic equation	10.24
A,B	Species in point groups	552
A,B	Jones-Dole viscosity parameters	9.15
A,B	Constants in a vapor pressure equation	8.12
$\mathcal{A}$	Affinity	17.31
$\mathcal{A}$	Area ($d\underline{\mathcal{A}}$ for a differential element)	19.2
$\mathcal{A},\mathcal{B}$	Einstein coefficients	21.46
a	Hard-sphere radius	19.9
a_{jk}	Expansion coefficients	4.25;21.25

a	Parameter in significant structure theory	2.13
a	Constant relating ΔH_{sol} to m	202
a	Radius of pipe	220
$\mathcal{a}$	Activity	17.20
$\mathcal{a},\mathcal{b}$	Parameters in fluctuations	3.46
$\mathcal{a},\mathcal{b}$	Van der Waals coefficients	2.4
B	Rotational energy parameter	18.25
B	Kerr constant	11.27
B	Virial coefficients	4.37
$\underline{\mathcal{B}}$	Magnetic induction	526
b	Turbidity	14.3
b	Scattering amplitude	16.1
$b_{j,n}$	Expansion coefficients	21.10
C_p	Heat capacity (p constant)	486
C_V	Heat capacity (V constant)	486
$C_{\mathcal{p}}$	Rotation by $360/\mathcal{p}$ degrees	551
C_{2v}	Point groups	551
$\mathcal{C}$	Capacitance	274
$\mathcal{C}_b$	Cabannes factor	14.6
$c(\mathcal{r})$	Direct correlation function	3.7
$c_j(t)$	Time dependent expansion coefficients	21.36
c	Concentration (mol l^{-1})	489
$c_{j,n}$	Expansion coefficients	21.10
c	Number of nearest neighbors, solvation number	37
$\mathcal{c}^{\bullet}$	Speed of light in free space (2.99793×10^8 m sec^{-1})	
$\underline{\mathcal{c}}$	Velocity of wave propagation	20.35
D	Diffusion coefficient	6.17
D*	Self-diffusion coefficient	211
D	Debye unit	293
$\underline{\mathcal{D}}$	Electric displacement	20.10
$\underline{\underline{\mathcal{D}}}$	Dipole-dipole interaction matrix	21.34
d	Atomic spacing	57

d	Distance of movement of boundary	216
d	Parameter in Cole-Davidson arc	11.17
E	Electromotive force of a cell	8.10
E	Constant in conductivity equation	9.4
E	Energy of a subsystem	18.11
$E^{\#}$	Activation energy	19.47
E_j	Eigenvalue of jth quantum state	539
$\underline{E}$	Electric field strength	20.1
e	Electron or proton charge (1.6021×10^{-19} coulomb)	
e	Base of natural logarithms (2.71828)	
$\underline{F}$	Force	509
$\mathcal{F}$	Faraday constant (9.6487×10^{4} coulomb mol^{-1})	
f	Scattering factor	432
f	Force per unit area	6.42
f	Rational activity coefficient	17.22
f_{ij}	Mayer function	18.33
$\mathscr{f}$	Factor in conductance equation	9.3
$\mathscr{f}$	Conformal theory parameter	4.32
$\mathscr{f}$	Universal function	2.3
$\mathscr{f}$	Force constant	532
$\mathscr{f}$	Generating function	19.38
$\mathscr{f}(t)$	Time dependent function	21.40
G	Gibbs free energy	17.4
G(t)	Time correlation function	157
$G(\nu)$	Spectral density function	18.17
$G(\underline{r},t)$	Van Hove function	151
$\underline{G}$	Magnetic field gradient	367
g	Conformal theory parameter	4.32
g	Integrals in cell theory	2.12
g	"g-factor"	20.20
g_j	Degeneracy of energy level j	550
$g(r)$	Distribution function	3.3
H	Enthalpy	17.4

H	Hamiltonian function	538
$\underline{H}$	Magnetic field strength	20.27
$h(r)$	Total correlation function	3.6
h	Parameter in significant structure theory	2.13
h	Parameter in Cole-Cole arc	11.16
h	Planck's constant (6.6256×10^{-34} J sec)	
$\hbar$	$h/2\pi$	
I	Intensity of absorption	316
I	Moment of inertia	18.25
I	Intensity of radiation or absorption (as $I(\omega)$)	
$\underline{I}$	Spin vector	544
I(q,t)	Intermediate scattering function	7.10
I	Ionic strength	5.9
I	Ionization potential	14
i(q)	Structure sensitive intensity	15.5
$\underline{i},\underline{j},\underline{k}$	Unit vectors in x, y, z directions	357
i	$\sqrt{-1}$	
J	Constant in conductivity equation	9.1
J	Total flux	6.78
J	Rotational quantum number	18.24
J	Thermodynamic flux	512
$\underline{J}$	Angular momentum of a molecule	364
$\underline{j}_i$	Diffusion current density	19.14
$\underline{j}_S$	Entropy current density	19.14
$\underline{j}$	Electric current density	20.11
K	Activity equilibrium constant	17.28
K_a	Ion pair association constant	209
k	Rate constant	19.47
k	Parameter in Berthelot rules	8.13
$\underline{k}$	Wave vector ($\lvert\underline{k}\rvert = 2\pi/\lambda$)	20.35
k	Boltzmann's constant (1.38054×10^{-23} J K^{-1})	
L	Inductance	287
L	Phenomenological coefficient	513
L	Persistance length	3.59

$\underline{L}$	Angular momentum	527
L	Length of box	21.19
L	Avogadro's number (6.0225×10^{23} mol^{-1})	
ℓ	Length of pipe	220
ℓ	Mean ion-ion distance	114
ℓ	Mean jump distance	6.37
ℓ, m	Quantum numbers	542
ℓ	Distance parameter	3.60
M	Molecular weight	
M	Function in x-ray scattering	15.10
M_I	z component of I	544
$\underline{M}$	Magnetization	20.21
m	Molality	489
m	Number of jumps	6.37
$\underline{m}$	Transition dipole	21.45
m	Number of atoms in structural unit	15.9
m,n,p,q	Hydration numbers	9.23
m_e	Mass of electron (9.1091×10^{-31} kg)	
$\underline{m}$	Magnetic moment (dipole)	20.17
N	Number of molecules	
N	Number of jumps	6.37
$\underline{N}$	Poynting vector	20.39
n	Number of moles	
n	Translational quantum number	18.2
n	Average number of molecules in cluster	44
$\underline{n}$	Unit normal vector	6.9
n	Refractive index	20.36
n	Bynber density	53
n	Number of carbon atoms in molecule	195
$\underline{P}$	Polarization	20.7
p	Pressure	
$p^{\#}$	Fugacity	17.19
$\underline{p}$	Momentum	500
p	Index for rotation in group theory	551
$\underline{p}$	Electric dipole	533

Q	Q-factor of a circuit	289
Q	General quantity	21.6
Q	Canonical partition function	18.2
Q	Electric quadrupole	7
$\mathcal{Q}, q$	Electric charge	523
q	Bjerrum distance	5.14
q	Partition function for subsystem	18.13
q	Heat absorbed in a system	484
$\underline{q}$	Wave vector	56
$\underline{q}$	Heat flow	6.32
R	Rayleigh ratio	14.4
R	Resistance	11.29
R	Rotation species in point group	552
R	Gas constant (8.314 J K^{-1} mol^{-1})	
$\underline{r}, \underline{r}$	Position vectors	
$r^{\#}$	Parameter in Lennard-Jones potential	1.1
S	Entropy	17.3
S_T	Soret coefficient	221
S	Electron spin	352
S_p	Rotation-reflection by 360/p degrees	551
S	Constant in conductivity equation	9.4
S(q)	Structure function	3.14
S(q,ω)	Scattering law	7.11
T	Translation species in point group	552
T	Function in x-ray scattering	15.10
T	Optical transmission	14.3
T_1	Spin-lattice relaxation time	355
T_2	Spin-spin relaxation time	356
t	Transport number	6.65
U	Internal energy	483
$\underline{u}$	Flow velocity	19.2
u	Mobility	6.57
u'	Electrical mobility	6.64
V	Potential energy	497

v	Vibrational quantum number	21.22
v	Ultrasonic speed	241
$\upsilon(r)$	Pair potential energy function	4
w	Work done on system	484
ω	Probability	18.4
X	Mol fraction	487
X	Thermodynamic force	512
x_i	Fraction of water molecules with i H bonds	44
$Y_{\ell,m}$	Spherical harmonic	542
y	Molar activity coefficient	17.22
y	Fraction of molecules with one H-bond	44
Z	Classical configuration integral	18.30
Z	Impedance	11.29
z	Configurational universal function	4.27
z_i, Z_i	Number of charges on ion species i	490
α	Pressure absorption coefficient of sound	241
α	Thermal expansion	486
α	Degree of dissociation	5.15
$\underline{\underline{\alpha}}$	Polarizability	10
α	Scattering angle	535
$\|\alpha\rangle, \|\beta\rangle$	Spin eigenfunctions	21.23
β	Expansion constant	19.22
β	Hyperpolarizability	10
β	Anisotropy	12.12
β_v	Thermal coefficient	187
β_j	Cluster integral	502
β_N	Nuclear magneton	13.1
β_e	Bohr magneton (9.2732×10^{-24} A m^2)	546
γ	Molal activity coefficient	17.22
γ	Radiation rate	20.46
γ	Ratio of specific heats	10.31
γ	Critical index	3.39
γ	Kinetic coefficients	19.31
γ_j	Variation parameters	547

γ	Gyromagnetic ratio	13.1
γ	Propagation factor	532
$\delta_{j,k}$	δ function	539
δ	Symbol in loss tangent (as tan δ)	288
δ	Critical index	32
δ	Solubility parameters	4.16
δ,θ,ρ	Intermolecular potential parameter	4.29
ε	Energy parameter in Lennard-Jones potential	1.1
ε	Permittivity or dielectric constant	525
$\varepsilon^{\bullet}$	Permittivity of free space (8.85419×10^{-12} $kg^{-1}\ m^{-3}\ sec^{4}\ A^{2}$)	
ε	Energy for diffusion and viscosity	6.43
ζ	Friction coefficient	6.12
ζ	Debye-Waller factor	442
ζ	General variable in system	514
η	Shear viscosity	6.2
η_{jk}	Second derivatives of entropy	19.36
η_{i}	Potential energy parameter	21.47
η	Factor indicating deviation from OZ relation	14.27
θ	Characteristic temperature	18.15
θ	Scattering angle	395
κ	Inverse persistence length	3.60
κ	Compressibility	486
κ	Debye-Hückel parameter	5.8
λ	Decay rate of fluctuations	19.34
λ	Wavelength	20.35
λ	Thermal conductivity	6.33
λ	Perturbation parameter	21.24
μ	Absorption per wavelength	10.20
μ	Reduced mass	20.21
μ	Chemical potential	486
μ	Permeability	528
$\mu^{\bullet}$	Permeability of free space ($4\pi \times 10^{-7}$ $kg^{-1}\ m^{-3}\ sec^{4}\ A^{2}$)	

ν	Stoichiometric doefficients	490
ν	Frequency	
$\tilde{\nu}$	Wave number	
ν	Rate of jumping	132
ν	Kinematic viscosity	220
ξ	Progress variable	508
ξ	Normal mode	21.21
ξ	General coordinate in molecule	20.18
ξ	Effective radius of droplets	422
π	Osmotic pressure	4.7
π	Constant (3.14159265)	
ρ	Density of mass	508
ρ	Density of charge	20.2
ρ_u	Depolarization ratio	14.6
$\rho(\nu)$	Radiation density	21.44
$\underline{\underline{\rho}}$	Density matrix	21.12
σ	Reflection in a plane	552
σ	Conductivity	20.11
σ	Scattering cross section	20.55
σ	Symmetry number	499
σ	Distance parameter	1.1
$\underline{\underline{\sigma}}$	Stress tensor	509
σ	Degree of dissociation	10.39
σ	Screening constant	354
τ	Relaxation time	6.67
τ	Differential orientation (as $d\tau$)	1.13
τ	Residence time	5.3
τ	Time between collisions	6.56
ϕ	Source term	508
ϕ	Electrical potential	20.3
ϕ	Universal function	18.37
ϕ	Volume fraction	4.16
ϕ	Apparent molar volume	8.14
ϕ	Variation function	21.35

ϕ_{me}	Potential of mean force	3.22
χ_m	Magnetic susceptibility	20.28
χ	Distance parameter	21.20
ψ	Stationary state wave function	21.3
ω	Frequency (radians sec^{-1})	
$\underline{\omega}$	Rotational velocity	6.13
Λ	DeBroglie wavelength	18.22
Λ	Conductivity	6.65
Ξ	Grand canonical function	18.41
Ψ	Time dependent wave function	538
Ω	Statistical weight	494
Ω	Element of solid angle (as $d\Omega$)	14.4
Δ	Difference (product-reagent)	491
Π	Multiplication	
Σ	Summation	
$\underline{\nabla}$	Differential operator (gradient)	
Φ	Universal function	18.39
Φ	Dissipation function	19.17
Γ	Gyromagnetic ratio	20.19
Γ	Wave lifetime	404

Prefixes

p	pico (x 10^{-12})	T	tera (x 10^{12})
n	nano (x 10^{-9})	G	giga (x 10^{9})
μ	micro (x 10^{-6})	M	mega (x 10^{6})
m	milli (x 10^{-3})	k	kilo (x 10^{3})
c	centi (x 10^{-2})		

Superscripts

•	Free space	^{e}	Excess
•	Pure component	^{id}	Ideal
•	Time derivative	*	Complex quantity
$^{\infty}$	Infinite dilution	*	Reduced quantity
$^{\#}$	Activated state	*	Complex conjugate
^	Operator	$^{\theta}$	Standard state
°	Unperturbed		

Energy Conversion Table

	kJ mol^{-1}	kcal mol^{-1}	erg $molecule^{-1}$	eV $molecule^{-1}$	cm^{-1}	Hz
1 kJ mol^{-1} =	1	2.390(-1)	1.660(-14)	1.0364(-2)	8.359(1)	2.506(12)
1 kcal mol^{-1} =	4.184	1	6.947(-14)	4.336(-2)	3.498(2)	1.048(13)
1 erg $molecule^{-1}$ =	6.023(13)	1.439(13)	1	6.242(11)	5.034(15)	1.510(26)
1 eV $molecule^{-1}$ =	9.649(1)	2.306(1)	1.602(-12)	1	8.065(3)	2.418(14)
1 cm^{-1} =	1.196(-2)	2.859(-3)	1.986(-16)	1.240(-4)	1	2.998(10)
1 Hz =	3.990(-13)	9.538(-14)	6.625(-27)	4.136(-15)	3.336(-11)	1

Powers of 10 are set in brackets, e.g., 6.023(16) = 6.023×10^{16}.

INDEX